P9-BUI-463

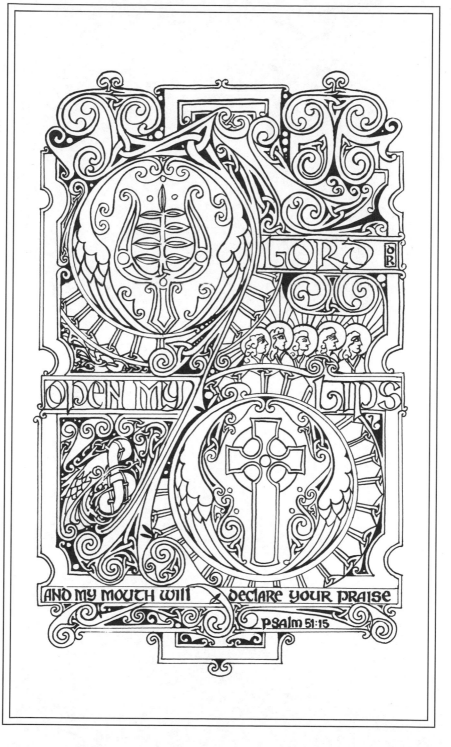

LORD
OR

OPEN MY LIPS

AND MY MOUTH WILL declare your praise

Psalm 51:15

THE BOOK OF PRAISE

The Book of Praise

Recommended for voluntary use in congregations by the 122nd General Assembly of The Presbyterian Church in Canada, 1996 / Recommandé pour un usage facultatif de la part des congrégations par la 122ième Assemblée Générale de l'Église Presbytérienne au Canada, 1996

ISBN 0-9699900-1-4

Printed and bound in Canada / Imprimé et fabriqué au Canada

Prepared by / Préparé par
The Task Force on the Revision of the Book of Praise
The Presbyterian Church in Canada / l'Église Presbytérienne au Canada
Editors / Rédacteurs: Donald Anderson & Andrew Donaldson
Celtic art / Art celtique: David Rankine
Typesetting / Gravure musicale: Simon Jutras Music Engraving,
114 Pine, Hudson, Quebec, Canada J0P 1H0

The Door of Peace

Table of Contents

* Service music is distributed throughout the book, with additional material grouped under Times and Occasions of Worship

Introduction

We will tell to the coming generation
the glorious deeds of the Lord,
and the mighty wonders that God has done.

(Psalm 78:1-4, from *The Book of Psalms*)

"We have no higher calling than to offer the worship that belongs to God day by day, Sunday by Sunday. Worship draws us into the work of Christ... In union with him, the church prays for the healing and the salvation of the world." (*Living Faith* 7.3.1, 7.3.3)

We worship and work as a part of the whole body of Christ present in the world. In many voices and languages, many sounds and rhythms, we sing the story of where we have been with God and where God is leading us. The present *Book of Praise* draws from the treasure house of hymn, psalm and spiritual song, offering scripture paraphrases, and choruses, prayers, responses and rounds, descants, spirituals, folk songs and chorales by which we pray and praise in language ancient and contemporary. May the Spirit enable us to sing a new song as we "tell to the coming generation... the mighty wonders that God has done."

Background

During the 1980s and 1990s, many denominations undertook hymn book revisions, e.g., the United Methodist, United Reformed and Baptist churches in Great Britain, the Methodist and Presbyterian churches in the U.S.A., the Church of Ireland, the United, Anglican and Roman Catholic churches in Canada, and The Brethren and Christian Reformed Churches in the United States and Canada. They faced similar challenges: to combine new hymnody with honoured and rich worship traditions that had nourished previous generations and to speak the gospel in the midst of changing customs and culture.

Spurred by the demand for fresh expressions of faith, hymn writers produced an extraordinary quantity of fine hymnody in many styles and genres, much of which became widely available through collections issued by publishers from every part of the globe. The development of indigenous Christian musical styles in South America, Africa and Asia, coupled with immigration and easier communication between cultures, presented to the churches of Europe and North America an astonishing body of newly composed and adapted worship music that crossed traditional cultural divides. Non-western churches experienced vigorous growth and churches in Europe and North America welcomed missionaries from these Christian communities. We have witnessed an outpouring of new hymnody which strives to express in fresh and appealing ways the ever-changing work of God's Spirit in the life and mission of the Christian church.

Knowledge of the resources became widespread. Presbyterians were moved by their experience of worship using new hymns and songs and wished to share with the whole Church the richness of expression and power of Christian witness embodied in this hymnody. The Synod of Saskatchewan and the Presbytery of Montréal brought overtures to the 1989 General Assembly, asking for the development of a revised hymn book. The General Assembly, granting the prayers of the overtures, established a task force to represent the theological and musical perspectives within the denomination. The task force brought back to subsequent General Assemblies guidelines concerning process and contents; later it presented annual progress reports as the book took shape. Through many surveys and workshops the task force asked the membership of the Presbyterian Church what it would like to see in a revised hymnbook. Church members, representing a large proportion of the denomination, helped the task force gain a clear picture of our use of hymns in worship. Approximately half of the hymns in *The Book of Praise* (1972) were in regular use. Use of the metrical (versified) psalms was in decline and congregations increasingly relied on hymn collections other than *The Book of Praise* (1972). Some respondents stated that many of the hymns were too high and that *The Book of Praise* (1972) separated tunes and words that should have been kept together. Many felt that the language of our hymns addressed only part of the worshipping community and requested language which would include all worshippers. Some stated that a wider spectrum of musical styles and origins would better reflect the diverse and changing ethnic makeup of the denomination. Others felt that the 1972 collection did not reflect the rich spectrum of worship practices current in the church and asked for music of a wider variety of genres such as Advent and adult baptism or expressing such themes as justice or personal faith in Christ. They looked for practical helps: a complete range of detailed indexes, tune cross-referencing, and helps and resources such as instrumental parts, percussion notation, descants and chord symbols.

Some voiced deep concern about aging or shrinking congregations and expressed the need for hymns and songs which could connect with the coming generation, the children and young adults, and with those not already members of a community of faith.

The Book of Praise (1997), the fourth in a series of hymn books serving the denomination since 1897 (hymn books appeared under this name in 1897, 1918 and 1972), addresses these needs. The task force gave its final report to the Church in 1996 and the General Assembly recommended the publication and voluntary use of the revised book in congregations.

Structure
The Book of Praise begins with Metrical Psalms; then follows The Church Year, God, The People of God, Times and Occasions of Worship. Service music—amens, hallelujahs, hosannas, etc.—is distributed throughout the book, with a few items grouped together under Times and Occasions of Worship. For a list of service music, please see the Service Music heading in the topical index. Following the example of the earlier collections, the metrical psalter and the church year are the first two main sections in *The Book of Praise*. For the largest part of the book—material under the general headings God and The People of God—the task force sought to organize the hymns under subheadings that were clear, concise, inclusive and comprehensive. We found such headings in *Living Faith* (published in French as *Foi Vivante*), a contemporary statement of faith already well known in Presbyterian congregations. Therefore, *The Book of Praise* borrows much of its internal structure from the categories in *Living Faith* which represent the main issues that we face in our week-by-week living out of the call to be Christ's body in the world.

Editorial Style
The editorial style for words in *The Book of Praise* is based on that adopted by the New Revised Standard Version Bible translation published by Thomas Nelson, Inc., Nashville Tennessee (©1989 by the Division of Christian Education of the National Council of the Churches of Christ). Capitalization is limited to beginnings of sentences, names in general and names of God, directly quoted speech and, occasionally, indirect speech when in the form of an acclamation. Punctuation and spelling have been standardized, except where copyright holders have stipulated a different style.

Many hymn texts exist in variant forms and most writers have from time to time recast their own hymns. In the present revision, the need of the church to sing its faith in clear, contemporary terms was a primary consideration in making editorial decisions. This need was balanced by a commitment on the part of the task force to respect the poetic diction of traditional texts. Texts by living authors have copyright information often showing the date of the latest revision. Significant alterations to other texts are indicated by the term "alt".

The present book facilitates sight-singing by placing as many as five or six verses between staves; hymns in several languages have the initial verses printed in this way— usually with at least one verse in each language underlaid, and with the final verses below the music.

Indexes
All standard hymn book indexes are provided, including two scripture indexes, one in Bible order and one in alphabetical order by first lines of hymns. The topical index includes over 200 headings designed for worship planning (e.g., headings include Processionals and Recessionals) with many cross-references. Also included are an index of items suggested for children and young adults and an index of copyright holders in alphabetical order with addresses, fax /phone numbers and the items under their copyright control.

In *The Book of Praise*, tune names are given immediately below the first line or title designation on the opening page of each hymn. The meter (the syllable count of each line of poetry), e.g., 8 6 8 6 D, is given beside the tune name.

Items without music
Prayers, poems, creeds and hymn words without music are interspersed throughout the book. The Great Prayer of Thanksgiving, divided for responsive reading, appears in the Communion section.

Metrical psalms and scripture paraphrases
The Book of Praise includes paraphrases of many of the Psalms, following the practice of all of our hymn books of the last one hundred years, and, in line with tradition, does not include a doxology at the end of each metrical psalm, preferring to allow each congregation to provide its own Christian context. The scripture paraphrases cover many musical styles and are drawn from both Old and New Testaments and the apochryphal books.

Cue notes
Cue notes are given where the rhythms, as traditionally sung, differ from the printed music, or where word rhythms change from verse to verse.

Amens
Amens in every relevant key are placed at end of the book and may be photocopied.

Chord symbols
Many musicians use chord symbols as a shorthand in realizing harmony, and so chord symbols are offered for most of the items in this book. The letter symbol (C, Fm, etc.) represents the basic chord (C major, F minor). A chord symbol followed by a slash (C/B^b) tells you that the chord is C major with the note B^b in the bass. When the slash–bass-note combination (/A) follows a symbol on a subsequent beat, it indicates that the harmony is maintained and only the bass note changes on that beat.

Descants and fauxbourdons
Descants are usually notated as the top staff and slightly reduced in size in this book. By convention, they are usually performed by sopranos for the final verse of the hymn (as indicated by the underlaid text), but can also be played on a treble instrument. There are some fauxbourdons (arrangements in which the melody appears in the tenor). They may be treated simply as alternative accompaniments for various verses, or may be presented as choral settings.

Languages

Though *The Book of Praise* is primarily for English-language singing, it offers some texts in French, Hungarian, Spanish, German, Chichewa, Shona, Xhosa, Zulu, Latin, Greek, Korean, Mandarin, and some North American Indian languages. Texts in languages that do not normally use the Latin alphabet, such as Korean, are romanized in order that they may be sung by an English-speaking congregation.

Acknowledgements

We are deeply grateful for the opportunity to serve the Church. Many individuals and organizations, boards and committees—more than can be named here—have helped us in the task. A few individuals to whom we have reported, and whose planning and expertise in the areas of budget and communications have been invaluable, must be named: Glen Davis, General Secretary of the Board of Congregational Life and of the Life and Mission Agency; Ian Morrison, General Secretary of the Life and Mission Agency; Margaret McNaughton, staff person for Worship under the Board of Congregational Life; Diane Strickland, Associate Secretary, Education for Discipleship, in the Life and Mission Agency; Judith Archer Green, Associate Secretary, Life and Mission Agency; Maureen Kelly, Muriel Barrington and Terry Ingram, Conveners of the Life and Mission Agency Committee; Karen Hincke, General Secretary of the Service Agency; Don Taylor, Comptroller and later Chief Financial Officer. The task of explaining to the Church the decisions of General Assembly and their implementation by the task force was entrusted to the co-editors, Andrew Donaldson and Donald Anderson, who joined the project in 1993 and provided administrative and technical support for development and production. Other executive staff within the Life and Mission Agency helped the task force in communicating with congregations in Canada and abroad: these include Glenn Cooper, Associate Secretary, Resource Production and Communications; Marjorie Ross, Associate Secretary, International Ministries; John Bannerman, Associate Secretary, Education for Discipleship; Joyce Hodgson, Associate Secretary, Education for Discipleship. Several other people have brought special abilities to various short- and long-term contracts: Anne Burleigh (Garvin); Liane Taylor, Loretta Jones, Jenny Franks, Virginia Lovering (database entry and punctuation), Karin Schemeit (manuscript preparation and copyright permissions), Carolyn Davidson and Grace-ann McIntyre. Daniel H. Forget and Jeanne LaRochelle-Reed supplied many French language texts: we thank them for their work, and also thank the individuals and committees who provided texts, translations and transliterations of the other languages included in the Book of Praise.

We reserve our deepest thanks for the many congregations and individuals who hosted workshops and festivals, tested hymns, communicated with the task force by phone or in writing, debated in the courts of the Church, responded to questionnaires, and who bought the book prior to publication. Through their prayers and by their gifts of time and their investment of money, they supported and enriched the work of the task force.

We pray that this book may repay the trust placed in the task force by the Church and inspire all who open it to a renewed sense of awe at "the mighty wonders that God has done" as they sing to God's glory. In selecting these hymns, we kept the past and present firmly in view though our knowledge the Church's history, our surveys, workshops and our weekly experience as worship leaders and participants in the life of our own congregations. And we aspire in faith to serve the next generation, those whom God will call, so that the church "reformed and always reforming" may continue to bear living witness to the One who was, who is and who is to come.

The Task Force on the Revision of the Book of Praise

Judee Archer Green, Keith Boyer (Convener), Jerry Crowdis, Richard Cunningham, John Derksen, Shirley Gale, Gerald Hobbs, Lois Klempa, Hans Kouwenberg, Iona MacLean, Peter Merrick, Jack Neil, Heidi Wehrmann, Yme Woensdregt.

1

How blest are they, who, fearing God

TALLIS' ORDINAL 8 6 8 6 CM

1. How blest are they, who, fear - ing God, from sin re-strain their feet,
2. How blest are they who make God's law their treas-ure and de - light
3. Their lives are nour-ished like a tree set by the riv - er's side;
4. The wick-ed, like the driv - en chaff, are blown a-cross the land;
5. The Lord will guard the right-eous well; their way to God is known,

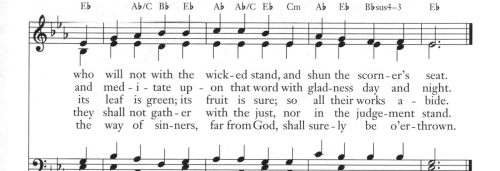

who will not with the wick-ed stand, and shun the scorn-er's seat.
and med - i - tate up - on that word with glad-ness day and night.
its leaf is green; its fruit is sure; so all their works a - bide.
they shall not gath-er with the just, nor in the judge-ment stand.
the way of sin-ners, far from God, shall sure-ly be o'er-thrown.

Alternate tune: Old 130 (Genevan 130)

Words: Psalm 1; paraphrase, Psalter 1912, alt Music: Thomas Tallis (c. 1505–1585)

Words: public domain Music: public domain

Psalm 3
How many are against me, Lord
ADON OLAM 8 8 8 8 LM

1. How man-y are a - gainst me, Lord: how man-y fierce at - tacks rise up! They say, "God will not come to help," and peo - ple taunt, "There is no hope."

2. But you are round me, Lord, my shield, but you, my glo - ry, lift my head! You hear me from your ho - ly hill and an - swer when I cry a - loud.

3. I go to rest, and sleep in peace— I wake a - gain; God keeps me safe: ten thou-sand shall not make me fear, for all their threats to take my life.

4. A - rise, O Lord, to res - cue me: a - rise and save me, O my God! You si - lence all my en - e - mies till scorn and spite are all de-stroyed.

Alternate tune: Solothurn

Words: Psalm 3; paraphrase, Christopher Idle (1938–) Music: Eliezer Gerovitch (1844–1914)

O God, defender of the poor

LIVERPOOL 8 6 8 6 CM

Alternate tunes: Abridge, Balerma

Words: Psalm 4; paraphrase, Christopher Idle (1938–) Music: American folk melody;
arrangement, John Barnard (1948–)

4

Psalm 5

Lord, as I wake I turn to you

DANIEL 8 8 8 8 LM

1. Lord, as I wake I turn to you,
   yourself the first thought of my day, my king, my God,
   whose help is sure, yourself the help for which I pray.
2. There is no bless - ing, Lord, from you
   for those who make their will their way, no praise for those
   who will not praise, no peace for those who will not pray.
3. Your lov - ing gifts of grace to me,
   those fa - vours I could nev - er earn, call for my thanks
   in praise and prayer, call me to love you in re - turn.
4. Lord, make my life a life of love,
   keep me from sin in all I do; Lord, make your law
   my on - ly law, your will my will, for love of you.

Words: Psalm 5; paraphrase, Brian Foley (1919–) Music: Irish traditional melody;
harmony, Martin Shaw (1875–1958)

Psalm 8

5

Lord, our Lord, your glorious name

GOTT SEI DANK DURCH ALLER WELT 7 7 7 7

1. Lord, our Lord, your glo - rious name all your
2. In - fant voic - es chant your praise, tell - ing
3. Moon and stars in shin - ing height night - ly
4. Who are we that we should share in your
5. With do - min - ion crowned, we stand o'er the

won - drous works pro - claim; in the heavens with
of your glo - rious ways; weak - est means work
tell their Mak - er's might; when I view the
love and ten - der care, raised to an ex -
crea - tures of your hand; all to us sub -

ra - diant signs ev - er - more your glo - ry shines.
out your will, migh - ty en - e - mies to still.
heavens a - far, then I know how small we are.
alt - ed height, crowned with hon - our in your sight?
jec - tion yield, in the sea and air and field.

Words: Psalm 8; paraphrase, Psalter 1912   Music: Geistreiches Gesangbuch (Freylinghausen), 1704

Words: public domain Music: public domain

Psalm 13

6

How long will you forget me, Lord

BANGOR 8 6 8 6 CM

1. How long will you for - get me, Lord, and
2. Look on my need, O Lord my God who
3. Look on their threats and hear my cry and
4. But since I trust your con - stant love, my

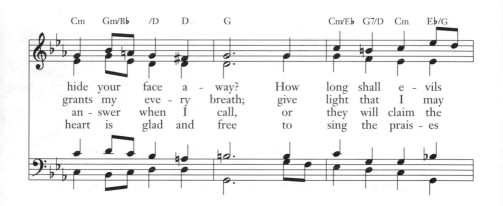

hide your face a - way? How long shall e - vils
grants my eve - ry breath; give light that I may
an - swer when I call, or they will claim the
heart is glad and free to sing the prais - es

tear my heart and trou - bles fill my day?
see your light, nor sleep the sleep of death.
vic - to - ry who long to see me fall.
of the Lord whose grace has res - cued me.

Words: Psalm 13; paraphrase, Christopher Idle (1938–)   Music: A Compleat Melody or Harmony of Zion 1734

Psalm 14

The foolish in their hearts deny

MAPLE AVENUE 8 6 8 6 D CMD

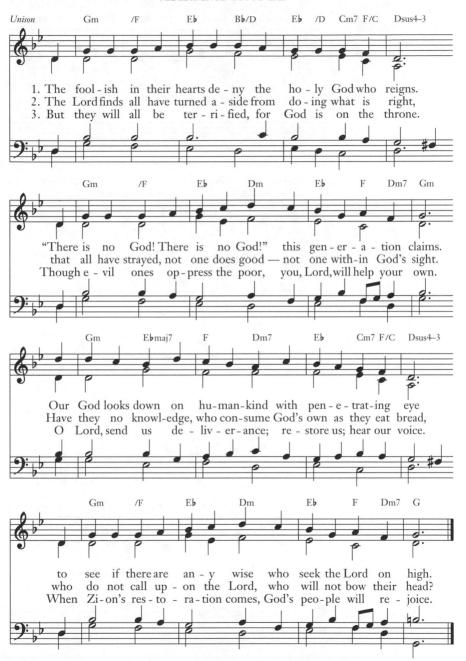

1. The fool-ish in their hearts de-ny the ho-ly God who reigns.
2. The Lord finds all have turned a-side from do-ing what is right,
3. But they will all be ter-ri-fied, for God is on the throne.

"There is no God! There is no God!" this gen-er-a-tion claims.
that all have strayed, not one does good — not one with-in God's sight.
Though e-vil ones op-press the poor, you, Lord, will help your own.

Our God looks down on hu-man-kind with pen-e-trat-ing eye
Have they no knowl-edge, who con-sume God's own as they eat bread,
O Lord, send us de-liv-er-ance; re-store us; hear our voice.

to see if there are an-y wise who seek the Lord on high.
who do not call up-on the Lord, who will not bow their head?
When Zi-on's res-to-ra-tion comes, God's peo-ple will re-joice.

Words: Psalm 14; paraphrase, Marie J. Post (1919–1990) Music: Richard L. Van Oss (1953–)

Psalm 15

8

Lord, who may dwell within your house

WITHINGTON 868886

1. Lord, who may dwell with-in your house and on your ho-ly hill? All those who walk a blame-less way, who love the right, who win the day with truth-ful words and, come what may, will speak no word of ill;

2. all those who love their neigh-bour well, who hate the way of sin, who hon-our all that fear the Lord, whose pro-mise is a bind-ing cord, who help, and seek no rich re-ward these, Lord, you wel-come in.

Words: Psalm 15; paraphrase, Paul Wigmore (1925–) Music: John Barnard (1948–)

Psalm 19

9

God's law is perfect

ST. ANDREW 8 6 8 6 CM

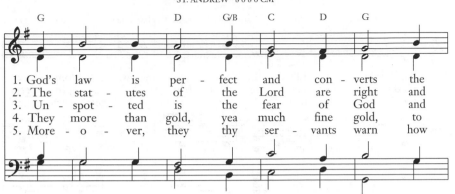

1. God's law is per - fect and con - verts the
2. The stat - utes of the Lord are right and
3. Un - spot - ted is the fear of God and
4. They more than gold, yea much fine gold, to
5. More - o - ver, they thy ser - vants warn how

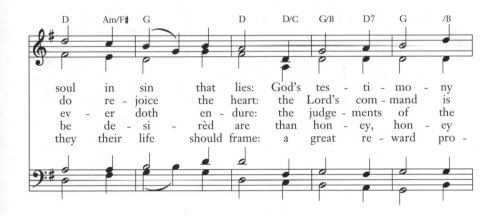

soul in sin that lies: God's tes - ti - mo - ny
do re - joice the heart: the Lord's com - mand is
ev - er doth en - dure: the judge - ments of the
be de - si - rèd are than hon - ey, hon - ey
they their life should frame: a great re - ward pro -

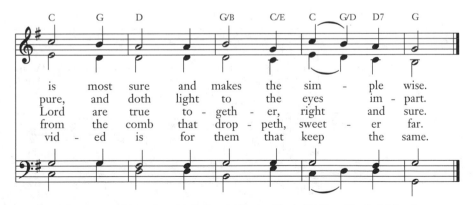

is most sure and makes the sim - ple wise.
pure, and doth light to the eyes im - part.
Lord are true to - geth - er, right and sure.
from the comb that drop - peth, sweet - er far.
vid - ed is for them that keep the same.

Words: Psalm 19; paraphrase, Scottish Psalter 1650, alt   Music: William Tans'ur's New harmony
of Zion 1764
Words: public domain Music: public domain

Psalm 19

10

God's glory fills the heavens

ST. PATRICK 8 8 8 8 D LMD

1. God's glo - ry fills the heavens with hymns, the domed sky
2. God's per - fect law re - vives the soul; its pre - cepts
3. God's ser - vant may I ev - er be: this world my

bears the Ma - ker's mark; new prais - es sound from
make the sim - ple wise; its just com - mands re -
joy, that word my guide. Oh cleanse me, Lord, from

day to day and e - cho through the know - ing dark. With -
joice the heart; its truth gives light un - to the eyes. For -
se - cret sin; de - li - ver me from sel - fish pride. Ac -

Words: Psalm 19; paraphrase, Carl P. Daw, Jr. (1944–) Music: Irish traditional hymn; C.V. Stanford (1852–1924)

out   a   word   their   songs   roll   on,   in - to   all   lands   their
ev - er   shall   this   law   en - dure: un - blem - ished, right - eous,
cept   my thoughts   and   words   and deeds;   let them   find   fav - our

voic - es   run.   And   with   a   champ - ion's strength and
true,   com - plete.   No   gold   was   ev - er   found   so
in   your   sight.   For   you   a - lone   can   make   me

grace   from   farth - est   heaven   comes forth   the   sun.
fine,   no   ho - ney   in   the   comb   more sweet.
whole,   O   Lord,   my   re - fuge   and   my   might.

Psalms

Psalm 23

The Lord's my shepherd

11

CRIMOND 8 6 8 6 CM

1. The Lord's my shepherd, I'll not want. He makes me down to lie in pastures green; he leadeth me the quiet waters by.
2. My soul he doth restore again, and me to walk doth make within the paths of righteousness even for his own name's sake.
3. Yea, though I walk in death's dark vale, yet will I fear none ill, for thou art with me, and thy rod and staff me comfort still.
4. My table thou hast furnished in presence of my foes; my head thou dost with oil anoint and my cup overflows.
5. Goodness and mercy all my life shall surely follow me and in God's house forevermore my dwelling place shall be.

Words: Psalm 23; paraphrase, Scottish Psalter 1650 Music: Jessie Seymour Irvine (1836–1887); harmony, Thomas C.I. Pritchard (1885–1960)

Words: public domain Music: harmony, copyright © Oxford University Press

Korean

1. Choo naw-eh mohk-jaw tweh-shee-nee
poo-johk-hawm uhp-suh-raw
Chuh poo-run pool-pawt mool-gaw-roh
nawl een-doh haw-sheen-daw

2. Meh maw-run yung-eh heem soh-saw
naw choo-rul daw-ru-nee
Chawm mohk-jaw ee-sheen ku ee-rum
chawn-yawng-ul paw-du-ree

3. Kawm-kawm hawn choo-gum keel-eh-doh
too-ryuh-oom uhp-su-myuh
Ku sohn-eh chee-pawng-ee poh-goh
naw-awn-sheem haw-ree-raw

French

1. Jésus est mon divin berger,
réjouis-toi, mon âme,
seul il délivre du danger,
tout en moi le réclame.

2. Non, je ne manquerai de rien,
car, ô grâce infinie,
Jésus est l'ami, le gardien,
en qui je me confie.

3. Jour après jour, il me conduit
dans ses verts pâturages,
de son amour il me nourrit
sous ses divins ombrages.

4. Je ne craindrai donc aucun mal,
quand au cours du voyage
il me faudra, du sombre val,
franchir le noir passage!

5. Toujours sa grâce et son amour
me suivront sur la terre,
et tout sera, dans son séjour:
paix, gloire, amour, lumière.

12

Lift up the gates eternal

LIFT UP THE GATES ETERNAL   12 12 with refrain (12 12)

Words: Psalm 24; paraphrase, Arlo D. Duba (1929–); refrain, Willard F. Jabusch (1930–)
Music: Israeli folk melody; arrangement, John Ferguson (1941–)

1. See, all the earth is God's, its peo - ple and na - tions;
2. Who can go up this moun-tain, who stand in prais - ing?
3. They shall re - ceive for - give - ness and have God's bless - ing
4. Come, lift your voic - es high: be lift - ed to glo - ry;
5. Who is this glo - rious one, for whom we are wait - ing?
6. Come, lift your heads with joy; come, lift up your tow - er;
7. Who is this King of glo - ry of whom we're sing - ing?

G (Am7 G/B C) D Cmaj7 G/B G (/F♯)

God built it on the deeps and laid its foun - da - tions.
Those who are pure, who come with clean hands up - rais - ing.
if they will search for God, their Sav-iour con - fess - ing. (Refrain)
the Lord our God ap-proach-es; come, shout the sto - ry.
We wait the might-y Lord, our God cel - e - brat - ing. (Refrain)
the King of glo - ry comes in full might and pow - er.
Our God, the Lord of Hosts, the vic - tory is bring - ing. (Refrain)

Em (/D Cmaj7 G/B Cmaj7) D7 G (/F♯)

Performance suggestion: gradually increase tempo.

13

Psalm 24

Ye gates, lift up your heads

ST. GEORGE'S, EDINBURGH   8 6 8 6 CMD with Coda

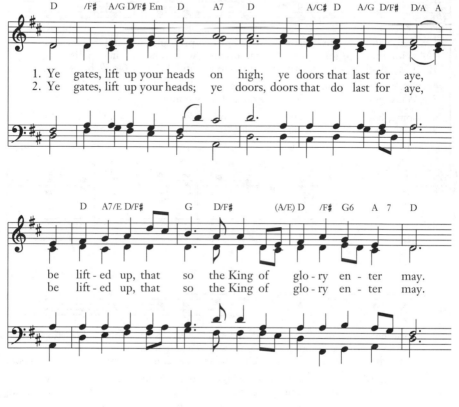

1. Ye gates, lift up your heads on high; ye doors that last for aye,
2. Ye gates, lift up your heads; ye doors, doors that do last for aye,

be lift - ed up, that so the King of glo - ry en - ter may.
be lift - ed up, that so the King of glo - ry en - ter may.

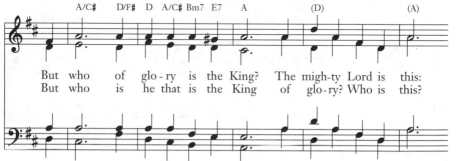

But who of glo - ry is the King? The migh - ty Lord is this:
But who is he that is the King of glo - ry? Who is this?

Words: Psalm 24; paraphrase, Scottish Psalter 1650   Music: Andrew Mitchell Thomson (1778–1831);
additional harmony, Henry Rosevear (1903–1982)

Words: public domain   Music: additional harmony, copyright © estate of Henry Rosevear

even that same Lord that great in might and strong in bat - tle is.
The Lord of hosts, and none but he the King of glo - ry is.

Even that same Lord that great in might and strong in bat - tle is.
The Lord of hosts, and none but he the King of glo - ry is.

Coda *To be sung after the last verse*

Hal - le - lu - jah, hal - le - lu - jah, hal - le - lu - jah, hal - le - lu - jah,

hal - le - lu - jah, a - men, a - men, a - men.

Psalm 27

14 Safe in your hands, O God who made me

SAFE IN THE HANDS 9 8 9 8

1. Safe in your hands, O God who made me,
2. This I have prayed and will seek af - ter,
3. God of my life, my help, my Sav - iour,
4. Teach me your way and lead me on - wards,

what can there be that I should fear? You are my
that I may walk with you each day; then will you
fa - ther and mo - ther now to me: come, shield me
save me from those who do me wrong; give me the

light and my sal - va - tion; strong is your
give me your pro - tec - tion; no trou - ble
from the threat of e - vil, lift up my
grace to wait with pa - tience; help me to

help when foes are near.
shall my heart dis - may.
soul and set me free!
trust, hold firm, be strong.

Words: Psalm 27; paraphrase, Michael Perry (1942–1996) Music: Christopher Norton (1953–)

Psalm 27

The Lord's my light

ST. MAGNUS 8 6 8 6 CM

1. The Lord's my light and sav - ing health; who
2. Though wars a - rise and ar - mies camp a -
3. One thing I asked of God the Lord, and
4. that I the beau - ty of the Lord may

shall make me dis - mayed? God is the strong - hold
gainst me, I'll not fear; I will stand firm and
will seek to ob - tain, that all days of my
wor - ship and ad - mire, that I in God's most

of my life: who shall make me a - fraid?
con - fi - dent: I know that God is near.
life I may with - in God's house re - main;
ho - ly place may rev - erent - ly en - quire.

5. In evil, troubled days, my God
   will hide and shelter me,
   and raise me high upon a rock
   above my enemy.

6. Now I will offer sacrifice
   for all God's saving grace,
   with melody unto the Lord
   and joyful shouts of praise!

Words: Psalm 27; paraphrase, Scottish Psalter 1650 Music: Jeremiah Clarke (c. 1674–1707), from Divine
Companion 1707; harmony, William Henry Monk (1823–1889) after John Pyke Hullah (19th cent.)

Words: this version, © The Presbyterian Church in Canada, 1997 Music: public domain

Psalm 30
I worship you, O Lord
BISHOP TUCKER 12 12 12

1. I wor-ship you, O Lord, for you have raised me up; I
2. Sing prais-es to the Lord, all those who know God's name, whose
3. I said, "I am so strong, I nev-er shall be moved", but
4. my mourn-ing you have turned to danc-ing and to joy; my

cried to you for help, and you re-stored my life. You
ho-ly wrath is brief, whose fav-our knows no end. Though
you, Lord, shook my life— my heart was in dis-tress. I
sad-ness you dis-pelled as glad-ness filled my soul, and

brought me back from death and saved me from the grave.
tears may flow at night, the morn-ing brings new joy.
cried to you for help and plead-ed for your grace:
so I'll sing your praise, my God, through all my days!

Words: Psalm 30; paraphrase, v. 1–3, 5 James Seddon (1915–1983); v.4 Calvin Seerveld (1930–)
Music: Norman Warren (1934–)

Words: paraphrase, copyright © 1973, 1982 by Hope Publishing Co. Music: copyright © 1990 by Hope Publishing Co.

Psalm 32

How blest are they whose trespass

GOSTERWOOD 7 6 7 6 D

1. How blest are they whose tres - pass has free - ly been for - given,
   whose sins are whol - ly cov - ered be - fore the sight of heaven, blest
2. While I kept guilt - y si - lence, my strength was spent with grief,
   your hand was heav - y on me, my soul found no re - lief; but
3. So let the god - ly seek you in times when you are near;
   no whelm-ing floods shall reach them, or cause their hearts to fear; O

they to whom the Lord God does not im - pute their sin, who
when I owned my tres - pass and did not hide my sin, then
Lord, you are my re - fuge, you are my hid - ing place, and

have a guile - less spir - it, whose heart is true with - in.
you for - gave my guilt, Lord, re - stored my life with - in.
you sur - round me al - ways with songs of sav - ing grace.

4. I graciously will teach you
   the way that you should go,
   and, with my eye upon you,
   help you my counsel know.
   Then do not be unruly
   or slow to understand;
   be not perverse, but willing
   to heed my wise command.

5. The sorrows of the wicked
   increase from year to year,
   but those who trust the Lord God
   know love instead of fear.
   Then in the Lord be joyful;
   in song lift up your voice;
   be glad in God, you righteous:
   rejoice, O saints rejoice!

Words: Psalm 32; paraphrase, Psalter 1912, alt   Music: English traditional; arrangement, Ralph
Vaughan Williams (1872–1958)

Psalm 34

Through all the changing scenes of life

WILTSHIRE 8 6 8 6 CM

1. Through all the chang - ing scenes of life, in
2. Oh mag - ni - fy the Lord with me; with
3. The hosts of God en - camp a - round the
4. Oh taste and see that God is good: ex -

trou - ble and in joy, the prais - es of my
me ex - alt God's name; when in dis - tress and
dwell - ings of the just; de - liv - erance God af -
pe - rience will de - cide how blest are they, and

God shall still my heart and tongue em - ploy.
fear I called, God to my res - cue came.
fords to all who seek and hope and trust.
on - ly they, who in God's truth con - fide.

5. O Saints, fear God, and you will then
have nothing else to fear;
make holy service your delight;
your wants shall be God's care.

6. The Lord preserves the souls of those
who on God's truth depend;
to them and their posterity
God's blessing shall descend.

Words: Psalm 34; paraphrase, Tate and Brady's New Version 1696, alt   Music: George Smart (1776–1867)

Words: public domain   Music: public domain

19

Psalm 36

High in the heavens, eternal God

SONG 34 8 8 8 8 LM

1. High in the heavens, e - ter - nal God, thy good-ness in full
2. For - ev - er firm thy jus - tice stands, as moun-tains their foun -
3. From the pro - vi - sions of thy house we shall be fed with
4. Life, like a foun - tain, rich and free, springs from the pres - ence

glo - ry shines: thy truth shall break through eve - ry
da - tions keep; wise are the won - ders of thy
sweet re - past; there mer - cy like a riv - er
of the Lord, and in thy light our souls shall

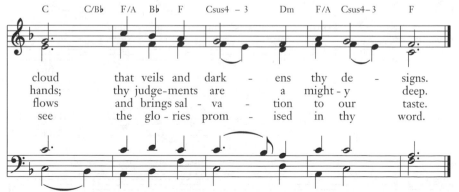

cloud that veils and dark - ens thy de - signs.
hands; thy judge-ments are a might - y deep.
flows and brings sal - va - tion to our taste.
see the glo - ries prom - ised in thy word.

Alternate tune: Truro

Words: Psalm 36; paraphrase, Isaac Watts (1674–1748) Music: Orlando Gibbons (1583–1625)

Lamentations 3

The steadfast love of the Lord

THE STEADFAST LOVE   Irregular

The stead - fast love of the Lord ne - ver ceas - es. Your mer-cies ne - ver come to an end; they are new eve-ry morn-ing, new eve-ry morn-ing: great is your faith - ful - ness, O Lord, great is your faith - ful - ness!

Fine

1.
1. You, Lord, are my por - tion, says my soul;

Words: Lamentations 3:21–26, 31–33, 40; paraphrase, Edith McNeill   Music: Edith McNeill;
arrangement, Chris Rollinson

there - fore I will hope in you.

2.–4.

2. You, Lord, are good to those who wait for you,
3. The Lord will not cast off for - ev - er,
4. So let us ex - a - mine all our ways,

to the soul that seeks you; it is good that we should wait
but will have com - pas - sion; for God does not will - ing -
and re - turn to the Lord, let us lift up our hearts and

qui - et - ly for the sal - va-tion of the Lord.
ly af - flict or grieve the right - eous ones.
hands to God in heaven.

D.C.

Psalm 37

21

Set thou thy trust upon the Lord

CAITHNESS 8 6 8 6 CM

1. Set thou thy trust up - on the Lord, and be thou do - ing good,
2. De - light thy - self in God who gives thine heart's de - sire to thee.
3. Rest in the Lord, and pa - tient - ly wait for God: do not fret
4. Mark thou the up - right ones, and watch the right-eous ones in - crease,

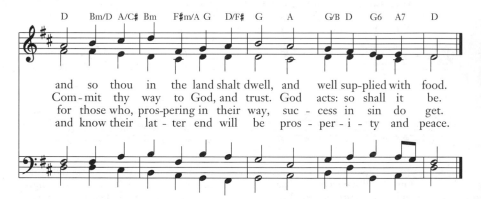

and so thou in the land shalt dwell, and well sup-plied with food.
Com - mit thy way to God, and trust. God acts: so shall it be.
for those who, pros-pering in their way, suc - cess in sin do get.
and know their lat - ter end will be pros - per - i - ty and peace.

Alternate tune: St. Andrew

Words: Psalm 37; paraphrase, Scottish Psalter 1650, alt   Music: The Psalms of David in Prose and
Meeter 1635; harmony, The English Hymnal, 1906

Words: this version, copyright © The Presbyterian Church in Canada, 1997   Music: public domain

Psalm 38

Rebuke me not in anger, Lord

ERHALT UNS, HERR 8 8 8 8 LM

1. Re - buke me not in an - ger, Lord; your ar - rows
2. My sin - ful fol - ly brought me low; bowed down, I
3. You know my sighs and weak-ness, Lord, my blind - ed
4. My mouth is mute: I can - not speak; my ear is
5. My pain is ev - er with me, Lord, for I have

wound and bring de - spair. My guilt is like a heav - y load
groan in an-guished grief. I have no strength, for I am crushed
eyes and throb-bing heart. Friends and com - pan - ions stand far off,
deaf: I can - not hear. I wait for you to an-swer, Lord,
sinned a - gainst your laws. My foes are might - y— those who hate

that is too much for me to bear.
and spend my days with no re - lief.
while oth - ers plot to seek my hurt.
to si - lence those who boast and jeer.
and slan - der me with - out a cause.

6. Do not forsake me, O my Lord;
   do not go far from me, my God.
   Come quickly, help me now, I pray,
   O Lord, my Saviour and my God.

See also: Erhalt uns, Herr 192

Words: Psalm 38; paraphrase, Helen Otte (1931–) Music: Geistliche Lieder (J. Klug), 1543

Psalm 40

I waited for the Lord my God

BALERMA 8 6 8 6 CM

1. I wait - ed for the Lord my God and
2. God took me from a fear - ful pit and
3. A new song now is in my mouth our
4. How man - y are your won - ders, Lord; none

pa - tient - ly did bear; at length to me God
from the mir - y clay; God set my feet up -
God to mag - ni - fy, and man - y now will
can com - pare with them, your gra - cious thoughts to

did in - cline, my voice and cry to hear.
on a rock es - tab - lish - ing my way.
see and fear, and on the Lord re - ly.
us be - yond my pow - er to pro - claim.

Words: Psalm 40; paraphrase, Scottish Psalter 1650, alt   Music: François H. Barthélémon (1741–1808)

Words: this version, copyright © The Presbyterian Church in Canada, 1997   Music: public domain

Psalm 40

I waited, I waited on you, Lord

I WAITED 9 9 9 5

I wait - ed, I wait - ed on you, Lord; I

wait-ed, I wait-ed on you, Lord. You bent down low and re -

mem - bered me when you heard my prayer.

Words: Psalm 40; paraphrase, John L. Bell (1949–) Music: John L. Bell (1949–)

Psalm 42

25
As longs the hart

O WALY, WALY   8 8 8 8 LM

1. As longs the hart for flow - ing streams, so longs my
2. My tears have fed me day and night, while oth - ers
3. Why do I mourn and toil with - in, when it is

soul for you, O God; my soul does thirst for the liv - ing
said, "Where is your God?" But I re - call, as my soul pours
mine to hope in God? I shall a - gain sing praise to

God: when shall I come to see your face?
dry, the days of praise with - in your house.
God, who is my help, who is my God.

See also: O Waly Waly 224 600

Words: Psalm 42; paraphrase, Danna Harkin   Music: English traditional;
arrangement, Noël Tredinnick (1949–)

26

As pants the hart

MARTYDROM 8 6 8 6 CM

1. As pants the hart for cool - ing streams when
2. For thee, my God, the liv - ing God, my
3. Why rest - less, why cast down, my soul? Trust
4. God of my strength, how long shall I, like
5. Why rest - less, why cast down, my soul? Hope

heat - ed in the chase, so longs my soul, O
thirst - y soul doth pine; oh when shall I be -
God, who will em - ploy sure aid for thee, and
one for - got - ten, mourn, for - lorn, for - sak - en
still, and thou shalt sing praise to thy God, the

God, for thee and thy re - fresh - ing grace.
hold thy face, thou maj - es - ty di - vine?
change these sighs to thank - ful hymns of joy.
and ex - posed to my op - pres - sor's scorn?
liv - ing God, thy health's e - ter - nal spring.

Words: Psalm 42; paraphrase, Tate and Brady's New Version 1696, alt   Music: Hugh Wilson (1766–1824)

Words: public domain   Music: public domain

Psalm 42

As the deer

AS THE DEER 87878987

Lyrics:

As the deer pants for the wa-ter so my soul longs aft - er you;

you a - lone are my heart's de - sire, and I long to wor - ship you.

Refrain
You a-lone are my strength, my shield; to you a-lone may my spir-it yield.

You a - lone are my heart's de - sire. and I long to wor - ship you.

Words: Psalm 42; paraphrase, Martin Nystrom (1956-) Music: Martin Nystrom (1956–)

Dieu Créateur et Souverain

2.1 Dieu crée et règne

2.1.1 Dieu vivant est Seigneur,
Créateur de tout, Soutien et Maitre de l'univers.
Dans le retour des saisons et les récoltes,
dans les succès et les défaites des nations,
la bonté et le jugement de Dieu se manifestent,
Tous les événements de ce monde
sont dans la main souveraine du Dieu éternel.

2.1.2. Nous honorons toute sa création,
comme le théâtre de la gloire et de l'oeuvre de Dieu
Dieu règne sur les individus et les nations
et pourtant il ne nie pas notre liberté ni notre responsabilité.
Toujours présent dans nos vies et dans le monde
Dieu dirige toute chose vers l'accomplissement en Jésus-Christ.

2.1.3. Nous affirmons les fins justes et charitables de Dieu
même dans un monde où le mal abonde.
Ces fins se révèlent de façon unique en Jésus-Christ.
En lui nous avons le plus grand paradoxe de la vie;
le Dieu puissant a choisi de venir en état de faiblesse
dans le monde.
Dans le Christ, Dieu a ressenti nos plus profondes souffrances.

2.1.4. Nous ne pouvons entièrement comprendre,
et il ne nous appartient pas de justifier
les actions de Dieu dans le monde.
Nous rencontrons le mal au cours de notre vie.
Mais il ne sera pas le plus fort,
car il va à l'encontre de la volonté de Dieu

Le résurrection de Christ
et la nouvelle vie qui'il nous apporte
nous assurent de sa victoire finale.

Words: from Foi Vivante (2nd edition) 1989
Words: copyright © The Presbyterian Church in Canada, 1989

29

Oh send thy light forth

ST. PAUL 8 6 8 6 CM

1. Oh send thy light forth and thy truth; let
2. Then to God's al - tar I will go to
3. Why art thou then cast down, my soul? What
4. Thou art my ref - uge and my help, my

them be guides to me, and bring me to thine
God, my chief - est joy; O God, my God, to
should dis - cour - age thee? And why with vex - ing
God that doth me raise. I hope in God; I

ho - ly hill, even where thy dwell - ings be.
praise thy name my harp I will em - ploy.
thoughts art thou dis - qui - et - ed in me?
will a - gain have cause to give thee praise.

Words: Psalm 43; paraphrase, Scottish Psalter 1650, alt Music: James Chalmers' Collection, 1749

Words: public domain Music: public domain

30
God is our refuge and our strength

STROUDWATER 8 6 8 6 CM

1. God is our ref - uge and our strength, a
2. though hills a - mid the seas be cast, though
3. A riv - er's there, whose streams make glad the
4. For God, our ref - uge dwell - eth there; that
5. The Lord of Hosts is on our side, our

ver - y pres - ent aid, and, there - fore, though the
wa - ters roar - ing make, and trou - bled be, yea
ci - ty of our God, the ho - ly place, where
ci - ty shall not move. God is its strength when
safe - ty to main - tain; the God of Ja - cob

earth be moved, we will not be a - fraid,
though the hills by swell - ing seas do shake.
God Most High hath made a strong a - bode.
morn - ing dawns, and will its help - er prove.
doth for us a ref - uge high re - main.

Words: Psalm 46; paraphrase, Scottish Psalter 1650, alt   Music: Wilkins' Psalmody 1730

Words: this version, copyright © The Presbyterian Church in Canada, 1997   Music: public domain

31

Psalm 47

Peoples, clap your hands

GENEVAN 47   10 10 10 10 10 10

1. Peo - ples, clap your hands! Shout to God with joy!
   King of all the earth is the Lord Most High;
   all hu - man - i - ty stands in awe of God.
   With a might - y hand God brings na - tions low,

2. God as - cends the throne with a joy - ful cry,
   and with trum - pet sound has gone up on high;
   sing your praise to God, sing with joy - ful voice!
   Rul - ers, peo - ples, now join to serve the Lord,

Words: Psalm 47; paraphrase, Joy F. Patterson (1931–)   Music: Genevan Psalter 1551;
arrangement, Claude Goudimel (c. 1505–1572)

Words: paraphrase, copyright © Joy F. Patterson, 1990   Music: public domain

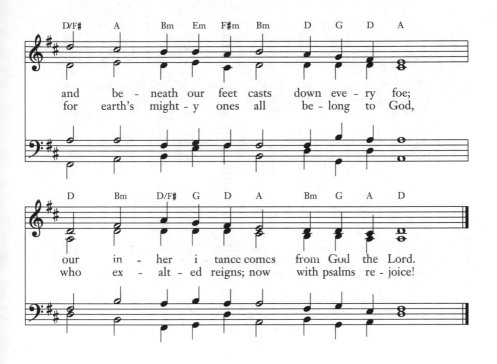

and   be - neath our feet casts   down eve - ry foe;
for earth's might - y ones all be - long to God,

our in - her i - tance comes from God the Lord.
who ex - alt - ed reigns; now with psalms re - joice!

Psalm 48
Within your temple, Lord
GOPSAL 6 6 6 6 8 8

1. With - in your tem - ple, Lord, your mer - cies we will tell,
2. Mount Zi - on, now re - joice! Let Ju - dah's daugh-ters praise
3. The towers of Zi - on tell; its pal - ac - es sur - vey;

for where your name is known there does your praise ex - cel:
with strong and cheer-ful voice, the just - ice God dis - plays;
mark its de - fenc - es well, and to your chil-dren say:

your prais - es sound through eve - ry land; with
go round the walls on Zi - on's mount its
"The Lord, our faith - ful God and guide, this

right - eous reign you shall com - mand.
man - y splen - dours to re - count.
God for - ev - er shall a - bide."

Words: Psalm 48; paraphrase, United Presbyterian Book of Psalms 1871   Music: Congregational
Church Music 1853

Words: public domain   Music: public domain

33

According to thy steadfast love

WINDSOR (DUNDEE) 8 6 8 6 CM

1. Ac - cord-ing to thy stead-fast love have mer - cy, Lord, on me; in
2. Wash me from sin; com - plete-ly cleanse me from in - iq - ui - ty, for
3. For thou de - sir - est truth, O Lord, with - in the in-ward part; thy
4. Purge me with hys-sop; make me clean and whit-er than the snow; thy
5. Blot out all my in - iq - ui - ties; thy face hide from my sin; cre -

thy com - pas - sion great, blot out all my in - iq - ui - ty.
my trans-gres-sions I con - fess; my sin I ev - er see.
wis-dom, Lord, then may I learn; oh teach my se - cret heart.
joy and glad - ness let me hear: thy heal - ing let me know.
ate in me a clean heart, Lord, a spir - it right with - in.

Words: Psalm 51; paraphrase, Scottish Psalter 1650, alt Music: Este's Psalter 1592

34

Psalm 51

God be merciful to me

PRESSBURG (NICHT SO TRAURIG) 7 7 7 7 D

1. God be mer - ci - ful to me; on thy grace I rest my plea.
2. Wash me, wash me pure with - in; cleanse, oh cleanse me from my sin;
3. Gra - cious God, my heart re - new, make my spir - it right and true;

Plen - teous in com - pas - sion thou, blot out my trans - gres - sions now;
I con - fess thy judge - ments just; speech - less, I thy mer - cy trust.
from my sins oh hide thy face, blot them out in bound - less grace.

my trans - gres - sions I con - fess; grief and guilt my soul op - press;
Thou a - lone my Sav - iour art; teach thy wis - dom to my heart;
Cast me not a - way from thee: let thy Spir - it dwell in me;

I have sinned a - gainst thy grace and pro - voked thee to thy face.
make me pure, thy grace be - stow; make me thus thy mer - cy know.
thy sal - va - tion's joy im - part; stead - fast make my will - ing heart.

Words: Psalm 51; parpahrase, Psalter 1912   Music: Geistreiches Gesangbuch (Freylinghausen) 1704

Words: public domain   Music: public domain

35

Psalm 61
Listen to my prayer, Lord

LISTENING 6 5 6 5

1. Lis - ten to my prayer, Lord; hear my hum - ble
2. In earth's far - thest cor - ner you will hear my
3. You have been my shel - ter when the foe was
4. I will rest for - ev - er in your care and
5. All that I have prom - ised, help me to ful -
6. May your truth and mer - cy keep me all my

cry; when my heart is faint - ing,
voice: set me on your rock, Lord;
near, as a tower of ref - uge
love, guard - ed and in all who love you
fil, and in all who love you
days; let my words and ac - tions

1. – 5.

to your throne I fly.
then I shall re - joice.
shield-ing me from fear.
as by wings a - bove.
work your per - fect will.

6.

6. be my songs of praise!

Alternate tune: Caswall (Bemerton)

Words: Psalm 61; paraphrase, James Seddon (1915–1983), alt Music: Norman Warren (1934–)

Psalm 62

I rest in God alone

WAINWRIGHT Irregular

Unison
Refrain

I rest in God a-lone,   from whom comes my sal-va-tion;

my souls finds rest in God,   my for-tress: I'll not be sha-ken.

1. My hope is in   the Lord, my hon-our and strength;   my
2. Oh trust in God,   you peo - ple; pour out your hearts,   for

ref- uge is the   Lord   for - ev - er,
God is our ref - uge   for - ev - er,

Words: Psalm 62; paraphrase, John Daniels (20th cent.)   Music: John Daniels (20th cent.)
arrangement, Christopher Norton (1953–)

my trust and all of my heart—

in God a-lone my soul finds rest.

rest.

Psalm 63

37 O God, thou art my God alone

WAINWRIGHT 8 8 8 8 LM

1. O God, thou art my God a - lone;
2. Yet through this rough and thorn - y maze
3. Thee in the watch - es of the night
4. Bet - ter than life it - self, thy love,
5. Praise with my heart, my mind, my voice,

ear - ly to thee my soul shall cry, a pil - grim in a
I fol - low hard on thee, my God; thy hand un - seen a up -
when I re-mem - ber on my bed, thy pres-ence makes the
dear - er than all be - side to me, for whom have I in
for all thy mer - cy I will give; my soul shall still in

land un-known, a thirst - y land whose springs are dry.
holds my ways; I safe - ly tread where thou hast trod.
dark - ness light; thy guard - ian wings are round my head.
heaven a - bove, or what on earth, com - pared with thee?
God re - joice; my tongue shall bless thee while I live.

Words: Psalm 63; paraphrase, James Montgomery (1771–1854) Music: Richard Wainwright (1758–1825)

Words: public domain Music: public domain

Psalm 65

38 Praise is your right, O God, in Zion

GENEVAN 65 9 6 9 6 D

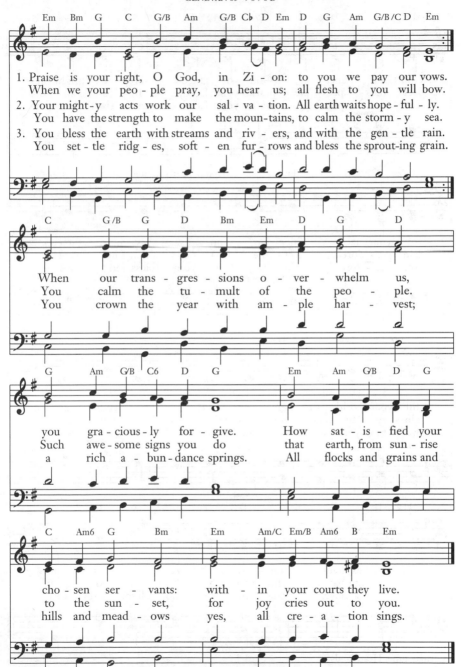

1. Praise is your right, O God, in Zi - on: to you we pay our vows.
   When we your peo - ple pray, you hear us; all flesh to you will bow.
2. Your might - y acts work our sal - va - tion. All earth waits hope - ful - ly.
   You have the strength to make the moun - tains, to calm the storm - y sea.
3. You bless the earth with streams and riv - ers, and with the gen - tle rain.
   You set - tle ridg - es, soft - en fur - rows and bless the sprout-ing grain.

When our trans - gres - sions o - ver - whelm us,
You calm the tu - mult of the peo - ple.
You crown the year with am - ple har - vest;

you gra - cious - ly for - give. How sat - is - fied your
Such awe - some signs you do that earth, from sun - rise
a rich a - bun - dance springs. All flocks and grains and

cho - sen ser - vants: with - in your courts they live.
to the sun - set, for joy cries out to you.
hills and mead - ows yes, all cre - a - tion sings.

Words: Psalm 65; paraphrase, Stanley Wiersma (1930–1986) Music: Genevan Psalter 1551;
harmony, Dale Grotenhuis (1931–)

39

God of mercy, God of grace

DIX 777777

1. God of mer-cy, God of grace, show the bright-ness
2. Let the peo-ple praise you, Lord; be by all that
3. Let the peo-ple praise you, Lord; earth shall then its

of your face. Shine up - on us, Sav - iour, shine;
live a - dored. Let the na - tions shout and sing
fruits af - ford. Un - to us your bless - ing give;

fill your world with light di - vine, and your sav - ing
glo - ry to their gra - cious King; at your feet their
we to you de - vot - ed live, all be - low and

health ex-tend un - to earth's re - mot - est end.
trib - ute pay, and your ho - ly will o - bey.
all a-bove, one in joy and light and love.

Alternate tune: Heathlands

Words: Psalm 66; paraphrase, Henry Francis Lyte (1793–1847), alt   Music: Conrad Kocher (1786–1872); arrangement, William Henry Monk (1823–1889)

40

Let us praise

BA NI NGYETI 8 8 8 with refrain

1. Let us praise the God of truth, let us praise the God of peace,
2. Ba ni ngye - ti Ba Ya - we, ba ni ngye - ti Ba Ya - we,
3. Ren-dons grâ - ce au Dieu saint, ren-dons grâ - ce au Dieu juste,

let us praise the God of love.
ba ni ngye - ti Ba Ya - we.
ren-dons grâ - ce au Dieu bon.

A - men.

Hal - le-lu-jah,
Al - lé-lu-ia,

hal - le-lu-jah, hal - le-lu-jah.
al - lé-lu-ia, al - lé-lu-ia.

A - men.

Words: traditional Mungaka (Cameroon); translation, R. Gerald Hobbs (1941–) Music: traditional Cameroon; arrangement, Andrew Donaldson (1951–)

Psalm 68

Great God, arise

OLD 113th 887887D

1. Great God, a-rise, and by your might de-feat all foes of truth and right;
2. But wid-ows and the fa-ther-less the Lord shall com-fort, heal and bless,
3. To God we lift our fer-vent praise, who o-ver-whelms us all our days
4. Come now all peo-ples of the earth: choose songs that nob-ly praise God's worth,

save us from e-vil's ter-ror. As smoke is driv-en by the storm,
who is their faith-ful fa-ther. God gives the des-o-late a place
with good things be-yond mea-sure, who cares for us: our Lord a-bove,
God's grace and gran-deur tell-ing. Praise God who reigns in glo-ry high,

as wax by fire is left no form, drive out all hu-man er-ror,
and pris-oners find re-lease and grace; the lost ones God will gath-er.
who shows e-ter-nal, faith-ful love by gifts from stores of trea-sure.
whose word like thun-der splits the sky, all power on earth com-pel-ling.

Words: Psalm 68; paraphrase, Norman Kansfield (1940–) Music: Matthäus Greiter (c. 1500–1552),
Strassburger Kirchenamt 1525; harmony, V. Earle Copes (1921–)

Words: paraphrase, copyright © Norman Kansfield, 1976, 1981 Music: harmony, copyright © Abingdon Press, 1964

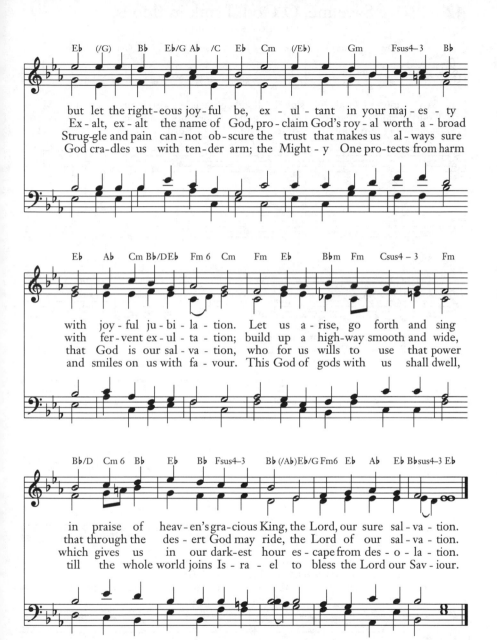

but let the right-eous joy-ful be, ex - ul - tant in your maj - es - ty
Ex - alt, ex - alt the name of God, pro - claim God's roy - al worth a - broad
Strug-gle and pain can-not ob-scure the trust that makes us al - ways sure
God cra-dles us with ten-der arm; the Might - y One pro-tects from harm

with joy - ful ju - bi - la - tion. Let us a - rise, go forth and sing
with fer-vent ex - ul - ta - tion; build up a high-way smooth and wide,
that God is our sal - va - tion, who for us wills to use that power
and smiles on us with fa - vour. This God of gods with us shall dwell,

in praise of heav-en's gra-cious King, the Lord, our sure sal - va - tion.
that through the des - ert God may ride, the Lord of our sal - va - tion.
which gives us in our dark-est hour es - cape from des - o - la - tion.
till the whole world joins Is - ra - el to bless the Lord our Sav - iour.

Psalms

Psalm 69

42   Save me, O God; I sink in floods

SALVATION 8 6 8 6 D CMD

1. Save me, O God; I sink in floods, plunged in - to mis - er - y. My
2. Your stead-fast mer - cy, Lord, is good; hide not your face from me. Hear
3. Though I am poor and sor-row - ful, O Lord, at - tend my cry. Let

con-stant weep-ing brings no help; Lord, hear and an - swer me. In
my dis - tress and an - swer, Lord; make haste and set me free. You
your sal - va - tion come to me and lift me up on high. Let

full as - sur - ance of your grace I turn to you in prayer. De -
know of my re - proach and shame; my heart de - spairs from grief. I
heaven and earth and seas re - joice; let all that move give praise. All

Words: Psalm 69; paraphrase, Marie J. Post (1919–1990) Music: Kentucky Harmony 1816;
harmony, Songs for Liturgy and More Hymns and Spiritual Songs 1971

liv - er me from surg-ing floods; draw near; reach out in care.
looked for pit - y, but I found no com - fort or re - lief.
those that love God's nameshall live in Zi - on all their days.

Psalm 72

43 God's name forever shall endure

DUNFERMLINE 8 6 8 6 CM

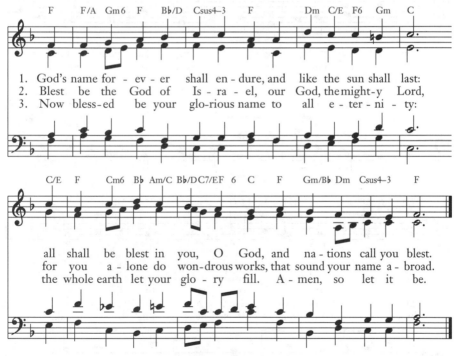

1. God's name for - ev - er shall en - dure, and like the sun shall last:
2. Blest be the God of Is - ra - el, our God, themight-y Lord,
3. Now bless-ed be your glo-rious name to all e - ter - ni - ty:

all shall be blest in you, O God, and na - tions call you blest.
for you a - lone do won-drous works, that sound your name a - broad.
the whole earth let your glo - ry fill. A - men, so let it be.

Words: Psalm 72; paraphrase, Scottish Psalter 1650, alt   Music: Scottish Psalter 1615

Words: this version, copyright © The Presbyterian Church in Canada, 1997 Music: public domain

Psalm 73

44 In sweet communion, Lord, with you

BEDFORDSHIRE MAY DAY CAROL 8 6 8 6 CM

1. In sweet com - mu - nion, Lord, with you I
2. Your coun - sel through my earth - ly way shall
3. Whom have I, Lord, in heaven but you, to
4. Though flesh and heart should faint and fail, the
5. To live a - part from God is death; 'tis

con - stant - ly a - bide; my hand you hold with -
guide me and con - trol, and then to glo - ry
whom my thoughts as - pire? And, hav - ing you, what
Lord will ev - er be the strength and por - tion
good God's face to seek. You are my ref - uge,

in your own to keep me near your side.
af - ter - ward you will re - ceive my soul.
more on earth is there I can de - sire?
of my heart, my God e - ter - nal - ly.
liv - ing God; your praise I long to speak.

Words: Psalm 73; paraphrase, Psalter 1912, alt Music: English traditional; arrangement, Paul Edwards (1955–)

Words: public domain Music: arrangement, copyright © Paul Edwards

Psalm 77

45

I cried out for heaven to hear me

HARVEST 9 8 9 8

Unison

1. I cried out for heav - en to hear me,
2. But in my de - spair I re - mem - bered
3. you spoke in the wind and the thun - der,

I reached out to God for my help, no coun - sel or
the songs of a long time a - go, and dreamed of the
the earth and the el - e-ments shook; your power tore the

com - fort would cheer me, my spir - it a - ban-doned all hope.
maj - es - ty splen-doured of God the al - might - y, the true:
wa - ters a - sun - der, as Shep-herd, you guid - ed your flock.

Words: Psalm 77; paraphrase, Michael Perry (1942–1996)   Music: Michael Metcalf

Psalm 78
We will tell each generation
RESTORATION 8 7 8 7

1. We will tell each gen - er - a - tion all that
2. tell the time of our re - bel - ling— how we
3. tell how once, when spite and ter - ror threat - ened
4. Tell the grace that falls from heav - en, an - gels'

you, our God, have done; how you called and
wan - dered from your way, how your law our
to en - gulf our land, you de - fend - ed
food as faith's re - ward; tell how sins may

led our na - tion, chose us out to be your own:
love com - pel - ling taught us hum - bly to o - bey:
us with vig - our, saved us by a might - y hand.
be for - giv - en through the mer - cy of the Lord.

Words: Psalm 78; paraphrase, Michael Perry (1942–1996) Music: Walker's Southern Harmony,
1835; harmony, Charles Webb (1933–), alt.

Psalm 79

Remember not, O God

SOUTHWELL (DAMAN) 6 6 8 6 SM

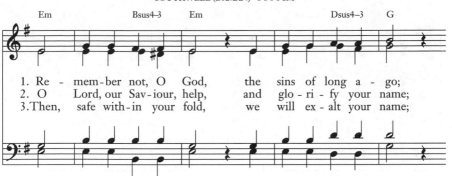

1. Re - mem-ber not, O God, the sins of long a - go;
2. O Lord, our Sav-iour, help, and glo - ri - fy your name;
3. Then, safe with-in your fold, we will ex - alt your name;

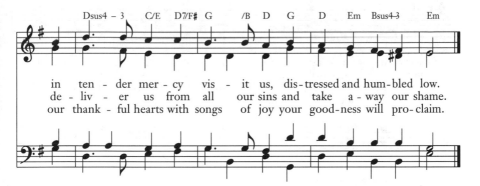

in ten - der mer - cy vis - it us, dis-tressed and hum-bled low.
de - liv - er us from all our sins and take a - way our shame.
our thank - ful hearts with songs of joy your good-ness will pro-claim.

Words: Psalm 79; paraphrase, Psalter 1912 Music: Daman's Psalter 1579

Words: public domain Music: public domain

48

God of hosts, you chose a vine

ST. BEES 7 7 7 7

1. God of hosts, you chose a vine meant to bear the fin-est wine, set it in a prom-ised land, nur-tured by your care-ful hand.
2. Like a ce-dar, it grew strong— deep its roots, its ten-drils long; yet, in en-vy those a-round stripped its branch-es to the ground.
3. Des-o-late, to God we cry: "Spare us from the en-e-my!" God of hosts, turn back a-gain, all such wick-ed-ness re-strain.
4. Turn us too, for we have failed, faith-ful-ness has not pre-vailed; vis-it, Lord, and heal your vine, on its fruit let glo-ry shine!

Alternate tune: Lübeck

Words: Psalm 80; paraphrase, David Mowbray (1938–)   Music: John Bacchus Dykes (1823–1876)

Words: paraphrase, copyright © 1990 by Hope Publishing Co.   Music: public domain

49
Oh hear our cry, O Lord

REDEMPTOR 6 6 8 6 SM with refrain

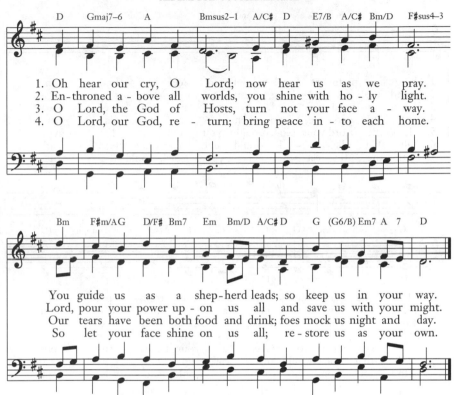

1. Oh hear our cry, O Lord; now hear us as we pray.
2. En-throned a - bove all worlds, you shine with ho - ly light.
3. O Lord, the God of Hosts, turn not your face a - way.
4. O Lord, our God, re - turn; bring peace in - to each home.

You guide us as a shep-herd leads; so keep us in your way.
Lord, pour your power up - on us all and save us with your might.
Our tears have been both food and drink; foes mock us night and day.
So let your face shine on us all; re - store us as your own.

Words: Psalm 80; paraphrase, Fred R. Anderson (1941–) Music: John W. Wilson (1905–1992)

Words: paraphrase, copyright © Fred R. Anderson, 1986; alt with permission, 1996 Music: copyright © Oxford University Press

50

Sing a psalm of joy
GENEVAN 81   5 6 9 5 9

1. Sing a psalm of joy! Shout in cel - e - bra - tion.
2. Sound the fes - tal horn, your thanks - giv - ing voic - ing.
3. When in need you cried, I was near and saved you.
4. O my peo - ple, hear; when I call you, lis - ten.
5. I, the Lord your God, brought you out of E - gypt.
6. Oh that Is - ra - el would but hear my plead - ing!
7. With the fin - est wheat I, your Lord, would feed you.

Let the tam - bou - rine and the trum - pet bring
Praise, O Is - ra - el, as God did com - mand
From the cloud I spoke, an - swered your re - quest —
Choose no for - eign god — lis - ten to my plea.
I re - moved your yoke, all your needs sup - plied.
Oh that they would turn, walk up - on my path;
Hon - ey from the rock I would glad - ly give

prais - es to our King for God's great sal - va - tion.
when from E - gypt's land you came forth re - joic - ing.
Mer - i - bah the test — I did not for - sake you.
Have no god but me; come and be for - giv - en.
O - pen your mouth wide: sure - ly I will fill it.
I would pour my wrath on their foes un - heed - ing.
that you all might live. Hear me, O my peo - ple.

Words: Psalm 81; paraphrase, Marie J. Post (1919–1990)   Music: Genevan Psalter 1562; harmony, Dale Grotenhuis (1931–)

Words: paraphrase, copyright © CRC Publications, 1987   Music: harmony, copyright © CRC Publications, 1987

Psalm 82

51

There where the judges gather

MUNICH 7676D

1. There where the judg - es gath - er, a great - er takes the seat;
2. Deal just - ly with the need - y; pro - tect the pow - er - less;
3. God speaks: "I named you rul - ers, to serve the Most High God,

"How long," God asks the judg - es, "will you pro - nounce de - ceit?
de - liv - er the af - flict - ed from those who would op - press,
but you shall die as mor - tals and per - ish by my rod."

How long show spe - cial fa - vour to those of ill re - pute?
but you are sure - ly blind - ed; you do not un - der - stand:
A - rise, O God, in judge - ment, your sov - ereign - ty make known,

How long ne - glect the or - phan, the poor and des - ti - tute?
there - fore foun - da - tions tot - ter; in - jus - tice rocks the land."
for yours are all the na - tions; the peo - ples are your own.

Alternate tune: St. Theodulph

Words: Psalm 82; paraphrase, Henry Zylstra (1909–1956), alt Music: Neuvermehrtes Gesangbuch 1693;
arrangement, Felix Mendelssohn (1809–1847)

Words: public domain Music: public domain

Psalm 84

52 How lovely is thy dwelling place

HARINGTON 8 6 8 6 CM

1. How love - ly is thy dwell - ing - place, O
2. My thirst - y soul longs vehe - ment - ly; it
3. Be - hold the spar - row find - eth out a
4. thine al - tars, where she might bring forth her
5. How blest are they that in thy house for -

Lord of hosts, to me! The tab - er - na - cles
faints thy courts to see: my ve - ry heart and
house where - in to rest; the swal - low al - so
young in safe a - bode, O thou Al - might - y
ev - er give thee praise. Blest are all those whose

of thy grace, how pleas - ant, Lord, they be!
flesh cry out, O liv - ing God, for thee.
for her young hath built her - self a nest,
Lord of hosts, my Sov - ereign and my God.
strength thou art, in whose heart are thy ways.

Words: Psalm 84; paraphrase, Scottish Psalter 1650, alt Music: Henry Harington (1727–1816)

Words: public domain Music: public domain

Psalm 84

53

How lovely, Lord, how lovely

MERLE'S TUNE 7 6 7 6 D

1. How love-ly, Lord, how love - ly is your a - bid - ing place;
2. In your blest courts to wor - ship, O God, a sin - gle day
3. A sun and shield for - ev - er are you, O Lord Most High;

my soul is long-ing, faint - ing, to feast up - on your grace.
is bet - ter than a thou - sand if I from you should stray.
you show-er us with bless - ings; no good will you de - ny.

The spar - row finds a shel - ter, a place to build her nest,
I'd rath - er keep the en - trance and claim you as my Lord,
The saints, your grace re - ceiv - ing, from strength to strength shall go,

and so your tem - ple calls us with - in its walls to rest.
than rev - el in the rich - es the ways of sin af - ford.
and from their life shall riv - ers of bless-ing o - ver - flow.

Words: Psalm 84; paraphrase, Arlo D. Duba (1929–) Music: Hal H. Hopson (1933–)
Words: paraphrase, copyright © 1986 by Hope Publishing Co. Music: copyright © 1983 by Hope Publishing Co.

Psalms
Psalm 89

54

My song forever shall record

ST. PETERSBURG 888888

1. My song for-ev-er shall re-cord the ten-der mer-cies
2. Al-might-y God, thy loft-y throne has jus-tice for its
3. The swell-ing sea o-beys thy will; its an-gry waves thy
4. With bless-ing is the na-tion crowned whose peo-ple know the

of the Lord; thy faith-ful-ness will I pro-claim, and
cor-ner-stone, and shin-ing bright be-fore thy face are
voice can still; the heavens and earth, by right di-vine, the
joy-ful sound; they in the light, O Lord, shall live, the

eve-ry age shall know thy name. I sing of mer-cies
truth and love and bound-less grace. The heavens shall join in
world and all there-in are thine; the whole cre-a-tion's
light thy face and fa-vour give. Their fame and might to

Words: Psalm 89; paraphrase, Psalter 1912   Music: Dmitri Stepanovich Bortnyanski (1751–1825)
Words: public domain Music: public domain

62

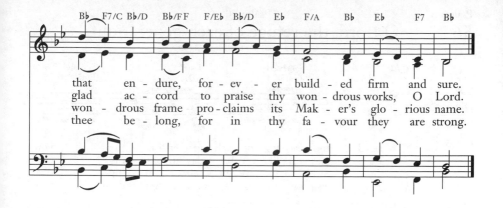

that en - dure, for - ev - er build - ed firm and sure.
glad ac - cord to praise thy won - drous works, O Lord.
won - drous frame pro - claims its Mak - er's glo - rious name.
thee be - long, for in thy fa - vour they are strong.

55   God moves in a mysterious way

1. God moves in a mysterious way
   his wonders to perform;
   he plants his footsteps in the sea,
   and rides upon the storm.

2. Deep in unfathomable mines
   of never failing skill
   he treasures up his bright designs,
   and works his sovereign will.

3. Ye fearful saints, fresh courage take;
   the clouds ye so much dread
   are big with mercy, and shall break
   in blessings on your head.

4. Judge not the Lord by feeble sense,
   but trust him for his grace;
   behind a frowning providence
   he hides a smiling face.

5. His purposes will ripen fast,
   unfolding every hour;
   the bud may have a bitter taste,
   but sweet will be the flower.

6. Blind unbelief is sure to err,
   and scan his work in vain;
   God is his own interpreter,
   and he will make it plain.

Words: William Cowper (1731–1800)
Words: public domain

Psalm 90

56   O Lord, the refuge of each generation

O LORD, THE REFUGE   11 10 11 10

Not too fast
Capo 3 (D)

O Lord, the re-fuge of each gen-er-a - tion, you
thou - sand years like yes-ter - day in pass - ing, our
ho - ly Lord, for-give our self-de-ceiv - ing— our
rush - es on: give us a heart of wis - dom that

reigned be-fore the u - ni - verse be - gan; we bear your
fleet - ing lives like half - re - mem-bered dreams, or weeds that
se - cret sins are clear be - fore your face: grant us re -
seeks your will and fol-lows your com - mands; show us your

stamp, the marks of your cre - a - tion, and yet how
flower at noon but die by eve - ning— so, Lord, to
lease, the joy of those be - liev - ing they are re -
deeds, your glo -ry to our chil - dren; work out your

Words: Psalm 90; paraphrase, Basil E. Bridge (1927–)   Music: Christopher Norton (1953–)

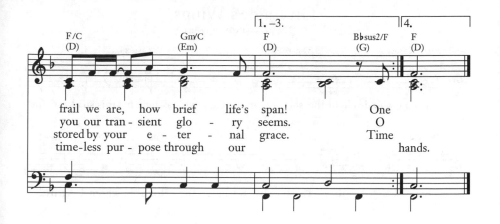

frail we are,	how	brief	life's	span!	One
you our tran-	sient	glo -	ry	seems.	O
stored by your	e - ter -	nal	grace.	Time
time-less pur -	pose through	our	hands.

Psalm 90
You who dwell in the shelter /
On Eagle's Wings
ON EAGLE'S WINGS Irregular

Solo or choir

1. You who dwell in the shel-ter of our God, who a - bide in this shad-ow for

life, say to the Lord: "My ref-uge, my Rock in whom I trust!"

Refrain

All "And I will raise you up on ea-gle's wings, bear you on the breath of dawn,

make you to shine like the sun, and hold you in the palm of my hand."

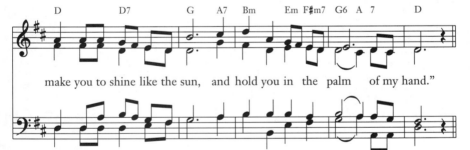

after last refrain (Solo or choir)

and hold you, hold you in the palm of my hand."

Words: Psalm 91 paraphrase, Michael Joncas (1951–) Music: Michael Joncas (1951–)

2. The snare of the fowl-er will nev-er cap-ture you, and fam-ine will bring you no fear: un - der God's wings your ref - uge, God's faith - ful - ness your shield.

3. You need not fear the ter-ror of the night, nor the ar-row that flies by day; though thou - sands fall a - bout you, near you it shall not come.

4. For to God's an - gels is giv - en a com-mand to guard you in all of your ways, up - on their hands they will bear you up, lest you dash your foot a-gainst a stone.

58

To render thanks unto the Lord

BISHOPTHORPE 8 6 8 6 CM

1. To ren - der thanks un - to the Lord, it
2. Thy lov - ing - kind - ness to show forth when
3. up - on a ten - stringed in - stru - ment, up -
4. For thou, Lord, by thy might - y works hast

is a come - ly thing, and to thy name, O
shines the morn - ing light, and to de - clare thy
on the psal - ter - y, and on the harp with
made my heart right glad, and I will tri - umph

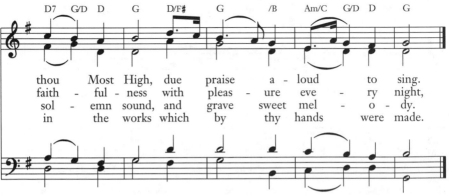

thou Most High, due praise a - loud to sing.
faith - ful - ness with pleas - ure eve - ry night,
sol - emn sound, and grave sweet mel - o - dy.
in the works which by thy hands were made.

Words: Psalm 92; paraphrase, Scottish Psalter 1650, alt   Music: Jeremiah Clarke (c. 1674–1707)

Words: public domain   Music: public domain

Psalms

59

To God in the highest

GLORIA (IONA) Irregular

Words: John L. Bell (1949-), and Iona Community (Scotland) Music: John L. Bell (1949-),
Iona Community (Scotland)

Psalm 93

60 God, our Sovereign Lord remaining

BRYN CALFARIA 878787

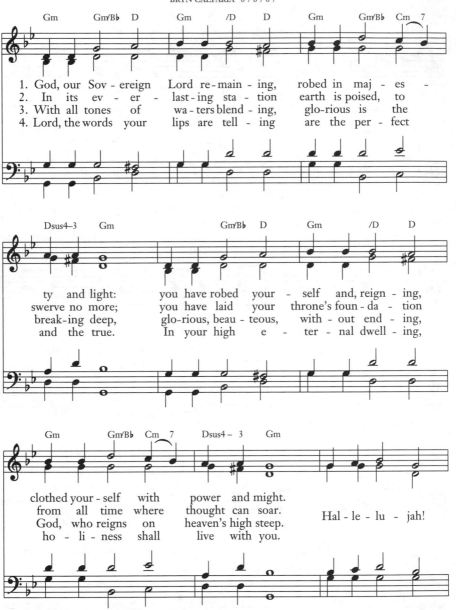

1. God, our Sov-ereign Lord re-main-ing, robed in maj - es -
2. In its ev - er - last-ing sta - tion earth is poised, to
3. With all tones of wa-ters blend - ing, glo-rious is the
4. Lord, the words your lips are tell - ing are the per - fect

ty and light: you have robed your - self and, reign-ing,
swerve no more; you have laid your throne's foun-da - tion
break-ing deep, glo-rious, beau - teous, with - out end - ing,
and the true. In your high e - ter - nal dwell-ing,

clothed your - self with power and might.
from all time where thought can soar.
God, who reigns on heaven's high steep. Hal - le - lu - jah!
ho - li - ness shall live with you.

Words: Psalm 93; paraphrase, John Keble (1792–1866)   Music: William Owen (1814–1893);
arrangement, Ralph Vaughan Williams (1872–1958)

Words: public domain   Music: arrangement, copyright © Oxford University Press

God our Lord in depth and height!
God our Lord in depth and height.

Hal-le-lu-jah! Hal-le-lu-jah!

Lord, you are for-ev-er-more!
Lord, you are for-ev-er-more!

Songs of o-cean nev-er sleep.
Songs of o-cean nev-er sleep.

Lord, your word is ev-er true.
Lord, your word is ev-er true.

Psalm 95

61

Oh come and sing unto the Lord

IRISH 8 6 8 6 CM

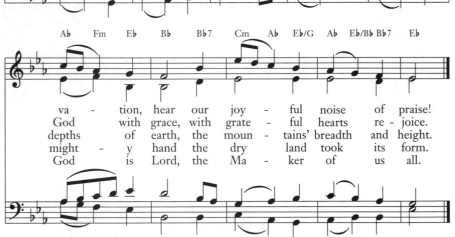

1. Oh come and sing un - to the Lord; to
2. Be - fore God's pres - ence let us come with
3. Our God is great and reigns su - preme a -
4. The sea be - longs to God a - lone who
5. Oh come and let us wor - ship God as

God our voic - es raise. O Rock of our sal -
praise and thank - ful voice; let us sing psalms to
bove all power and might; God's hand still holds the
made both calm and storm, and from the Ma - ker's
to our knees we fall; we are God's peo - ple;

va - tion, hear our joy - ful noise of praise!
God with grace, with grate - ful hearts re - joice.
depths of earth, the moun - tains' breadth and height.
might - y hand the dry land took its form.
God is Lord, the Ma - ker of us all.

Words: Psalm 95; paraphrase, Psalter, 1912, alt   Music: A Collection of Hymns and Sacred Poems, 1749

Words: this version, copyright © Andrew Donaldson, 1996 Music: public domain

Psalm 98
New songs of celebration render
RENDEZ À DIEU 9 8 9 8 D

1. New songs of cel - e - bra-tion ren - der to God who has great won-ders done.
2. Joy - ful - ly, heart - i - ly re - sounding, let eve - ry in - stru-ment and voice
3. Riv - ers and seas and tor-rents roar - ing, hon-our the Lord with wild ac-claim;

Love sits en-throned in age-less splen-dour; come and a - dore the might-y One.
peal out the praise of grace a-bound-ing, call - ing the whole world to re - joice.
moun-tains and stones, look up a - dor - ing and find a voice to praise God's name.

God has made known the great sal-va- tion which all the saints with joy con-fess.
Trum-pets and or - gans, set in mo-tion such sounds as make the heav-ens ring;
Right-teous, com - mand-ing, ev - er glo-rious, prais - es be sung that nev - er cease:

God has re-vealed to eve - ry na-tion truth and un - end - ing right-teous-ness.
all things that live in earth and o - cean, sound forth the song, your prais-es bring.
just is our God, whose truth vic-to-rious es - tab - lish - es the world in peace.

Words: Psalm 98; paraphrase, Erik Routley (1917–1982) Music: Louis Bourgeois (c. 1510–1561)

63

Psalm 98

O sing a new song to the Lord

JACKSON 8 6 8 6 CM

1. Oh sing a new song to the Lord, for won - ders God has done, whose right hand and whose ho - ly arm great vic - to - ry has won.
2. The Lord makes known the vic - to - ry— we tri - umph in God's might!— for jus - tice now has been re - vealed in all the na - tions' sight.
3. The Lord re - mem - bers stead - fast love, with Is - rael's house has stood, and all the ends of earth have seen the vic - tory of our God.
4. Let all the earth un - to the Lord send forth a joy - ful noise; lift up your voice a - loud to God, sing prais - es, and re - joice.
5. Let seas and all their full - ness roar, the world, and dwell - ers there; let floods clap hands be - fore the Lord; let hills their joy de - clare.
6. Oh sing for joy be - fore the Lord who comes in vic - to - ry to judge the world with righ - teous - ness, and rule with eq - ui - ty.

Words: Psalm 98; paraphrase, Scottish Psalter 1650, alt   Music: Thomas Jackson (1715–1781)

Words: this version, copyright © The Presbyterian Church in Canada, 1997 Music: public domain

64

Be still and know that I am God

BE STILL AND KNOW 8 8 8

1. Be still and know that I am God.
2. I am the Lord that heal - eth thee.
3. In thee, O Lord, I put my trust.

Be still and know that I am God.
I am the Lord that heal - eth thee.
In thee, O Lord, I put my trust.

Be still and know that I am God.
I am the Lord that heal - eth thee.
In thee, O Lord, I put my trust.

Words: anonymous Music: anonymous

Words: public domain Music: public domain

Psalm 100

65 All people that on earth do dwell

OLD 100th 8 8 8 8 LM

1. All peo - ple that on earth do dwell, sing
2. Know that the Lord is God in - deed; with -
3. Oh en - ter then his gates with praise; ap -
4. For why, the Lord our God is good; his

to the Lord with cheer - ful voice. Him serve with mirth; his
out our aid he did us make; we are his flock, he
proach with joy his courts un - to; praise, laud and bless his
mer - cy is for - ev - er sure; his truth at all times

praise forth tell. Come ye be - fore him and re - joice.
doth us feed, and for his sheep he doth us take.
name al - ways, for it is seem - ly so to do.
firm - ly stood, and shall from age to age en - dure.

Words: Psalm 100; paraphrase, William Kethe (c. 1535–1594) as in Scottish Psalter 1650
Music: Genevan Psalter 1551; last line from Ravencroft's Psalter 1621; fauxbourdon, John Dowland (1563–1626)

Words: public domain Music: public domain

Fauxbourdon
Congregation

Alternate choral or instrumental accompaniment.

66

Psalm 100

Shout for joy to the Lord

SHOUT FOR JOY   Irregular

Shout for joy to the Lord, all the earth; serve the Lord with glad-ness.

Come with thanks-giv-ing, sing joy-ful songs; it is God who made us.

We are God's peo - ple, the sheep of God's pas - ture.

En - ter God's gates with thanks - giv - ing. En - ter the gates with thanks-

Words: Psalm 100; paraphrase, Andrew Donaldson (1951–) Music: Andrew Donaldson (1951–)

79

Psalm 102

67

Thou shalt arise

DUKE STREET 8 8 8 8 LM

1. Thou shalt a - rise, and mer - cy yet thou to mount
2. Thy ser - vants trea - sure Zi - on's stones; its ver - y
3. With glo - ry God shall soon ap - pear to build up
4. The des - ti - tute God will not scorn: this for all

Zi - on shalt ex - tend: the time is come, the
dust to them is dear. Na - tions and lands and
Zi - on and re - pair; with true com - pas - sion
time let us re - cord, that gen - er - a - tions

time that's set, when thou shalt grace and fa - vour send.
powers and thrones on earth thy glo - rious name shall fear.
God shall hear and not de - spise the need - y prayer.
yet un - born may praise and mag - ni - fy the Lord.

Words: Psalm 102; paraphrase, Scottish Psalter 1650, alt   Music: John Warrington Hatton
(c. 1710–1793)

Words: this version, copyright © The Presbyterian Church in Canada, 1997 Music: public domain

68

Psalm 103

Bless the Lord, O my soul

BLESS THE LORD, O MY SOUL 12 8 12 8

Unison
Refrain

Bless the Lord, O my soul, and all with-in me hon-our God's name;

bless the Lord, O my soul, and ne-ver for-get all God's bless-ings.

Words: Psalm 103; paraphrase, Michael Baughen (1930–), alt Music: Michael Baughen (1930–);
arrangement, Noël Tredinnick (1949–)

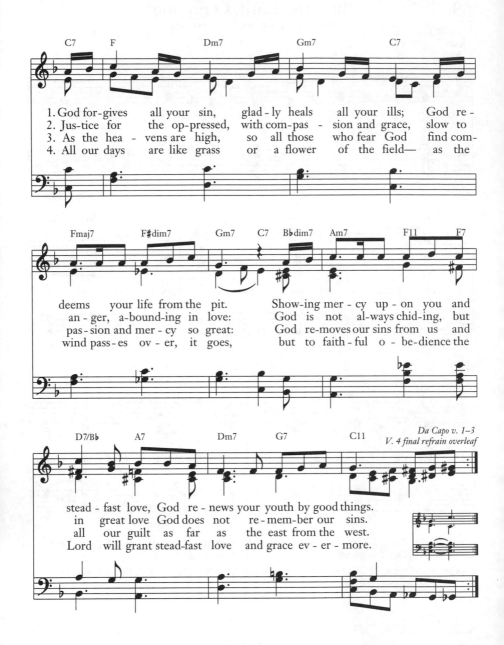

C7   F   Dm7   Gm7   C7

1. God for-gives   all your sin,   glad - ly heals   all your ills;   God re -
2. Jus-tice for   the op-pressed,   with com-pas -   sion and grace,   slow to
3. As the hea -   vens are high,   so all those   who fear God   find com-
4. All our days   are like grass   or a flower   of the field—   as the

Fmaj7   F♯dim7   Gm7   C7 B♭dim7 Am7   F11   F7

deems   your life from the pit.   Show-ing mer - cy up - on you and
an - ger, a-bound-ing in love: God is not al-ways chid-ing, but
pas - sion and mer - cy so great: God re-moves our sins from us and
wind pass-es ov - er, it goes,   but to faith-ful o - be-dience the

D7/B♭   A7   Dm7   G7   C11

Da Capo v. 1–3
V. 4 final refrain overleaf

stead - fast love, God re - news your youth by good things.
in great love God does not re - mem - ber our sins.
all our guilt as far as the east from the west.
Lord will grant stead-fast love and grace ev - er - more.

82

Final Refrain

Bless the Rul-er of all, all you the an-gels do-ing God's word;

bless the Lord, all the hosts and all of God's works in cre - a - tion!

Bless the Lord, O my soul!

83

Psalm 103

69

O thou, my soul, bless God the Lord

ST. PAUL 8 6 8 6 CM

1. O thou, my soul, bless God the Lord, and
2. Bless now my soul, the Lord thy God, and
3. In - iq - ui - ties and sins God will most
4. My God re - deems my life, that I to
5. The Lord will sat - is - fy my soul a -

all that is with - in, a - wake to praise and
not for - get - ful be, of all the gra - cious
gra - cious - ly for - give: all thy dis - eas - es
death might not go down; with mer - cy and with
bun - dant - ly with good, so ev - en as the

mag - ni - fy and bless God's ho - ly name.
ben - e - fits God hath be - stowed on thee.
and thy pain most ten - der - ly re - lieve.
stead - fast love the Lord my soul will crown.
ea - gle's life my youth will be re - newed.

Words: Psalm 103; paraphrase, Scottish Psalter 1650, alt Music: James Chalmers' Collection 1749

Words: this version, copyright © The Presbyterian Church in Canada, 1997 Music: public domain

70

Psalm 104

All things I see

SAN ROCCO 8 6 8 6 CM

1. All things I see, Lord, call to me to
2. I see your beau - ty in the dawn, your
3. Your wa - ters gath - er in the skies and
4. All things that grow, all things that live, and

speak their Mak - er's praise: how you have brought them
good-ness in the light; I see your power in
fall to fill the seas; your lands, the moun - tains
I my - self make known what praise, what glo - ry

all to be and guide them in their ways.
winds and storm, your wis - dom in the night.
where they rise, are or - dered as you please.
I must give to you, my God, a - lone.

Words: Psalm 104; paraphrase, Brian Foley (1919–) Music: Derek Williams (1945–)

Psalm 106

71 ## It is good to give thanks to you, Lord

NEW 106TH Irregular

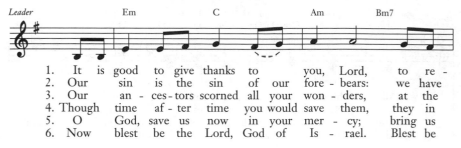

1. It is good to give thanks to you, Lord, to re -
2. Our sin is the sin of our fore - bears: we have
3. Our an - ces-tors scorned all your won - ders, at the
4. Though time af - ter time you would save them, they in
5. O God, save us now in your mer - cy; bring us
6. Now blest be the Lord, God of Is - rael. Blest be

mem - ber all you have done; then you will re - mem-ber our
wronged you and have done e - vil, like those who once lived un - der
Red Sea, ques-tioned their God; they fell from their faith in the
mal - ice dared to de - fy you; des - pite this, you came to their
back from all that of - fends you. Lord, look not a - lone at our
God both now and for - ev - er. Let na - tions and peo - ple cry,

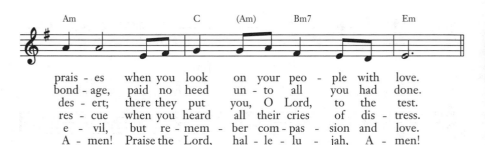

prais - es when you look on your peo - ple with love.
bond - age, paid no heed un - to all you had done.
des - ert; there they put you, O Lord, to the test.
res - cue when you heard all their cries of dis - tress.
e - vil, but re - mem - ber com - pas - sion and love.
A - men! Praise the Lord, hal - le - lu - jah, A - men!

Words: Psalm 106; paraphrase, John L. Bell (1949–) Music: John L. Bell (1949–)

Refrain
Harmony

All: Oh give thanks to the Lord, for God's love en-dures for - ev - er;

oh give thanks to the Lord, for the Lord a-lone is good.

72 Oh give thanks, for God is gracious

WYLDE GREEN 8 7 8 7 4 7

1. "Oh give thanks, for God is gra - cious!" now may Is - rael
2. When God's peo - ple walked the des - ert, hun - gry, thirst - y,
3. Those who steer their ships through trou - ble, ride the storm and
4. Oh give thanks for all God's mer - cies: fields are wa - tered,

F   Am7   Dm   Bb/C   Gm/Bb D7/A   Gm   /F   C7/E F#dim7 Gm   C7

tru - ly say; through great tri - als God has brought us
faint of heart, God pre - pared for them a ci - ty,
plumb the deep, reach at length their prom- ised ha - ven,
crops are sown, sheep and cat - tle fill the pas - tures,

Dm   Gm   C7sus4–3   F   Am7   Dm   Bb/C   Gm/Bb D7/A   Gm   C#dim7

Alternate tune: St. Osmund

Words: Psalm 107; paraphrase, David Mowbray (1938–), alt   Music: Peter Cutts (1937–)

to   the dawn of   this new   day.
gave   them hope and   took their part.
bless   that grace which brings them sleep.   All God's chil - dren,
babes   in arms have safe - ly grown.

A7/C#   Bb   Dm/F Gm6 A7   Dmsus4–3 F/A G/B C   /Bb

praise the won   -   ders God has   done.

F/A Cm6/G D7/F#   D7/Bb Gm F/C C7   F

Psalm 113

Praise to the Lord

RICHARDSON–BURTON Irregular

1. Praise to the Lord, all of you, God's ser-vants.
2. There is none like our God in the heavens or on earth, who
1. Lou - ez l'É - ter - nel, ser - vi - teurs de Dieu.
2. Qui est comme no - tre Dieu, dans les cieux, sur la ter - re, qui

Bless - ed be the name of our God now and
lifts the poor from the dust, seat - ing them with the
Bé - ni soit son nom, main - te - nant, à ja -
ex - al - te les pauvres au rang des grands de son

ev - er. From the ris - ing up of the sun
might-y, who, stoops to raise the weak and low:
mais. Du le - ver du so - leil,
peu - ple, qui ma - ni - feste mi - sé - ri - corde?

Refrain

may the Lord be praised, praise to the name of the Lord!
bé - ni soit son nom! Lou-é soit Dieu, l'É - ter - nel!

Words: Psalm 113; paraphrase, Ron Klusmeier (1946–); French, R. Gerald Hobbs (1941–)
Music: Ron Klusmeier (1946–)

74

When Israel fled from Egypt land

CHARMINSTER 8 8 8 8 LM

1. When Is - rael fled from E - gypt land, from
2. The sea rolled back to form dry land, the
3. What made you part, O might - y sea? Why,
4. Now trem - ble, earth, the Lord is near; bow

for - eign tongue and cru - el hand, the Lord took Ju - dah
Jor - dan fled at God's com-mand. The moun-tains skipped like
Jor - dan, did you turn to flee? Why, moun-tains, skip like
down and see your God ap - pear, whose might makes springs to

for a home and Is - ra - el to be a throne.
joy - ful rams, the lit - tle hills like play - ful lambs.
joy - ful rams, and lit - tle hills, like play - ful lambs?
gush and glow; from flint the cool - ing wa - ters flow.

Alternate tunes: Daniel, Truro

Words: Psalm 114, paraphrase, Henrietta Ten Harmsel (1921–)   Music: Cyril Vincent Taylor (1907–1991)

Words: paraphrase, copyright © CRC Publications, 1987   Music: copyright © 19   by Hope Publishing Co.

Psalm 116
I love you, Lord,
for you have heard my voice

GENEVAN 116   10 11 11 10

1. I love you, Lord, for you have heard my voice.
2. Our God is gra - cious, mer - ci - ful and just,
3. For you, O Lord, have saved my soul from death.
4. How can I pay you, Lord, for all your gifts?
5. Pre - cious to you the dy - ing of your saints.

You turned to me and heard my cry for mer - cy.
who watch - es o - ver all the sim - ple - heart - ed.
You kept my eyes from tears, my feet from stum - bling.
I will lift up the cup of full sal - va - tion.
I am your faith - ful ser - vant, freed from bond - age.

An - guished by death and o - ver - come by sor - row,
Rest, O my soul, and trust God for sal - va - tion.
I kept my faith, though I was much af - flict - ed.
I will ful - fil my vows to you, my Sav - iour.
I'll pay my vows and with your peo - ple thank you.

Words: Psalm 116; paraphrase, Helen Otte (1931–), alt   Music: Genevan Psalter 1562;
harmony, Seymour Swets (1900–1982)

Words: paraphrase, copyright © CRC Publications, 1987   Music: public domain

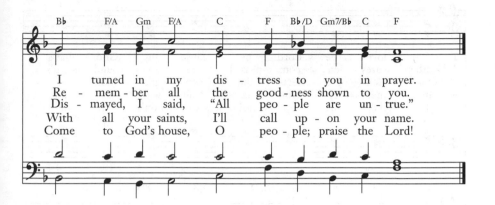

I turned in my dis - tress to you in prayer.
Re - mem - ber all the good - ness shown to you.
Dis - mayed, I said, "All peo - ple are un - true."
With all your saints, I'll call up - on your name.
Come to God's house, O peo - ple; praise the Lord!

Psalm 116
I love the Lord

ST. PAUL 8 6 8 6 CM

1. I love the Lord be - cause my God has
2. Death's snares en - com - passed me a - round; death's
3. Our God pro - tects the sim - ple ones, all -
4. In mer - cy God has dealt with me and
5. I will lift up sal - va - tion's cup and

heard my voice, my prayer; so while I live, I'll
pain laid hold on me. In an - guish and dis -
gra - cious, mer - ci - ful. I was brought low; God
saved my soul from death, my eyes from tears, my
call up - on God's name; I'll pay my vows un -

praise the one who turned a gra - cious ear.
tress I called, "Oh save me, Lord, I pray."
res - cued me: re - turn to rest, my soul.
feet from snares; through pain, I kept my faith.
to the Lord who res - cued me from shame.

6. How precious in your sight, O God,
   the death of faithful ones!
   Child of your servant, Lord, I am
   your servant, freed from bonds.

7. I pay the vows that I have made
   within your house, O God;
   and in your midst, Jerusalem,
   still thank and praise the Lord!

Words: Psalm 116; paraphrase, Andrew Donaldson (1951–) Music: James Chalmers' Collection, 1749
Words: this version, copyright © Andrew Donaldson, 1996 Music: public domain

Psalm 117

From all that dwell below the skies

CHURCH TRIUMPHANT 8 8 8 8

1. From all that dwell be - low the skies let
the Cre - a - tor's praise a - rise: let the Re - deem - er's
name be sung through eve - ry land, in eve - ry tongue.

2. E - ter - nal are your mer - cies, Lord; e -
ter - nal truth at - tends your word: your praise shall sound from
shore to shore, till suns shall rise and set no more.

Words: Psalm 117; paraphrase, Isaac Watts (1674–1748) Music: James William Elliott (1833–1915)

Words: public domain Music: public domain

Psalm 118

This is the day

THIS IS THE DAY Irregular

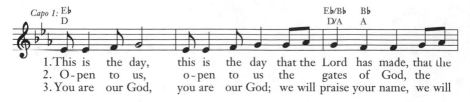

1. This is   the day,   this is   the day   that the Lord has made, that the
2. O-pen   to   us,   o-pen   to   us   the   gates of God, the
3. You are   our God,   you are   our God; we will praise your name, we will

Lord   has   made.   We will   re - joice,   we will   re - joice   and be
gates of   God;   we will   go   in,   we will   go   in   and
praise your name;   we will   give thanks,   we will   give thanks for your

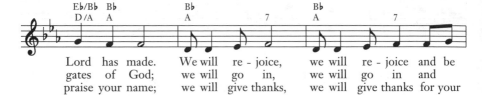

glad   in   it,   and be   glad   in   it.   This is   the day   that the
praise the Lord, and   praise the Lord.   O-pen   to   us   the
faith - ful - ness, for your faith - ful - ness.   You are   our God; we will

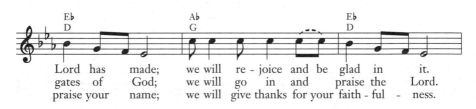

Lord   has   made;   we will   re - joice and be glad   in   it.
gates of   God;   we will   go   in   and   praise the   Lord.
praise your   name;   we will   give thanks for your faith - ful - ness.

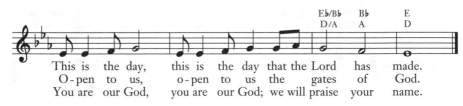

This is   the   day,   this is   the   day that the Lord   has   made.
O-pen   to   us,   o-pen   to   us   the   gates   of   God.
You are our God,   you are our God; we will praise your   name.

Words: Psalm 118:19, 24, 28   Music: Fijian folk melody

Words: public domain   Music: public domain

Praise God from whom all blessings flow

COME TOGETHER 8 8 8 8 LM

Praise God from whom all bless - ings flow;
La grâ - ce de no - tre Sau - veur,

praise him, all crea - tures here be - low:
l'a - mour du Père et sa fa - veur,

praise him a - bove, ye heav - en - ly host;
et l'onc - ti - on du Saint - Es - prit,

praise Fa - ther, Son and Ho - ly Ghost.
soient a - vec nous par Jé - sus - Christ!

Words: Thomas Ken (1637-1711) Music: Jimmy Owens (1930-); arrangement, David Peacock (1949-)

Psalm 119
Teach me, O Lord, your way of truth
EISENACH 8 8 8 8 LM

Descant

5. I thirst for your com - mand - ments, Lord, and

D   A7/E   D/F♯ Bm   A7/C♯ D   A

1. Teach   me,   O   Lord, your   way   of   truth,   and
2. In   your   com -   mand - ments   make   me   walk,   for
3. Your   word   sheds   light   up - on   my   path;   a
4. Your   won - drous   tes - ti - mo - nies,   Lord,   my
5. I   thirst   for   your   com - mand - ments,   Lord,   and

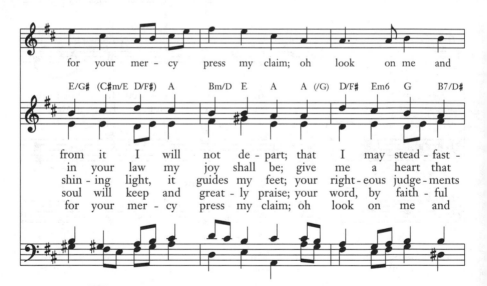

for   your   mer - cy   press   my   claim;   oh   look   on me   and

E/G♯ (C♯m/E D/F♯) A   Bm/D E   A   A (/G) D/F♯ Em6 G   B7/D♯

from   it   I   will   not   de - part;   that   I   may   stead - fast -
in   your   law   my   joy   shall   be;   give   me   a   heart that
shin - ing   light,   it   guides   my   feet;   your   right - eous   judge - ments
soul   will   keep   and   great - ly   praise;   your   word,   by   faith - ful
for   your   mer - cy   press   my   claim;   oh   look   on   me   and

Words: Psalm 119; paraphrase, Psalter, 1912   Music: J.H. Schein (1586–1630); harmony, J.S. Bach (1685–1750), alt; descant, John Wilson (1905–1992)

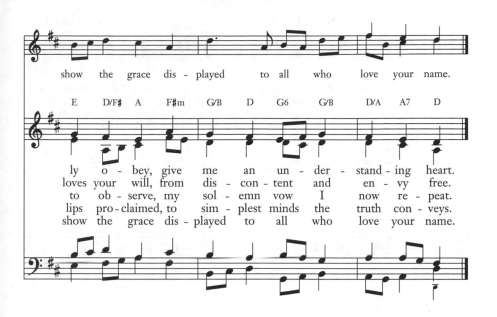

show the grace dis - played to all who love your name.

E   D/F#   A   F#m   G/B   D   G6   G/B   D/A   A7   D

ly   o - bey,   give   me   an   un - der - stand - ing   heart.
loves your will, from   dis - con - tent   and   en - vy   free.
to   ob - serve, my   sol - emn   vow   I   now   re - peat.
lips   pro - claimed, to   sim - plest minds   the   truth   con - veys.
show the grace dis - played   to   all   who   love   your   name.

Psalm 121

Unto the hills around

SANDON 10 4 10 4 10 10

1. Un - to the hills a - round do I lift up my long - ing
2. He will not suf - fer that thy foot be moved: safe shalt thou
3. Je - ho - vah is him - self thy keep - er true, thy change-less
4. From eve - ry e - vil shall he keep thy soul, from eve - ry

eyes: oh whence for me shall my sal - va - tion come, from
be. No care - less slum - ber shall his eye - lids close, who
shade; Je - ho - vah thy de - fence on thy right hand him -
sin: Je - ho - vah shall pre - serve thy go - ing out, thy

whence a - rise? From God the Lord doth come my cer - tain
keep - eth thee. Be - hold, he sleep - eth not, he slum - bereth
self hath made, and thee no sun by day shall ev - er
com - ing in. A - bove thee watch - ing, he whom we a -

Words: Psalm 121; paraphrase, John, Duke of Argyll (1845–1914) Music: Charles Purday (1799–1885)

Words: public domain Music: public domain

| F | F/A | Bb | F/A | C7/G | F | Bb6 | F/C | C7 | F |

aid, from God the Lord who heaven and earth hath made.
ne'er, who keep - eth Is - rael in his ho - ly care.
smite; no moon shall harm thee in the si - lent night.
dore shall keep thee hence - forth, yea, for - ev - er - more.

Psalm 121

82   I to the hills will lift my cyes

DUNDEE (FRENCH) 8 6 8 6 CM

| D | | G | D/F♯ D | C | D7/A G | D | A | Bm G | A | D |

1. I to the hills will lift my eyes; from whence shall come my aid?
2. God will not let your foot be moved; your Guard-ian nev - er sleeps.
3. Your faith - ful keep - er is the Lord, your shel - ter and your shade;
4. From e - vil God will keep you safe, pro - vide for all you need;

| D | | A | Bm A/C♯ Bm/D E | A | D | Em/G Bm | Asus4–3 | D |

My help is from the Lord a - lone, who heaven and earth has made.
God's watch - ful and un - slum - bering care pro - tects and safe - ly keeps.
'neath sun or moon, by day or night, you shall not be a - fraid.
your go - ing out, your com - ing in, God will for - ev - er lead.

Words: Psalm 121; paraphrase, Psalter 1912 Music: Scottish Psalter 1615

Words: public domain Music: public domain

Psalm 122

83

I was glad when they said to me

I WAS GLAD 8 9 9 8

Pray for peace; pray for peace;

Bb Ebmaj7 Cm7 F7

I was glad when they said to me,

pray for peace for the ci - ty of God:

D Gm Gm/F Eb F D7/F#

let us go to the house of the Lord:

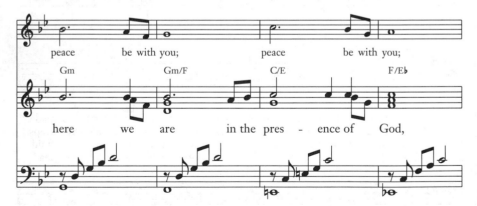

peace be with you; peace be with you;

Gm Gm/F C/E F/Eb

here we are in the pres - ence of God,

Words: Psalm 122; paraphrase, Michael Saward Music: Norman Warren (1934–);
arrangement, Christopher Norton (1953–)

peace be with you; peace be with you. you.

giv - ing thanks to our might - y Lord. Lord.

Psalm 122

84   I joyed when to the house of God

ST. PAUL 8 6 8 6 CM

1. I joyed when "To the house of God go up," they said to me.
2. Je - ru - sa - lem— a cit - y—built, bound firm - ly; strong it stands.
3. Pray that Je - ru - sa - lem may have peace and fe - lic - i - ty;
4. There - fore, I wish that peace may still with - in thy walls re - main,
5. Now, for my friends' and kind-red's sake, "Peace be in thee," I'll say.

Je - ru - sa - lem, with - in thy gates our feet shall stand-ing be.
The pil-grims go to wor - ship there, God's faith-ful from its lands.
let them that love thee and thy peace en - joy pros - per - i - ty.
and ev - er may thy pal - ac - es pros - per - i - ty re - tain.
"And for the house of God our Lord I'll seek thy good al - way."

Words: Psalm 122:1–4, 6–9; paraphrase, Scottish Psalter 1650, v. 2 alt   Music: James Chalmers'
Collection 1749

Words: v.2 copyright © The Presbyterian Church in Canada, 1997   Music: public domain

Psalm 124

85

Now Israel may say

OLD 124TH 10 10 10 10 10

1. Now Is - ra - el may say, and that in truth: if that the
2. Yea, when their wrath a - gainst us fierce-ly rose, the swell-ing
3. Blest be the Lord, who made us not their prey; as from the

Lord had not our right main - tained, if that the Lord had
tide had o'er us spread its wave, the rag-ing stream had
snare a bird es - cap - eth free, their net is rent and

not with us re-mained when cru - el foes a - gainst us rose to
then be-come our grave, the surg-ing flood, in proud-ly swell-ing
so es-caped are we; our on - ly help is in God's ho - ly

strive, we sure - ly had been swal-lowed up a - live.
roll, most sure - ly then had o - ver-whelmed our soul.
name, who made the earth and all the heaven - ly frame.

Words: Psalm 124; paraphase, Psalter, 1912 Music: Genevan Psalter 1551; harmony, Martin Shaw (1875–1958)

Psalm 125

86

Those who rely on the Lord

WAS LEBET 12 10 12 10

1. Those who re - ly on the Lord are un - shake - ab - le,
2. E - vil shall not al - ways rule o - ver right - eous-ness;

firm as mount Zi - on, su - preme - ly as - sured;
God's time will come when op - press - ion shall cease:

just as the moun-tains en - cir - cle Je - ru - sa-lem,
Lord, bless the right-eous; re - strain the im - pen - i - tent;

round us for - ev - er is stand - ing the Lord.
grant to your peo - ple the gift of your peace.

Words: Psalm 125; paraphrase, Christopher Idle (1938–)   Music: J.H. Rheinhardt (1754)

Words: paraphrase, copyright © 1987 by Hope Publishing Co. Music: public domain

Psalm 126

87 When God restored our common life

RESIGNATION 8 6 8 6 D CMD

1. When God re-stored our com-mon life, our hope, our lib - er - ty,
2. We went forth weep-ing, sow-ing seeds in hard, un-yield-ing soil;
3. Great lib - er - at - ing God, we pray for all who are op-pressed.

at first it seemed a pass-ing dream, a wak-ing fan - ta - sy.
with laugh-ing hearts we car-ry home the fruit of all our toil.
May those who long for what is right with jus-tice now be blest.

A shock of joy swept o - ver us, for we had wept so long;
We praise the One who gave the growth, with voic-es full and strong.
We pray for those who mourn this day, and all who suf - fer wrong;

Words: Psalm 126; paraphrase, Ruth Duck (1947–) Music: American folk hymn, Walker's
Southern Harmony 1835; harmony, Erik Routley (1917–1982)

the   seeds   we wa-tered once with tears sprang up   in - to   a   song.
The   seeds   we wa-tered once with tears sprang up   in - to   a   song.
may   seeds they wa - ter   now with tears spring up   in - to   a   song.

Psalm 127

88   Unless the Lord constructs the house

BRISTOL   8 6 8 6 CM

1. Un - less the Lord con-structs the   house, the build-ers work in   vain; the
2. Un - less the Lord is keep-ing   watch, the   cit - y can-not stand; the
3. In   vain you la - bour night and   day, by   con-stant care op-pressed;the
4. The Lord de-signed the fam - i - ly, pro - vid-ing earth-ly   love; our
5. Like weap-ons in   a   war-rior's   hand are those who bear our name; with

Lord a - lone de - signs and builds foun - da - tions that re - main.
sen - try guards the gates in   vain with - out God's might-y   hand.
Lord sup-plies your loved ones' needs and   grants them sleep and   rest.
chil-dren are God's her - i - tage—   a   gift from heaven a - bove.
them we face a   hos - tile world as - sured and free from shame.

Words: Psalm 127; paraphrase, Mollie Knight, alt Music: Ravenscroft's Psalter 1621

Psalm 128

Bless all who trust in God

SANDYS 6 6 8 6 SM

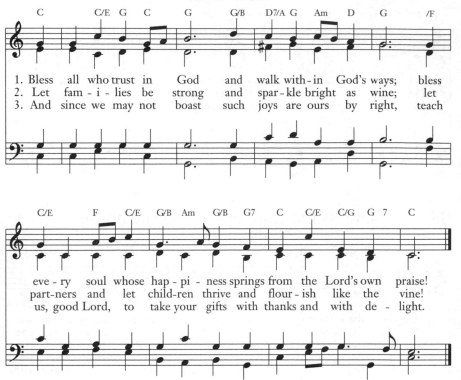

1. Bless all who trust in God and walk with-in God's ways; bless
2. Let fam - i - lies be strong and spar-kle bright as wine; let
3. And since we may not boast such joys are ours by right, teach

eve - ry soul whose hap - pi - ness springs from the Lord's own praise!
part-ners and let child-ren thrive and flour - ish like the vine!
us, good Lord, to take your gifts with thanks and with de - light.

Words: Psalm 128; paraphrase, David Mowbray (1938–)   Music: English traditional melody, W. Sandy's Christmas Carols 1833

Words: paraphrase, copyright © 1990 by Hope Publishing Co. Music: public domain

Psalm 130

Up from the depths I cry to you

MACPHERSON'S FAREWELL   8 6 8 6 with refrain

1. Up from the depths   I   cry to God: oh   lis - ten, Lord, to   me;   oh
2. If   you, my   God, should mea-sure guilt, who   then could   ev - er   stand?   But
3. O   Is - rael,   set   your hope in   God whose mer - cy   is   su - preme: the

hear my   voice in   this dis-tress, this   mire of   mi - se - ry.
those who   fear your   name will find for - give-ness from your   hand.   I
na-tion mourn-ing   for   its   sin he*   sure-ly   will   re - deem.

wait for God* with   all   my heart; my   hope is   in   his*   word,   and

more than watch-men*   for   the dawn   I'm   long-ing   for   the*   Lord.

*God, you, your, watchers, you

Alternate tune: Kingsfold   See also: MacPherson's Farewell 750

Words: Psalm 130; paraphrase, Christopher Idle (1938–), alt Music: Scottish traditional;
arrangement, David Iliff (1939–)

91

Psalm 130

Out of the depths I cry

STARLIGHT 6 6 6 6

1. Out of the depths I cry: O God, re - mem - ber me! What earth - ly help have I if you watch si - lent - ly?
2. If you watch si - lent - ly and mark things done a - miss, to whom then may I fly at such a time as this?
3. At such a time as this my soul waits for the Lord; no joy is there, no bliss, with - out God's sav - ing word.
4. With - out God's sav - ing word all hope for - ev - er dies: speak now, most might - y Lord, and from the depths I rise!

Words: Psalm 130; paraphrase, David Mowbray (1938–) Music: Robin Sheldon (1931–)

Words: paraphrase, copyright © 1990 by Hope Publishing Co. Music: copyright © Robin Sheldon

Psalm 131

Before the Lord my soul is bowed

HERONGATE 8 8 8 8 LM

1. Be - fore the Lord my soul is bowed in
2. But I have made my spir - it calm; my
3. Let grate - ful voic - es tell a - broad the

trust and quiet hu - mil - i - ty; I do not let my
soul is like a child at rest who knows that it is
might - y name that we a - dore: O Is - rael, hope in

heart grow proud or pon - der things too great for me.
safe from harm and sleeps up - on its moth - er's breast.
God the Lord, your glo - ry now and ev - er - more!

Words: Psalm 131; paraphrase, Stephen Horsfall   Music: English traditional;
arrangement, Ralph Vaughan Williams (1872–1958)

Psalms
93

Psalm 133

Oh look and wonder

OH, LOOK AND WONDER   Irregular

Unison

Oh look and won - der, how good it is!
¡Mi - ren qué bue - no, qué bue-no es!

1.-4. How good it is when kin-dred live in har-mo - ny to - geth - er,

1. joy-ous and sweet as pre-cious oil a - noint - ing Aar-on's head.
2. joy-ous and sweet as pre-cious oil that flows down Aar-on's beard.
3. joy-ous and sweet as dew that falls on Zi - on, new and pure.
4. joy-ous and sweet as life God gives on Zi - on ev - er - more.

1. Miren qué bueno es cuando los hermanos están juntos:
   es como aceite bueno derramado sobre Aarón.

2. Miren qué bueno es cuando los hermanos están juntos:
   se parece al rocío sobre los montes de Síon.

3. Miren qué bueno es cuando los hermanos están juntos:
   porque el Señor ahí manda vida eterna y bendición.

Words: Psalm 133; Spanish paraphrase, Pablo Sosa (1933–); translation, Andrew Donaldson
(1951–)   Music: Pablo Sosa (1933)

*Words: Spanish, copyright © Pablo Sosa ISEDET, 1974; English, copyright © Andrew Donaldson, 1996   Music: copyright © Pablo Sosa,
ISEDET, 1974*

Psalm 134

94

Bless the Lord as day departs

ASTHALL 7 8 7 8

Words: Psalm 134; paraphrase, Timothy Dudley–Smith (1926–) Music: John Barnard (1948–)

Psalm 134

95
Come bless the Lord

COME BLESS THE LORD   Irregular

Come bless the Lord, all you ser-vants of the Lord who stand by night in the house of the Lord; lift up your hands to the ho-ly place and bless the Lord: come bless the Lord, come bless the Lord, come bless the Lord!

Words: Psalm 134; paraphrase, Philip Lawson–Johnston   Music: Philip Lawson–Johnston; arrangement, Christopher Norton (1953–)

Psalm 136
Let us with a gladsome mind
MONKLAND 7 7 7 7

Descant

5. Let us then with glad-some mind praise the Lord so good and kind:

Bb   (Gm F/A   Bb)   Eb   Cm   Bb   Bb   /D   F   Bb/D   F   C 7   F

1. Let us with a glad-some mind praise the Lord, so good and kind,
2. Let us blaze God's name a - broad; of all gods the Lord is God,
3. God with all - com-mand-ing might filled the new-made world with light,
4. All things liv - ing God doth feed; with full hand sup - plies their need,
5. Let us then with glad-some mind praise the Lord, so good and kind,

for God's mer - cies shall en-dure, ev - er faith-ful, ev - er sure.

F   C/E   F   /Eb   Bb/D Bb   F   Bb   F/C   /Eb   Bb/D   Fsus4–3   Bb

for God's mer - cies shall en - dure, ev - er faith - ful, ev - er sure.

Words: Psalm 136:1–3, 7, 23, 25, 26; paraphrase, John Milton (1608–1674), alt   Music: Hymn
Tunes of the United Brethren, 1824; descant, C.S. Lang (1891–1971)
Words: public domain Music: descant; copyright © Novello & Co Ltd

Psalm 136

97 We thank you, Lord, for you are good

WAS GOTT TUT 8 7 8 7 8 8 7

1. We thank you, Lord, for you are good;
2. You, Lord, a - lone did won-drous deeds;
3. You made the star - ry lights to rise;
4. You res - cue us from eve - ry foe;

your mer-cy lives for - ev - er.

Your kind - ness from of old has stood;
From you a - lone all good pro - ceeds;
Your glo - ries shine in ra - diant skies;
You feed your crea - tures here be - low;

your love will keep us ev - er.

O God of gods, O sov - ereign Lord, we bless you
Your wis - dom made the heavens to be; you formed the
Your glow - ing moon en - hanc - es night. Your sun brings
We give you thanks, Cre - a - tor, Lord; we sing the

Words: Psalm 136; paraphrase, John G. Dunn   Music: Severus Gastorius (1646–1682); harmony,
Common Service Book, 1917

Words: paraphrase, copyright © John G. Dunn   Music: public domain

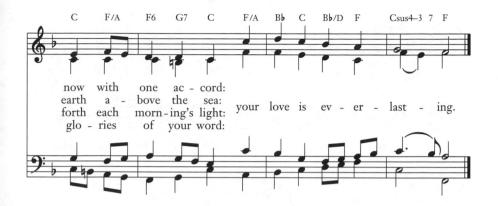

now with one ac - cord:
earth a - bove the sea:
forth each morn-ing's light: your love is ev - er - last - ing.
glo - ries of your word:

Psalm 137

98   By the Babylonian rivers
LATVIAN MELODY   8 7 8 7

1. By the Bab - y - lo - nian ri - vers we sat down   in grief and wept,
2. There our cap - tors in de - ri - sion did re - quire   of us a song;
3. How shall we sing songs of Zi - on in a strange and bit - ter land?

hung our harps up - on a wil - low, mourned for Zi - on while we slept.
so we sat with star - ing vi - sion, and the days were hard and long.
Can our voic - es veil the sor - row? O God, hear your lone - ly band.

Words: Psalm 137; paraphrase, Ewald Bash (1924–)   Music: Latvian traditional; arrangement, Darryl Nixon (1952–)

99

Psalm 137

By the waters, the waters of Babylon

BY THE WATERS   Irregular (?)

By the wa - ters, the wa - ters of Bab - y - lon,

we sat down and wept, and wept for you Zi - on.

We re-mem-ber, we re-mem-ber, we re-mem-ber Zi - on.

May be sung as a round

Words: Psalm 137   Music: Jewish melody

Words: public domain   Music: public domain

100

Psalm 138

I'll praise you, Lord

HIGHWOOD   11 10 11 10

1. I'll praise you, Lord, with heart con - tent and joy - ful;
2. Be - yond the skies you set your time - less king - dom;
3. Though set on high, you look up - on the low - ly—
4. For - ev - er you will keep your face to - wards us;

Words: Psalm 138; paraphrase, Michael Perry (1942–1996)   Music: Richard Runciman Terry (1865–1938)

Words: paraphrase, copyright © 1989 by Hope Publishing Co. Music: copyright © Oxford University Press

be - fore the world, I'll tell your right-eous ways;
your word shall last; your throne shall nev - er fall;
the proud you see with sor - row from a - far;
your mer - cy and your love will nev - er cease.

I will bow down to - wards your ho - ly tem - ple,
the lords of earth will mar - vel at your wis - dom
in all my trou - ble you are swift to save me,
Then come ful - fil in us your might - y pur - pose,

ex - alt your name and sing your wor - thy praise.
and kneel be - fore the might - y Lord of all.
and with your arm re - strain the threat of war.
and grant to your cre - a - tion per - fect peace.

Psalm 139

You are before me, Lord

SURSUM CORDA   10 10 10 10

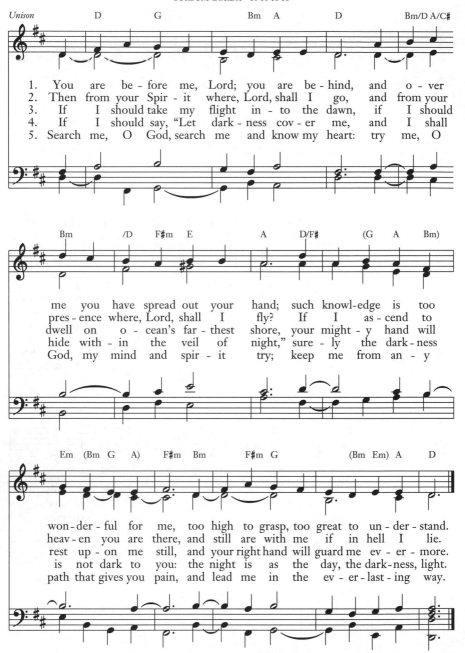

Unison

1. You are be-fore me, Lord; you are be-hind, and o-ver
2. Then from your Spir-it where, Lord, shall I go, and from your
3. If I should take my flight in-to the dawn, if I should
4. If I should say, "Let dark-ness cov-er me, and I shall
5. Search me, O God, search me and know my heart: try me, O

me you have spread out your hand; such knowl-edge is too
pres-ence where, Lord, shall I fly? If I as-cend to
dwell on o-cean's far-thest shore, your might-y hand will
hide with-in the veil of night," sure-ly the dark-ness
God, my mind and spir-it try; keep me from an-y

won-der-ful for me, too high to grasp, too great to un-der-stand.
heav-en you are there, and still are with me if in hell I lie.
rest up-on me still, and your right hand will guard me ev-er-more.
is not dark to you: the night is as the day, the dark-ness, light.
path that gives you pain, and lead me in the ev-er-last-ing way.

Words: Psalm 139; paraphrase, Ian Pitt–Watson (1923–1995)   Music: Alfred Morton Smith (1879–1971)

Words: paraphrase, copyright © the estate of Ian Pitt–Watson, 1973   Music: copyright © the estate of Doris Wright Smith

Psalm 142

When I lift up my voice

WHEN I LIFT UP MY VOICE   6 6 10 with refrain

1. When I lift up my voice, and I cry for your help, and I pour out my trou-bles be - fore you: I say,
2. When I see no - one cares, and I walk all a - lone, and my spir - it grows wea-ry with - in me: I say, "You are my ref - uge;
3. When you come to my side and you an - swer my prayers and you set my soul free from its pris - on: I say,

I will praise your name; you are good to me, O

Lord!"

Lord!"

Words: Psalm 142; paraphrase, Michael Perry (1942–1996)   Music: Michael Perry (1942–1996); arrangement, David Peacock (1949–)

103 O Lord, thou art my God and King

Psalm 145

DUKE STREET 8 8 8 8 LM

1. O Lord, thou art my God and King; thee will I
2. Thee will I bless each day I rise, and praise thy
3. Thy saints shall praise thy glo - rious name; thy might-y
4. Thy might shall be by all ex - tolled; thy glo-rious
5. Thy faith - ful shall make known the fame of thy great

mag - ni - fy and praise: I will thee bless and
name, time with - out end; much to be praised and
acts they shall de - clare; thy won-drous works I
grace I will re - cord; with all my strength I
good - ness and shall bless the splen-dour of thy

glad - ly sing un - to thy ho - ly name al - ways.
great God is, whose great-ness none can com - pre - hend.
will pro - claim and med - i - tate on them with prayer.
will un - fold thy great and might - y acts, O Lord.
glo - rious name, prais - ing a - loud thy right-eous - ness.

Alternate tune: Warrington

Words: Psalm 145:1–7; paraphrase, Scottish Psalter, 1650, alt
Music: John Warrington Hatton (c.1710–1793)

Words: this version, copyright © The Presbyterian Church in Canada, 1997 Music: public domain

104

Your faithfulness, O Lord, is sure

MORNING HYMN 8 8 8 8

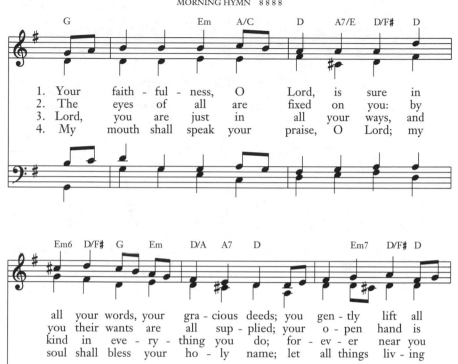

1. Your faith - ful - ness, O Lord, is sure in
2. The eyes of all are fixed on you: by
3. Lord, you are just in all your ways, and
4. My mouth shall speak your praise, O Lord; my

all your words, your gra - cious deeds; you gen - tly lift all
you their wants are all sup - plied; your o - pen hand is
kind in eve - ry - thing you do; for - ev - er near you
soul shall bless your ho - ly name; let all things liv - ing

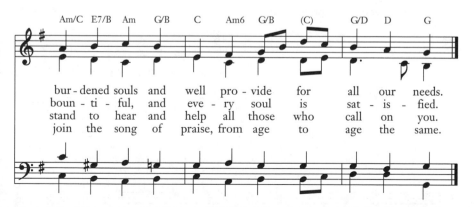

bur - dened souls and well pro - vide for all our needs.
boun - ti - ful, and eve - ry soul is sat - is - fied.
stand to hear and help all those who call on you.
join the song of praise, from age to age the same.

Words: Psalm 145; paraphrase, Joy F. Patterson (1931–)   Music: François H. Barthélémon (1741–1808)

Words: paraphrase, copyright © Joy F. Patterson, 1990   Music: public domain

Psalm 146

105 I'll praise my Maker while I've breath

OLD 113TH 888888

1. I'll praise my Mak - er while I've breath, and when my voice
2. Hap - py are those whose hopes re - ly on Is - rael's God,
3. The Lord gives eye - sight to the blind; the Lord sup - ports
4. I'll praise you while you lend me breath, and, when my voice

is lost in death, praise shall em - ploy my no - bler powers.
who made the sky, the earth and seas, with all their train.
the faint - ing mind, and sends the trou - bled con - science peace.
is lost in death, praise shall em - ploy my no - bler powers.

My days of praise shall ne'er be past while life and thought
This truth for - ev - er stands se - cure: God saves the op-pressed,
God helps the strang - er in dis - tress, the wid - ow and
My days of praise shall ne'er be past, while life and thought

and be - ing last, or im - mor - tal - i - ty en - dures.
God feeds the poor, and none shall find this prom - ise vain.
the fa - ther - less, and grants the pris - oner sweet re - lease.
and be - ing last, or im - mor - tal - i - ty en - dures.

Words: Psalm 146; paraphrase, Isaac Watts (1674–1748), John Wesley (1703–1791) Music:
Matthäus Greiter (c. 1500–1552), Strassburger Kirchenamt 1525; harmony, V. Earle Copes (1921–)

Psalm 148

Let all creation bless the Lord

LUTHER'S HYMN 8 7 8 7 8 8 7

1. Let all cre - a - tion bless the Lord, till heaven with praise is ring - ing.
   Sun, moon and stars peal out a chord, stir up the an - gels' sing - ing.
2. All liv - ing things up - on the earth, green fer - tile hills and moun - tains,
   sing to the God who gave you birth; be joy - ful, springs and foun - tains.
3. O men and wom - en eve - ry-where, lift up a hymn of glo - ry;
   all you who know God's stead-fast care, tell out sal - va - tion's sto - ry.

Sing, wind and rain! Sing, snow and sleet! Make mus - ic, day, night,
Lithe wa - ter - life, bright air - borne birds, wild rov - ing beasts, tame
No tongue be si - lent; sing your part, you hum - ble souls and

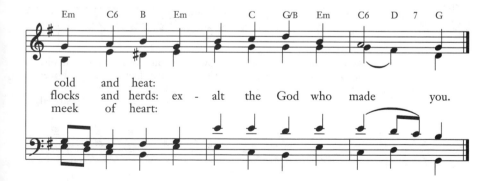

cold and heat:
flocks and herds: ex - alt the God who made you.
meek of heart:

Words: orig. a paraphrase of the canticle "Benedicite, omnia opera Domini", Apocryphal book
The Prayer of Azariah and the Song of the Three Jews 35-65, Carl P. Daw, Jr. (1944–)
Music: Martin Luther (1483–1546)

107

Sing praise to the Lord

TETHERDOWN 10 10 11 11

1. Sing praise to the Lord; sing praise in the height;
2. Sing praise to the Lord; sing praise on the earth
3. Sing praise to the Lord, all things that give sound;
4. Sing praise to the Lord, thanks - giv - ing and song

re - joice in God's word, all an - gels of light.
in tune - ful ac - cord, you heirs of new birth;
each ju - bi - lant chord re - ech - o a - round;
to God be out - poured all ag - es a - long;

Now wor - ship your Mak - er by whom you were made;
praise God who has brought you rich grace from a - bove;
loud or - gans God's glo - ry forth - tell in deep tone,
for love in cre - a - tion, for heav - en re - stored,

Alternate tune: Laudete Dominum

Words: Psalm 150; paraphrase, Henry Williams Baker (1821–1877), alt Music: Gerald L. Barnes (1935–)

Words: this version, copyright © The Presbyterian Church in Canada, 1997 Music: copyright © G. L. Barnes

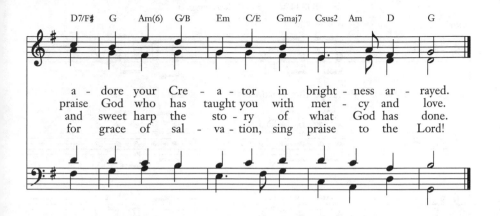

a - dore your Cre - a - tor in bright - ness ar - rayed.
praise God who has taught you with mer - cy and love.
and sweet harp the sto - ry of what God has done.
for grace of sal - va - tion, sing praise to the Lord!

Psalm 150
Praise ye the Lord
CLEVELAND 8 7 8 7 with refrain (8 7)

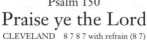

Refrain

Choir or Congregation: Praise ye the Lord,   hal - le - lu - jah!

Eve - ry - bod - y praise the Lord.   Lord.

1.   2. *Fine*

D   D   G

Em/G   D/A   A7   D   (G/DD)   D   (G/D D)   /C

Words: Psalm 150; paraphrase, J. Jefferson Cleveland (1937–1986)
 Music: J. Jefferson Cleveland (1937–1986)

1. Praise God with the sound of the trum - pet; praise God with the
2. Praise God with ho - ly cym - bals; praise God with
3. Praise God in the ho - ly tem - ple; praise God for
4. Praise God on top of the moun-tains; praise God both

lute and the harp; praise God with the tim-brel and danc - ing;
strings and with pipes; praise God with clash - ing cym - bals;
al - might - y deeds; praise God for those boun-ti - ful mer - cies;
day and night; praise God down in the low val - leys;

praise God wher - ev - er you are. *D.S. al Fine*
praise God with all of your might.
for God ful - fils our needs.
praise God be - cause it's all right.

All earth is waiting

TAULE 11 12 12 11

1. All earth is wait-ing to see the Prom-ised One,
2. Thus says the proph-et to those of Is - ra - el:
3. Moun - tains and val - leys will have to be made plain;
4. In low - ly sta - ble the Prom-ised One ap - peared;

and o - pen fur-rows a - wait the seed of God. All the
"A vir - gin moth - er will bear Em-man - u - el," one whose
o - pen new high-ways, new high-ways for the Lord. He is
yet feel his pres-ence through-out the earth to - day, for he

world, bound and strug-gling, seeks true lib - er - ty; it
name is "God-with - us" our Sav - iour shall be; with
now com - ing clos - er, so come all and see, and
lives in all Chris-tians and is with us now; a -

cries out for jus - tice and search-es for the truth.
him hope will blos - som once more with-in our hearts.
o - pen the door-ways as wide as wide can be.;
gain, with his com-ing he brings us lib-er-ty.

Words: Alberto Taulé (1932–); translation, Gertrude C. Suppe (1911–) Music: Alberto Taulé (1932–); harmony, Skinner Chávez-Melo (1944–1992)

Come, thou long–expected Jesus

HYFRYDOL 8 7 8 7 D

1. Come, thou long - ex - pect - ed Je - sus, born to set thy
from our fears and sins re - lease us; let us find our

2. Born thy peo - ple to de - liv - er; born a child and
born to reign in us for - ev - er; now thy gra - cious

peo - ple free; Is - rael's strength and con - so - la - tion,
rest in thee.
yet a king;
king - dom bring. By thine own e - ter - nal Spir - it

hope of all the earth thou art, dear de - sire of
rule in all our hearts a - lone; by thine all - suf -

eve - ry na - tion, joy of eve - ry long - ing heart.
fi - cient mer - it raise us to thy glo - rious throne.

Words: Charles Wesley (1707–1788) Music: Rowland Hugh Pritchard (1812–1887);
harmony, Ralph Vaughan Williams (1872–1958)

Words: public domain Music: harmony, copyright © Oxford University Press from The English Hymnal

111 Creator of the stars of night

CONDITOR ALME SIDERUM 8 8 8 8 LM

Alternate rhythm:

1. Cre - a - tor of the stars of night, your peo - ple's
2. To you the la - bour pain was known that made the
3. Old was the world that drew toward night; you came, but
4. At your great name, Christ Je - sus, now all knees must
5. Come in your ho - ly might, we pray; re - deem us
6. To God the Fa - ther, God the Son and God the

ev - er - last - ing light, O Christ, the Sav - iour of us all,
whole cre - a - tion groan, un - til the time that you would free
not in splen - dour bright, as mon - arch, but the hum - ble child
bend; all hearts must bow; all things in heaven your name shall bless.
for e - ter - nal day, when all your judge - ments will be known
Spir - it, Three - in - One, laud, hon - our, might and glo - ry be

Words: Latin, anonymous, 9th century; translation, John Mason Neale (1818–1866), alt
Music: Sarum plainsong; arrangement, Bruce Neswick (1956–)

we pray, oh hear us when we call.
your own in glo-rious lib - er - ty.
of Ma - ry, faith - ful moth - er mild.   A - men.
All things on earth your power con - fess.
and power of dark-ness o - ver-thrown.
from age to age e - ter - nal - ly.

112   Prepare the way of the Lord

PREPARE THE WAY 7 7 13

Pre-pare the way of the Lord. Pre-pare the way of the Lord,

and all peo-ple will see the sal - va - tion of our God.

Note: May be sung as a four–part round.

Words: Isaiah 40:3; 52:10 Music: Jacques Berthier (1923–1994), Taizé Community (France)

113   Comfort, comfort you my people

GENEVAN 42   8 7 8 7 7 7 8 8

1. Com-fort, com-fort you my peo-ple; tell of peace, thus says our God;
2. For the her-ald's voice is call-ing in the des-ert far and near,
3. Make you straight what long was crook-ed; make the rough-er plac-es plain;

com-fort those who sit in dark-ness bowed be-neath op-pres-sion's load.
bid-ding us to make re-pent-ance since the king-dom now is here.
let your hearts be true and hum-ble, as be-fits God's ho-ly reign,

Speak you to Je-ru-sa-lem of the peace that waits for them;
Oh that warn-ing cry o-bey! Now pre-pare for God a way;
for the glo-ry of the Lord now o'er earth is shed a-broad,

tell them that their sins I cov-er, and their war-fare now is o-ver.
let the val-leys rise in meet-ing and the hills bow down in greet-ing.
and all flesh shall see the to-ken that God's word is nev-er bro-ken.

Words: German, Johannes Olearius (1611–1684); translation, Catherine Winkworth (1827–1878)
Music: Genevan Psalter 1551

Words: public domain   Music: public domain

Advent

114

Emmanuel, Emmanuel

EMMANUEL 8 8 7 8

Note: the accompaniment may be simplified by playing only the low notes in the left hand.
Words: Bob McGee (1944–) Music: Bob McGee (1944–)

115 Hail to the Lord's Anointed

ST. THEODULPH 7676D

1. Hail to the Lord's A - noint - ed, great Da - vid's great - er Son;
2. He brings sal - va - tion speed - y to those who suf - fer wrong;
3. He shall come down like show - ers up - on the fruit - ful earth,
4. All powers shall bow be - fore him, and gold and in - cense bring;
5. O'er eve - ry foe vic - to - rious, Christ on his throne shall rest,

hail, in the time ap - point - ed, his reign on earth be - gun!
he saves the poor and need - y, and helps the weak be strong;
and love, joy, hope, like flow - ers, spring in his path to birth.
all na - tions shall a - dore him, his praise all peo - ple sing,
from age to age more glo - rious, all - bless - ing and all - blest:

He comes to break op - pres - sion, to set the cap - tive free,
they sing who once were sigh - ing, their dark-ness turned to light,
Be - fore him on the moun-tains shall peace, the her - ald, go,
for he shall have do - min - ion o'er riv - er, sea and shore,
the tide of time shall nev - er his cov - e - nant re - move;

See also: St. Theodulph 115 214 Alternate tune: Crüger

Words: James Montgomery (1771–1854), alt Music: Melchior Teschner (1584–1635)

Words: public domain Music: public domain

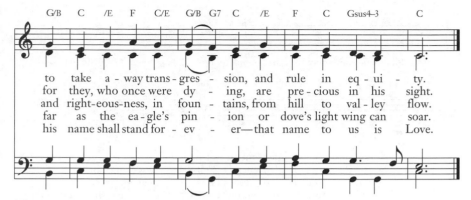

to take a - way trans - gres - sion, and rule in eq - ui - ty.
for they, who once were dy - ing, are pre - cious in his sight.
and right-eous-ness, in foun - tains, from hill to val - ley flow.
far as the ea - gle's pin - ion or dove's light wing can soar.
his name shall stand for - ev - er—that name to us is Love.

Advent

116 Hark! a thrilling voice is sounding

MERTON 8 7 8 7

1. Hark! a thrill-ing voice is sound-ing: "Christ is nigh," it seems to say;
2. Wak-ened by the sol - emn warn-ing, let us all from sleep a - rise;
3. Lo! the Lamb, so long ex - pect - ed, comes with par-don down from heaven;
4. When our Sav-iour comes in glo - ry, though the world be wrapped in fear,
5. Hon - our, glo - ry, might and bless-ing to the Fa-ther and the Son,

"Cast a - way the dreams of dark-ness, O ye chil-dren of the day!"
Christ, our sun, all ill dis - pel - ling, shines up - on the morn-ing skies.
let us haste, with tears of sor - row, one and all to be for - given.
with his mer - cy he will shield us, and with words of love draw near.
with the ev - er - last-ing Spir - it while e - ter - nal a - ges run.

Words: Latin, anonymous, 6th century; translation, Edward Caswell (1814–1848), alt
Music: William Henry Monk (1823–1889)

Words: public domain   Music: public domain

117 Herald! Sound the note of judgement

UNSER HERRSCHER 8 7 8 7 8 7

Descant

1. Her - ald! Sound the note of tri - umph! Christ has come to share our life,

C   G/B   C   /E   C   F/A   G   Am   /G   C/E   C   F6   G   C

1. Her-ald! Sound the note of judge-ment, warn-ing souls of right and wrong,
2. Her-ald! Sound the note of glad - ness! Tell the   news that Christ is here;
3. Her-ald! Sound the note of par - don! Those re - pent-ing are for - given;
4. Her-ald! Sound the note of tri - umph! Christ has come to share our life,

bring - ing God's own love and pow - er, grant - ing vic - tory in our strife.

C   G/B   C   /E   C   F/A   G   Am   /G   C/E   C   F6   G   C

turn-ing them from sin and sad - ness, till once more they sing the song.
make a path-way through the des - ert for the one who brings God near.
God re-ceives us way - ward child-ren, and to all new life is given.
bring-ing God's own love and pow - er, grant-ing vic - tory in our strife.

Words: Moir A.J. Waters (1906–1980), alt   Music: Joachim Neander (1650–1680);
descant, John Dykes Bower (1905–1981)

Sound the trum-pet! Tell the mess-age! Christ the Sav-iour King has come!

Sound the trum-pet! Tell the mess-age! Christ the Sav-iour King has come!

Hark the glad sound

RICHMOND 8 6 8 6 CM

1. Hark the glad sound! The Sav - iour comes, the
2. You come the pris - oners to re - lease in
3. You come the bro - ken heart to bind, the
4. Our glad ho - san - nas, Prince of Peace, your

Sav - iour prom - ised long; let eve - ry heart pre -
Sa - tan's bond - age held; the gates of brass be -
wound - ed soul to cure, to bring the treas - ures
wel - come shall pro - claim, and heaven's e - ter - nal

pare a throne, and eve - ry voice a song!
fore you burst, the i - ron fet - ters yield.
of God's grace, good ti - dings for the poor.
arch - es ring with your most hon - oured name.

Words: Philip Doddridge (1701–1751), Scottish Paraphrases, alt Music: Thomas Haweis (1734–1820);
arrangement, Samuel Webbe the younger (1770–1843)

Words: public domain Music: public domain

Hope is a star

MOON BEAMS Irregular

1. Hope is a star that shines in the night,
2. Peace is a rib - bon that cir - cles the earth,
3. Joy is a song that wel - comes the dawn,
4. Love is a flame that burns in our heart.

lead - ing us on till the morn - ing is bright.
giv - ing a prom - ise of safe - ty and worth.
tell - ing the world that the Sav - iour is born.
Je - sus has come and will nev - er de - part.

Refrain

When God is a child there's joy in our song. The last shall be first

and the weak shall be strong, and none shall be a - fraid.

Words: Brian A. Wren (1936–) Music: Joan Collier Fogg (1949–)

120   Lo! Christ comes with clouds

HELMSLEY 878747

1. Lo! Christ comes with clouds de - scend - ing,
2. Eve - ry eye shall now be - hold thee
3. Now re - demp - tion long a - wait - ed,
4. Ev - er - more let all a - dore thee,

Lamb of God for sin - ners slain;
robed in awe and maj - es - ty;
see in glo - rious life ap - pear!
high on thine e - ter - nal throne;

thou - sand thou - sand saints at - tend - ing
we, who scorned and mocked and sold thee,
All God's crea - tures freed from groan - ing,
crowns and em - pires fall be - fore thee:

Words: Charles Wesley (1707–1788), alt; v.3, James P. Martin (1923–)
Music: adaptation, Thomas Olivers (1725–1799)

Words: this version, copyright © The Presbyterian Church in Canada, 1997; v.3, copyright © James P. Martin Music: public domain

swell   the Lord's tri - um - phant   train.
pierced   and nailed thee   to   the   tree,
sounds   of li - ber - a - tion   hear:
thou   shalt reign and   thou   a - lone.

Hal - le - lu - jah hal - le - lu - jah, hal - le -
deep - ly griev - ing, deep - ly griev - ing, deep - ly
Hal - le - lu - jah, hal - le - lu - jah, hal - le -
Come, Lord Je - sus; come, Lord Je - sus; come, Lord

lu - jah! God ap - pears on   earth   to   reign.
griev - ing, shall the   true Mes - si - ah   see.
lu - jah! See the   day of   God ap - pear.
Je - sus! Claim all   glo - ry   for thine   own.

121 Long ago, prophets knew

THEODORIC (PERSONENT HODIE) 6 6 6 6 6 with refrain

1. Long a go,
2. God in time,
3. Ma - ry, hail!
4. Jour - ney ends!

pro - phets knew Christ would come, born a Jew,
God in man, this is God's time - less plan:
Though a - fraid, she be - lieved; she o - beyed.
Where a - far Beth - lehem shines, like a star,

come to make all things new, bear all peo - ple's
he will come as a man, born him - self of
In her womb, God is laid till the time ex -
sta - ble door stands a - jar: un - born son of

Words: Fred Pratt Green (1903–) Music: Piae Cantiones, 1582; harmony, Gustav T. Holst (1874–1934)

Words: copyright © 1971 by Hope Publishing Co. Music: harmony, copyright © J. Curwen & Sons, Ltd.

bur - den, free - ly love and par - don.
wom - an, God di - vine - ly hu - man.
pect - ed, nur - tured and pro - tect - ed.
Ma - ry, Sav - iour do not tar - ry!

Refrain

Ring, bells, ring, ring, ring! Sing, choirs, sing, sing, sing!

When he comes, when he comes, who will make him wel - come?
(last verse) we will make him wel - come!

Advent

122

Oh come, oh come, Emmanuel

VENI EMMANUEL 888888

Unison

1. Oh come, oh come, Em-man - u - el, and ran-som cap-tive
2. Oh come, oh come, thou Lord of might, who to thy tribes on
3. Oh come, thou Wis-dom from on high, and or - der all things
4. Oh come, thou Branch of Jes - se, free thine own from Sa - tan's
5. Oh come, thou Key of Da - vid, come and o - pen wide our

Is - ra - el, that mourns in low - ly ex - ile here,
Si - nai's height, in an - cient times didst give the law
far and nigh; to us the path of knowl - edge show,
tyr - an - ny; from the depths of hell thy peo - ple save,
heaven - ly home; make safe the way that leads on high

6. Oh come, thou Dayspring, come and cheer
our spirits by thine advent here;
disperse the gloomy clouds of night,
and death's dark shadows put to flight. Rejoice!...

7. Oh come, desire of nations, bind
all peoples in one heart, one mind;
bid envy, strife and discord cease,
and be thyself our source of peace.
Rejoice!...

Words: Latin, 13th century; translation, John Mason Neale (1818–1866); French, H. Écuyer
Music: Gregorian plainsong; arrangement, Healey Willan (1880–1968)

un - til the Son of God ap - pear.
in cloud and maj - es - ty and awe.
and cause us in her ways to go. Re-joice, re-joice!
and give them vic-tory o'er the grave.
and close the path to mis - er - y.

Em-man - u - el shall come to thee, O Is - ra - el.

1. Oh! viens bientôt, Emmanuel,
   nous délivrer du joug cruel,
   et du péché briser la loi;
   ton peuple entier s'attend à toi.
   Joyeux, levez les yeux au ciel,
   voici venir Emmanuel!

2. Oh! viens bientôt, que ta clarté
   dissipe nos obscurités.
   Errants et tristes dans la nuit,
   nous appelons le jour qui luit.
   Joyeux, levez les yeux au ciel,
   Voici venir Emmanuel!

3. Oh! viens bientôt, descends vers nous,
   Saint Fils du ciel, aimant et doux.
   Aux coeurs troublés apporte donc
   la paix divine du pardon.
   Joyeux, levez les yeux au ciel,
   voici venir Emmanuel!

4. Oh! viens bientôt, puissant Sauveur,
   nous réveiller de nos langueurs!
   Il n'est que toi, céleste Pain,
   qui puisse apaiser notre faim.
   Joyeux, levez les yeux au ciel,
   voici venir Emmanuel!

123 My soul gives glory to my God

MORNING SONG 8 6 8 6 CM

1. My soul gives glo - ry to my God. My
2. My God has done great things for me; yes,
3. From age to age to all who fear, such
4. Love casts the might - y from their thrones, pro -
5. Praise God, whose lov - ing cov - e - nant sup -

heart pours out its praise. God lift - ed up my
ho - ly is this name. All peo - ple will de -
mer - cy love im - parts, dis - pens - ing jus - tice
motes the in - se - cure, leaves hun - gry spir - its
ports those in dis - tress, re - mem - ber - ing past

low - li - ness in man - y mar-vel-ous ways.
clare me blessed, and bless - ings they shall claim.
far and near, dis - miss - ing self - ish hearts.
sat - is - fied; the rich seem sud-den - ly poor.
prom - is - es with pres - ent faith - ful - ness.

See also: Morning Song 711

Words: Miriam Therese Winter (1938–)   Music: anonymous, 1811; in Wyeth's Repository of
Sacred Music 1813; harmony, C. Winfred Douglas (1867–1944)

Words: paraphrase, copyright © Medical Mission Sisters, 1978, 1987 Music: public domain

124

People in darkness

PEOPLE IN DARKNESS 10 6 10 5 11 8

1. Peo-ple in dark-ness are look-ing for light.
2. Peo-ple with sick-ness are pray-ing for health.   Come,   come,
3. Peo-ple in trou-ble would like to be free.
4. Peo-ple in sad-ness are try-ing to sing.

come, Je-sus Christ.   Peo-ple with blind-ness are long-ing for sight.
Peo-ple in pov - er - ty want to have wealth.
Peo-ple with ar - gu-ments want to a - gree.
Bells in the stee-ple are wait-ing to ring.

Come,   Lord Je - sus Christ.   These days of ad-ven-ture when

all peo - ple wait   are   days for the ad - vent of (1) love.
(2) hope.
(3) peace.
(4) joy.

Words: Dosia Carlson (20th cent.); v.4 Ken Stright (1952–), Jeanne Stright (1953–)   Music: Dosia Carlson (20th cent.)

125   People, look east

BESANÇON 879887

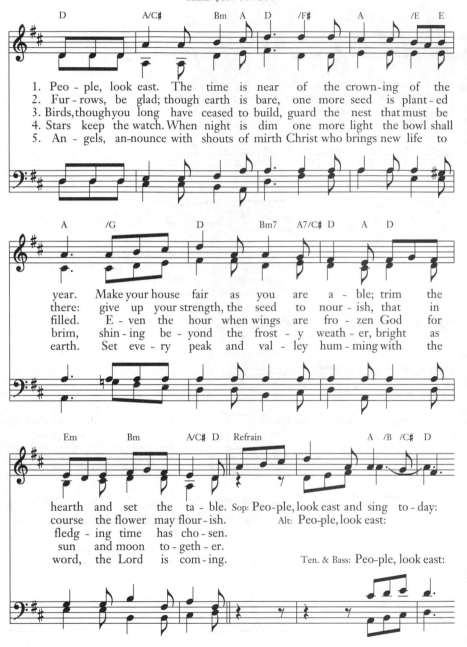

1. Peo - ple, look east. The time is near of the crown-ing of the
2. Fur - rows, be glad; though earth is bare, one more seed is plant - ed
3. Birds, though you long have ceased to build, guard the nest that must be
4. Stars keep the watch. When night is dim one more light the bowl shall
5. An - gels, an-nounce with shouts of mirth Christ who brings new life to

year. Make your house fair as you are a - ble; trim the
there: give up your strength, the seed to nour - ish, that in
filled. E - ven the hour when wings are fro - zen God for
brim, shin - ing be - yond the frost - y weath - er, bright as
earth. Set eve - ry peak and val - ley hum - ming with the

hearth and set the ta - ble. Sop: Peo-ple, look east and sing to - day:
course the flower may flour - ish.   Alt: Peo-ple, look east:
fledg - ing time has cho - sen.
sun and moon to - geth - er.
word, the Lord is com - ing.   Ten. & Bass: Peo-ple, look east:

Words: Eleanor Farjeon (1881–1965), from The Children's Bells   Music: French traditional;
harmony, Martin Shaw (1875–1958), from Oxford Book of Carols

Words: copyright © David Higham Assocociates Ltd.   Music: harmony, copyright © Oxford University Press Press, 1928

(1) guest
(2) rose
Love the (3) bird is on the way.
(4) star
(5) Lord
Ten.: Love is on the way.

Advent

126 On Jordan's bank

WINCHESTER NEW 8 8 8 8 LM

1. On Jor-dan's bank the Bap-tist's cry an-nounc-es that the Lord is nigh;
2. Then cleansed be eve-ry breast from sin; make straight the way for God with-in;
3. For thou art our sal-va-tion, Lord, our ref-uge and our great re-ward;
4. To heal the sick, stretch out thine hand, and bid the fall-en sin-ner stand;
5. All praise, et-er-nal Son, to thee, whose ad-vent sets thy peo-ple free,

a-wake and heark-en, for he brings glad ti-dings of the King of kings.
pre-pare we in our hearts a home where such a might-y guest may come.
with-out thy grace, we waste a-way, like flowers that with-er and de-cay.
shine forth and let thy light re-store earth's own true love-li-ness once more.
whom, with the Fath-er, we a-dore, and Ho-ly Spir-it, ev-er-more.

Words: Latin, Charles Coffin (1676–1749); translation, John Chandler (1806–1876)
Music: Musik Handbuch, Hamburg 1690; arrangement, William Henry Havergal (1793–1870)

Sleepers, wake!

WACHET AUF 89889866488

1. "Sleep-ers, wake!" A voice a - stounds us, the
2. Zi - on hears the watch - men sing - ing; her
3. Lamb of God, the heavens a - dore you; let

shout of ram - part-guards sur - rounds us: "A -
heart with joy - ful hope is spring - ing, she
saints and an - gels sing be - fore you, as

wake, Je - ru - sa - lem, a - rise!" Mid-night's peace their
wakes and hur - ries through the night. Forth he comes, her
harps and cym - bals swell the sound. Twelve great pearls, the

cry has bro - ken, their ur - gent sum-mons clear - ly spo -
Bride-groom glo - rious in strength of grace, in truth vic - to -
ci - ty's por - tals: through them we stream to join the im - mor -

Words: German, Philipp Nicolai (1556–1608); translation, Carl P. Daw, Jr. (1944–) Music: Hans
Sachs (1494–1576); adaptation, Philipp Nicolai (1556–1608); harmony, J.S. Bach (1685–1750)

ken: "The time has come, O maid - ens wise!
rious: her star is risen; her light grows bright.
tals as we with joy your throne sur - round.

Rise up, and give us light; the Bride - groom is in
Now come, most wor - thy Lord, God's Son, In - car - nate
No eye has known the sight, no ear heard such de -

sight. Your lamps pre - pare and
Word. Hal - le - lu - jah! We fol - low all and
light: There - fore we sing to

has - ten there, that you the wed - ding feast may share."
heed your call to come in - to the ban - quet hall.
greet our King; for - ev - er let our prais - es ring.

153

Advent

128   There's a voice in the wilderness crying

ASCENSION   Irregular

1. There's a voice in the wil-der-ness cry-ing, a call from the ways un-trod: pre-pare in the de-sert a high-way, a high-way for our God! The
2. O Zi-on, that bring-est good ti-dings, go up to the heights and sing! Pro-claim to a de-so-late peo-le the com-ing of their King. Like the
3. but the word of our God is stead-fast; the arm of the Lord is strong; God stands in the midst of na-tions, and soon will right the wrong. God shall

Words: James Lewis Milligan (1876–1961), alt   Music: Henry Hugh Bancroft (1904–1988)

Words: public domain   Music: copyright © the estate of Henry Hugh Bancroft

154

val - leys shall be ex - alt - ed,   the lof - ty hills brought
flowers of the field they per - ish,   like grass our works de -
feed the flock like a shep-herd,   the lambs will gent - ly

low;   make straight all the crook - ed pla - ces
cay,   the power and pomp of na - tions
hold,   to pas - tures of peace will lead them,

where the Lord our God may go!
shall pass like a dream a - way,
and bring them safe to the fold.

129 Prepare the way, O Zion

BEREDEN VAG FOR HERRAN 7 6 7 6 7 7 6 6

1. Pre - pare the way, O Zi - on: your Christ is draw - ing near!
2. He brings God's rule, O Zi - on; Christ comes from heaven a - bove.
3. Fling wide your gates, O Zi - on; your Sav - iour's rule em - brace,

Let eve - ry hill and val - ley a lev - el way ap - pear.
His rule is peace and free - dom, and jus - tice, truth, and love.
and tid - ings of sal - va - tion pro - claim in eve - ry place.

Greet One who comes in glo - ry, fore - told in sa - cred sto - ry.
Lift high your praise re - sound - ing, for grace and joy a - bound - ing.
All lands will bow re - joic - ing, their ad - o - ra - tion voic - ing.

Refrain

Oh blest is Christ that came in God's most ho - ly name.

Words: Frans Mikael Franzen (1771/2–1847); alt Charles P. Price (1920–)
Music: Then Swenska Psalmboken 1697; arrangement, American Lutheran Hymnal 1930

Advent

130 To a maid whose name was Mary

ANNUNCIATION 767676

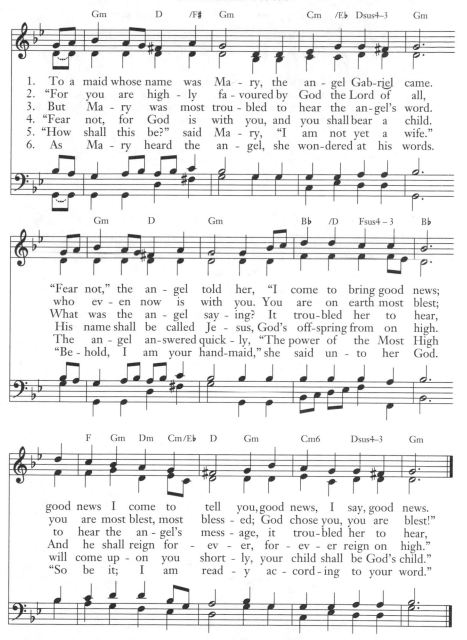

1. To a maid whose name was Ma - ry, the an - gel Gab-ri̯el came.
2. "For you are high - ly fa - voured by God the Lord of all,
3. But Ma - ry was most trou - bled to hear the an-gel's word.
4. "Fear not, for God is with you, and you shall bear a child.
5. "How shall this be?" said Ma - ry, "I am not yet a wife."
6. As Ma - ry heard the an - gel, she won-dered at his words.

"Fear not," the an - gel told her, "I come to bring good news;
who ev - en now is with you. You are on earth most blest;
What was the an - gel say - ing? It trou-bled her to hear,
His name shall be called Je - sus, God's off-spring from on high.
The an - gel an-swered quick - ly, "The power of the Most High
"Be - hold, I am your hand-maid," she said un - to her God.

good news I come to tell you, good news, I say, good news.
you are most blest, most bless - ed; God chose you, you are blest!"
to hear the an - gel's mess - age, it trou-bled her to hear,
And he shall reign for - ev - er, for - ev - er reign on high."
will come up - on you short - ly, your child shall be God's child."
"So be it; I am read - y ac - cord-ing to your word."

Words: Gracia Grindal (1943–) Music: Rusty Edwards (1955–)

Words: copyright © 1984 by Hope Publishing Co. Music: copyright © 1984 by Hope Publishing Co.

157

Advent

131

Tomorrow Christ is coming

LITTLE BADDOW 7 6 7 6 D

1. To - mor - row Christ is com - ing, as yes - ter - day he came;
2. To - mor - row will be Christ - mas, the feast of love di - vine,
3. There will be no to - mor - rows for man-y a ba - by born;
4. Our Lord be - comes in - car - nate in eve - ry hu-man birth.

a child is born this mo - ment; we do not know its name.
but, for the name-less mil - lions, the star will nev - er shine.
Good Fri - day falls on Christ - mas when life is sown as corn,
Cre - at - ed in God's im - age, we must make peace on earth.

The world is full of dark - ness: a - gain there is no room;
Still is the cen - sus tak - en, with peo - ple on the move;
but Je - sus Christ is ris - en and comes a - gain in bread
God will ful - fil love's pur - pose, and this shall be the sign:

Words: Fred Kaan (1929–) Music: Cecil Armstrong Gibbs (1889–1960)

Words: copyright © 1968 by Hope Publishing Co. Music: copyright © G. Schirmer Inc., (ASCAP). International copyright secured. All rights reserved. Reprinted by permission.

158

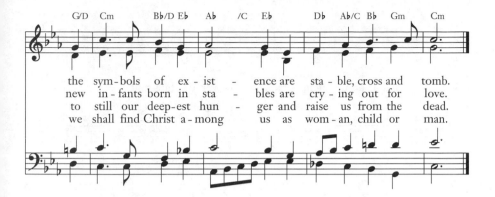

the sym-bols of ex-ist - ence are sta-ble, cross and tomb.
new in-fants born in sta - bles are cry-ing out for love.
to still our deep-est hun - ger and raise us from the dead.
we shall find Christ a-mong us as wom-an, child or man.

Advent

132 What is the crying at Jordan

ST. MARK'S, BERKELEY 8 8 8 6

1. What is the cry-ing at Jor-dan? Who hears, O God, the pro-phe-cy?
2. Who then shall stir in this dark-ness, pre-pare for joy in the win-ter night?
3. Lord, give us grace to a-wake us, to see the branch that be-gins to bloom;
4. Now comes the day of sal-va-tion, in joy and ter-ror the Word is born!

Dark is the sea-son, dark our hearts and shut to mys-ter-y.
Mor-tal in dark-ness we lie down, blind-heart-ed, see-ing no light.
in great hu-mil-i-ty is hid all heaven in a lit-tle room.
God comes as gift in-to our lives; oh let sal-va-tion dawn!

Words: Carol Christopher Drake (1933–) Music: Irish melody, Danta De: Hymns to God,
Ancient and Modern; harmony, Norman Mealy (1923–1987)

Words: copyright © Carol C. Stone, 1971 Music: harmony, copyright © Margaret W. Mealy, executor of estate of Norman Mealy. Used by permission

133 Go, tell it on the mountain

GO, TELL IT   7 6 7 6 with refrain

Refrain

Go, tell it on the moun - tain, o - ver the hills and eve - ry - where.

Go, tell it on the moun - tain that Je - sus Christ is born.

1. While shep-herds kept their watch-ing o'er si - lent flocks by night,
2. The shep-herds feared and trem-bled, when lo, a - bove the earth
3. Down in a low - ly man - ger the hum - ble Christ was born,

be - hold, through-out the heav-ens there shone a ho - ly light.
rang out the an-gel cho-rus that hailed our Sav-iour's birth!
and God sent us sal - va - tion that bless-ed Christ-mas morn.

Words: African-American traditional; adaptation, John W. Work (1901–1967)
Music: African-American traditional; arrangement, John W. Work (1901–1967), alt

Words: adaptation, copyright © John W. Work, 1940   Music: arrangement, copyright © John W. Work, 1940

134

Lord, you were rich

FRAGRANCE 9 8 9 8 9 8

D   (A/D) D6   Dmaj7 D6   Bm   G/B   D/F♯   A7/E   D   A

1. Lord, you were rich be - yond all splen - dour, yet, for love's sake, be -
2. You are our God be - yond all prais - ing, yet, for love's sake, be -
3. Lord, you are love be - yond all tell - ing; Sav-iour and King, we

Bm   G6   A7   Dsus4 – 3   D   (maj7) G/D   D   Bm   /D   F♯m

came so poor; lea - ving your throne in glad sur - ren - der,
came a man; stoop-ing so low, but sin - ners rais - ing
wor-ship you. Em-man - u - el, with - in us dwell - ing,

D/F♯   Gmaj7 A7   Bm /A G6 D   G/B Asus4 – 3   D   (A/D) D6   A/D

sap - phire-paved courts for sta - ble floor. Lord, you were rich be -
heaven-wards by your e - ter - nal plan. You are our God be -
make us and keep us pure and true. Lord, you are love be -

Bm/D   D   Bm   G/B   D/F♯   G6   D/A   A   7   D

yond all splen - dour, yet, for love's sake, be - came so poor.
yond all prais - ing, yet, for love's sake, be - came a man.
yond all tell - ing, Sav-iour and King, we wor-ship you.

Words: Frank Houghton (1894–1972), revision, Hymns for Today's Church
Music: French traditional carol; harmony, C.H. Kitson (1874–1944)

135

Christians, awake

YORKSHIRE 10 10 10 10 10 10

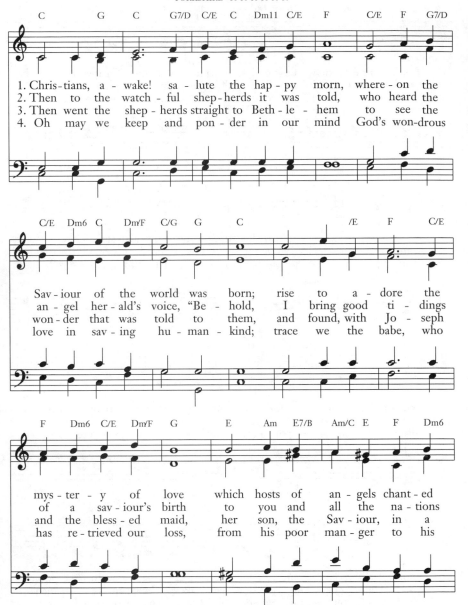

1. Chris - tians, a - wake! sa - lute the hap - py morn, where - on the
2. Then to the watch - ful shep - herds it was told, who heard the
3. Then went the shep - herds straight to Beth - le - hem to see the
4. Oh may we keep and pon - der in our mind God's won-drous

Sav - iour of the world was born; rise to a - dore the
an - gel her - ald's voice, "Be - hold, I bring good ti - dings
won - der that was told to them, and found, with Jo - seph
love in sav - ing hu - man - kind; trace we the babe, who

mys - ter - y of love which hosts of an - gels chant - ed
of a sav - iour's birth to you and all the na - tions
and the bless - ed maid, her son, the Sav - iour, in a
has re - trieved our loss, from his poor man - ger to his

Words: Luke 2:8–17; paraphrase, John Byrom (1692–1763), alt Music: John Wainwright (1723–1768)

Words: public domain Music: public domain

from a - bove; with them the joy - ful ti - dings first be -
on the earth; God has this day ful - filled the prom - ised
man - ger laid; joy - ful, the won - drous sto - ry they pro -
bit - ter cross; saved by his love, un - ceas - ing we shall

gun of God In - car - nate and the vir - gin's son.
word: this day is born a sav - iour, Christ the Lord."
claim, the first a - pos - tles of his in - fant fame.
sing e - ter - nal praise to heaven's al - might - y King.

136

The first nowell

THE FIRST NOWELL Irregular

1. The first now - ell the an - gel did say was to
2. They look - ed up and saw a star shin-ing
3. And by the light of that same star three
4. This star drew nigh to the north - west; o'er
5. Then en - tered in those wise men three full

cer - tain poor shep-herds in fields as they lay, in
in the east be - yond them far, and
wise men came from coun - try far; to
Beth - le - hem it took its rest; and
rev - erent - ly up - on their knee, and

fields where they lay keep-ing their sheep, on a cold win-ter's
to the earth it gave great light, and so it con -
search for a king was their in - tent, and to fol-low the
there it did both stop and stay right o - ver the
of - fered there in his pres - ence their gold and

6. Then let us all with one accord
    sing praises to our heavenly Lord,
    that hath made heaven and earth of nought,
    and with his blood our souls has bought.
    Refrain:

Words: English traditional, 17th century Music: English traditional carol, Sandy's Christmas
Carols, 1833; descant and alternate harmony, Healey Willan (1880–1968)

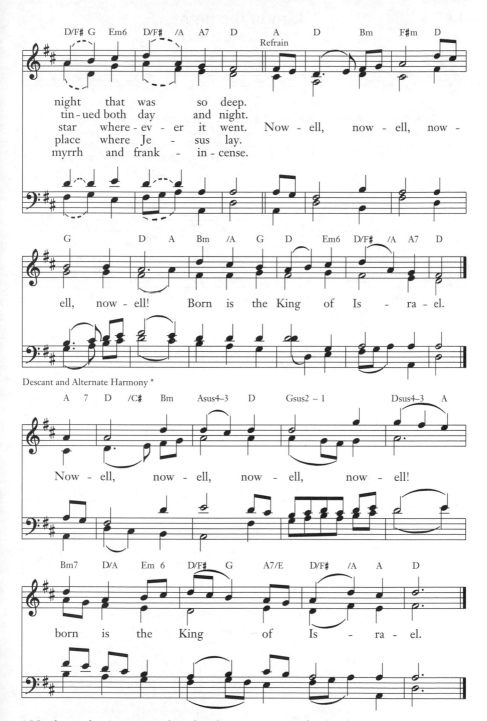

Chords above staves, top system, left to right: D/F♯ G Em6 D/F♯ /A A7 D A D Bm F♯m D

Refrain

night   that   was   so   deep.
tin - ued both   day   and   night.
star   where - ev - er   it   went.   Now - ell,   now - ell,   now -
place   where   Je - sus   lay.
myrrh   and   frank - in - cense.

Chords, second system: G D A Bm /A G D Em6 D/F♯ /A A7 D

ell,   now - ell,   now - ell!   Born   is   the   King   of   Is - ra - el.

Descant and Alternate Harmony *

Chords, third system: A 7 D /C♯ Bm Asus4–3 D Gsus2 – 1 Dsus4–3 A

Now - ell,   now - ell,   now - ell,   now - ell!

Chords, fourth system: Bm7 D/A Em 6 D/F♯ G A7/E D/F♯ /A A D

born   is   the   King   of   Is - ra - el.

* May be used as instrumental or choral accompaniment for the chorus.

165

137

Born in the night

MARY'S CHILD 7 6 7 6

1. Born in the night,   Ma-ry's child,   a   long way from your home;
2. Clear shin-ing light,   Ma-ry's child,   your face lights up   our way;
3. Truth of our life,   Ma-ry's child,   you   tell   us God   is   good;
4. Hope of the world,   Ma-ry's child, you're com-ing soon   to   reign;

com - ing in need,   Ma-ry's child,   born   in a   bor-rowed room.
Light   of the world, Ma-ry's child,   dawn on our dark-ened day.
prove   it is true,   Ma-ry's child,   go   to your cross of   wood.
King   of the earth, Ma-ry's child,   walk in our streets a - gain.

Words: Geoffrey Ainger (1925–) Music: Geoffrey Ainger (1925–); harmony, Richard D. Wetzel (1935–)

While shepherds watched

WINCHESTER OLD 8 6 8 6 CM

Descant

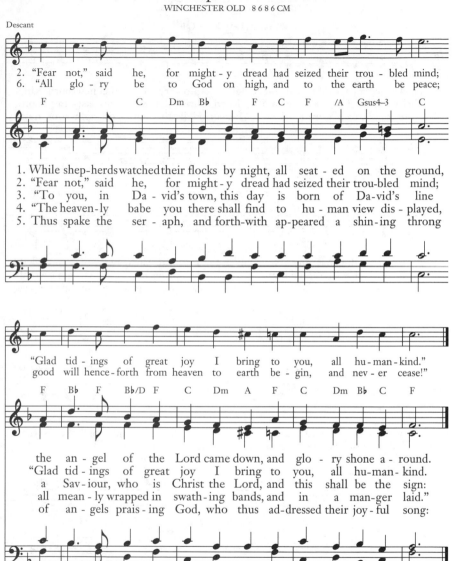

2. "Fear not," said he, for might-y dread had seized their trou - bled mind;
6. "All glo - ry be to God on high, and to the earth be peace;

1. While shep-herds watched their flocks by night, all seat - ed on the ground,
2. "Fear not," said he, for might-y dread had seized their trou-bled mind;
3. "To you, in Da - vid's town, this day is born of Da-vid's line
4. "The heaven-ly babe you there shall find to hu - man view dis - played,
5. Thus spake the ser - aph, and forth-with ap-peared a shin-ing throng

"Glad tid - ings of great joy I bring to you, all hu - man - kind."
good will hence - forth from heaven to earth be - gin, and nev - er cease!"

the an - gel of the Lord came down, and glo - ry shone a - round.
"Glad tid - ings of great joy I bring to you, all hu - man - kind.
a Sav - iour, who is Christ the Lord, and this shall be the sign:
all mean - ly wrapped in swath-ing bands, and in a man-ger laid."
of an - gels prais - ing God, who thus ad-dressed their joy - ful song:

6. "All glory be to God on high,
   and to the earth be peace;
   good will henceforth from heaven to earth
   begin, and never cease!"

Words: Nahum Tate (1652–1715) Music: Este's Psalter 1592; descant, Alan Gray (1885–1935)

Words: public domain Music: descant, copyright © Cambridge University Press

139   Hark! the herald angels sing

MENDELSSOHN 7 7 7 7 D with refrain

1. Hark! the her - ald an - gels sing glo - ry to the new-born King,
2. Christ, by high - est heaven a - dored, Christ, the ev - er - last - ing Lord,
3. Hail the heaven-born Prince of Peace! Hail the sun of right-eous-ness!

peace on earth and mer - cy mild, God and sin - ners re - con - ciled.
late in time be - hold him come, off-spring of a vir - gin's womb.
Light and life to all he brings, risen with heal - ing in his wings.

Joy - ful, all ye na - tions, rise; join the tri - umph of the skies;
Veiled in flesh the God-head see! Hail the in - car - nate de - i - ty!
Mild, he lays his glo - ry by, born that we no more may die,

with the an - gel - ic host pro - claim, "Christ is born in Beth - le - hem."
Pleased on earth with us to dwell, Je - sus, our Em - man - u - el.
born to raise the lost of earth, born to give us sec - ond birth.

Words: Charles Wesley (1707–1788), alt; French, Edmond L. Budry (1854–1932)
Music: Felix Mendelssohn (1809–1847); arrangement, William Hayman Cummings (1831–1915)

Hark! the her-ald an-gels sing glo-ry to the new-born King.

<table>
</table>

French	Hungarian
1. Ecoutez! le chant des anges,	1. Halld mint zeng az egész ég;

French

1. Ecoutez! le chant des anges,
vient d'éclater dans les airs;
joignons aussi nos louanges
à leurs sublimes concerts:
gloire à Dieu! paix sur la terre!
Aujourd'hui le Christ est né!
Jésus s'est fait notre frère,
un Sauveur nous est donné.
Jésus s'est fait notre frère,
un Sauveur nous est donné.

2. Son palais est une étable,
une crèche est son berceau,
et pourtant, c'est l'Admirable,
c'est le Fils du Dieu très-haut.
Il vient à nous débonnaire
et de grâce couronné.
Jésus s'est fait notre frère,
un Sauveur nous est donné.
Jésus s'est fait notre frère,
un Sauveur nous est donné.

3. Avec vous, bergers et mages,
aux pieds de notre Seigneur
nous déposons nos hommages,
nous lui sonnons notre coeur.
Tout son peuple sur la terre
dit, avec nous prosterné:
Jésus, s'est fait notre frère,
un Sauveur nous est donné.
Jésus, s'est fait notre frère,
un Sauveur nous est donné.

Hungarian

1. Halld mint zeng az egész ég;
"A Királynak dicsőség!
Békesség a földön lenn,
Istentől jő kegyelem."
Népek, örvendezzetek!
Visszhangozzák a mennyek!
Hirdesse a természet:
Krisztusunk megszületett!
Halld mint zeng az egész ég:
"A Királynak dicsőség!"

2. Krisztus, kit imád a menny,
Úr a nagy világ előtt,
Köztünk íme megjelent,
Szent szűz az, ki szülte Őt.
Dicsősége eget áthat,
Isten Ő, ki porruhánkat
Földön élni vette fel.
Jézus O, Immánuel!
Halld mint zeng...

3. Dicsőség! Ő a Király,
Békesség és Igazság,
Éltető világos nap,
Bajainkra gyógyírt ad.
Kis gyermek lett mi érettünk,
Született, hogy mi élhessünk,
Porból, hogy feltámasszon
S ujjászületést adjon.
Halld mint zeng...

140 In Bethlehem a newborn boy

IN BETHLEHEM 8 8 8 8 LM

1. In Beth - le - hem a new-born boy was hailed with songs of
2. (The) sol - diers sought the Child in vain: not yet was he to
3. (Still) rage the fires of hate to - day, and in - no - cents the
4. (Lord) Je - sus, through our night of loss shines out the won - der
5. (May) that great love our lives con - trol and con - quer hate in

praise and joy. Then warn - ing came of dan - ger near: King
share our pain, but down the a - ges rings the cry of
price must pay, while ach - ing hearts in eve - ry land cry
of your cross, the love that can - not cease to bear our
eve - ry soul, till, pledged to build and not des - troy, we

Words: Rosamond E. Herklots (1905–1987)   Music: Wilbur Held (1914–)

Words: copyright © by permission of Oxford University Press   Music: copyright © Wilbur Held, 1983

1.–4.   Final Ending

He - rod's troops would soon ap - pear.   The
those who saw their chil-dren die.   Still
out, "We can - not un - der - stand!"   Lord
hu - man an - guish eve - ry - where.   May
share your pain and find your joy.

Dm7   Dm6/F   Am   Gsus2/A   Am   Amsus4   Am   (sus4)

141 Good Christians, all rejoice

IN DULCI JUBILO Irregular

Good Chris-tians, all re-joice with heart and soul and voice;

1. now give heed to what we say: Je - sus Christ is born to-day,
2. now you hear of end - less bliss: Je - sus Christ was born for this.
3. now you need not fear the grave: Je - sus Christ was born to save,

ox and ass be - fore him bow, and he is in the man-ger now.
He has o - pened heav-en's door, and we are blest for - ev - er-more.
calls you one and calls you all to gain the ev - er - last-ing hall.

Christ is born to - day; Christ is born to - day.
Christ was born for this; Christ was born for this.
Christ was born to save; Christ was born to save.

Words: Latin, anonymous; translation, John Mason Neale (1818–1866), alt Music: German carol melody, 14th century; arrangement, anonymous

Words: public domain Music: public domain

142

I wonder as I wander

I WONDER AS I WANDER 11 11 11 11

1. I won - der as I wan - der, out un - der the sky, how
2. When Ma - ry birth'd Je - sus, 'twas in a cow's stall, with
3. If Je - sus had want - ed for an - y wee thing, a
4. I won - der as I wan - der, out un - der the sky, how

Je - sus the Sav - iour did come for to die for
wise men and farm - ers and shep - herds and all, but
star in the sky, or a bird on the wing, or
Je - sus the Sav - iour did come for to die for

poor or'n - 'ry peo - ple like you and like I; I
high from God's heav - en a star's light did fall; the
all of God's an - gels in heav'n for to sing, he
poor or'n - 'ry peo - ple like you and like I; I

won - der as I wan - der, out un - der the sky.
prom - ise of a - ges it then did re - call.
sure - ly could have it, 'cause he was the King.
won - der as I wan - der, out un - der the sky. Out un - der the sky.

Words: traditional Appalachian carol; adaptation, John Jacob Niles (1892–1980)
Music: American traditional, John Jacob Niles (1892–1980); arrangement, Donald P. Hustad (1918–)

143

Infant holy, Infant lowly

POLISH CAROL 8 7 8 7 8 8 7 7

1. In - fant ho - ly, in - fant low - ly, for his bed a
2. Flocks were sleep - ing, shep - herds keep - ing vig - il till the

cat - tle stall; ox - en low - ing, lit - tle know - ing
morn - ing new, saw the glo - ry, heard the sto - ry,

Christ the babe is Lord of all. Swift are wing - ing
tid - ings of a gos - pel true. Thus re - joic - ing,

Words: translation, Edith M.G. Reed (1885–1933)   Music: Polish traditional carol; harmony, A.E. Rusbridge (1917–1969)

an - gels sing - ing,   no - wells ring - ing,   tid - ings bring - ing:
free from sor - row,   prais - es voic - ing   greet the mor - row:

Christ the babe is Lord of all.
Christ the babe was born for you.

Christ the babe is Lord of all.
Christ the babe was born for you.

*Alternate melody: C B

175

144

'Twas in the moon of wintertime

JESOUS AHATONHIA 868688647

1. 'Twas in the moon of win-ter-time, when all the birds had fled,
2. With-in a lodge of bro-ken bark the ten-der Babe was found;
3. The ear-liest moon of win-ter-time is not so round and fair
4. O chil-dren of the for-est free, the kin of Man-i-tou,

that might-y Git-chi Man-i-tou sent an-gel choirs in-stead;
a rag-ged robe of rab-bit skin en-wrapped his beau-ty round,
as was the ring of glo-ry on the help-less in-fant there.
the ho-ly child of earth and heaven is born to-day for you.

be-fore their light the stars grew dim, and wan-dering hunt-ers
but, as the hunt-er braves drew nigh, the an-gel song rang
The chiefs from far be-fore him knelt with gifts of fox and
Come kneel be-fore the ra-diant boy, who brings you beau-ty,

Words: Huron, Jean de Brébeuf (1593–1649), translation, J. Edgar Middleton (1872–1960), alt
Music: Anonymous; arrangement, Frederick Jackisch (1922–)

heard   the   hymn:
loud   and   high:
bea - ver   pelt.
peace   and   joy.

Je - sus your King is born, Je - sus is born, in ex - cel - sis glo - ri - a.

In the bleak mid–winter

CRANHAM Irregular

1. In the bleak mid-win-ter, fros-ty wind made moan;
2. Our God, heaven can-not hold him, nor earth sus-tain;
3. An-gels and arch-an-gels may have gath-ered there,
4. What can I give him, poor as I am?

earth stood hard as i - ron, wa-ter like a stone;
heaven and earth shall wel-come him when he comes to reign:
cher-u-bim and ser-a-phim throng - ed the air;
If I were a shep - herd, I would bring a lamb;

snow had fall-en, snow on snow, snow on snow,
in the bleak mid-win-ter a sta-ble place suf-ficed the
but his mo-ther on-ly, in her maid-en bliss,
if I were a Wise Man, I would do my part; yet

in the bleak mid-win-ter, long a-go.
Lord God in-car-nate, Je-sus Christ.
wor-shipped the Be-lov-èd with a kiss.
what I can I give him — give my heart.

Words: Christina G. Rossetti (1830–1894) Music: Gustav T. Holst (1874–1934)

Christmas

146   Angels from the realms of glory

REGENT SQUARE   8 7 8 7 8 7

1. An - gels from the realms of glo - ry, wing your flight o'er all the earth;
2. Shep-herds in the field a - bid - ing, watch-ing o'er your flocks by night,
3. Sa - ges, leave your con - tem-pla - tions; bright-er vis - ions beam a - far;
4. Saints, be - fore the al - tar bend-ing, watch-ing long in hope and fear,
5. Though an in - fant now we view him, he shall fill his Fa-ther's throne,

ye who sang cre - a - tion's sto - ry, now pro-claim Mes - si - ah's birth.
God with us is now re - sid - ing; yon-der shines the in - fant Light.
seek the great de - sire of na - tions; ye have seen his na - tal star.
sud - den - ly the Lord, de-scend-ing, in his tem - ple shall ap - pear.
ga - ther all the na - tions to him; eve - ry knee shall then bow down.

Come and wor - ship, come and wor-ship; wor-ship Christ, the new-born King.

Words: James Montgomery (1771–1854)   Music: Henry T. Smart (1813–1879)

Words: public domain   Music: public domain

147 Angels we have heard on high

IRIS (GLORIA) 7 7 7 7 with refrain (9 9)

1. An - gels we have heard on high, sweet - ly sing-ing o'er the plains,
2. Shep-herds, why this ju - bi - lee? Why your joy - ous strains pro - long?
3. Come to Beth - le - hem and see Christ whose birth the an - gels sing;
4. See him in a man - ger laid, whom the choirs of an - gels praise;

and the moun-tains in re - ply ech - o - ing their joy - ous strains.
What the glad - some tid - ings be which in - spire your heaven-ly song?
come, a - dore on bend - ed knee, Christ, the Lord, the new-born King.
Ma - ry, Jo - seph, lend your aid, while our hearts in love we raise.

Refrain

Glo -

Glo -

Words: Luke 2:6–20; traditional French carol   Music: traditional; arrangement; Martin Shaw
(1875–1958) from Oxford Book of Carols

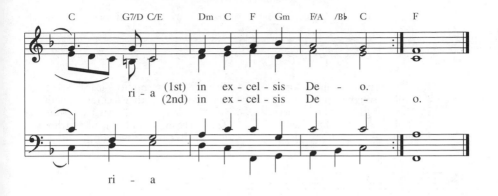

ri - a (1st) in ex - cel - sis De - o.
(2nd) in ex - cel - sis De - o.

ri - a

1. Les anges dans nos campagnes
   ont entonné l'hymne des cieux,
   et l'écho de nos montagnes
   redit ce chant mélodieux.
   Refrain
   Gloria in excelsis Deo!
   Gloria in excelsis Deo!

2. Bergers, pour qui cette fête?
   quei est l'objet de tous ces chants?
   quel vainqueur ou quel prophète
   méritent ces choeurs triomphants?
   Refrain

3. Ils annoncent la naissance
   du libérateur d'Israël
   et pleins de reconnaissance
   chantent en ce jour solennel:
   Refrain

148 It came upon the midnight clear

CAROL 8 6 8 6 D CMD

Alternate tune: Noel

Words: Edmund Hamilton Sears (1810–1876), alt   Music: Richard Storrs Willis (1819–1900)

Words: public domain   Music: public domain

"To all the earth good-will and peace, from
a - bove its sad and low - ly plains they
but we, through din of war, hear not the
look now! for glad and gold - en hours come
when peace shall o - ver all the earth God's

heaven's all - gra - cious King"; the world in sol - emn
bend on hov - ering wing, and ev - er o'er its
love - song which they bring. Oh hush the noise, Oh
swift - ly on the wing. Oh rest be - side the
pro - mised splen - dours fling, and all the world take

still - ness lay to hear the an - gels sing.
ba - bel sounds the bless - ed an - gels sing.
still the strife and hear the an - gels sing.
wea - ry road and hear the an - gels sing.
up the song, which now the an - gels sing.

149

Away in a manger

CRADLE SONG 11 11 11 11

1. A - way in a man - ger, no crib for a bed, the lit - tle Lord
2. The cat - tle are low - ing, the ba - by a - wakes, but lit - tle Lord
3. Be near me, Lord Je - sus, I ask you to stay close by me for -

Je - sus laid down his sweet head. The stars in the bright sky looked
Je - sus no cry - ing he makes. I love you, Lord Je - sus! Look
ev - er, and love me, I pray. Bless all the dear chil - dren in

down where he lay, the lit - tle Lord Je - sus a - sleep on the hay.
down from the sky, and stay by my side un - til morn - ing is nigh.
your ten - der care, and fit us for hea - ven to live with you there.

Words: v.1, 2, Little Children's Book for School and Families c. 1885; v.3, Gabriel's Vineyard Songs 1892;
alt Music: William James Kirkpatrick (1838–1921); harmony, Eric H. Thiman (1900–1975)

150 Jesus, our brother, kind and good

ORIENTIS PARTIBUS Irregular

1. Je - sus, our bro - ther, kind and good, was hum - bly
2. "I," said the don - key, shag - gy and brown, "I car - ried his
3. "I," said the cow, all white and red, "I gave him my
4. "I," said the sheep, with curl - y horn, "I gave him my

born in a sta - ble rude, and the friend - ly beasts a -
mo - ther up - hill and down; I car - ried his mo - ther to
man - ger for his bed; I gave him hay to
wool for his blan - ket warm, he wore my coat on

round him stood, Je - sus, our bro - ther, kind and good.
Beth - le - hem town; I," said the don - key, shag - gy and brown.
pil - low his head; I," said the cow, all white and red.
Christ - mas morn; I," said the sheep, with curl - y horn.

Words: French carol, 12th century; translation, anonymous Music: Medieval French melody;
harmony, Richard Redhead (1820–1901)

Words: public domain Music: public domain

151 Lo, how a Rose e'er blooming

ES IST EIN' ROS' ENTSPRUNGEN 7 6 7 6 6 7 6

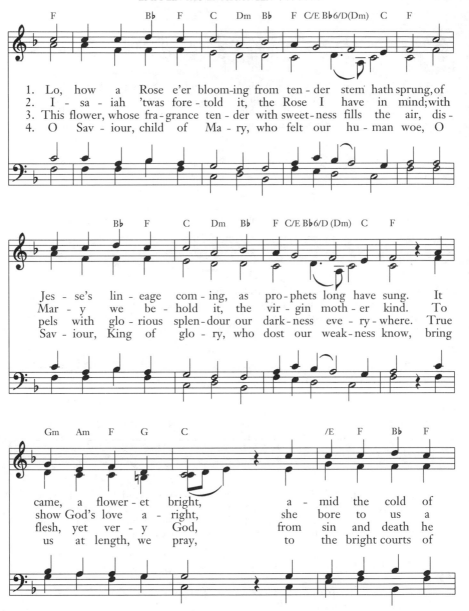

1. Lo, how a Rose e'er bloom-ing from ten - der stem hath sprung, of
2. I - sa - iah 'twas fore - told it, the Rose I have in mind; with
3. This flower, whose fra-grance ten - der with sweet-ness fills the air, dis -
4. O Sav - iour, child of Ma - ry, who felt our hu - man woe, O

Jes - se's lin - eage com - ing, as pro-phets long have sung. It
Mar - y we be - hold it, the vir - gin moth - er kind. To
pels with glo - rious splen-dour our dark-ness eve - ry - where. True
Sav - iour, King of glo - ry, who dost our weak-ness know, bring

came, a flower - et bright, a - mid the cold of
show God's love a - right, she bore to us a
flesh, yet ver - y God, from sin and death he
us at length, we pray, to the bright courts of

Words: German, anonymous; translation v.1,2, Theodore Baker (1851–1934); v.3, Harriet R. Krauth (1845–1925); v.4, John Caspar Mattes (1876–1948); alt
Music: Michael Praetorius (1571–1621), Geistliche Kirchengesänge, Cologne 1599

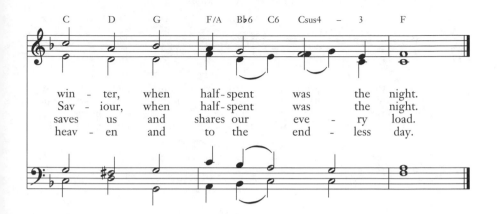

win - ter, when half - spent was the night.
Sav - iour, when half - spent was the night.
saves us and shares our eve - ry load.
heav - en and to the end - less day.

152 Still, still, still

STILL, STILL, STILL 3 6 9 8 3 6

1. Still, still, still, he sleeps this night so chill! The
2. Sleep, sleep, sleep, he lies in slum - ber deep, while
1. Still, still, still, weil's Kind-lein schla-fen will. Die
2. Schlaf, schlaf, schlaf, mein lie - bes Kind-lein, schlaf. Ma -

Vir-gin's ten - der arms en - fold-ing, warm and safe the child are hold-ing.
an - gel hosts from heaven come wing-ing, sweet-est songs of joy are sing-ing.
En-gel tun schön ju - bi - lie-ren, bei dem Kripp-lein mu - si - zie-ren.
ri - a will dich nie - der - sing-en, ih - re keu - sche Brust dar-bring-en.

Words: Austrian traditional; translation, George K. Evans (1917–) Music: Austrian traditional; arrangement, Walter Ehret (1918–)

153

Joy to the world

ANTIOCH 8 6 8 6 CM with repeat

1. Joy to the world! the Lord is come: let earth re-
2. Joy to the earth! the Sav-iour reigns: let us our
3. No more let sins and sor-rows grow, nor thorns in-
4. He rules the world with truth and grace, and makes the

ceive its King; let eve-ry heart pre-pare him
songs em-ploy, while fields and floods, rocks, hills and
fest the ground; he comes to make his bless-ings
na-tions prove the glo-ries of his right-eous-

room and heaven and na-ture sing, and heaven and na-ture
plains re-peat the sound-ing joy, re-peat the sound-ing
flow far as the curse is found, far as the curse is
ness and won-ders of his love, and won-ders of his-

Tenor and bass v.1 And heaven and na-ture sing *(Bass)*, and

Words: Isaac Watts (1674–1748), alt Music: Lowell Mason (1792–1872);
harmony, Henry Rosevear (1903–1982)

Words: public domain Music: harmony, copyright © estate of Henry Rosevear

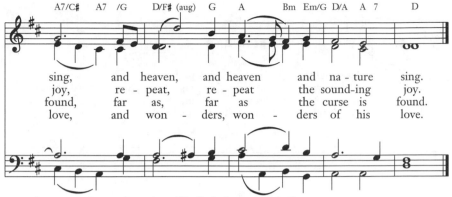

	A7/C♯	A7	/G	D/F♯ (aug)	G	A	Bm Em/G D/A	A 7	D

sing,   and heaven,   and heaven   and na - ture   sing.
joy,   re - peat,   re - peat   the sound-ing   joy.
found,   far as,   far as   the curse is   found.
love,   and won - ders, won - ders of his   love.

heaven and na - ture   sing *(Similarly for vv 2, 3 & 4)*

Korean

1. Kee-pu-daw koo-joo oh-shut-neh
   mawn pek-sung maw-jaw-raw
   Ohn kyo-hweh yuh taw il-uh-naw
   Taw chawn-yawng haw-yuh-raw
   Taw chawn-yawng haw-yuh-raw
   Taw chawn-yawng chawn-yawng haw-yuh-raw

2. Koo-seh-joo tawn-seng hess-u-nee
   taw chawn-yawng haw-yuh-raw
   Ee seh-sawng-eh mawn-mool-dul-aw
   Taw hwaw-dawp haw-yuh-raw
   Taw hwaw-dawp haw-yuh-raw
   Taw hwaw-dawp hwaw-dawp haw-yuh-raw

3. Ohn seh-sawng chweh-rul saw-haw-ruh
   choo yeh-soo oh-shut-neh
   Chweh wah sul-poom moo-raw-neh-goh
   Taw koo-wun haw-shi-neh
   Taw koo-wun haw-shi-heh
   Taw koo-wun koo-wun haw-shi-neh

4. Un-heh wah chill-lee tweh-shin joo
   taw choo-gwahn haw-shi-nee
   Mahn-gook pek-sung koo-joo aw-peh
   Taw kyung-beh haw-yuh-raw
   Taw kyung-beh haw-yuh-raw
   Taw kyung-beh haw-yuh-raw
   Taw kyung-beh kyung-beh haw-yuh-raw

154

Silent night

STILLE NACHT Irregular

1. Si - lent night! ho - ly night! All is calm,
2. Si - lent night! ho - ly night! Shep - herds quake
3. Si - lent night! ho - ly night! Son of God,
1. Stil - le Nacht, hei - li - ge Nacht! Al - les schläft,

all is bright round yon vir - gin moth - er and child,
at the sight: glo - ries stream from heav - en a - far,
love's pure light ra - diant beams from thy ho - ly face,
ein - sam wacht nur das trau - te hoch - hei - li - ge Paar.

ho - ly in - fant so ten - der and mild, sleep in heav - en - ly
heaven - ly hosts sing "Hal - le - lu - jah, Christ, the Sav - iour is
with the dawn of re - deem - ing grace, Je - sus, Lord, at thy
Hol - der Kna - be im lok - ki - gen Haar, schlaf in himm-lisch-er

Words: German, Joseph Mohr (1792–1848), translation, John Freeman Young (1820–1885)
Music: Franz Gruber (1787–1863)

peace;	sleep	in	heav -	en - ly	peace.	
born!	Christ,	the	Sav -	iour is	born!"	
birth,	Je -	sus,	Lord,	at thy	birth.	
Ruh',	schlaf	in	himm -	lisch-er	Ruh'.	

Hungarian

1. Csendes éj, szentséges éj!
   Mindenek nyugta mély;
   Nincs fenn más, csak a szent szüle pár,
   Drága kisdednük álmainál.
   Szent Fiú aludjál,
   Szent Fiú aludjál!

2. Csendes éj, szentséges éj!
   Angyalok hangja kél;
   Halld a mennyei halleluját,
   Szerte zengi e drága szavát:
   Krisztus megszabadít,
   Krisztus megszabadít!

3. Csendes éj, Szentséges éj!
   Szív örülj, higyj, remélj
   Isten szent Fia hinti reád
   Ajka vigaszadó mosolyát!
   Krisztus megszületett,
   Krisztus megszületett!

Chinese (Mandarin)

Píng ān yè! Shèng shàn yè!
Zhēn níng jìng, zhēn guāng míng,
Guāng huī huán zhào shèng mǔ shèng yīng,
Shèng jié yīng hái Chún zhēn kě ài,
Jìng xiǎng tiān cì ān mián,
Jìng xiǎng tiān cì ān mián.

155 That boy–child of Mary

BLANTYRE 5 5 9 with refrain (12 10)

That boy-child of Ma - ry was born in a sta - ble, a man-ger his
cra - dle in Beth - le - hem.

1. What shall we call him,
2. His name is Je - sus,
3. How can he save us,
4. Gift of the Fa - ther,
5. One with the Fa - ther,
6. Glad - ly we praise him,

child of the man - ger? What name is giv - en in Beth-le - hem?
God ev - er with us, God giv - en for us in Beth-le - hem.
how can he help us, born here a - mong us in Beth-le - hem?
to hu-man moth - er, makes him our broth - er of Beth-le - hem.
he is our Sav - iour, heav - en - sent help - er of Beth-le - hem.
love and a - dore him, give our-selves to him of Beth-le - hem.

Words: Tom Colvin (1925–) Music: Malawi traditional; adaptation, Tom Colvin (1925–)

156   The angel Gabriel from heaven

GABRIEL'S MESSAGE   10 10 12 10

1. The an - gel Ga - bri - el from heav - en came,
2. "For know a bless - ed moth - er you shall be,
3. Then gen - tle Ma - ry meek - ly bowed her head,
4. Of her, Em-man - u - el, the Christ, was born

his wings as drift - ed snow, his eyes as flame;
all gen - er - a - tions praise con - tin - ual - ly,
"To me be as it pleas - es God," she said,
in Beth - le-hem, all on a Christ - mas morn,

"All hail," said he, "O low - ly maid - en Ma - ry,"
your son shall be Em - man - u - el, by seers fore - told,"
"my soul shall laud and mag - ni - fy God's ho - ly name,"
and Chris-tian folk through-out the world will ev - er say:

most high-ly fa-voured la - dy: Glo - ri - a!

Words: paraphrase, Sabine Baring–Gould (1834–1924)   Music: Basque traditional melody;
arrangement, C. Edgar Pettman (1866–1943)

157 The snow lay on the ground

VENITE ADOREMUS   10 10 10 10 with refrain (10 10)

1. The snow lay on the ground, the stars shone bright, when Christ our Lord was born on Christ-mas night. Ve-ni-te a-do-re-mus Do-mi-num. Ve-ni-te a-do-re-mus Do-mi-num.
2. 'Twas gen-tle Ma-ry maid, so young and strong, who wel-comed here the Christ-child with a song. She laid him in a stall at Beth-le-hem; the ass and ox-en shared the roof with them.
3. And Jo-seph too was there to tend the Child, to guard him, and pro-tect his moth-er mild. The an-gels hov-ered round and sang this song: Ve-ni-te a-do-re-mus Do-mi-num.
4. And thus that man-ger poor be-came a throne, for he whom Ma-ry bore was God the Son. Oh come, then, let us join the heaven-ly host, to praise the Fa-ther, Son and Ho-ly Ghost.

Ve-ni-te a-do-re-mus Do-mi-num. Ve-ni-te a-do-re-mus Do-mi-num.

Words: Anglo–Irish carol; alt   Music: English melody; adaptation, C. Winfred Douglas (1867–1944); harmony, Leo Sowerby (1895–1968)

158 The hands that first held Mary's child

NOEL 8 6 8 6 D CMD

1. The hands that first held Ma-ry's Child were hard from work-ing wood,
2. When Jo-seph mar-veled at the size of that small breath-ing frame,
3. "This Child shall be Em - man-u-el, not God up - on the throne
4. The tools which Jo-seph laid a - side a mob would lat - er lift

from boards they sawed and planed and filed and splin-ters they with-stood.
and gazed up - on those bright new eyes and spoke the In-fant's name,
but God with us, Em - man - u - el, as close as blood and bone."
and use with an - ger, fear and pride to cru - ci - fy God's gift.

This day they gripped no tool of steel, they drove no i - ron nail,
the an-gel's words he once had dreamed poured down from heav-en's height,
The ti - ny form in Jo-seph's palms con - firmed what he had heard,
Let us, O Lord, not on - ly hold the Child who's born to - day,

but cra - dled from the head to heel our Lord, new-born and frail.
and, like the host of stars that beamed, blessed earth with wel-come light.
and from his heart rose hymns and psalms for heav - en's hu - man word.
but, charged with faith, may we be bold to fol - low in his way.

Words: Thomas H. Troeger (1945–) Music: English traditional; arrangement, Arthur Seymour Sullivan (1842–1900)

Oh come, all ye faithful

ADESTE FIDELES   Irregular

Descant

5. Yea, Lord, we greet thee, born this hap-py morn - ing:

1. Oh come, all ye faith - ful, joy - ful and tri - um - phant; oh
2. God of God, Light of light,
3. See how the shep - herds, sum-moned to his cra - dle,
4. Sing, choirs of an - gels, sing in ex - ul - ta - tion;
5. Yea, Lord, we greet thee, born this hap-py morn - ing;

Je - sus, to thee be all glo - ry given;

come ye, oh come ye to Beth - le - hem.
born un - to Ma - ry, the vir - gin blest,
leav - ing their flocks draw nigh with ho - ly fear;
sing, all ye ci - ti - zens of heaven a - bove:
Je - sus, to thee be glo - ry given;

Words: Latin, John Francis Wade (1711–1786), translation, F. Oakeley (1802–1880), alt; French, Claude
Rozier (1924–) Music: anonymous; arrangement and descant, Hymns Ancient and Modern Ltd. 1947

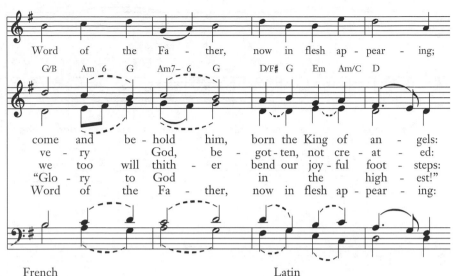

Word of the Fa - ther, now in flesh ap - pear - ing;

G/B   Am 6   G   Am7– 6   G   D/F♯   G   Em   Am/C   D

come and be - hold him, born the King of an - gels:
ve - ry God, be - got - ten, not cre - at - ed:
we too will thith - er bend our joy - ful foot - steps:
"Glo - ry to God in the high - est!"
Word of the Fa - ther, now in flesh ap - pear - ing:

French

1. Peuple fidèle! Ton Seigneur t'appelle:
c'est féte sur terre, le Christ est né.
Viens à la crèche, voir le Roi du monde:

   Refrain:
   en lui, viens reconnaître,
   en lui, viens reconnaître,
   ton Dieu, ton Sauveur!

2. Verbe, Lumière, et Splendeur du Père,
il naît d'une mère, petit enfant;
Dieu véritable, le Seigneur fait homme:
Refrain:

3. Peuple, acclame, avec tous les anges,
le Maître du monde qui vient chez nous,
Dieu qui se donne à tous ceux qu'il aime:
Refrain:

4. Peuple fidèle, en ce jour de fête,
proclame la gloire de ton Seigneur.
Dieu se fait homme; vois donc comme
il t'aime:
Refrain:

Latin

1. Adeste, fideles, laeti triumphantes,
venite, venite, in Bethlehem;
natum videte regem angelorum:

   Refrain:
   Venite, adoremus,
   venite, adoremus,
   venite, adoremus
   Dominum.

2. Deum de Deo, Lumen de Lumine,
parturit virgo mater;
Deum verum, genitum, non factum:
Refrain:

3. Cantet nunc hymnos chorus
  angelorum;
cantet nunc aula caelestium:
gloria in excelsis Deo!
Refrain:

4. En grege relicto, humiles ad cunas
vocati pastores approperant;
et nos ovanti gradu festinemus:
Refrain:

5. Ergo qui natus die hodierna,
Jesu, tibi sit gloria:
Patris aeterni verbum caro factum:
Refrain:

Refrain

Oh come, oh come,

G   D/F♯ G   D7/A G   D/F♯

Oh come, let us a - dore him; oh come, let us a - dore him;

oh come, let us a - dore him, Christ the Lord.

G   D7/A G   D   A7/E D   /C G/B C   G/D D   G

oh come, let us a - dore him, Christ the Lord.

French Refrain
en lui, viens reconnaître
en lui, viens reconnaître
en lui, viens reconnaître
ton Dieu, ton Sauveur!

Latin Refrain
venite, adoremus,
venite, adoremus,
venite, adoremus
Dominum.

160 Unto us a child is born

PUER NOBIS NASCITUR 7 6 7 7

1. Un - to us a child is born! Sov-ereign of cre - a - tion,
2. Cra - dled in a cat - tle stall, held by love ma - ter - nal,
3. Now may Ma - ry's son, who came so long a - go to love us,
4. "Christ the Source and Christ the End!" Let the or - gan thun - der

came once to a world for - lorn, the Lord of eve - ry
see the Sove-reign of us all, our Lord of lords e -
lead us all with hearts a - flame un - to the joys a -
while our hap - py voic - es rend the joy - ful air a -

na - tion, the Lord of eve - ry na - tion.
ter - nal, our Lord of lords e - ter - nal.
bove us, un - to the joys a - bove us.
sun - der, the joy - ful air a - sun - der!

Words: Latin, 15th century, translation, Percy Dearmer (1867–1936), alt; v.2 revision, Hymns for Today's Church Music: 15th century carol melody, Piae Cantiones 1582; arrangement, Derek Holman (1931–)

Words: translation, copyright © Oxford University Press Music: arrangement, copyright © Derek Holman

161 What child is this

GREENSLEEVES 87876867

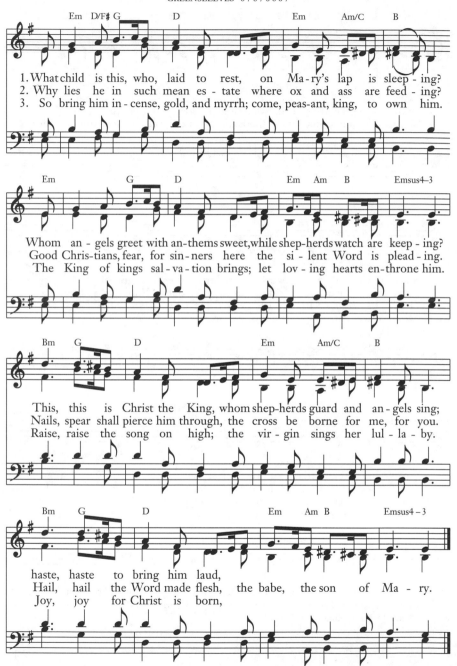

1. What child is this, who, laid to rest, on Ma - ry's lap is sleep - ing?
2. Why lies he in such mean es - tate where ox and ass are feed - ing?
3. So bring him in - cense, gold, and myrrh; come, peas-ant, king, to own him.

Whom an - gels greet with an-thems sweet, while shep-herds watch are keep - ing?
Good Chris-tians, fear, for sin-ners here the si - lent Word is plead - ing.
The King of kings sal - va - tion brings; let lov - ing hearts en-throne him.

This, this is Christ the King, whom shep-herds guard and an - gels sing;
Nails, spear shall pierce him through, the cross be borne for me, for you.
Raise, raise the song on high; the vir - gin sings her lul - la - by.

haste, haste to bring him laud,
Hail, hail the Word made flesh, the babe, the son of Ma - ry.
Joy, joy for Christ is born,

Words: William Chatterton Dix (1837–1898) Music: English traditional

Words: public domain Music: public domain

162   On Christmas night all Christians sing

SUSSEX CAROL   8 8 8 8 8 8

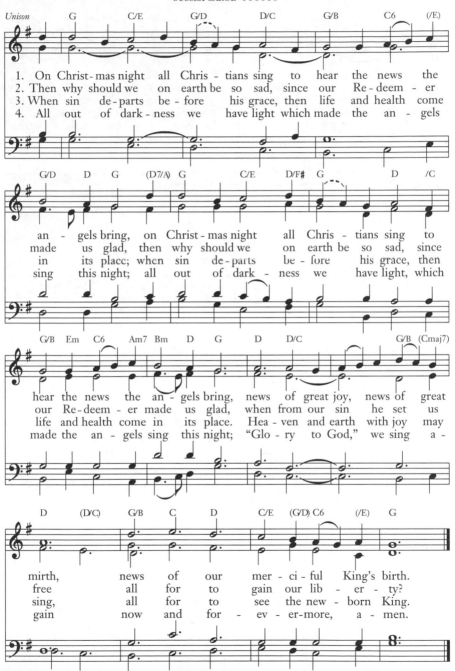

1. On Christ-mas night all Chris-tians sing to hear the news the
2. Then why should we on earth be so sad, since our Re-deem - er
3. When sin de-parts be - fore his grace, then life and health come
4. All out of dark - ness we have light which made the an - gels

an - gels bring, on Christ-mas night all Chris - tians sing to
made us glad, then why should we on earth be so sad, since
in its place; when sin de-parts be - fore his grace, then
sing this night; all out of dark - ness we have light, which

hear the news the an - gels bring, news of great joy, news of great
our Re-deem - er made us glad, when from our sin he set us
life and health come in its place. Hea - ven and earth with joy may
made the an - gels sing this night; "Glo - ry to God," we sing a -

mirth, news of our mer - ci - ful King's birth.
free all for to gain our lib - er - ty?
sing, all for to see the new - born King.
gain now and for - ev - er-more, a - men.

Words: English traditional, alt Music: English traditional; arrangement, Ralph Vaughan Williams (1872–1958)

163 Of eternal love begotten

DIVINUM MYSTERIUM 8 7 8 7 8 7 7

1. Of e - ter - nal love be - got - ten un - cre - at - ed One-in-Three,
2. This, the one whom heaven-taught sing - ers sang of old with one ac-cord,
3. Oh that birth for - ev - er bless - ed when the vir - gin, full of grace,
4. All the heights of heaven a - dore him; an - gels end-less prais - es sing,
5. God Re - deem - er, God Cre - a - tor, God the Spir - it, now to thee

Christ, the Al - pha and O - me - ga, Christ, the Source, the End will be
whom the scrip-tures of the pro-phets pro-mised in their faith - ful word;
by the Spi - rit's power con-ceiv-ing, bore the Sav - iour of our race,
all earth bow to Christ our Sov-ereign, and our joy - ful tri - bute bring;
hymn and chant and high thanks-giv - ing and un - wea - ried prais - es be,

Words: Latin, Aurelius Clemens Prudentius (348–413); translation, John Mason Neale (1818–1866), alt;
v.3, The Psalter Hymnal 1987   Music: Plainsong, 12th century; arrangement, Healey Willan (1880–1968)

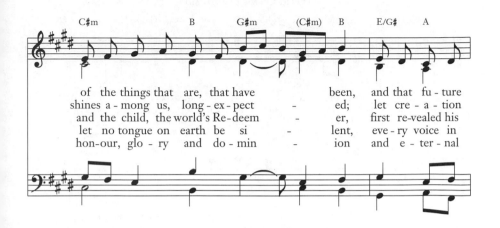

| | C#m | | B | G#m | (C#m) | B | E/G# | A |

of the things that are, that have been, and that fu - ture
shines a - mong us, long - ex - pect - ed; let cre - a - tion
and the child, the world's Re - deem - er, first re-vealed his
let no tongue on earth be si - lent, eve - ry voice in
hon - our, glo - ry and do - min - ion and e - ter - nal

| C#m | G#m | C#m | G#m | (C#m) | B | E |

years shall see,
praise its Lord,
sa - cred face, ev - er - more and ev - er - more.
con - cert ring,
vic - to - ry,

164   O little town of Bethlehem

FOREST GREEN   8 6 8 6 D CMD

1. O lit - tle town of Beth - le - hem, how still we see thee lie!
2. For Christ is born of Ma - ry, and, gath-ered all a - bove,
3. How si - lent-ly, how si - lent - ly, the won-drous gift is given!
4. O ho - ly child of Beth - le - hem, de - scend to us, we pray;

A - bove thy deep and dream-less sleep the si - lent stars go by:
while mor-tals sleep, the an - gels keep their watch of won-dering love.
So God im-parts to hu - man hearts the bless-ings born of heaven.
cast out our sin and en - ter in; be born in us to - day.

yet in thy dark streets shin - eth the ev - er - last - ing light;
O morn-ing stars, to - geth - er pro - claim the ho - ly birth,
No ear may hear his com - ing, but in this world of sin,
We hear the Christ-mas an - gels the great glad tid - ings tell;

Words: Phillips Brooks (1835–1893), alt   Music: English traditional; harmony, Ralph Vaughan Williams (1872–1958)

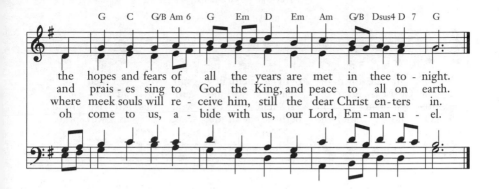

| | G | | C | G/B | Am 6 | | G | | Em | D | | Em | Am | G/B | Dsus4 | D | 7 | G |

the   hopes and fears of   all   the years are   met   in   thee to - night.
and   prais - es sing to   God   the King, and peace   to   all   on   earth.
where meek souls will re - ceive him, still the   dear Christ en - ters   in.
oh   come   to   us,   a - bide with us,   our Lord, Em - man - u -   el.

Christmas

165   O little town of Bethlehem

ST. LOUIS 8 6 8 6 D CMD

1. O lit-tle town of Beth-le-hem, how still we see thee lie!
2. For Christ is born of Mar - y, and, gath-ered all a - bove,
3. How si - lent-ly, how si - lent-ly, the won-drous gift is given!
4. O ho - ly child of Beth-le-hem, de - scend to us, we pray;

A - bove thy deep and dream-less sleep the si - lent stars go by:
while mor-tals sleep, the an - gels keep their watch of won-dering love.
So God im-parts to hu - man hearts the bless-ings born of heaven.
cast out our sin and en - ter in; be born in us to - day.

yet in thy dark streets shin - eth the ev - er-last-ing light;
O morn-ing stars, to - geth - er pro - claim the ho - ly birth,
No ear may hear his com - ing, but in this world of sin,
We hear the Christ-mas an - gels the great glad tid-ings tell;

the hopes and fears of all the years are met in thee to-night.
and prais - es sing to God the King, and peace to all on earth.
where meek souls will re - ceive him, still the dear Christ en - ters in.
oh come to us, a - bide with us, our Lord, Em-man-u - el.

Words: Phillips Brooks (1835–1893), alt Music: Louis Henry Redner (1831–1908)

Words: public domain Music: public domain

206

166   Once in royal David's city

IRBY 878777

1. Once in roy - al Da - vid's ci - ty stood a low - ly cat - tle shed, where a moth - er laid her ba - by in a man - ger for his bed: Ma - ry was that moth - er mild, Je - sus Christ her lit - tle child.

2. Christ came down to earth from heav - en, who is God and Lord of all, shel - tered by a hum - ble sta - ble, cra - dled in a cat - tle stall: with the poor, op-pressed and low - ly, lived on earth our Sav - iour ho - ly,

3. and our eyes at last shall see him, through his own re-deem - ing love, for that child so dear and gen - tle is our Lord in heaven a - bove, and he leads his chil - dren on to the place where he is gone.

4. Not in that poor low - ly sta - ble, with the ox - en stand - ing by, we shall see him, but in heav - en, set at God's right hand on high; there God's chil - dren ga - ther round, bright like stars, with glo - ry crowned.

Words: Cecil Frances Alexander (1823–1895), alt
Music: Henry John Gauntlett (1805–1876); harmony, A.H. Mann (1850–1929)

167 Where shepherds lately knelt

MANGER SONG 12 12 10 10

Unison

1. Where shep-herds late-ly knelt and kept the an-gel's word,
2. In that un-like-ly place I find him as they said:
3. How should I not have known I-sa-iah would be there,
4. Can I, will I for-get how love was born, and burned

I come in half be-lief, a pil-grim strange-ly stirred,
sweet new-born babe, how frail! and in a man-ger bed,
his proph-e-cies ful-filled? With pound-ing heart I stare:
its way in-to my heart un-asked, un-forced, un-earned,

but there is room and wel-come there for me,
a still, small voice to cry one day for me,
a child, a son, the Prince of Peace for me,
to die, to live, and not a-lone for me,

but there is room and wel-come there for me.
a still, small voice to cry one day for me.
a child, a son, the Prince of Peace for me.
to die, to live, and not a-lone for me?

Words: Jaroslav J. Vajda (1919–) Music: Carl F. Schalk (1929–)

168 See amid the winter's snow

HUMILITY 7 7 7 7 with refrain

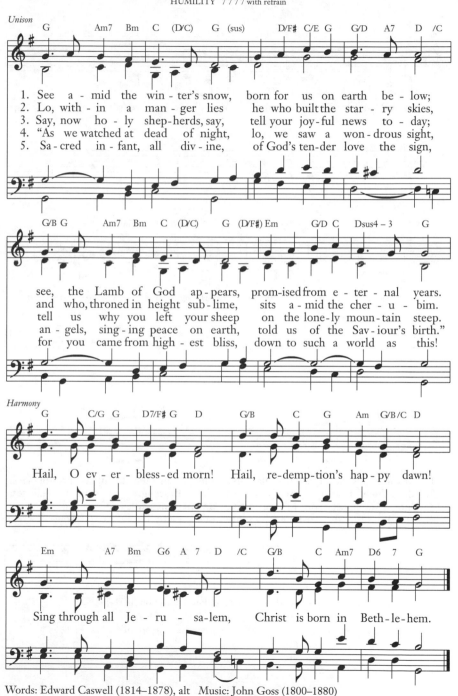

1. See a-mid the win-ter's snow, born for us on earth be-low;
2. Lo, with-in a man-ger lies he who built the star-ry skies,
3. Say, now ho-ly shep-herds, say, tell your joy-ful news to-day;
4. "As we watched at dead of night, lo, we saw a won-drous sight,
5. Sa-cred in-fant, all div-ine, of God's ten-der love the sign,

see, the Lamb of God ap-pears, prom-ised from e-ter-nal years.
and who, throned in height sub-lime, sits a-mid the cher-u-bim.
tell us why you left your sheep on the lone-ly moun-tain steep.
an-gels, sing-ing peace on earth, told us of the Sav-iour's birth."
for you came from high-est bliss, down to such a world as this!

Hail, O ev-er-bless-ed morn! Hail, re-demp-tion's hap-py dawn!

Sing through all Je-ru-sa-lem, Christ is born in Beth-le-hem.

Words: Edward Caswell (1814–1878), alt Music: John Goss (1800–1880)

169

Il est né

IL EST NÉ 8 9 8 8 with refrain (8 11 8 8)

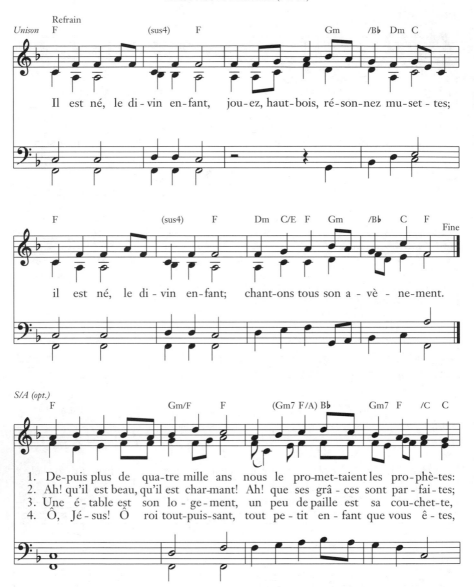

Il est né, le di - vin en - fant, jou - ez, haut - bois, ré - son - nez mu - set - tes;

il est né, le di - vin en - fant; chant-ons tous son a - vè - ne-ment.

1. De-puis plus de qua-tre mille ans nous le pro-met-taient les pro-phè-tes:
2. Ah! qu'il est beau, qu'il est char-mant! Ah! que ses grâ - ces sont par - fai-tes;
3. Une é - table est son lo - ge-ment, un peu de paille est sa cou-chet-te,
4. Ô, Jé - sus! Ô roi tout-puis-sant, tout pe - tit en - fant que vous ê - tes,

Words: 19th century French carol; English translation, Andrew Donaldson (1951–)
Music: 18th century French carol; harmony, Andrew Donaldson (1951–)

Words: English translation, copyright © Andrew Donaldson, 1997 Music: arrangement copyright © Andrew Donaldson 1997

de-puis plus de qua-tre mille ans nous at-tend-ions cet heu-reux temps.
Ah! qu'il est beau, qu'il est char-mant! Qu'il est doux, ce di-vin en - fant!
une é-table est son lo - ge-ment, pour un Dieu, quel a - bais - se - ment!
ô Jé-sus! Ô roi tout-puis-sant, rei-gnez sur nous en - tiè - re - ment!

Refrain
He is born! Now the child has come!
Fill all the air with our merry carolling!
Play the pipe, beat the joyful drum!
Hope is born, for the child has come!

1. Faithful sages through ages long,
   prophets sang of the Saviour's coming:
   faithful sages through ages long,
   prophets sang of the promised dawn.
   Refrain:

2. See what light from his face has shone,
   grace and mercy of God revealing;
   see what light from his face has shone,
   from this child, from the promised one!
   Refrain:

3. Christ embraced our human form,
   made the stable a holy dwelling;
   Christ embraced our human form:
   dwell in us, well-beloved Son!
   Refrain:

4. Jesus, Sovereign and Holy One,
   we adore you, before you kneeling;
   Jesus, Sovereign and Holy One,
   dwell in us, make our hearts your throne!
   Refrain:

What star is this

PUER NOBIS 8 8 8 8 LM

1. What star is this, with beams so bright,
2. 'Tis now ful - filled what God de - creed,
3. O Je - sus, while the star of grace
4. To God the Fa - ther, God the Son,

more love - ly than the noon - day light?
"From Ja - cob shall a star pro - ceed,"
im - pels us on to seek your face,
and Ho - ly Spir - it, Three - in - One,

'Tis sent to an - nounce a new - born King,
and lo! the East - ern sag - es stand
let not our sloth - ful hearts re - fuse
may eve - ry tongue and na - tion raise

Words: Matthew 2:1–12; paraphrase, Latin, Charles Coffin (1676–1749), translation, Hymns Ancient and Modern, 1861; alt, John Chandler (1806–1876)   Music: 15th-century carol melody, Pie Cantiones 1582; adaptation, Michael Praetorius (1571–1621); harmony, G.R. Woodward (1848–1935)

Words: public domain   Music: harmony, copyright © A.R. Mowbray and Co. Ltd., (an imprint of Cassell plc) from The Cowley Carol Book

(Em)	A/C#	D	A	(F#m)	D	A	D

glad   ti - dings   of   our   God   to   bring.
to   read   in   heaven   the   Lord's   com - mand.
the   guid - ance   of   your   light   to   use.
an   end - less   song   of   thank - ful   praise.

171   The people that in darkness

DUNFERMLINE 8 6 8 6 CM

E	/G#	F#m6	E	A/C#	Bsus4–3	E	C#m	B/D#	E6	F#	B

1. The peo - ple that in dark-ness pined have seen   a glo-rious light;
2. To hail your rise, O   bet - ter Sun, the gath-ering na-tions come,
3. To   us   a   Child of hope is born, to   us   a   Son is   given,
4. His name shall be   the Prince of Peace, for - ev - er-more a - dored,
5. His reign of right-eous gov-ern-ment shall   o - ver all ex - tend,

B/D#	E	Bm6	A	G#m/B	B7/D#	E	B	E	F#m/A	C#m	Bsus4–3	E

the peo - ple dwell in day, who dwelt in death's sur-round-ing night.
re - joic - ing as when reap - ers bear the har - vest treas-ures home.
and on his shoul-ders ev - er rests all power in earth and heaven.
the Won-der - ful, the Coun - sel - or, the great and might-y   Lord.
for peace and jus - tice shall a - bound in this world with-out end.

See also: Dunfermline 43 221

Words: John Morison (1750–1798), Scottish Paraphrase; alt   Music: Scottish Psalter, 1615

Words: public domain   Music: public domain

172
As with gladness men of old
DIX 777777

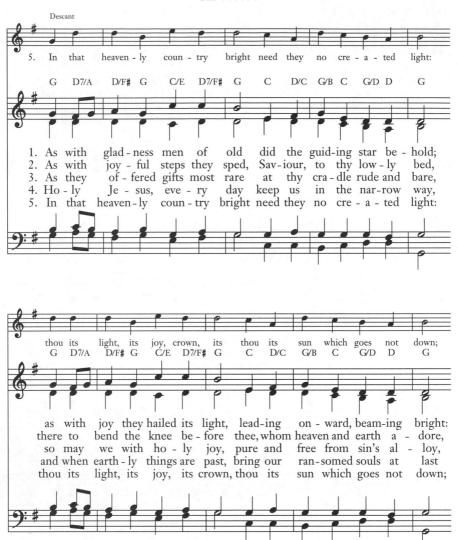

5. In that heaven-ly coun-try bright need they no cre-a-ted light:

G D7/A D/F♯ G C/E D7/F♯ G C D/C G/B C G/D D G

1. As with glad - ness men of old did the guid-ing star be - hold;
2. As with joy - ful steps they sped, Sav-iour, to thy low - ly bed,
3. As they of - fered gifts most rare at thy cra - dle rude and bare,
4. Ho - ly Je - sus, eve - ry day keep us in the nar-row way,
5. In that heaven-ly coun - try bright need they no cre - a - ted light:

thou its light, its joy, crown, its thou its sun which goes not down;
G D7/A D/F♯ G C/E D7/F♯ G C D/C G/B C G/D D G

as with joy they hailed its light, lead-ing on - ward, beam-ing bright:
there to bend the knee be - fore thee, whom heaven and earth a - dore,
so may we with ho - ly joy, pure and free from sin's al - loy,
and when earth - ly things are past, bring our ran-somed souls at last
thou its light, its joy, its crown, thou its sun which goes not down;

Words: William Chatterton Dix (1837–1898) Music: Conrad Kocher (1786–1872);
harmony, William H. Monk (1823–1889); descant, Sydney H. Nicholson (1875–1947)

Words: public domain Music: descant, copyright © The Royal School of Church Music

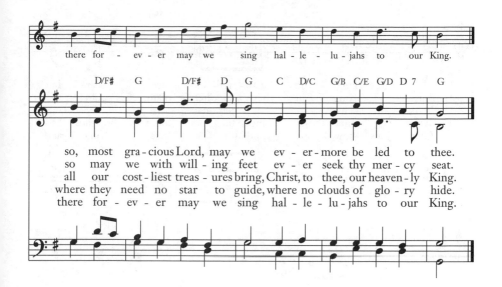

there for - ev - er may we sing hal - le - lu - jahs to our King.

D/F♯   G   D/F♯   D   G   C   D/C   G/B   C/E   G/D   D 7   G

so,   most   gra - cious Lord, may   we   ev - er - more be   led   to   thee.
so   may   we   with will - ing feet   ev - er seek thy mer - cy   seat.
all   our   cost - liest treas - ures bring, Christ, to   thee, our heaven - ly King.
where they   need   no   star   to   guide, where no clouds of   glo - ry   hide.
there   for - ev - er   may   we sing   hal - le - lu - jahs to   our   King.

173 We three kings

KINGS OF ORIENT 8 8 8 6 with refrain

1. We three kings of O - ri - ent are; bear - ing
2. Born a King on Beth - le - hem's plain, gold I
3. Frank - in - cense to of - fer have I; in - cense
4. Myrrh is mine; its bit - ter per - fume breathes a
5. Glo - rious now be - hold him a - rise, King and

gifts we tra - verse a - far, field and foun - tain,
bring to crown him a - gain, King for - ev - er,
owns a De - i - ty nigh, prayer and prais - ing,
life of gath - er - ing gloom, sor - rowing, sigh - ing,
God and sac - ri - fice: hal - le - lu - jah,

moor and moun - tain, fol - low - ing yon - der star.
ceas - ing nev - er, o - ver us all to reign.
voic - es rais - ing, wor - ship - ping God on high.
bleed - ing, dy - ing, sealed in the stone - cold tomb.
hal - le - lu - jah, sounds through the earth and skies.

Words: John H. Hopkins Jr. (1820–1891) Music: traditional carol;
arrangement, John H. Hopkins Jr. (1820–1891)

Words: public domain Music: public domain

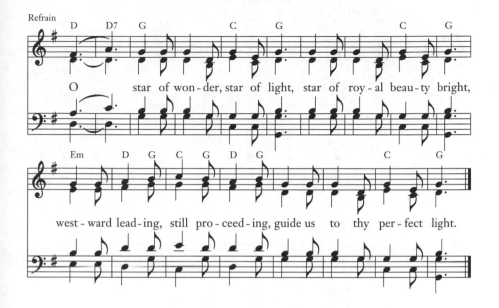

O star of won-der, star of light, star of roy-al beau-ty bright, west-ward lead-ing, still pro-ceed-ing, guide us to thy per-fect light.

Epiphany

174   Worship the Lord in the beauty of holiness

MORDUN 12 10 12 10

1. Wor - ship the Lord in the beau - ty of
2. Low at his feet lay thy bur - den of
3. Fear not to en - ter God's courts in the
4. These, though we bring them in trem - bling and
5. Wor - ship the Lord in the beau - ty of

ho - li - ness; bow down in rev - erence, God's
care - ful - ness; high on his heart Je - sus
slen - der - ness of the poor wealth thou wouldst
fear - ful - ness, God will ac - cept for the
ho - li - ness; bow down in rev - erence, God's

glo - ry pro - claim; gold of o - be - dience and
bears it for thee, com - forts thy sor - rows and
reck - on as thine; truth in its beau - ty and
name that is dear; morn - ings of joy give for
glo - ry pro - claim; gold of o - be - dience and

Alternate tune: Was Lebet

Words: John Samuel Bewley Monsell (1811–1875), alt   Music: Henry T. Smart (1813–1879)

Words: public domain   Music: public domain

218

| Em | D/A | A | /G | D/F# | | D6 | C/E | | Am/C |

in - cense of low - li - ness bring now, a -
an - swers thy prayer - ful - ness, guid - ing thy
love in its ten - der - ness: these are the
eve - nings of tear - ful - ness, trust for our
in - cense of low - li - ness bring now, a -

| B | | Em | Am | D | | 7 | G |

dor - ing the Lord's ho - ly name.
steps as may best for thee be.
of - ferings to lay on his shrine.
trem - bling and hope for our fear.
dor - ing the Lord's ho - ly name.

175 Brightest and best of the stars of the morning

STELLA ORIENTIS 11 10 11 10

1. Bright-est and best of the stars of the morn - ing,
2. Cold on his cra - dle the dew-drops are shin - ing;
3. Say, shall we yield him, in cost - ly de - vo - tion,
4. Vain - ly we of - fer each am - ple ob - la - tion,
5. Bright - est and best of the stars of the morn - ing,

dawn on our dark - ness and lend us thine aid;
low lies his head with the beasts of the stall;
o - dours of E - dom and of - ferings di - vine,
vain - ly with gifts would his fa - vour se - cure;
dawn on our dark - ness and lend us thine aid;

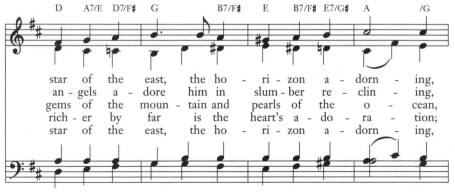

star of the east, the ho - ri - zon a - dorn - ing,
an - gels a - dore him in slum - ber re - clin - ing,
gems of the moun - tain and pearls of the o - cean,
rich - er by far is the heart's a - do - ra - tion;
star of the east, the ho - ri - zon a - dorn - ing,

Words: Reginald Heber (1783–1826), alt Music: Healey Willan (1880–1968)

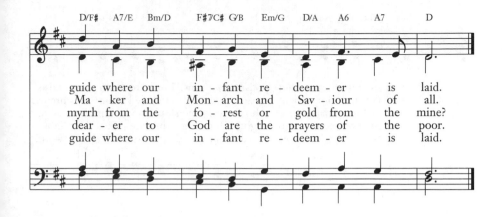

guide where our in - fant re - deem - er is laid.
Ma - ker and Mon - arch and Sav - iour of all.
myrrh from the fo - rest or gold from the mine?
dear - er to God are the prayers of the poor.
guide where our in - fant re - deem - er is laid.

176 Songs of thankfulness and praise

SALZBURG (HINTZE) 7 7 7 7 D

1. Songs of thank-ful - ness and praise Je - sus, Lord, to you we raise,
2. God re-vealed at Jor - dan's stream God's be - lov - ed Son su - preme,
3. God re-vealed in mak - ing whole weak-ened limbs and faint - ing soul,
4. Man - i - fest on moun - tain height, shin - ing in re - splen-dent light,
5. Grant us grace to see you, Lord, mir-rored in your ho - ly word;

God re-vealed by guid - ing star to the sag - es from a - far,
and at Ca - na, wed - ding-guest, in your pow - er man-i - fest,
God re-vealed in val - iant fight quell-ing all the dev-il's might,
where dis - ci - ples filled with awe your trans-fig-ured glo-ry saw;
may we im - i - tate you still and o - bey your per-fect will,

branch of roy - al Da-vid's stem, in your birth at Beth - le - hem:
God re-vealed in works di - vine, chang - ing wa - ter in - to wine:
God re-vealed in gra-cious will, ev - er bring-ing good from ill:
from that place you went with them stead - fast to Je - ru - sa - lem;
that we like to you may be, at your great E - pi - pha - ny:

Words: Christopher Wordsworth (1807–1885), alt   Music: Jakob Hintze (1622–1702), alt; harmony, J.S. Bach (1685–1750)

Words: public domain   Music: public domain

| D | G A | Bm7 E7/B A | G D Em6 | D/F♯ G6 A | D |

(1–3) an-thems be to you ad-dressed,
(4) cross and East-er day at-test God in Christ made man-i-fest.
(5) may your glo-ry be con-fessed,

177   Christ, whose glory fills the skies

HEATHLANDS 777777

| C/E | C | G | C/E | F | /A | C | F/A | G/B | C | F/A | C/E F | G |

1. Christ, whose glo-ry fills the skies, Christ, the true, the on-ly Light,
2. Dark and cheer-less is the morn un-ac-com-pan-ied by thee;
3. Vis-it, then, this soul of mine; pierce the gloom of sin and grief;

| G/B G | C | G/B Am6 | G/B | D | D/F♯ D | G | C/E | Am D | G |

Sun of right-eous-ness, a-rise, tri-umph o'er the shades of night.
joy-less is the day's re-turn, till thy mer-cy's beams I see,
fill me, ra-dian-cy di-vine; scat-ter all my un-be-lief;

| Em | C6 F | G7/D | Am | F | C/E F/A C/G | Dm7/F G7 | C |

Day-spring from on high, be near; Day-star, in my heart ap-pear.
till thy in-ward light im-part, glad my eyes and warm my heart.
more and more thy-self dis-play, shin-ing to the per-fect day.

Words: Charles Wesley (1707–1788) Music: Henry T. Smart (1813–1879)

Words: public domain Music: public domain

Epiphany

178 When heaven's bright with mystery

MEADVILLE 888888

1. When heav-en's bright with mys-ter-y and sci-ence search-es na-ture's art, when all cre-a-tion yearns for peace and hope sinks deep in hu-man hearts, ap-pear to
2. When Her-od bar-ters power and lives and Ra-chel's weep-ing fills the night, when suf-fering's mask marks eve-ry face and Love's a ref-u-gee in flight, re-veal to
3. When fra-gile faith like des-ert wind blows dry and emp-ty, hope e-rased, when with-ered grass and fad-ing flower pro-claim a-gain our day's brief space, breathe on the
4. When heav-en's bright with mys-ter-y and stars still lead an un-known way, when love still lights a gen-tle path where courts of power can hold no sway, there with the

Alternate tune: Melita

Words: Rob Johns (1942–1986) Music: Walter Pelz (1926–); adaptation, W. Thomas Jones (1956–)

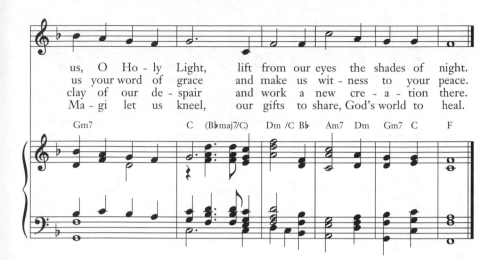

us, O Ho - ly Light,   lift from our eyes the shades of night.
us your word of grace   and make us wit - ness to your peace.
clay of our de - spair   and work a new cre - a - tion there.
Ma - gi let us kneel,   our gifts to share, God's world to heal.

179 Arise, shine out, your light has come

VOM HIMMEL HOCH 8 8 8 8 LM

1. A - rise, shine out, your light has come,	un - fold - ing
2. A - bove earth's val - leys, thick with night,	high on your
3. From walls sur - pas - sing time and space,	un - num - bered
4. The sounds of vi - o - lence shall cease,	as dwel - lings
5. The danc - ing air shall glow with light	and sun and

ci - ty of our dreams.	On dis - tant hills a
walls the dawn ap - pears,	and his - to - ry shall
gates, like o - pen hands,	shall ga - ther gifts from
of sal - va - tion rise,	to spar - kle in e -
moon give up their place,	when love shines out of

glo - ry gleams:	the new cre - a - tion has	be - gun.
dry its tears,	as na - tions stream to - wards	your light.
all the lands,	and wel - come all the hu -	man race.
ter - nal skies	from a - ven - ues of praise	and peace.
eve - ry face:	our good, our glo - ry, our	de - light.

Words: Brian A. Wren (1936–) Music: Schumann's Geistliche Lieder, 1539; harmony, Hans Leo Hassler (1564–1612)

Epiphany

180 How brightly beams the morning star

WIE SCHÖN LEUCHTET 8 8 7 D 8 8 8

1. How bright-ly beams the morn-ing star! What sud-den ra-diance
Bright-ness of God, that breaks our night and fills the dark-ened
2. All praise the One who came to save, who con-quered death and
the Truth, the Life who once was slain, the Friend whom none shall

from a-far doth glad us with its shin - ing?
souls with light, who long for truth were pin - ing. New-ly,
scorned the grave; each day new praise re - sound - eth;
trust in vain, with grace for aye a - bound - eth. Sing then;

tru - ly, God's word feeds us, right-ly leads us, life be-stow -
ring then; tell the sto-ry filled with glo-ry, till these prais -

ing. Praise, oh praise such love o'er-flow - ing.
es flood with light earth's dark - est plac - es.

Words: German, Johann Adolf Schlegel (1721–1793); translation, Catherine Winkworth (1827–1878)
Music: Philipp Nicolai (1556–1608); harmony, J.S. Bach (1685–1750)

227

181
All praise to you, O Lord
ST. ETHELWALD 6 6 8 6 SM

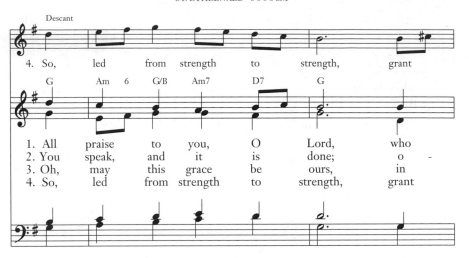

Descant

4. So, led from strength to strength, grant

G   Am 6 G/B Am7 D7 G

1. All praise to you, O Lord, who
2. You speak, and it is done; o -
3. Oh, may this grace be ours, in
4. So, led from strength to strength, grant

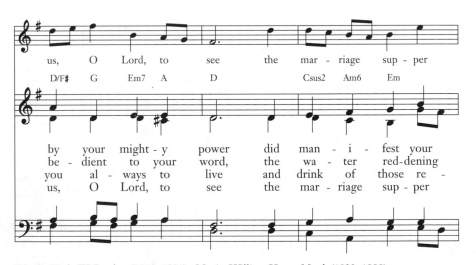

us, O Lord, to see the mar - riage sup - per

D/F# G Em7 A D   Csus2 Am6 Em

by your might - y power did man - i - fest your
be - dient to your word, the wa - ter red-dening
you al - ways to live and drink of those re -
us, O Lord, to see the mar - riage sup - per

Words: Hyde W. Beadon (1812–1891) Music: William Henry Monk (1823–1889)

Words: public domain Music: public domain

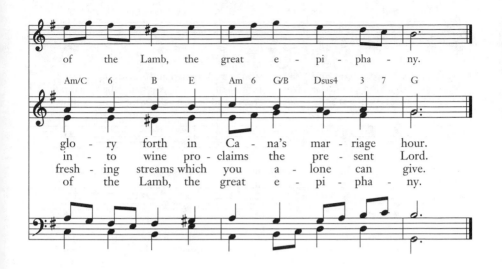

of the Lamb, the great e - pi - pha - ny.

Am/C   6   B   E   Am   6   G/B   Dsus4   3   7   G

glo - ry forth in Ca - na's mar - riage hour.
in - to wine pro - claims the pre - sent Lord.
fresh - ing streams which you a - lone can give.
of the Lamb, the great e - pi - pha - ny.

Baptism of Jesus

182

What was your vow and vision

GENEVAN 130 7 6 7 6 D

1. What was your vow and vi - sion, re - vealed and re - cog - nized,
2. Was this God's call, the crow - ning of all you had be - come:
3. We meet you at the wa - ter and pon - der why and how,

Christ, when you came to Jor - dan and asked to be bap - tized?
"Go, show and tell my com - ing, my own, my cho - sen one"?
in hope that we may fol - low where God is go - ing now,

Was there a sud - den splen - dour of pro - phets, priests and kings,
Did scrip-ture join with scrip - ture, re - veal - ing in sur - prise
a - noin-ted with your Spir - it, re - born, and e - ner - gized,

a wind that stirred the wa - ters, a blur of might - y wings?
the tri - umph of a ser - vant re - jec - ted and de - spised?
through deed and word pro-claim - ing: "In Christ we are bap - tized!"

Words: Brian A. Wren (1936–) Music: Genevan Psalter 1542

183   Christ, when for us you were baptized

JACKSON 8 6 8 6 CM

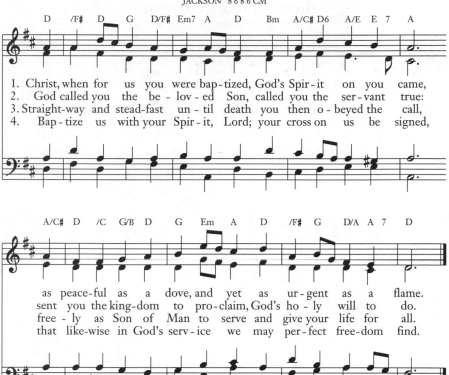

1. Christ, when for us you were bap-tized, God's Spir-it on you came,
2. God called you the be - lov - ed Son, called you the ser - vant true:
3. Straight-way and stead-fast un - til death you then o - beyed the call,
4. Bap - tize us with your Spir - it, Lord; your cross on us be signed,

as peace-ful as a dove, and yet as ur - gent as a flame.
sent you the king-dom to pro-claim, God's ho - ly will to do.
free - ly as Son of Man to serve and give your life for all.
that like-wise in God's serv - ice we may per - fect free-dom find.

Words: F. Bland Tucker (1895–1984), alt   Music: Thomas Jackson (1715–1781);
harmony, David Evans (1874–1948)

184

What king would wade through murky streams

STANTON 8 6 8 6 CM with refrain (7 8 8 4)

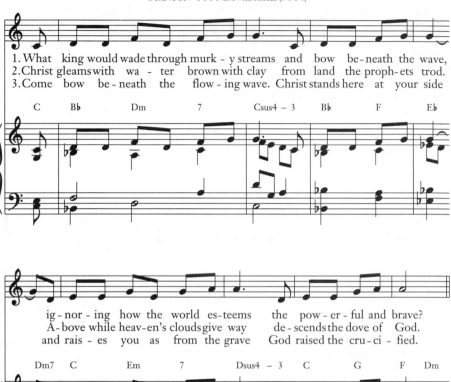

1. What king would wade through murk - y streams and bow be-neath the wave,
2. Christ gleams with wa - ter brown with clay from land the proph-ets trod.
3. Come bow be - neath the flow - ing wave. Christ stands here at your side

ig - nor - ing how the world es-teems the pow - er - ful and brave?
A - bove while heav-en's clouds give way de - scends the dove of God.
and rais - es you as from the grave God raised the cru - ci - fied.

Words: Thomas H. Troeger (1945–) Music: David Hurd (1950–)

Words: copyright © Oxford University Press, 1984, 1993 Music: copyright © The Pilgrim Press, 1994

Wa-ter, Riv-er, Spir-it, Grace, sweep o-ver me, sweep o-ver me!

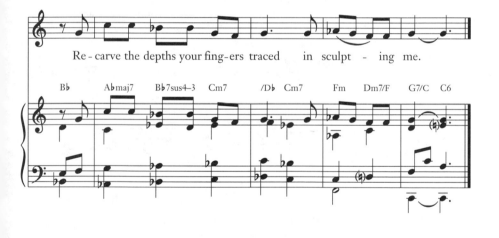

Re - carve the depths your fing-ers traced in sculpt - ing me.

Transfiguration

185 Jesus on the mountain peak

MOWSLEY 7 8 7 8 4

1. Je - sus on the moun - tain peak stands a - lone in
2. Trem-bling at his feet we saw Mo - ses and E -
3. Swift the cloud of glo - ry came, God pro - claim - ing,
4. This is God's be - lov - ed Son! Law and proph - ets

glo - ry blaz - ing; let us, if we dare to speak,
li - jah speak - ing. All the proph - ets and the law
in its thun - der, Je - sus as the Son by name!
sing be - fore him, first and last and on - ly one.

join the saints and an - gels prais - ing:
shout through them their joy - ful greet - ing: hal - le - lu - jah!
Na - tions, cry a - loud in won - der:
All cre - a - tion shall a - dore him:

Words: Brian A. Wren (1936–) Music: Cyril Vincent Taylor (1907–1991)

Words: copyright © 1977, 1995 by Hope Publishing Co. Music: copyright © 1985 by Hope Publishing Co.

234

Transfiguration

186 Swiftly pass the clouds of glory

GENEVA 8 7 8 7 D

1. Swift - ly pass the clouds of glo - ry, heav - en's voice, the daz - zling light;
2. Glimpsed and gone the rev - e - la - tion, they shall gain and keep its truth,
3. Lord, trans-fig - ure our per-cep - tion with the pur - est light that shines

Mo-ses and E - li - jah van - ish; Christ a - lone com-mands the height!
not by build-ing on the moun-tain an - y shrine or sa - cred booth,
and re-cast our life's in - ten-tions to the shape of your de - signs,

Pe-ter, James and John fall si - lent, turn - ing from the sum-mit's rise
but by fol - low - ing the Sav-iour through the val - ley to the cross
till we seek no oth - er glo - ry than what lies past Cal-vary's hill

down-ward toward the shad - owed val - ley where their Lord has fixed his eyes.
and by test - ing faith's re - sil-ience through be - tray - al, pain and loss.
and our liv - ing and our dy - ing and our ris - ing by your will.

Words: Thomas H. Troeger (1945–)   Music: George Henry Day (1883–1966)

Words: copyright © Oxford University Press   Music: copyright © Church Pension Fund, 1943, 1961, 1985

Transfiguration

187   We have come at Christ's own bidding

BREWER 8 7 8 7 D

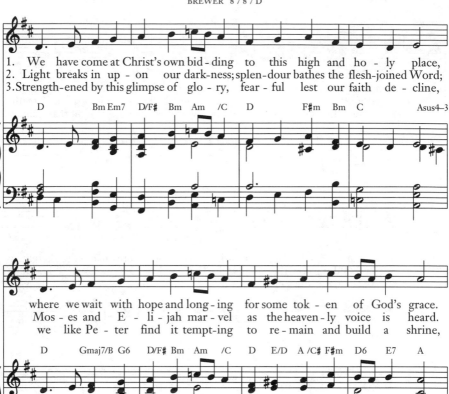

1. We have come at Christ's own bid-ding to this high and ho - ly place,
2. Light breaks in up - on our dark-ness; splen-dour bathes the flesh-joined Word;
3. Strength-ened by this glimpse of glo - ry, fear - ful lest our faith de - cline,

where we wait with hope and long-ing for some tok - en of God's grace.
Mos - es and E - li - jah mar - vel as the heaven-ly voice is heard.
we like Pe - ter find it tempt-ing to re - main and build a shrine,

Alternate tune: Hyfrydol

Words: Carl P. Daw, Jr. (1944–) Music: David Ashley White (1944–)

Words: copyright © 1988 by Hope Publishing Co. Music: copyright © Selah Publishing Co., Inc., 1991

236

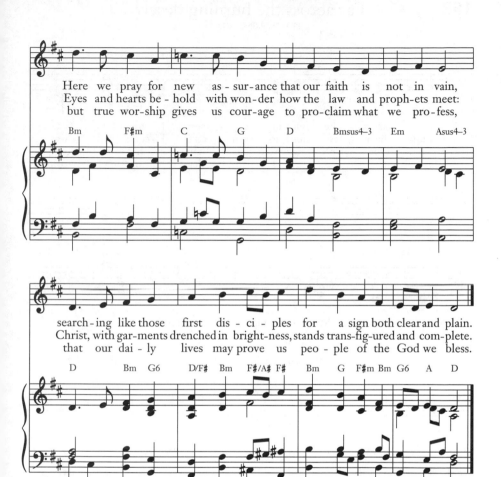

Here we pray for new as - sur-ance that our faith is not in vain,
Eyes and hearts be - hold with won-der how the law and proph-ets meet:
but true wor-ship gives us cour-age to pro-claim what we pro-fess,

Bm   F♯m   C   G   D   Bmsus4–3   Em   Asus4–3

search-ing like those first dis - ci - ples for a sign both clear and plain.
Christ, with gar-ments drenched in bright-ness, stands trans-fig-ured and com-plete.
that our dai - ly lives may prove us peo - ple of the God we bless.

D   Bm   G6   D/F♯   Bm   F♯/A♯   F♯   Bm   G   F♯m   Bm   G6   A   D

Lent

188

Far across the burning desert

BEACH SPRING 8 7 8 7 D

1. Far a-cross the burn-ing de-sert Ja-cob fled a
2. Lone-ly, cheer-less, none to com-fort, Ja-cob's bed was
3. Signs of God were no-where pre-sent in that dis-tant,
4. Ja-cob, sleep-ing, saw a lad-der reach-ing high from

bro-ther's wrath. Star-less night ob-scured his vi-sion;
bar-ren ground. Worn by guilt-y flight and fear-ful,
al-ien place. Of the hand that once had led him,
earth to sky. Faith, whose wings till then were fold-ed,

track-less sands his on-ly path. Light, un-seen with-in our
trou-bled sleep at length he found. Rest of eve-ry anx-ious
Ja-cob's eye could find no trace. Un-seen hand whose hid-den
stirred with Ja-cob's wak-ing cry: "Sure-ly God, un-seen, is

Alternate tune: Geneva

Words: Herman G. Stuempfle, Jr. (1923–) Music: attributed to Benjamin Franklin White (1800–1879) from Sacred Harp 1844, harmony, James H. Wood

dark - ness, shin-ing where no eye can see: God of
wan - derer, heal - er of the heart's dis - tress: God of
pres - ence leads us by an un - known way: God of
with me in this bar - ren, cheer - less place." God of

Ja - cob, si - lent search - er, seek us, when from you we flee.
Ja - cob, friend of sin - ners, meet us in our wil - der - ness.
Ja - cob, help us trust you when in dark - est night we pray.
Ja - cob, grant us vi - sion in the night to glimpse your face.

Lent

189   As when the Hebrew prophet raised

ABRIDGE 8 6 8 6 CM

1. As when the He - brew proph - et raised the
2. so from the Sav - iour on the cross a
3. for God gave up the Son to death, so
4. Not to con - demn us, or to judge, the
5. Christ came to raise our fal - len state, and

braz - en ser - pent high the wound - ed looked and
heal - ing vir - tue flows; who looks to him with
gen - erous was that love, that all the faith - ful
Lamb of God ap - peared; no wea - pons in his
our lost hopes re - store; faith leads us to the

straight were cured; the peo - ple ceased to die,
liv - ing faith is saved from end - less woes,
might en - joy e - ter - nal life a - bove.
hands are seen, nor voice of ter - ror heard.
mer - cy seat and bids us fear no more.

Words: Isaac Watts (1674–1748), Scottish Paraphrase, alt   Music: Isaac Smith (c.1735–1805)

Words: public domain   Music: public domain

190

You thirsty ones

BELMONT 8 6 8 6 CM

1. You thirst - y ones! come to the spring! Have
2. Why do you work and earn and spend on
3. This food de - lights and sa - tis - fies, the
4. Re - turn while God may still be found and
5. My word like heav - en's snow de - scends; it

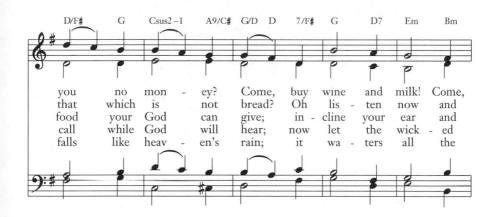

you no mon - ey? Come, buy wine and milk! Come,
that which is not bread? Oh lis - ten now and
food your God can give; in - cline your ear and
call while God will hear; now let the wick - ed
falls like heav - en's rain; it wa - ters all the

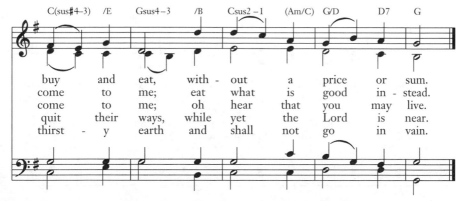

buy and eat, with - out a price or sum.
come to me; eat what is good in - stead.
come to me; oh hear that you may live.
quit their ways, while yet the Lord is near.
thirst - y earth and shall not go in vain.

Words: Isaiah 55:1–11; paraphrase, Andrew Donaldson (1951–) Music: William Gardiner (1770–1853)
Words: this version, copyright © Andrew Donaldson, 1996 Music: public domain

191

Now quit your care

QUITTEZ 11 10 11 6 12 12

1. Now quit your care and anx-ious fear and wor - ry, for schemes are vain and fret - ting brings no gain. Lent calls to prayer, to trust and ded - i - ca - tion; God brings new beau-ty

2. To bow the head in sack-cloth and in ash - es, or rend the soul, such grief is not Lent's goal, but to be led where heav - en's glo - ry flash - es, God's beau-ty to come

3. "For is not this the fast that I have cho - sen," the pro - phet spoke, "to shat - ter eve - ry yoke, of wick - ed - ness the griev - ous bands to loos - en, op - pres-sion put to

4. For right - eous - ness and peace will show their fa - ces to those who feed the hun - gry in their need, and wrongs re - dress, who build the old waste pla - ces, and in the dark-ness

5. Then shall your light break forth as doth the morn - ing; your health shall spring; the friends you make shall bring God's glo - ry bright, your way through life a - dorn - ing; and love shall be the

Words: Percy Dearmer (1867–1936) Music: French traditional carol; harmony, Martin Shaw (1875–1958) from Oxford Book of Carols

Words: copyright © Oxford University Press Music: harmony, copyright © Oxford University Press, 1928

nigh; re - ply, re - ply, re - ply with love to love most high;
near. Make clear, make clear, make clear where truth and light ap - pear;
flight, to fight, to fight, to fight till eve - ry wrong's set right,
shine. Di - vine, di - vine, di - vine it is when all com - bine;
prize. A - rise, a - rise, a - rise! and make a par - a - dise;

re - ply, re - ply, re - ply with love to love most high.
make clear, make clear, make clear where truth and light ap - pear.
to fight, to fight, to fight till eve - ry wrong's set right?"
di - vine, di - vine, di - vine it is when all com - bine!
a - rise, a - rise, a - rise! and make a par - a - dise!

Lent

192

The glory of these forty days

ERHALT UNS, HERR 8 8 8 8 LM

1. The glo - ry of these for - ty days we
2. A - lone and fast - ing Mo - ses saw the
3. So Dan - iel trained his mys - tic sight, de -
4. Then grant us, Lord, like them to be full
5. O Fa - ther, Son, and Spir - it blest, to

cel - e - brate with songs of praise, for Christ, through whom all
lov - ing God who gave the law, and to E - li - jah,
liv - ered from the li - ons' might, and John, the Bride-groom's
oft in fast and prayer with thee; our spir - its strength - en
thee be eve - ry prayer ad - dressed, who art in three - fold

things were made, him - self has fast - ed and has prayed.
fast - ing, came the steeds and char - i - ots of flame.
friend, be - came the her - ald of Mes - si - ah's name.
with thy grace, and give us joy to see thy face.
name a - dored, from age to age, the on - ly Lord.

Words: Latin, 6th century; translation, Maurice F. Bell (1862–1947) Music: Geistliche Lieder (J. Klug)
1543; harmony, J.S. Bach (1685–1750)

Lent

193 Out of my bondage, sorrow and night

OUT OF MY BONDAGE 989869996

1. Out of my bond-age, sor-row and night,
2. Out of my shame-ful fail-ure and loss,
3. Out of un-rest and ar-ro-gant pride,
4. Out of the fear and dread of the tomb,

Je-sus, I come; Je-sus, I come;

in-to thy free-dom, glad-ness and light,
in-to the glo-rious gain of thy cross,
in-to thy bless-ed will to a-bide,
in-to the joy and light of thy home,

Je-sus, I come to thee;

out of my sick-ness in-to thy health, out of my want and in-to thy wealth,
out of earth's sor-rows in-to thy balm, out of life's storms and in-to thy calm,
out of my-self to dwell in thy love, out of de-spair in-to rap-tures a-bove,
out of the depths of ru-in un-told, in-to the peace of thy shel-ter-ing fold,

out of my sin and in-to thy-self,
out of dis-tress to ju-bi-lant psalm,
up-ward for aye on wings like a dove,
ev-er thy glo-rious face to be-hold,

Je-sus, I come to thee.

Words: William T. Sleeper (1819–1904) Music: George C. Stebbins (1846–1945)

Words: public domain Music: public domain

Come, let us to the Lord our God

KILMARNOCK 8 6 8 6 CM

1. Come, let us to the Lord our God with
2. God's voice commands the tempest forth and
3. The night of sorrow long has reigned, but
4. Then let us know, let us press on to

con-trite hearts re-turn; our God is gra-cious,
stills the storm-y wave; God's arm is strong and
dawn shall bring us light; God shall ap-pear, and
know our God the Lord, whose com-ing is as

nor will leave the de-so-late to mourn.
swift to strike, but al-so strong to save.
we shall rise with glad-ness in God's sight.
sure as dawn, whose name shall be a-dored.

5. As dew upon the tender grass
diffusing fragrance round,
as rain that ushers in the spring
and cheers the thirsty ground,

6. so shall God's presence bless our souls
and shed a joyful light,
that hallowed morn shall chase away
the sorrows of the night.

Alternate tune: Belmont

Words: John Morison (1750–1798), Scottish Paraphrase, alt   Music: Neil Dougall (1776–1862)

Words: public domain   Music: public domain

Lent

195

Come, ye disconsolate

CONSOLATION 11 10 11 10

1. Come, ye dis-con-so-late, where'-er ye lan-guish; come to the mer-cy seat;
2. Joy of the des-o-late, light of the stray-ing, hope of the pen-i-tent,
3. Here see the bread of life; see wa-ters flow-ing forth from the throne of God,

fer-vent-ly kneel; here bring your woun-ded hearts; here tell your an-guish:
fade-less and pure! here speaks the com-fort-er, ten-der-ly say-ing,
pure from a-bove: come to the feast of love; come ev-er know-ing

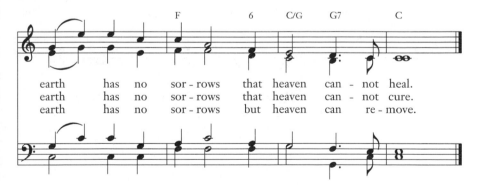

earth has no sor-rows that heaven can-not heal.
earth has no sor-rows that heaven can-not cure.
earth has no sor-rows but heaven can re-move.

Words: Thomas Hastings (1784–1872), Thomas Moore (1779–1852) Music: Samuel Webbe, the younger (1770–1843)

Words: public domain Music: public domain

196

Throughout these
Lenten days and nights

BRESLAU 8 8 8 8 LM

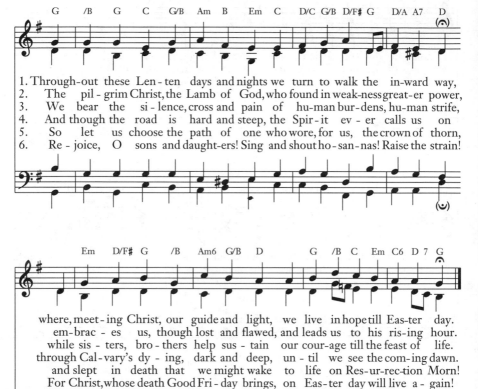

1. Through-out these Len-ten days and nights we turn to walk the in-ward way,
2. The pil-grim Christ, the Lamb of God, who found in weak-ness great-er power,
3. We bear the si-lence, cross and pain of hu-man bur-dens, hu-man strife,
4. And though the road is hard and steep, the Spir-it ev-er calls us on
5. So let us choose the path of one who wore, for us, the crown of thorn,
6. Re-joice, O sons and daught-ers! Sing and shout ho-san-nas! Raise the strain!

where, meet-ing Christ, our guide and light, we live in hope till Eas-ter day.
em-brac-es us, though lost and flawed, and leads us to his ris-ing hour.
while sis-ters, bro-thers help sus-tain our cour-age till the feast of life.
through Cal-vary's dy-ing, dark and deep, un-til we see the com-ing dawn.
and slept in death that we might wake to life on Res-ur-rec-tion Morn!
For Christ, whose death Good Fri-day brings, on Eas-ter day will live a-gain!

Words: James Gertmenian (1947–)   Music: Christian Gall's 'As hymnodus sacer', Leipzig 1625

197

Forty days and forty nights

AUS DER TIEFE 7 7 7 7

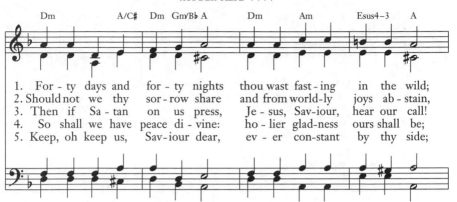

1. For - ty days and   for - ty nights   thou wast fast - ing   in   the   wild;
2. Should not we thy   sor - row share   and from world-ly   joys ab - stain,
3. Then if   Sa - tan   on   us press,   Je - sus, Sav-iour,   hear our   call!
4. So   shall we have peace di - vine: ho - lier glad-ness   ours shall   be;
5. Keep, oh keep us,   Sav-iour dear,   ev - er   con-stant   by   thy   side;

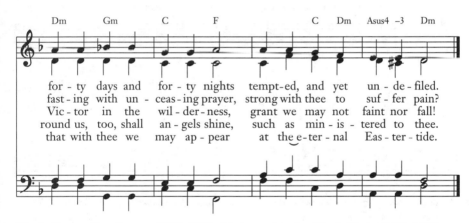

for - ty days and   for - ty nights   tempt-ed, and yet   un - de - filed.
fast - ing with un - ceas-ing prayer, strong with thee to   suf - fer pain?
Vic - tor   in   the   wil - der-ness,   grant we may not faint nor fall!
round us, too, shall an - gels shine,   such as min - is - tered to thee.
that with thee we   may ap - pear   at the e - ter - nal Eas - ter - tide.

Words: George Hunt Smyttan (1822–1870)   Music: attributed to Martin Herbst (1654–1681);
harmony, William Henry Monk (1823–1889)

Words: public domain   Music: public domain

198
I hunger and I thirst
QUAM DILECTA 6 6 6 6

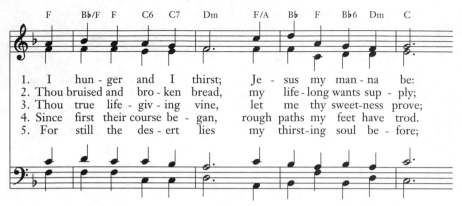

| F | Bb/F F | C6 | C7 | Dm | F/A | Bb | F | Bb6 | Dm | C |

1. I hun - ger and I thirst; Je - sus my man - na be:
2. Thou bruised and bro - ken bread, my life - long wants sup - ply;
3. Thou true life - giv - ing vine, let me thy sweet-ness prove;
4. Since first their course be - gan, rough paths my feet have trod.
5. For still the des - ert lies my thirst-ing soul be - fore;

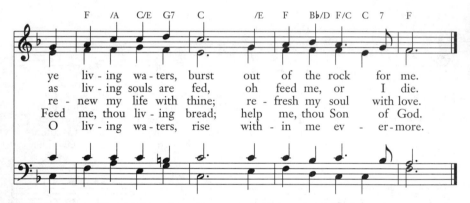

| F | /A | C/E | G7 | C | /E | F | Bb/D F/C | C | 7 | F |

ye liv - ing wa - ters, burst out of the rock for me.
as liv - ing souls are fed, oh feed me, or I die.
re - new my life with thine; re - fresh my soul with love.
Feed me, thou liv - ing bread; help me, thou Son of God.
O liv - ing wa - ters, rise with - in me ev - er - more.

Words: John Samuel Beweley Monsell (1811–1875), alt   Music: Henry Lascelles Jenner (1820–1898)
Words: public domain   Music: public domain

199 If I have been the source of pain

CAMACUA 10 10 10 4

Unison

1. If I have been the source of pain, O God, if to the
2. If I have spo-ken words of cru - el - ty, if I have
1. Si fui mo - ti - vo de do - lor, oh Dios, si por mi
2. Si va-na y fú - til mi pa - la - bra fue, si al que su -

weak I have re - fused my strength, if in re - bel - lion
left some suf-fering un - re - lieved, con-demn not my in -
cau-sa el dé - bil tro - pe - zó, si en tus ca - mi - nos
frí - a en su do - lor de - jé, no me con - de - nes,

I have strayed a - way, for - give me, God.
sen - si - ti - vi - ty: for - give me, God.
yo no qui-se an - dar, ¡per - dón, oh Dios!
tú, por mi mal - dad, ¡per - dón, oh Dios!
(Verse 4) A - men, a - men.

3. If I've insisted on a peaceful life,
far from the struggles that the
gospel brings,
when you prefer to guide me to the strife,
forgive me, God.

3. Si por la vida quise andar en paz,
tranquilo, libre y sin luchar por ti
cuando anhelbas verme en la lid,
¡perdón, oh Dios!

4. Receive, O God, this ardent word of prayer,
and free me from temptation's
subtle snare;
with tender patience, lead me to your care.
Amen, amen.

4. Escucha, oh Dios, mi humilde
confesión
y líbrame de tentación sutil;
preserva siempre mi alma en
tu redil.
Amén, amén.

Words: Sara M. de Hall, based on text by C. Maude Battersby, (19th–20th cent.);
translation, Janet W. May (20th cent.) Music: Pablo Sosa (1933–)

200 Lord Jesus, who through forty days

ST. FLAVIAN 8 6 8 6 CM

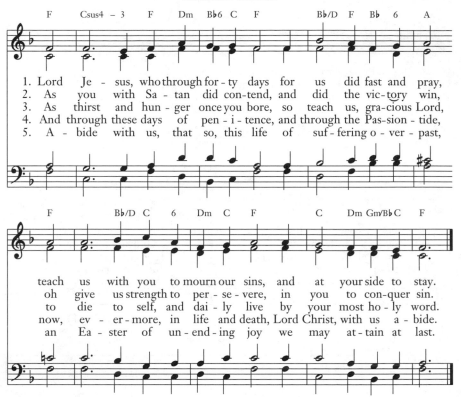

1. Lord Je - sus, who through for - ty days for us did fast and pray,
2. As you with Sa - tan did con-tend, and did the vic-to-ry win,
3. As thirst and hun - ger once you bore, so teach us, gra-cious Lord,
4. And through these days of pen - i - tence, and through the Pas-sion - tide,
5. A - bide with us, that so, this life of suf - fering o - ver - past,

teach us with you to mourn our sins, and at your side to stay.
oh give us strength to per - se - vere, in you to con-quer sin.
to die to self, and dai - ly live by your most ho - ly word.
now, ev - er-more, in life and death, Lord Christ, with us a - bide.
an Ea - ster of un - end-ing joy we may at-tain at last.

Words: Claudia Frances Hernaman (1838–1898), alt Music: Day's Psalter 1652

201 We come to ask your forgiveness

WE COME TO ASK 10 10 13 9 with refrain (10 10 13 9)

Refrain

We come to ask your for-give-ness, O Lord, and we

Words: Carey Landry (1944–) Music: Carey Landry (1944–); arrangement, Tom Tilden

seek for-give-ness from each oth-er. Some-times we build up walls in-stead of

bridg-es to peace, and we ask your for-give-ness, O Lord.

Verses

1. Some-times we hurt by what we do to oth - ers. Some-times we
2. For the times when we've been rude and self - ish, for the

hurt with words that are un - true. Some-times we cause oth-ers pain by
times when we have been un - kind, and for the times we re-fused to

what we fail to do, and we ask your for-give-ness, O Lord.
help our friends in need, we ask your for-give-ness, O Lord.

Lent

202

We lay our broken world
in sorrow at your feet

GARELOCHSIDE 6 6 8 6 SM

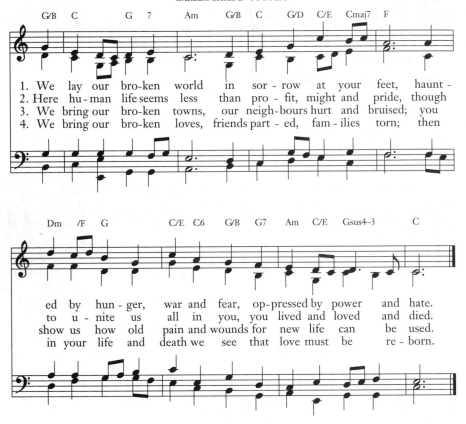

1. We lay our bro-ken world in sor - row at your feet, haunt -
2. Here hu - man life seems less than pro - fit, might and pride, though
3. We bring our bro-ken towns, our neigh-bours hurt and bruised; you
4. We bring our bro-ken loves, friends part - ed, fam - ilies torn; then

ed by hun - ger, war and fear, op-pressed by power and hate.
to u - nite us all in you, you lived and loved and died.
show us how old pain and wounds for new life can be used.
in your life and death we see that love must be re - born.

5. We bring our broken selves,
   confused and closed and tired;
   then through your gift of healing grace
   new purpose is inspired.

6. O Spirit, on us breathe
   with life and strength anew;
   find in us love, and hope, and trust,
   and lift us up to you.

Words: Anna Briggs (1947–) Music: Kenneth G. Finlay (1882–1974)

Lent

203

When Jesus the healer
passed through Galilee

WHEN JESUS THE HEALER 11 6 11 5

1. When Je-sus the heal-er passed through Gal-i-lee,
2. A par-a-lyzed man was let down through a roof.
3. The death of his daugh-ter caused Jai-rus to weep.
4. When blind Bar-ti-mae-us cried out to the Lord,

the deaf came to hear and the
us, heal us to-day! His sins were for-giv-en, his
The Lord took her hand, and he
his faith made him whole and his

blind came to see.
walk-ing the proof.
raised her from sleep.
sight was re-stored.

Heal us, Lord Je-sus!

5. The lepers were healed and the demons cast out. Heal us, heal us today!
A bent woman straightened to laugh and to shout. Heal us, Lord Jesus.

6. The twelve were commissioned and sent out in twos, Heal us, heal us today!
to make the sick whole and to spread the good news. Heal us, Lord Jesus.

7. There's still so much sickness and suffering today. Heal us, heal us today!
We gather together for healing, and pray: Heal us, Lord Jesus.

Words: Peter D. Smith (1938–)   Music: Peter D. Smith (1938–)

Thou didst leave thy throne

MARGARET Irregular

1. Thou didst leave thy throne and thy king - ly crown
2. E - ven fox - es found rest, and the birds had their nest
3. When thou cam - est, O Lord, with the liv - ing word,
4. Heav-en's arch - es shall ring and its choirs shall sing

when thou cam - est to earth for me, but in
in the shade of the for - est tree, but thy
'twas to set all thy peo - ple free, but with
at thy com - ing to vic - to - ry; let thy

Beth - le - hem's home was there found no room for thy
couch was the sod, O thou Son of God, in the
mock - ing scorn and with crown of thorn, then we
voice call me home, say - ing, "Yet there is room, there is

Words: Emily Elizabeth Steele Elliott (1836–1897), alt   Music: Timothy Richard Matthews
(1826–1910)

	A	/C#	Esus4 – 3	A	7	D	/E /F#

ho - ly na - tiv - i - ty: oh come to my heart,
des - erts of Gal - i - lee: oh come to my heart,
bore thee to Cal - va - ry: oh come to my heart,
room at my side for thee!" My heart shall re-joice,

	D	Em7			D/F#	Bm6	D/A	A	7	D

Lord Je - sus; there is room in my heart for thee.
Lord Je - sus; there is room in my heart for thee.
Lord Je - sus; now thy cross is my on - ly plea.
Lord Je - sus, when thou com - est and call - est me.

205   O love, how deep, how broad, how high

PUER NOBIS NASCITUR   8 8 8 8 LM

1. O love, how deep, how broad, how high,
2. For us bap - tized, for us he bore
3. For us he prayed; for us he taught;
4. For us to wick - ed hands be - trayed,

how pass - ing thought and fan - ta - sy,
his ho - ly fast and hung - ered sore;
for us his dai - ly works he wrought:
scourged, mocked, in pur - ple robe ar - rayed,

that God, the Son of God, should take
for us temp - ta - tions sharp he knew,
by words and signs and ac - tions, thus
he bore the shame - ful cross and death,

See also: Puer nobis nascitur 160 170

Words: Latin, 15th century; English translation, anonymous   Music: 15th century carol melody, Pie Cantiones 1582; adaptation, Michael Praetorius (1571–1621); harmony, George Ratcliffe Woodward (1848–1934)

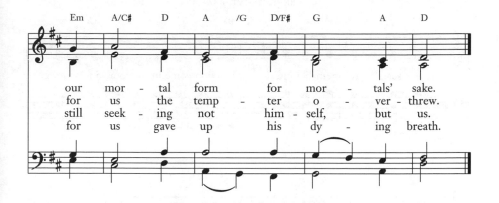

| Em | A/C# | D | A | /G | D/F# | G | A | D |

our mor - tal form for mor - tals' sake.
for us the temp - ter o - ver - threw.
still seek - ing not him - self, but us.
for us gave up his dy - ing breath.

5. For us he rose from death again;
   for us he went on high to reign;
   for us he sent his Spirit here
   to guide, to strengthen and to cheer.

6. All glory to our Lord and God
   for love so deep, so high, so broad,
   the Trinity whom we adore
   forever and forevermore.

Jesus, remember me

REMEMBER ME 6 8 6 8

Je - sus, re - mem-ber me when you come in - to your king - dom.

Je - sus, re - mem-ber me when you come in - to your king - dom.

Accompaniment

Words: Luke 23:42   Music: Jacques Berthier (1923–1994), Taizé Community (France)

Instrumental Descant

(Je-sus,   re-mem-ber me)

207 Lord Jesus, think on me

SOUTHWELL (DAMAN) 6 6 8 6 SM

1. Lord Jesus, think on me and purge a - way my sin;
2. Lord Jesus, think on me a - mid the bat - tle's strife;
3. Lord Jesus, think on me, nor let me go a - stray;
4. Lord Jesus, think on me, that, when this life is past,

from earth-born pas-sions set me free and make me pure with-in.
in all my pain and mis - er - y be thou my health and life.
through dark-ness and per - plex - i - ty point thou the heaven-ly way.
I may the e-ter - nal bright-ness see and share thy joy at last.

See also: Southwell (Daman) 47

Words: Greek, Synesius of Cyrene (c.370–413); translation, Allen William Chatfield (1808–1896)
Music: Daman's Psalter, 1579

Words: public domain Music: public domain

208 In the cross of Christ I glory

CROSS OF JESUS 8 7 8 7

1. In the cross of Christ I glo - ry, tower-ing o'er the wrecks of time;
2. When the woes of life o'er - take me, hopes de-ceive and fears an - noy,
3. When the sun of bliss is beam-ing light and love up - on my way,
4. Bane and bless-ing, pain and pleas-ure, by the cross are sanc - ti - fied;

all the light of sa - cred sto - ry gath - ers round its head sub-lime.
nev - er shall the cross for - sake me: lo! it glows with peace and joy.
from the cross the ra-diance stream-ing adds more lus - tre to the day.
peace is there that knows no meas-ure, joys that through all time a - bide.

Words: John Bowring (1792–1872) Music: John Stainer (1840–1901)

Words: public domain Music: public domain

O Love that wilt not let me go

ST. MARGARET 8 8 8 8 6

1. O Love that wilt not let me go,
2. O Light that fol - lowest all my way,
3. O Joy that seek - est me through pain,
4. O Cross that lift - est up my head,

I rest my wea - ry soul in thee;
I yield my flick - ering torch to thee;
I can - not close my heart to thee;
I dare not ask to fly from thee;

I give thee back the life I owe,
my heart re - stores its bor - rowed ray,
I trace the rain - bow through the rain,
I lay in dust life's glo - ry dead,

Words: George Matheson (1842–1906) Music: Albert Lister Peace (1844–1912)

Words: public domain Music: public domain

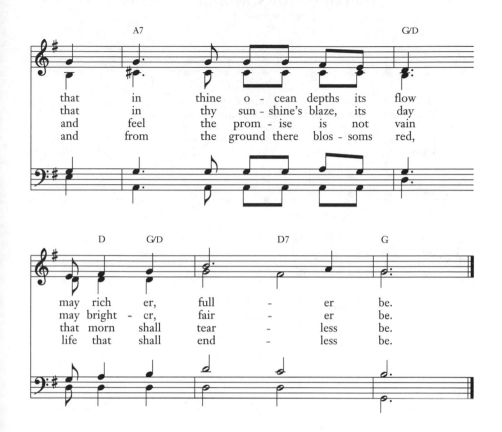

that in thine o - cean depths its flow
that in thy sun - shine's blaze, its day
and feel the prom - ise is not vain
and from the ground there blos - soms red,

may rich er, full - er be.
may bright - er, fair - er be.
that morn shall tear - less be.
life that shall end - less be.

210 Man of sorrows, wondrous name

MAN OF SORROWS 7 7 7 8

1. Man of sor - rows, won - drous name for the Son of God who came ru - ined sin - ners to re - claim: Hal - le - lu - jah! Gra - cious Sav - iour!
2. Bear - ing shame and scoff - ing rude, in my place con - demned he stood, sealed my par - don with his blood: Hal - le - lu - jah! Lov - ing Sav - iour!
3. Guilt - y, help - less, lost were we; spot - less Lamb of God was he; full a - tone - ment— can it be? Hal - le - lu - jah! Bles - sed Sav - iour!
4. Lift - ed up was he to die; "It is fin - ished" was his cry, now in heaven ex - alt - ed high: Hal - le - lu - jah! Might - y Sav - iour!
5. When Christ comes, our glo - rious King, all the ran - somed home to bring, then a - new this song we'll sing: Hal - le - lu - jah! Won - drous Sav - iour!

Words: Philip Bliss (1838–1876), alt   Music: Philip Bliss (1838–1876)

Words: public domain   Music: public domain

Lent

211

Take up your cross

HESPERUS 8 8 8 8 LM

1. Take up your cross, the Sav - iour said, if my dis -
2. Take up your cross; let not its weight fill fright-ened
3. Take up your cross, nor heed the shame, nor let your
4. Take up your cross, then, in Christ's strength, and eve - ry
5. Take up your cross and fol - low Christ, nor think till

ci - ple you would be; de - ny your - self, the
spir - it with a - larm; his strength shall bear your
fool - ish pride re - bel: for you the Sav - iour
dan - ger calm - ly brave; 'twill guide you to a
death to lay it down, for on - ly those who

world for - sake, and hum - bly fol - low af - ter me.
spir - it up, and brace your heart, and nerve your arm.
bore the cross, to save your soul from death and hell.
heaven - ly home, and lead to vic - tory o'er the grave.
bear the cross may hope to wear the glo - rious crown.

Alternate tune: Breslau

Words: Charles William Everest (1814–1877), alt   Music: Henry Baker (1835–1910)

Words: public domain   Music: public domain

212 God marked a line and told the sea

KEDRON 8888 LM

1. God marked a line and told the sea its
2. God set one lim - it in the glade where
3. The line, the lim - it and the law are
4. But, dis - con - tent with fi - nite pow - ers,
5. We are not free when we're con - fined to

surg - ing tides and waves were free to trav - el up the
tempt - ing, fruit - ed branch - es swayed, and that first lim - it
pat - terns meant to help us draw a bound be - tween what
we reach to take what is not ours, and then de - fend
eve - ry wish that sweeps the mind, but free when free - ly

slop - ing strand, but not to o - ver - take the land.
stands be - hind the lim - its that the law de - fined.
life re - quires and all the things our heart de - sires.
our claims by force and swerve from life's in - tend - ed course.
we ac - cept the sac - red bounds that must be kept.

Words: Thomas H. Troeger (1945–) Music: attributed to Elkanah Kelsay Dare (1782–1826)

Words: copyright © Oxford University Press, 1989 Music: public domain

213

Hosanna

HOSANNA (NAMETH) Irregular

Ho -
san - na, ho - san - na, ho - san - na in the
high - est; ho - san - na, ho - san - na, ho - san - na to the
Lord.   Ho - Lord.

Words: traditional Music: Bart Nameth (1954–)

Words: public domain Music: copyright © Bart Nameth

214

All glory, laud and honour

ST. THEODULPH 7 6 7 6 D

4. All glo-ry, laud, and hon - our to thee, Re-deem - er, King,

(1.–4.) All glo-ry, laud, and hon - our to thee, Re-deem-er, King,

to whom the lips of chil - dren made sweet ho - san-nas ring!

to whom the lips of chil - dren made sweet ho - san-nas ring!

See also: St. Theodulph 115

Words: Latin, Theodulph of Orleans (750–821); translation, John Mason Neale (1818–1866)
Music: Melchior Teschner (1584–1635); harmony, J.S. Bach (1685–1750); descant, Randall De Bruyn (1947–)

Thou didst ac - cept their prais - es; ac - cept the prayers we bring,

Bb   Gm C/E C   F C7 F   /Eb Bb/D F/C Bb6 C 7   F

1. Thou art the King of Is - rael, thou Da - vid's roy - al   son,
2. The peo - ple of the He - brews with palms be - fore thee   went;
3. To thee be - fore thy pas - sion they sang their hymns of   praise;
4. Thou didst ac - cept their prais - es; ac - cept the prayers we   bring,

who in all good de - light - test, thou good and gra - cious   King.

F/A Bb /Ab Eb/G Bdim7 Cmsus Gm Bb/Ab Eb/G Bb/F Eb6 F 7   Bb

who in the Lord's name com - est, the King and bless - ed   one.
our praise and prayer and an - thems be - fore thee we pre - sent.
to thee, now high ex - alt - ed, our mel - o - dy we   raise.
who in all good de - light - est, thou good and gra - cious   King.

215

Filled with excitement

HOSANNA   10 10 10 10 with refrain

Words: Spanish, Rubén Ruiz Avila (20th cent.); translation, Gertrude C. Suppe (1911–)   Music: Rubén Ruiz Avila (20th century); arrangement, Alvin Schutmaat (1921–1988)

prais - es to him who comes in the name of God.
san - na al que vie - ne en el nom - bre del Se - ñor,

With one great shout of ac - cla - ma - tion loud tri - um - phant songs break
Con un a - lien - to de gran ex - cla - ma - ción pro - rrum - pen con voz triun -

forth: "Ho - san - na,
fal: "¡Ho - san - na!

ho - san - na to the King! Ho -
¡Ho - san - na al Rey!" "¡Ho -

san - na, ho - san - na to the King!"
san - na! ¡Ho - san - na al Rey!"

Palm/Passion Sunday

216

Hosanna

HOSANNA 7 6 5 8 7

Words: Carl Tuttle Music: Carl Tuttle

Words: copyright © Mercy/Vineyard, 1985 Music: copyright © Mercy/Vineyard, 1985

274

217
Ride on, ride on in majesty

WINCHESTER NEW 8 8 8 8 LM

Words: Henry Hart Milman (1791–1868), alt Music: Musikalisches Handbuch, Hamburg 1690; arrangement, William Henry Havergal (1793–1870)

Words: public domain Music: public domain

218 Hosanna, loud hosanna

ELLACOMBE 7 6 7 6 D

1. Ho - san - na, loud ho - san - na, the lit - tle chil - dren sang;
2. From O - li - vet they fol - lowed a - mid the shout-ing crowd,
3. "Ho - san - na in the high - est!" that an - cient song we sing,

through pil-lared court and tem - ple the joy - ful an - them rang.
the vic - tor palm branch wav - ing and chant-ing clear and loud;
for Christ is our Re - deem - er, the Lord of heaven our King.

To Je - sus, who had held them close fold - ed to his breast,
Mes - si - ah, God's a - noint - ed, rode there in hum - ble state,
Oh may we ev - er praise him with heart and life and voice,

the chil - ren sang their prais - es, the sim - plest and the best.
"Ho - san - na, in the high - est!" rang out their prais-es great.
and in God's joy - ful pres - ence e - ter - nal - ly re - joice!

See also: Ellacombe 801

Words: Jennette Threlfall (1821–1880), alt   Music: Mainz Song Book, 1833

Words: this version, copyright © The Presbyterian Church in Canada, 1996 Music: public domain

219
A stable lamp is lighted
TOLLEFSON 76766676

1. A sta - ble lamp is light-ed / whose glow shall wake the sky;
2. This child through Da-vid's ci - ty / shall ride in tri-umph by;
3. Yet he shall be for-sak-en, / and yield-ed up to die;
4. But now, as at the end-ing, / the low is lift-ed high;

the stars shall bend their voic-es, / and eve-ry stone shall cry.
the palm shall strew its branch-es,
the sky shall groan and dark-en,
the stars shall bend their voic-es,

And eve - ry stone shall cry, and straw like gold shall shine;
And eve - ry stone shall cry, though hea-vy, dull and dumb,
And eve - ry stone shall cry for gifts of love a - bused;
And eve - ry stone shall cry in prais-es of the child

a barn shall har-bour heav - en, a stall be-come a shrine.
and lie with-in the road-way to pave his king-dom come.
God's blood up-on the spear-head, God's blood a-gain re - fused.
by whose de-scent a-mong us the worlds are rec-on - ciled.

Words: Richard Wilbur (1921–), alt Music: Paulette Tollefson (1950–)

220 My song is love unknown

LOVE UNKNOWN 666688

1. My song is love un - known, my Sav-iour's love to me,
2. He came from his blest throne sal - va - tion to be - stow,
3. Some - times they strew his way and his sweet prais-es sing,
4. Here might I stay and sing, no sto - ry so di - vine;

love
but
re -
nev-

love to the love - less shown, that they might love - ly be.
but we made strange, and none the longed-for Christ would know.
re-sound-ing all the day ho - san - nas to their King;
nev - er was love, dear King, nev - er was grief like thine.

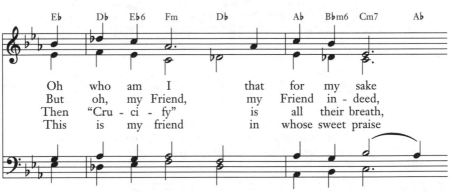

Oh who am I that for my sake
But oh, my Friend, my Friend in - deed,
Then "Cru - ci - fy" is all their breath,
This is my friend in whose sweet praise

Words: Samuel Crossman (c.1624–1683), alt   Music: John Ireland (1879–1962)

Words: public domain   Music: copyright © The John Ireland Trust

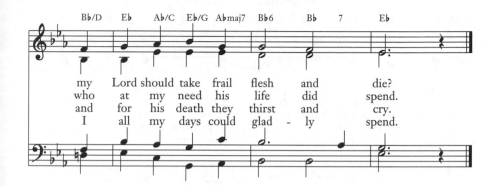

	Bb/D	Eb	Ab/C	Eb/G	Abmaj7	Bb6	Bb	7	Eb

my Lord should take frail flesh and die?
who at my need his life did spend.
and for his death they thirst and cry.
I all my days could glad - ly spend.

221   O dearest Lord

DUNFERMLINE 8 6 8 6 CM

1. O dear-est Lord, thy sa-cred head with thorns was pierced for me:
2. O dear-est Lord, thy sa-cred hands with nails were pierced for me:
3. O dear-est Lord, thy sa-cred feet with nails were pierced for me:
4. O dear-est Lord, thy sa-cred heart with spear was pierced for me:

pour out thy bless-ing on my head that I may think for thee.
pour out thy bless-ing on my hands that they may work for thee.
pour out thy bless-ing on my feet that they may fol-low thee.
pour out thy spir-it in my heart that I may live for thee.

Words: Henry Ernest Hardy (1869–1946), alt   Music: Scottish Psalter, 1615

Words: public domain   Music: public domain

222 The flaming banners of our King

GONFALON ROYAL 8 8 8 8 LM

1. The flam - ing ban - ners of our King
2. A Ro - man sol - dier drew a spear
3. The crowd would have been sa - tis - fied
4. With what strange light the rough trunk shone,
5. The best are shamed be - fore that wood;

ad - vance through his self - of - fer - ing.
to mix his blood with wa - ter clear.
to see a pro - phet cru - ci - fied.
its pur - ple limbs a roy - al throne,
the worst gain pow - er to be good.

He lived to rob death of its sting;
That blood re - tains its liv - ing power:
They stum - bled on a mys - ter - y:
its load a roy - al treas - ur - y:
Oh grant, most bless - ed Trin - i - ty,

Words: Latin, Venantius Honorius Fortunatus (c.540–c.609); translation, John Webster Grant (1919–) Music: Percy Carter Buck (1871–1947)

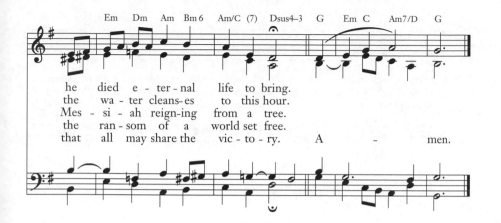

he   died e - ter - nal   life to bring.
the   wa - ter cleans- es   to   this hour.
Mes - si - ah reign-ing from a   tree.
the   ran - som of a   world set free.
that   all may share the   vic - to - ry.   A   -   men.

223   To mock your reign, O dearest Lord

THE THIRD TUNE 8 6 8 6 D CMD

1. To mock your reign, O dear-est Lord, they made a crown of thorns,
2. In mock ac - claim, O gra-cious Lord, they snatched a pur-ple cloak,
3. A scep-tered reed, O pa-tient Lord, they thrust in - to your hand,

set you with taunts a - long that road from which no one re - turns.
your pas-sion turned, for all they cared, in - to a sol-dier's joke.
and act - ed out their grim cha-rade to its ap-point-ed end.

They did not know, as we do now, that glo - rious is your crown;
They did not know, as we do now, that though we mer - it blame
They did not know, as we do now, though em - pires rise and fall,

that thorns would flower up - on your brow, your sor - rows heal our own.
you will your robe of mer - cy throw a-round our na-ked shame.
your king - dom shall not cease to grow till love em - bra-ces all.

The bracketed notes are to be treated as triplet groups.
Alternate tune: Kingsfold See also: The Third Tune 720

Words: Fred Pratt Green (1903–) Music: Thomas Tallis (c.1505–1585); edited by John W. Wilson (1905–1992)

224 An upper room did our Lord prepare

FOLKSONG (O WALY, WALY) 9 8 9 8

1. An up-per room did our Lord pre-pare for those he
2. A last-ing gift Je-sus gave his own— to share his
3. And af-ter sup - per he washed their feet, for ser-vice,
4. No end there is! We de-part in peace; he loves be -

loved un-til the end, and his dis - ci - ples still ga-ther
bread, his lov-ing cup; what-ev - er bur - dens may bow us
too, is sac-ra - ment; in him our joy shall be made com -
yond the ut-ter - most; in eve-ry room in our Fa-ther's

there to ce - le - brate their ri - sen Friend.
down, he by his cross shall lift us up.
plete— sent out to serve, as he was sent.
house he will be there, as Lord and Host.

See also: O Waly Waly 600 25

Words: Fred Pratt Green (1903–)   Music: English traditional; arrangement, John W. Wilson (1905–1992)

Words: copyright © 1974 by Hope Publishing Co.   Music: arrangement, copyright © 1974 by Hope Publishing Co.

Maundy Thursday
225   A new commandment

A NEW COMMANDMENT   Irregular

Words: John 13:34,35; French translation, Andrew Donaldson (1951–) Music: Anonymous;
arrangement, Lawrence Bartlett (1933–)

Words: French translation, copyright © Andrew Donaldson, 1996 Music: arrangement, copyright © from the Australian Hymn Book, 1977

you are my dis - ci - ples: if you have love one for an -
vous êtes mes dis - ci - ples si vous ai - mez les uns les

o - ther; by this shall all know you are my dis -
au - tres, et tous ver - ront que vous êtes mes dis -

ci - ples: if you have love one for an - o - ther."
ci - ples si vous ai - mez les uns les au - tres."

226 Great God, your love has called us here

ABINGDON 888888

1. Great God, your love has called us here,
2. We come with self - in - flict - ed pains
3. Great God, in Christ you call our name
4. Then take the towel, and break the bread,
5. Great God, in Christ you set us free,

as we, by love for love were made. Your liv - ing
of bro - ken trust and cho - sen wrong, half - free, half -
and then re - ceive us as your own, not through some
and hum - ble us, and call us friends. Suf - fer and
your life to live, your joy to share. Give us your

like - ness still we bear, though marred, dis - hon - oured,
bound by in - ner chains, by so - cial forc - es
mer - it, right or claim, but by your gra - cious
serve till all are fed, and show how grand - ly
Spir - it's lib - er - ty to turn from guilt and

Words: Brian A. Wren (1936–) Music: Erik Routley (1917–1982)

Words: copyright © 1977, 1995 by Hope Publishing Co. Music: copyright © 1977 by Hope Publishing Co.

286

dis - o - beyed. We come, with all our heart and
swept a - long, by powers and sys - tems close con -
love a - lone. We strain to glimpse your mer - cy
love in - tends to work till all cre - a - tion
dull de - spair and to of - fer all that faith can

mind, your call to hear, your love to find.
fined yet seek - ing hope for hu - man - kind.
seat and find you knee - ling at our feet.
sings, to fill all worlds, to crown all things.
do, while love is mak - ing all things new.

227 God is love, and where true love is

UBI CARITAS   12 12 12 12 with refrain

God is love, and where true love is, God is pre-sent there.

1. Here in Christ we gath - er, love of Christ our call - ing.
2. When we Chris-tians gath - er, mem-bers of one bo - dy,
3. Grant us love's ful - fil - ment, joy with all the bless - ed,

Christ, our love, is with us, glad-ness be his greet - ing.
let there be in us no dis-cord but one spi - rit.
when we see your face, O Sa-viour, in its glo - ry.

Let us fear and love him, ho - ly God e - ter - nal.
Ban-ished now be an - ger, strife and eve-ry quar - rel.
Shine on us, O pur - est Light of all cre - a - tion;

Words: Latin, anonymous; translation, James Quinn (1919–), alt   Music: A. Gregory Murray (1905–1992)

Words: translation, copyright © James Quinn   Music: copyright © A. Gregory Murray

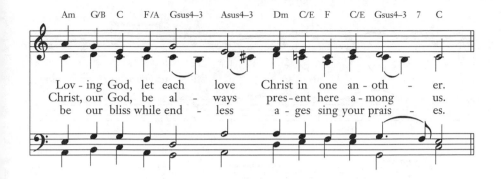

Lov - ing God, let each love Christ in one an - oth - er.
Christ, our God, be al - ways pres - ent here a - mong us.
be our bliss while end - less a - ges sing your prais - es.

228   Drop, drop, slow tears

SONG 46   10 10

1. Drop, drop, slow tears, and bathe those beau-teous feet,
2. Cease not, wet eyes, his mer - cies to en - treat;
3. In your deep floods, drown all my faults and fears;

which brought from heaven the news and Prince of Peace.
to cry for ven-geance, sin doth nev - er cease.
nor let his eye see sin, but through my tears.

Words: Phineas Fletcher (1582–1650)   Music: Orlando Gibbons (1583–1625)

Words: public domain   Music: public domain

Maundy Thursday

229 Jesu, Jesu, fill us with your love

CHEREPONI 7 7 8 with refrain

Refrain

Je - su,   Je - su,   fill   us with your love;   show

us how to serve   the neigh-bours we have   from   you.

1. Kneels at the feet of his   friends,   si - lent - ly wash - es their
2. Neigh-bours are rich   and   poor,   var - ied in col - our and
3. These are the ones we should serve;   these are the ones we should
4. Kneel at the feet of our   friends,   si - lent - ly wash-ing their

feet,   mas - ter who acts as   a   slave   to them.
race;   neigh-bours are near   and   far   a - way.
love;   all   are neigh-bours to   us   and you.
feet;   this   is the way we should live   with you.

Words: Tom Colvin (1925–) Music: Ghanaian folk melody; arrangement, Jane Marshall (1924–);
adaptation, Tom Colvin (1925–)

Words: copyright © 1969 by Hope Publishing Co. Music: adaptation, copyright © 1969 and this arrangement © 1982 by Hope Publishing Co.

Good Friday

230 Go to dark Gethsemane

REDHEAD NO. 76 7 7 7 7 7 7

1. Go to dark Geth - sem - a - ne, you that feel the tempt - er's power; your Re - deem - er's con - flict see, watch with him one bit - ter hour. From his grief turn not a - way; learn of Je - sus Christ to pray.

2. Fol - low to the judge - ment hall; see him beat - en, bound, ar - raigned; pa - tient - ly he bears it all, all our pain his soul sus - tained. Shun not suf - fering, shame or loss; learn of Christ to bear the cross.

3. Climb to Cal - vary's mourn - ful site: there the Lord of glo - ry reigns; there, through weak - ness, wins the fight, o - ver sin our vic - tory gains. "It is fin - ished!" hear him cry; there, in Christ, we dare to die.

Words: James Montgomery (1771–1854); revision, Andrew Donaldson (1951–)
Music: Richard Redhead (1820–1901)

Words: this version, copyright © The Presbyterian Church in Canada, 1997 Music: public domain

231 When I survey the wondrous cross

ROCKINGHAM 8 8 8 8 LM

1. When I sur-vey the won-drous cross on
2. For-bid it, Lord, that I should boast, save
1. Quand je me tour-ne vers la croix où
2. Qui donc pour-rait cal-mer ce coeur hor-

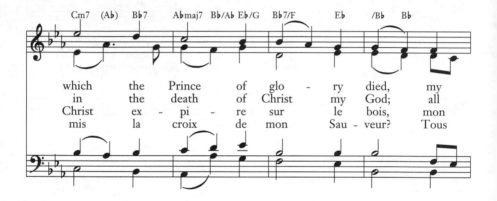

which the Prince of glo - ry died, my
in the death of Christ my God; all
Christ ex - pi - re sur le bois, mon
mis la croix de mon Sau - veur? Tous

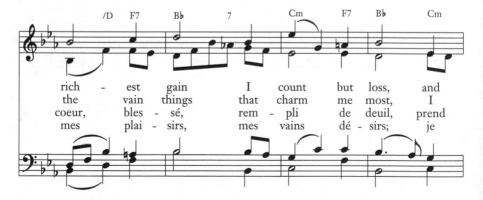

rich - est gain I count but loss, and
the vain things that charm me most, I
coeur, bles - sé, rem - pli de deuil, prend
mes plai - sirs, mes vains dé - sirs; je

See also: Rockingham 537

Words: Isaac Watts (1674–1748) Music: Psalmody in Miniature, Second Supplement, c.1780; adaptation, Edward Miller (1731–1807); harmony, Samuel Webbe, the elder (1740–1816) Webbe's Collection of Psalm-Tunes

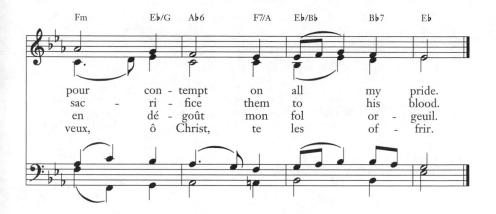

| Fm | | Eb/G | Ab6 | | F7/A | Eb/Bb | | Bb7 | Eb |

pour | con - tempt | on | all | my | pride.
sac - | ri - fice | them | to | his | blood.
en | dé - goût | mon | fol | or - | geuil.
veux, | ô Christ, | te | les | of - | frir.

3. See from his head, his hands, his feet,
   sorrow and love flow mingled down!
   Did e'er such love and sorrow meet,
   or thorns compose so rich a crown?

4. Were the whole realm of nature mine,
   that were an offering far to small;
   love so amazing, so divine,
   demands my soul, my life, my all.

3. Oh vois, des mains, de son côté,
   du front d'épines couronné,
   douleur, angoisse, amour mêlés,
   descendre pour nous racheter.

4. Si je t'offrais le monde entier,
   ce don serait pris en pitié.
   Amour si grand, si pur, si doux
   veut âme, corps, mon coeur, mon tout!

232 Alone you once went forth, O Lord

BANGOR 8 6 8 6 CM

1. A - lone you once went forth, O Lord, in
2. Our sins, not yours, you bore then, Lord: make
3. This was earth's dark - est hour, but you did
4. Grant us with you to suf - fer, Lord, that,

sac - ri - fice to die; does not your sor - row
us your sor - row feel, till through our pi - ty
light and life re - store; then let us give all
as we share this hour, your cross may bring us

touch the hearts of peo - ple pass - ing by?
and our shame love an - swers love's ap - peal.
praise to you who live for - ev - er - more.
to your joy and res - ur - rec - tion power.

Words: Latin, Peter Abelard (1079–1142); translation, F. Bland Tucker (1895–1984)
Music: William Trans'ur (1706–1783)

Words: translation, copyright © Church Pension Fund Music: public domain

233
Were you there
WERE YOU THERE 10 10 14 10

1. Were you there when they cru-ci-fied my Lord? Were you there?

Were you there when they cru-ci-fied my Lord? Oh!

1.–5. Some-times it caus-es me to trem-ble, trem-ble, trem-ble.
6. Some-times I feel like shouting "Glo-ry, glo-ry, glo-ry!"

Were you there when they cru-ci-fied my Lord? Were you there?

2. ...nailed him to the tree...
3. ...pierced him in the side...
4. ...the sun refused to shine...

5. ...laid him in the tomb...
6. ...he rose up from the dead...

Words: African-American traditional Music: African-American spiritual;
arrangement, Melva Wilson Costen (1933–)

Good Friday
234   Ah! holy Jesu, how hast thou offended

HERZLIEBSTER JESU 11 11 11 5

Words: Johann Heermann (1585–1647), translation, Yattendon Hymnal, 1899, alt
Music: Johann Crüger (1598–1662); harmony, J.S. Bach (1685–1750)

Words: public domain Music: public domain

296

235 Alas, and did my Saviour bleed

MARTYRDOM 8 6 8 6 CM

1. A - las, and did my Sav - iour bleed, and did my Sov ereign die? Would he de - vote that sa - cred head for sin - ners such as I?
2. Was it for sins that I have done he groaned up - on the tree? A - maz - ing pit - y, grace un - known, and love be - yond de - gree!
3. Well might the sun in dark - ness hide, and shut its glo - ries in, when Christ the great re - deem - er died for fall - en crea - tures' sin.
4. I, too, in shame would hide my face, while that dread cross ap - pears; dis - solve my heart in thank - ful - ness and melt mine eyes to tears.
5. But drops of grief can ne'er re - pay the debt of love I owe; here, Lord, I give my - self a - way: 'tis all that I can do.

Words: Isaac Watts (1674–1748), alt Music: Hugh Wilson (1766–1824)

Words: public domain Music: public domain

Good Friday

236   At the cross her vigil keeping

STABAT MATER 8 8 7

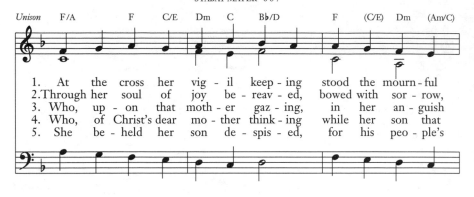

1. At the cross her vig - il keep - ing stood the mourn - ful
2. Through her soul of joy be - reav - ed, bowed with sor - row,
3. Who, up - on that moth - er gaz - ing, in her an - guish
4. Who, of Christ's dear mo - ther think - ing while her son that
5. She be - held her son de - spis - ed, for his peo - ple's

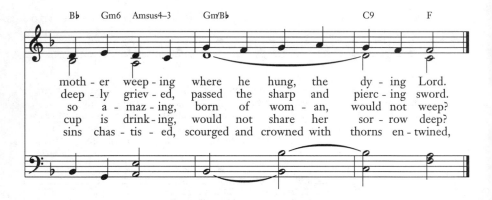

moth - er weep - ing where he hung, the dy - ing Lord.
deep - ly griev - ed, passed the sharp and pierc - ing sword.
so a - maz - ing, born of wom - an, would not weep?
cup is drink - ing, would not share her sor - row deep?
sins chas - tis - ed, scourged and crowned with thorns en - twined,

6. saw him then from judgement taken,
and in death by all forsaken,
till his spirit he resigned.

7. Near thy cross, O Christ, abiding,
grief and love my heart dividing,
I with her would take my place:

8. by thy saving cross uphold me,
in thy dying, Christ, enfold me
with the deathless arms of grace.

Words: Italian, Jacopone da Todi (12??–1306); translation, Edward Caswall (1814–1878)
Music: Maintz Gesangbuch 1661; harmony, Winfred C. Douglas (1867–1944)
Words: public domain Music: public domain

Good Friday

237 Oh come and mourn with me awhile

ST. CROSS 8 8 8 8 LM

1. Oh come and mourn with me awhile; oh come ye to the Sav-iour's side; oh come, to-geth-er let us mourn; Je-sus, our Lord, is cru-ci-fied.

2. Have we no tears to shed for him, while sol-diers scoff and foes de - ride? Ah! look how pa-tient - ly he hangs: Je-sus, our Lord, is cru-ci-fied.

3. Seven times he spoke, seven words of love, and all three hours his si - lence cried, "For-give: they know not what they do." Je-sus, our Lord, is cru-ci-fied.

4. O love of God! O hu - man sin! In this dread act your strength is tried, and vic - to-ry re - mains with love: for Christ, our Lord, is cru-ci-fied.

Words: Frederick William Faber (1814–1863), alt Music: John Bacchus Dykes (1823–1876)

Words: public domain Music: public domain

238 Beneath the cross of Jesus

ST. CHRISTOPHER 76 8 6 8 6 8 6

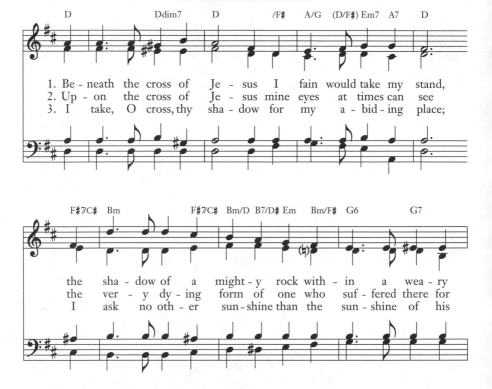

1. Be - neath the cross of Je - sus I fain would take my stand,
2. Up - on the cross of Je - sus mine eyes at times can see
3. I take, O cross, thy sha - dow for my a - bid - ing place;

the sha - dow of a might - y rock with - in a wea - ry
the ver - y dy - ing form of one who suf - fered there for
I ask no oth - er sun - shine than the sun - shine of his

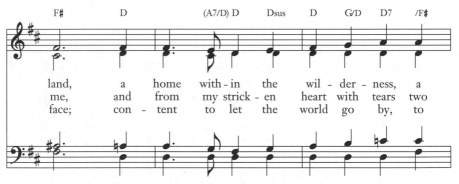

land, a home with - in the wil - der - ness, a
me, and from my strick - en heart with tears two
face; con - tent to let the world go by, to

Words: Elizabeth Cecilia Clephane (1830–1869) Music: Frederick Charles Maker (1844–1927)

Words: public domain Music: public domain

rest up-on the way, from the burn - ing of the
won - ders I con - fess: the won - ders of re -
know no gain nor loss; my sin - ful self my

noon - tide heat and the bur - den of the day.
deem - ing love and my own un - worth - i - ness.
on - ly shame, my glo - ry all, the cross.

239 O sacred head, sore wounded

HERZLICH TUT MICH VERLANGEN 7 6 7 6 D

1. O sa - cred head, sore wound - ed, with grief and shame weighed down,
2. What thou, my Lord, hast suf - fered was all for sin - ners' gain;
1. Chef cou-vert de bles - sur - es, meur-tri pour nous pé - cheurs,
2. C'est ain - si que tu pai - es le prix de ma ran - çon.

now scorn-ful - ly sur - round - ed with thorns, thine on - ly crown;
mine, mine was the trans - gres - sion, but thine the dead - ly pain;
chef ac - ca - blé d'in - jur - es, d'op - pro - bre, de dou - leurs;
Tes lan-gueurs et tes plai - es, voi - là ma gué - ri - son.

how art thou pale with an - guish, with sore a - buse and scorn;
lo, here I fall, my Sav - iour; 'tis I de - serve thy place;
des splen-deurs é - ter - nel - les na-guère en - vi - ron - né,
Mon â - me cri - mi - nel - le est à tes pieds, Sei - gneur,

Words: Latin, Bernard of Clairvaux (1091–1153); German, Paul Gerhardt (1607–1676);
translation, James Waddell Alexander (1804–1859), alt   Music: Hans Leo Hassler (1564–1612);
harmony, J.S. Bach 1685–1750)

Words: public domain   Music: public domain

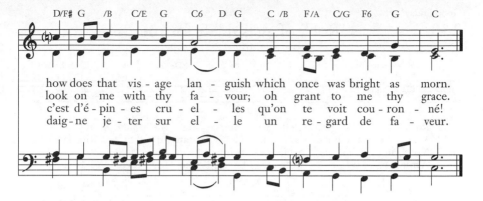

| D/F# | G | /B | C/E | G | | C6 | D | G | | C | /B | F/A | C/G | F6 | G | | C |

how does that vis - age lan - guish which once was bright as morn.
look on me with thy fa - vour; oh grant to me thy grace.
c'est d'é - pin - es cru - el - les qu'on te voit cou - ron - né!
daig - ne je - ter sur el - le un re - gard de fa - veur.

English (cont.)

3. What language shall I borrow
to thank thee, dearest friend,
for this, thy dying sorrow,
thy pity without end?
Oh make me thine forever,
and should I fainting be,
oh let me never, never
outlive my love for thee.

4. Be near when I am dying;
oh show thy cross to me,
and to my rescue flying,
come, Lord, and set me free:
these eyes, new faith receiving,
from Jesus shall not move,
for those who die believing
die safely through thy love.

French (cont.)

3. Au sein de ma misère,
sauvé par ton amour,
pour toi que puis-je faire?
Que t'offrir en retour?
Ah! du moins, Dieu suprême,
prends à jamais mon coeur;
qu'il te serve et qu'il t'aime,
plein d'une sainte ardeur.

4. Pour ta longue agonie,
pour ta sainte douleur,
je veux, toute ma vie,
te bénir, mon Sauveur.
Ta grâce est éternelle,
et rien jusqu'à la fin
ne pourra, Dieu fidèle,
me ravir de ta main.

Hungarian

1. O Krisztusfő, te zuzott, Te véres szenvedő,
Te toviskoszorúzott Kigúnyolt, drága fő,
Ki széség tükre voltál, Ékes, csodás remek,
De most megesúfolodtal: Szent fő, köszöntelek!

2. Mind, ami kin s ütés ért, Magam hoztam Reád,
Uram e szenvedésért Lelkemben ég a vád.
Feddo szot érdemelve itt állok én, szegény,
S kérlek, lelked kegyelme Sugározzék felém.

3. Ó láy érette áldott, Jézus Egyetlenem,
Hogy szorny kinhalálod Nagy jót akar velem.
Add, hogy hódolva hiven Tőled ne térjek el,
S ha hini kezed a szivem, Benned pihenjek el.

4. Légy pajzsom és reményem, Ha kétség látogat,
Véssem szivembe mélyen Kereszthalálodat.
Rád nézzek, Rád szünetlen, S ha majd szivem megáll,
Öleljen át a lelkem-igy halni: jó halál.

303

Rock of ages, cleft for me

TOPLADY 777777

1. Rock of a - ges, cleft for me, let me hide my-self in
2. Not the la - bours of my hands can ful - fil thy law's de -
3. Noth - ing in my hand I bring, sim - ply to thy cross I
4. While I draw this fleet - ing breath, when my eye - lids close in

thee; let the wa - ter and the blood, from thy
mands; could my zeal no res - pite know, could my
cling: na - ked, come to thee for dress; help - less,
death, when I soar through tracts un - known, see thee

riv - en side which flowed, be of sin the
tears for - ev - er flow, all for sin could
look to thee for grace; foul, I to the
on thy judge - ment throne, rock of a - ges,

dou - ble cure: cleanse me from its guilt and power.
not a - tone; thou must save, and thou a - lone.
foun - tain fly; wash me, Sav - iour, or I die.
cleft for me, let me hide my - self in thee.

Alternate tune: Redhead 76 (Petra)

Words: Augustus Montague Toplady (1740–1778) Music: Thomas Hastings (1784–1872)

241

What are these wounds
in your hands, dear Saviour

MIKHAEL GIDEON JAKOB 10 7 10 7

1. hands,
2. feet,
What are these wounds in your 3. brow, dear Sav - iour?
4. side,
5. heart,

hands?
feet?
What are these wounds in your brow?   "These are the wounds with which
side?
heart?

I was wound - ed,   here in the house of my friends."

Words: Zechariah 13:6; paraphrase, Rae E. Whitney (1927–) Music: Amanda Husberg (20th cent.)
Words: copyright © Selah Publishing Co. Inc., 1994 Music: copyright © Selah Publishing Co. Ltd., 1994

What wondrous love is this

WONDROUS LOVE 12 9 12 12 9

1. What won-drous love is this, O my soul, O my soul!
2. To God and to the Lamb, I will sing, I will sing,
3. And when from death I'm free, I'll sing on, I'll sing on,

What won-drous love is this, O my soul!
to God and to the Lamb, I will sing.
and when from death I'm free, I'll sing on.

What won-drous love is this, that caused the Lord of bliss
To God and to the Lamb, who is the great I Am,
And when from death I'm free, I'll sing and joy-ful be,

to lay a-side his crown for my soul, for my soul,
while mil-lions join the theme, I will sing, I will sing,
and through e-ter-ni-ty I'll sing on, I'll sing on,

Words: American folk hymn, c.1811   Music: Walker's Southern Harmony 1835;
harmony, Cantate Domino 1980

Words: public domain   Music: harmony, copyright © World Council of Churches

306

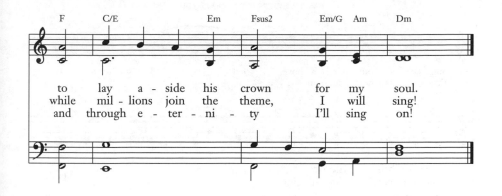

to   lay   a - side   his   crown   for   my   soul.
while   mil - lions join   the   theme,   I   will   sing!
and   through e - ter - ni - ty   I'll   sing   on!

Easter

243

Jesus Christ is risen today

EASTER HYMN 7 7 7 7 with hallelujahs

Descant

4. Sing we to our God a-bove, hal - le - lu - jah!
4. Puis-que ta mort fut sui - vi - e, al - lé - lu - ia!

1. Je - sus Christ is risen to-day, hal - le - lu - jah!
2. Hymns of praise then let us sing
1. Bri-sant ses li - ens fu - nè-bres, al - lé - lu - ia!
2. Les sol-dats, le sceau, la pier-re,

praise e - ter - nal as his love; hal - le - lu - jah!
du tri-om - phe de la vi - e, al - lé - lu - ia!

our tri-um-phant ho - ly day, hal - le - lu - jah!
un-to Christ our heaven-ly King,
Christ est sor - ti des té - nè-bres, al - lé - lu - ia!
n'ont pu le gar - der en ter - re,

Words: Latin, anonymous; translation, Tate and Brady's New Version 1698; vs.4, Charles Wesley (1707–1788); French translation, Ruben Saillens Music: Lyra Davidica 1708, 1749; descant, Derek Holman (1931–).

Words: public domain Music: descant, copyright © Derek Holman

3. But the pains which he endured hallelujah!
   our salvation have procured; hallelujah!
   now above the sky he's King, hallelujah!
   where the angels ever sing, hallelujah!

4. Sing we to our God above, hallelujah!
   praise eternal as his love; hallelujah!
   praise him, all ye heavenly host, hallelujah!
   Father, Son and Holy Ghost, hallelujah!

3. Il vit notre roi de gloire! alléluia!
   sépulchre, où est ta victoire? alléluia!
   le Christ est le vainqueur fort, alléluia!
   qui triomphe sur la mort, alléluia!

4. Puisque ta mort fut suivie, alléluia!
   du triomphe de la vie, alléluia!
   Je veux, ô mon divin Roi, alléluia!
   mourir et naître avec toi! alléluia!

244 Hail, O festival day

SALVE FESTA DIES 7 9 7 7 with refrain

Refrain

Hail, O fest-i-val day! blest day that all a-ges will cher - ish:

day when the Christ was raised, break-ing the bond-age of death. death.

First time only

1. See how the grace of the world, re-born, blos-soms forth from the win - ter,
3. God the Al-might-y, you fill the cos - mos and all you cre-at - ed;
5. We praise you, Spir-it of life, O fount, the sus - tain-er of all things,

Words: Latin, Venantius Honorius Fortunatus (c.540–c.609c.); 3, 5, 6 and Pentecost from York
Processionals 1530; translation, The New Century Hymnal 1995, alt
Music: Ralph Vaughan Williams (1872–1958)

Words: translation, copyright © The Pilgrim Press, 1995 Music: copyright © Oxford University Press

Repeat Refrain once after each stanza, using second ending.

bears wit-ness to Christ's re - turn: life's ver - y gift is re - newed.
cleanse us with - in, make us pure, that we your ves - sel may be.
O ra-diant life - giv-ing Light, re - new-ing life with your grace.

2. Now on the third day re-turned, a - rise now, O Christ, who was bur - ied;
4. O Christ, Re-deem-er of all, our Sav - iour, the au - thor of good-ness,
6. Sov-ereign of all that is good, your sweet balm of peace pour up-on us;

Repeat Refrain once after each stanza, using second ending

fill - ing your prom-ise of faith; nour-ish-ing pow - er a - rise.
on - ly be - got-ten of God, touch us with your heal - ing grace.
give us the wis-dom that guides the un - i - verse on its way.

See overleaf for Ascension and Pentecost words for Refrain and verses 1–2. Verses 3–6 may be used for Easter, Ascension and Pentecost.

Ascension Words

Refrain:
Hail, O festival day!
blest day that all ages will cherish:
day when Christ transcends earth,
ever in heaven to reign.

1. Christ now in triumph ascends;
now Satan's dominion is vanquished;
heaven's mighty gates open wide,
spilling forth increase of light.
Refrain:

2. The laws of hell now oppressed,
creation resounds in thanksgiving;
field and sea, light and sky sing
at the return of their God,
Refrain:

Pentecost Words

Refrain:
Hail, O festival day!
blest day that all ages will cherish:
day when God shone with grace,
over the whole, wide earth,

1. God to the faithful returned:
the Spirit in image of fire;
those gathered tell of Christ's deeds,
in every language on earth,
Refrain:

2. Now to our lips the brights coal
touch gently, so we, too, ar kindled—
your love aflame in our hearts,
lit fom your own endless love.
Refrain:

245   You choirs of new Jerusalem

ST. FULBERT 8 6 8 6 CM

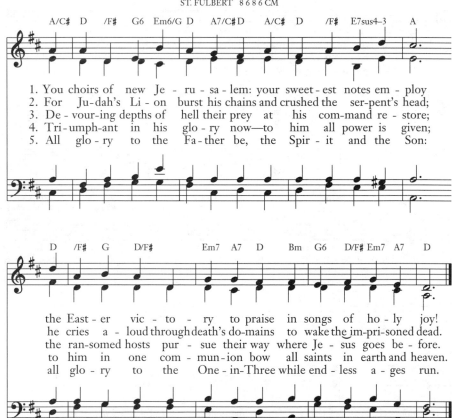

1. You choirs of new Je - ru - sa - lem: your sweet - est notes em - ploy
2. For Ju-dah's Li - on burst his chains and crushed the ser-pent's head;
3. De - vour-ing depths of hell their prey at his com-mand re - store;
4. Tri - umph-ant in his glo - ry now—to him all power is given;
5. All glo - ry to the Fa - ther be, the Spir - it and the Son:

the East - er vic - to - ry to praise in songs of ho - ly joy!
he cries a - loud through death's do-mains to wake the im-pri-soned dead.
the ran-somed hosts pur - sue their way where Je - sus goes be - fore.
to him in one com - mun-ion bow all saints in earth and heaven.
all glo - ry to the One - in-Three while end - less a - ges run.

Words: Latin, Fulbert of Chartres (9??–1028); translation, Robert Campbell (1814–1868)
Music: Henry John Gauntlett (1805–1876)

Words: public domain Music: public domain

This is the feast of victory

FESTIVAL CANTICLE   9 11 with refrain

Refrain
Unison

This is the feast of vic-to-ry for our God.

Hal-le - lu - jah, hal-le - lu-jah, hal-le - lu - jah!   lu - jah!

1. Wor - thy is Christ, the Lamb who was slain, whose
2. Pow - er, rich - es, wis - dom and strength and
3. Sing with all the peo - ple of God, and
4. Bless - ing, hon - our, glo - ry and might be to
5. For the Lamb who was slain has be -

blood set us free to be peo - ple of God.
hon - our, bless - ing and glo - ry are his.
join in the hymn of all cre - a - tion.
God and the Lamb for - ev - er. A - men.
gun his reign. Hal - le - lu - jah!

Words: Revelation 6:12–14; paraphrase, John W. Arthur (1922–1980)   Music: Richard Hillert (1923–)

247

Christ the Lord is risen today

ST. GEORGE'S, WINDSOR 7 7 7 7 D

1. "Christ the Lord is risen to-day," all cre - a - tion join to say.
2. Vain the stone, the watch, the seal; Christ hath burst the gates of hell.
3. Soar we now where Christ hath led, fol-lowing our ex - alt - ed Head;

Raise your joys and tri - umphs high; sing, ye heavens, and earth, re - ply.
Death in vain for - bids him rise; Christ hath o - pened par - a - dise.
made like him, like him we rise; ours the cross, the grave, the skies.

Descant

Hail! the Lord of earth and heaven! Praise to thee by

Love's re-deem - ing work is done, fought the fight, the
Lives a - gain our glo - rious King: where, O death, is
Hail! the Lord of earth and heaven! Praise to thee by

Words: Charles Wesley (1707–1788), alt   Music: George Job Elvey (1816–1893);
descant, C.S. Lang (1891–1971)

Words: public domain   Music: descant, copyright © Novello & Co. Ltd., 1953

both be given; eve - ry knee to thee shall

Bb/D Cm7-6 Bb   D/F#   D   Gm   C/E   C

bat - tle won: lo! our sun's e - clipse is
now thy sting? Once he died our souls to
both be given; eve - ry knee to thee shall

bow, ris - en Christ tri - um - phant now.

F   Bb/D Bb   F/A   Dm   F/C   C   7   F

o'er; lo! he sets in blood no more.
save; where thy vic - to - ry, O grave?
bow, ris - en Christ tri - um - phant now.

Chinese (Mandarin)

Jī Dū Yē Sū jìn fù shēng, Hā lī lù yà!
Tiān shǐ shi rén tóng huān hū, Hā lī lù yà!
Gāo chàng huān lè kǎi xuan gē, Hā lī lù yà!
Zhū tiān dā dī tóng chang hē, Hā lī lù yà!

248

At the dawning of salvation

NETTLETON 8 7 8 7 D Iambic

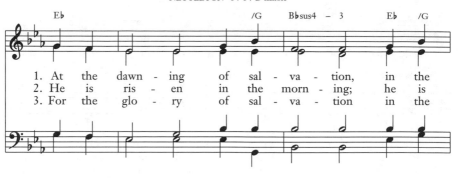

1. At the dawn - ing of sal - va - tion, in the
2. He is ris - en in the morn - ing; he is
3. For the glo - ry of sal - va - tion in the

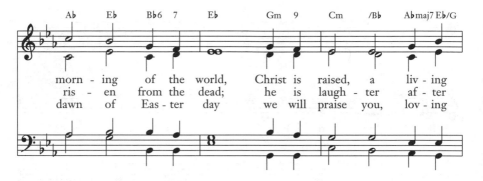

morn - ing of the world, Christ is raised, a liv - ing
ris - en from the dead; he is laugh - ter af - ter
dawn of Eas - ter day we will praise you, lov - ing

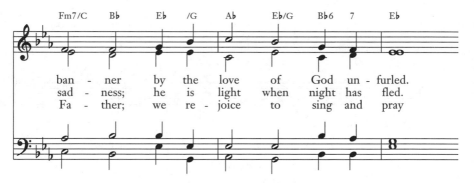

ban - ner by the love of God un - furled.
sad - ness; he is light when night has fled.
Fa - ther; we re - joice to sing and pray

Words: Jock Curle   Music: American folk melody; harmony, John Wilson (1905–1992)

Through the day - light, through the dark - ness, Christ leads
He has suf - fered; he has tri - umphed; life is
with the Son and with the Spir - it. Lead us

on his great ar - ray: all the saints and all the
his a - lone to give: as he gave it once, he
on, your great ar - ray, saints and sin - ners cel - e -

sin - ners he has gath - ered on his way.
gives it ev - er - more, that we may live.
brat - ing your tri - um - phant love to - day.

249

The day of resurrection

ELLACOMBE 7 6 7 6 D

Descant

3. Now let the heavens be joy - ful; let earth its song be - gin;

A/C♯ F♯m   E   A   D   A/C♯ D6 E   A

1. The day of re - sur - rec - tion—earth, tell it out a - broad,
2. Our hearts be pure from e - vil, that we may see a - right
3. Now let the heavens be joy - ful; let earth its song be - gin;

let the round world keep tri - umph, and all that is there - in;

A/C♯ F♯m   E   A   D   F♯m Esus4-3   A

the Pass - o - ver of glad - ness, the Pass - o - ver of God!
the Lord in rays e - ter - nal of re - sur - rec-tion light,
let the round world keep tri - umph, and all that is there - in;

Words: Greek, John of Damascus (c.696–c.754); translation, John Mason Neale (1818–1866)
Music: Mainz Song Book 1833; descant, Cyril Winn (1884–1973)

Words: public domain   Music: descant, copyright © Oxford University Press

in - vis - i - ble and vis - i - ble, their notes to - geth - er blend,

E/G♯ A   D   E   (F♯m E/G♯)A   E/G♯ A   D   E

From death to life e - ter - nal, from earth un - to the sky,
and, lis-tening to his ac - cents, may hear, so calm and plain,
in - vis - i - ble and vis - i - ble, their notes to - geth-er blend,

for Christ the Lord hath ris - en, our joy that hath no end.

A/C♯ F♯m   E   A   D   F♯m Esus4–3   A

our Christ hath brought us o - ver with hymns of vic - to - ry.
his own "All hail!" and, hear - ing, may raise the vic-tor strain.
for Christ the Lord hath ris - en, our joy that hath no end.

250

I danced in the morning /
Lord of the dance

LORD OF THE DANCE Irregular with refrain

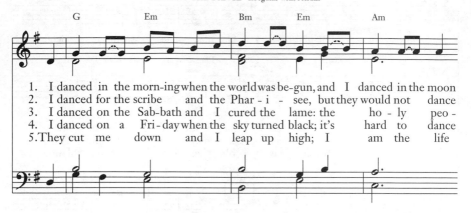

1. I danced in the morn-ing when the world was be-gun, and I danced in the moon
2. I danced for the scribe   and the Phar - i - see, but they would not   dance
3. I danced on the Sab-bath and I cured the   lame: the   ho - ly   peo -
4. I danced on a   Fri - day when the sky turned black; it's   hard to   dance
5. They cut me   down   and I leap up   high; I   am the   life

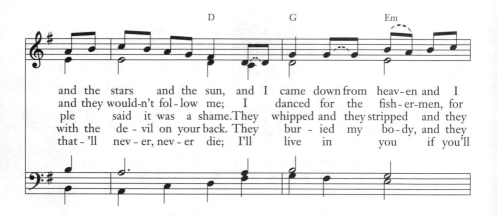

and the stars   and the sun, and I came down from heav-en and I
and they would-n't fol - low me;   I   danced for the   fish - er-men, for
ple   said it was a shame. They   whipped and they stripped   and they
with the   de - vil on your back. They   bur - ied my   bo - dy, and they
that - 'll   nev - er, nev - er   die; I'll   live   in   you   if you'll

Words: Sydney Carter (1915–) Music: 19th century, Shaker tune; adaptation by Sydney Carter (1915–);
arrangement, John Birch

danced on the earth; at Beth - le - hem I had my birth.
James and John; they came with me and the dance went on.
hung me high, and they left me there on a cross to die.
thought I'd gone, but I am the dance, and I still go on.
live in me; I am the Lord of the Dance, said he.

Refrain

Dance, then, wher-ev-er you may be; I am the Lord of the Dance, said he, and I'll

lead you all, wher-ev-er you may be, and I'll lead you all in the dance, said he.

251

Christ is alive

TRURO 8 8 8 8 LM

1. Christ is a - live! Let Chris-tians sing. His cross stands emp - ty to the
2. Christ is a - live! No long - er bound to dis - tant years in Pal - es -
3. In eve-ry in - sult, rift and war, where col - our, scorn or wealth di -
4. Wom-en and men, in age and youth, can feel the Spir - it, hear the
5. Christ is a - live and comes to bring good news to this and eve - ry

sky. Let streets and homes with prais - es ring. His love in
tine, he comes to claim the here and now and dwell in
vide, Christ suf - fers still, yet loves the more, and lives, where
call, and find the life, the way, the truth, re-vealed in
age, till earth and all cre - a - tion ring with joy, with

death shall nev - er die.
eve - ry place and time.
e - ven hope has died.
Je - sus, freed for all.
jus - tice, love and praise.

Words: Brian A. Wren (1936–) Music: Psalmodia Evangelica 1789

Words: copyright © 1975, 1996 by Hope Publishing Co., Music: public domain

252

He is Lord

HE IS LORD 6 11 10 6

He is Lord, he is Lord; he is
ris-en from the dead and he is Lord! Eve-ry knee shall bow, eve-ry
tongue con - fess that Je - sus Christ is Lord.

Words: Philippians 2:10–11   Music: traditional; harmony, Norman Warren (1934–)

Words: public domain   Music: harmony, copyright © 1982 by Hope Publishing Co.

Come, ye faithful, raise the strain

AVE VIRGO VIRGINUM 7 6 7 6 D Trochaic

1. Come, ye faith-ful, raise the strain of tri-um-phant glad - ness;
2. 'Tis the spring of souls to - day; Christ hath burst his pris - on,
3. Hal - le - lu - jah! now we cry to our King im - mor - tal,

God hath brought forth Is - ra - el in - to joy from sad - ness,
and from three-days' sleep in death as a sun hath ris - en;
who tri - um - phant burst the bars of the tomb's dark por - tal;

loosed from Phar-aoh's bit - ter yoke Ja - cob's sons and daugh - ters,
all the win - ter of our sins, long and dark, is fly - ing
hal - le - lu - jah! with the Son, God the Fa - ther prais - ing;

led them with un - moist-ened foot through the Red Sea wa - ters.
from his light, to whom we give laud and praise un - dy - ing.
hal - le - lu - jah! yet a - gain to the Spir - it rais - ing.

Words: Greek, John of Damascus (c.696–c.754); translation, John Mason Neale (1818–1866), alt
Music: Gesangbuch der Brüder (Johann Horn), Nürnberg 1544

254

Jesus is risen from the grave

JESUS IS RISEN FROM THE GRAVE 8 8 8 4

1. Je - sus is ris - en from the grave; Je - sus is ris - en from the grave;
2. Je - sus was seen by Mar - y; Je - sus was seen by Mar - y;
3. Pe - ter will soon be smil - ing; Pe - ter will soon be smil - ing;
4. Tho-mas will stop his doubt - ing; Tho-mas will stop his doubt - ing;
5. Je - sus will meet his peo - ple; Je - sus will meet his peo - ple;
6. Je - sus is here in bread and wine; Je - sus is here in bread and wine;
7. Je - sus will live for - ev - er; Je - sus will live for - ev - er;

Je - sus is ris - en from the grave.
Je - sus was seen by Mar - y.
Pe - ter will soon be smil - ing.
Tho-mas will stop his doubt - ing. Hal - le - lu - jah!
Je - sus will meet his peo - ple.
Je - sus is here in bread and wine.
Je - sus will live for - ev - er.

Words: Iona Community (Scotland)   Music: Iona Community (Scotland)

Now let the vault of heaven resound

LASST UNS ERFREUEN 8 8 4 4 D with hallelujahs

1. Now let the vault of heaven resound in praise of love that doth a - bound, "Christ hath tri - umphed, hal - le - lu - jah"; sing, choirs of an - gels, loud and
2. E - ter - nal is the gift he brings; where - fore our heart with rap - ture sings, "Christ hath tri - umphed, Je - sus liv - eth!" now doth he come and give us
3. Oh fill us, Lord, with daunt-less love; set heart and will on things a - bove, that we con - quer through thy tri - umph, grant grace suf - fi - cient for life's
4. A - dor - ing prais - es now we bring, and with the heaven-ly bless - ed sing, "Christ hath tri - umphed, hal - le - lu - jah!" Be to the Fath - er and our

See also: Lasst uns erfreuen with descant 433 607

Words: Paul Zeller Strodach (1876–1947) Music: Geistliche Kirchengesänge, Cologne 1623

Words: public domain Music: public domain

Bbsus4 – 3   Eb/G   Bb7/F Eb   Ab/C Eb/Bb Ab   Eb/G (Bb/F Eb Bb/D)

clear,   re - peat their song of glo - ry here,
life;   now   doth his pres - ence still all strife
day,   that by our life we ev - er say,
Lord,   to   Spir - it blest, most ho - ly God,

Harmony

Ab/C Eb/Bb Ab6 Bb/Ab Eb/G   Fm7   Eb/G Ab6 Bb7 Cm   Bb/D Eb6 F7 Bb

"Christ hath tri - umphed, Christ hath tri - umphed!"
through his tri - umph; Je - sus reign - eth!   Hal-le - lu - jah,
"Christ hath tri - umphed, and he liv - eth!"
thine the glo - ry nev - er end - ing!

Unison

Cm Bb/D Eb6 Fm   Bb/D C7/E Fm   Eb/G Ab6   Bb   7   Eb

hal - le - lu - jah, hal - le - lu - - jah!

256

Now the green blade rises

FRENCH CAROL 11 11 10 11

1. Now the green blade ris - es from the bur - ied grain,
2. In the grave they laid him, love by ha - tred slain,
3. Forth he came at Eas - ter, like the ris - en grain,
4. When our hearts are win - try, griev-ing or in pain,

wheat that in the dark earth man - y days has lain;
sure that he would nev - er, ne - ver wake a - gain,
he that for these three days in the grave had lain;
then your touch can call us back to life a - gain,

love lives a - gain, that with the dead has been:
laid in the earth like grain that sleeps un - seen:
raised from the dead my liv - ing Lord is seen:
fields of our hearts that dead and bare have been:

love is come a - gain like wheat new - spring-ing green.

Words: J.M.C. Crum (1872–1958), alt from Oxford Book of Carols Music: French traditional carol "Noël Nouvelet"; harmony, Martin Shaw (1875–1958) from Oxford Book of Carols

Words: copyright © Oxford University Press Music: harmony, copyright © Oxford University Press. 1928

Easter
257
The strife is o'er, the battle done
VICTORY 8 8 8 with hallelujahs

Antiphon *(at the beginning and end)*

Hal - le - lu — jah, hal - le - lu — jah, hal - le - lu — jah!

1. The strife is o'er, the bat — tle done; the vic - to -
2. Death's might-iest powers have done their worst, but Christ their
3. The three sad days have quick - ly sped; Christ ris - es
4. Lord, from your wounds God's bless - ings spring: free us, we

ry of life is won; the song of tri - umph
le - gions has dis - persed: let shouts of praise and
glo - rious from the dead: all glo - ry to our
pray, from death's dread sting that we may live, and

has be - gun.
joy out - burst.
ris - en Head! Hal - le - lu — jah!
ev - er sing *[Ant.]*

Alternate tunes: Christus, der ist mein Leben Vulpius

Words: Latin, anonymous, c.1695; translation, Francis Pott (1832–1909), alt Music: Giovanni Pierluigi da Palestrina (c.1525–1594); arrangement, William Henry Monk (1823–1889)

Words: public domain Music: public domain   329

258

Thine be the glory

MACCABAEUS 10 11 11 11 with Refrain

1. Thine be the glo - ry, ris - en, con-quering son,
2. Lo! Je - sus meets us, ris - en from the tomb;
1. À toi la gloi - re, O Res - sus - ci - té!
2. Vois - le pa - raî - tre: c'est lui, c'est Jé - sus,

end - less is the vic - tory thou o'er death hast won;
lov - ing - ly he greets us, scat - ters fear and gloom;
A toi la vic - toi - re pour l'é - ter - ni - té!
ton Sau - veur, ton maî - tre! Oh! ne dou - te plus!

an - gels in bright rai - ment rolled the stone a - way,
let the church with glad - ness hymns of tri - umph sing,
Bril - lant de lu - miè - re, l'ange est des - cen - du,
Sois dans l'al - lé - gres - se, peu - ple du Sei - gneur,

kept the fold - ed grave clothes, where thy bo - dy lay.
for her Lord now liv - eth; death hath lost its sting.
il rou - le la pier - re du tom - beau vain - cu.
et re - dis sans ces - se que Christ est vain - queur.

Words: French, Edmond L. Budry (1854–1932); translation, R. Birch Hoyle (1875–1939)
Music: George Frideric Handel (1685–1759)

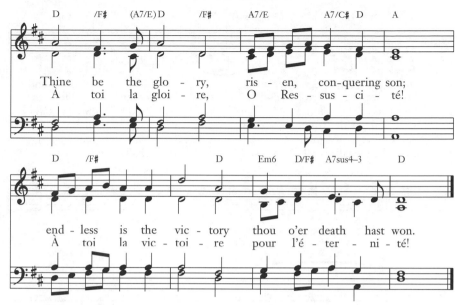

| | D | /F♯ | (A7/E) D | /F♯ | A7/E | A7/C♯ | D | A |

Thine be the glo - ry, ris - en, con-quering son;
À toi la gloi - re, O Res - sus - ci - té!

| | D | /F♯ | | D | Em6 | D/F♯ | A7sus4–3 | D |

end - less is the vic - tory thou o'er death hast won.
À toi la vic - toi - re pour l'é - ter - ni - té!

3. No more we doubt thee,
   glorious prince of life;
   life is nought without thee:
   aid us in our strife;
   make us more than conquerors,
   through thy deathless love:
   bring us safe through Jordan
   to thy home above.

3. Craindrais–je encore?
   Il vit à jamais,
   celui que j'adore,
   le Prince de paix;
   il est ma victoire,
   mon puissant soutien,
   ma vie et ma gloire:
   non, je ne crains rien.

Korean
1. Choo-neem-keh yung-gwawng taw-shee saw-sheen joo
   saw-mawng kwun-seh moh-doo ee-gee-shee-uht-neg
   Heen-oht ee-bun chun-saw tohl-ul ohom-gyut-neh
   Noo-oo-shut-ton goh-sun pee-uh ee-sut-heh
   Refrain:
   Heen-oht ee-bun chun-saw tohl-ul ohom-gyut-neh
   noo-oo-shut goh-sun pee-uh ee-sut-neh

2. Poo-hwawl-eh choo-neem naw-taw-naw-shee-saw
   Too-ryuh--oom gwaw ui-sheem mool-lee chee-shut-neg
   Choo-eh kyoh-hweh keep-puh chawn-sohng haw-yuh-raw
   Taw-shee saw-sheen choo-neem choo-gum ee-gyut-neh
   Refrain:

3. Seng-myung eh eem-gum yung-gwawng eh choo-neem
   Choo-neem uhp-nun sawlm-un huht-twell poon-ee-raw
   Choo-eh saw-rawng-u-roh seh-sawng ee-gee-goh
   Yoh-dawn knu-nug pohn-yawng kaw-geh hawp-soh-sub
   Refrain:

259

This joyful Eastertide

VREUCHTEN 6 7 6 7 with refrain

1. This joy-ful Eas-ter-tide, a-way with sin and sad - ness!
   My love, the cru-ci-fied, has sprung to life in glad - ness.

2. My bo-dy, too, at last shall rest with-in God's keep - ing:
   un-til, with trum-pet blast, the dead shall wake from sleep - ing.

   Had

3. Death's flood hath lost its chill, since Je-sus crossed the riv - er,
   and love shall reach me still, and shall my soul de - liv - er.

Refrain

Words: George Ratcliffe Woodward (1849–1934), alt   Music: J. Oudaen's David's Psalmen 1685; harmony, Charles Wood (1866–1926)

Words: copyright © A.R. Mowbray and Co. Ltd. (an imprint of Cassell plc), from the Crowley Carol Book   Music: public domain

Christ, that once was slain, ne'er burst his three-day pris-on, our faith had been in vain, but now has Christ a-ris - en, a - ris - en, a - ris - en, a - ris - en.

Easter
260

Alleluia, alleluia, give thanks to
the risen Lord / Alleluia No. 1

ALLELUIA NO. 1   8 8 with refrain

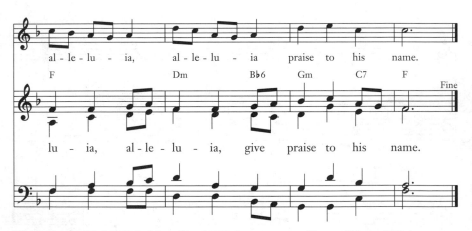

Words: Donald Fishel (1950–);   Music: Donald Fishel;   arrangement, Norman Warren (1952–);
descant, Angela Reith (1952–)

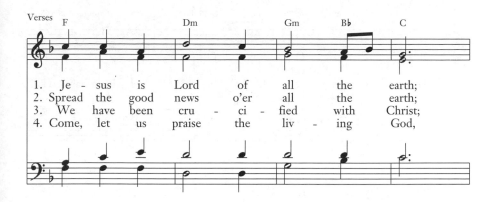

Verses

1. Je - sus is Lord of all the earth;
2. Spread the good news o'er all the earth;
3. We have been cru - ci - fied with Christ;
4. Come, let us praise the liv - ing God,

he is the King of cre - a - tion:
Je - sus has died and has ris - en:
now we shall live for - ev - er:
joy - ful - ly sing to our Sav - iour:

261

Hallelujah! Hallelujah! Hallelujah!

O FILII ET FILIAE 8 8 8 with hallelujahs

Refrain (at beginning and after v.9)

Hal - le - lu-jah! Hal - le - lu-jah! Hal - le-lu-jah! Hal -

le - lu - jah!

1. O sons and daugh - ters, let us sing!
2. That East - er morn, at break of day,
3. An an - gel clad in white they see,
4. That night the a -pos - tles met in fear;
5. When Tho - mas first the ti - dings heard,

The king of heaven, the glo - rious King, o'er death to - day rose
the faith - ful wom - en went their way to seek the tomb where
who sat, and spake un - to the three, "Your Lord doth go to
a - midst them came their Lord most dear, and said, "My peace be
how they had seen the ris - en Lord, he doubt - ed the dis -

Words: Latin, Jean Tisserand (14??–1494); translation, John Mason Neale (1818–1866)
Music: Anonymous French, Airs sur les hymnes sacrez, odes et noëls, 1623;
harmony, anonymous, last 2 measures from the Hymnal 1982

Words: public domain Music: harmony, copyright © The Church Pension Fund

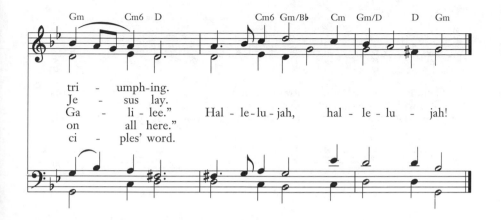

| Gm | Cm6 D | Cm6 Gm/B♭ | Cm Gm/D | D Gm |

tri - umph-ing.
Je - sus lay.
Ga - li - lee." Hal - le-lu-jah, hal - le - lu - jah!
on all here."
ci - ples' word.

6. "My pierced side, O Thomas, see;
   my hands, my feet, I show to thee;
   not faithless, but believing be."
   Hallelujah! Hallelujah!

7. No longer Thomas then denied;
   he saw the feet, the hands, the side.
   "Thou art my Lord and God," he cried.
   Hallelujah! Hallelujah!

8. How blest are they who have not seen,
   and yet whose faith has constant been,
   for they eternal life shall win.
   Hallelujah! Hallelujah!

9. On this most holy day of days,
   to God your hearts and voices raise
   in laud and jubilee and praise.
   Hallelujah! Hallelujah!

Refrain:
Hallelujah! Hallelujah! Hallelujah! Hallelujah!

Easter

262

<h1 style="text-align:center">Come to us, beloved Stranger</h1>

BEACH SPRING 8 7 8 7 D

1. Come to us, be - lov - ed Stran - ger, as you came that
2. Stay with us and give us bless - ing, that our hopes a -
3. We would nev - er fail to see you as you walk with

East - er day. Walk with us to our Em - ma - us,
gain may rise. Of - fer us your bro - ken bo - dy;
us each day. As a friend and not a stran - ger

for we need you still to - day. Come to us when we are
o - pen our un - see - ing eyes. Come to us, God's love em -
you would join us on our way. Help us trust that through your

Words: Edith Sinclair Downing (1922–)   Music: attributed to Benjamin Franklin White (1800–1879) from Sacred Harp 1844; harmony, James H. Wood

bro - ken,   when our dear - est   hopes are lost,   speak to
bod - ied;   touch our hearts with   burn - ing flame.   Ris - en
mer - cy   we can doubt and   fear tran-scend,   and to

us   the pro-phets' mes - sage you ful - filled up - on the cross.
Christ, once dead, now liv - ing, come to us through joy, through pain.
oth - ers be a bless - ing. Keep us faith - ful till life's end!

263 They set out on their homeward road

RYBURN 888888

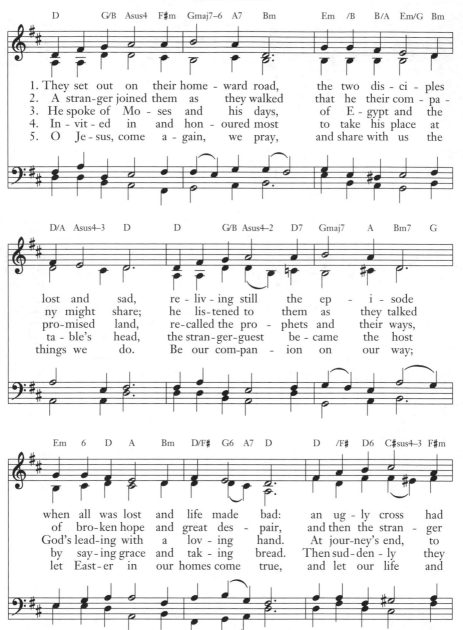

1. They set out on their home - ward road, the two dis - ci - ples
2. A stran-ger joined them as they walked that he their com - pa -
3. He spoke of Mo - ses and his days, of E - gypt and the
4. In - vit - ed in and hon - oured most to take his place at
5. O Je - sus, come a - gain, we pray, and share with us the

lost and sad, re - liv - ing still the ep - i - sode
ny might share; he lis-tened to them as they talked
pro-mised land, re-called the pro - phets and their ways,
ta - ble's head, the stran-ger-guest be - came the host
things we do. Be our com-pan - ion on our way;

when all was lost and life made bad: an ug - ly cross had
of bro-ken hope and great des - pair, and then the stran - ger
God's lead-ing with a lov - ing hand. At jour-ney's end, to
by say-ing grace and tak - ing bread. Then sud-den - ly they
let East-er in our homes come true, and let our life and

Words: Fred Kaan (1929–) Music: Norman Cocker (1889–1953)

Words: copyright © 1968 by Hope Publishing Co. Music: copyright © Oxford University Press

264 Sing amen

AMEN (ASITHI) 8 8 8 8

Words: Xhosa, S.C. Molefe (1921–1983) Music: S.C. Molefe (1921–1983); arrangement, David Dargie (1938–)

265   Hail the day that sees Christ rise

LLANFAIR 7 4 7 4 D

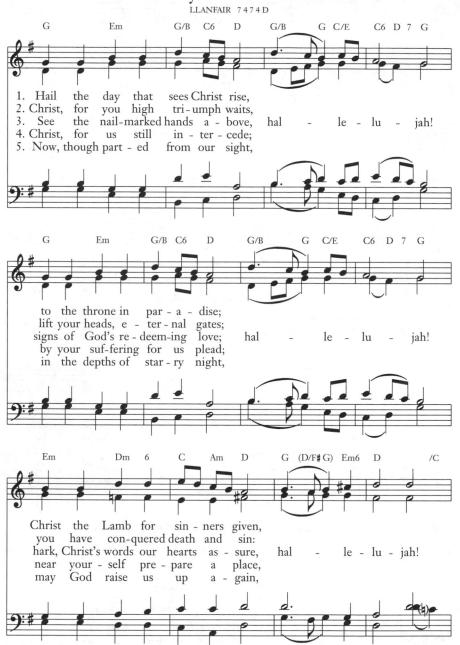

1. Hail the day that sees Christ rise,
2. Christ, for you high tri - umph waits,
3. See the nail-marked hands a - bove,   hal - le - lu - jah!
4. Christ, for us still in - ter - cede;
5. Now, though part - ed from our sight,

to the throne in par - a - dise;
lift your heads, e - ter - nal gates;
signs of God's re - deem-ing love;   hal - le - lu - jah!
by your suf-fering for us plead;
in the depths of star - ry night,

Christ the Lamb for sin - ners given,
you have con-quered death and sin:
hark, Christ's words our hearts as - sure,   hal - le - lu - jah!
near your - self pre - pare a place,
may God raise us up a - gain,

Words: anonymous, Thomas Cotterill (1779–1823), Charles Wesley (1707–1788), alt
Music: Robert Williams (1781–1821)

Words: public domain   Music: public domain

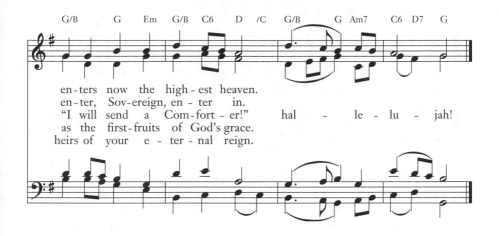

en - ters now the high - est heaven.
en - ter, Sov-ereign, en - ter in.
"I will send a Com-fort - er!" hal - le - lu - jah!
as the first-fruits of God's grace.
heirs of your e - ter - nal reign.

266   King of Kings

KING OF KINGS Irregular

King of kings and Lord of lords, glo - ry, hal - le - lu - jah!
Roi des rois, Sei - gneur des sei-gneurs, gloi-re, al - lé - lu - ia!

Je - sus, Prince of Peace, glo - ry, hal - le - lu - jah!
Jé - sus, Prince de paix, gloi-re, al - lé - lu - ia!

* May be sung as a round.

Words: Naomi Batya, Sophie Conty   Music: Jewish traditional

Words: copyright © Maranatha! Music, 1980, 1983   Music: public domain

267 Rejoice, the Lord is King

DARWALL'S 148TH 6 6 6 6 8 8

Descant

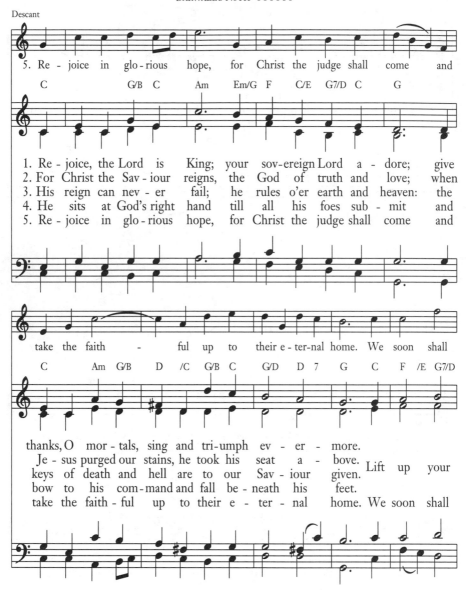

5. Re - joice in glo - rious hope, for Christ the judge shall come and

1. Re - joice, the Lord is King; your sov-ereign Lord a - dore; give
2. For Christ the Sav - iour reigns, the God of truth and love; when
3. His reign can nev - er fail; he rules o'er earth and heaven: the
4. He sits at God's right hand till all his foes sub - mit and
5. Re - joice in glo - rious hope, for Christ the judge shall come and

take the faith - ful up to their e - ter-nal home. We soon shall

thanks, O mor - tals, sing and tri-umph ev - er - more.
Je - sus purged our stains, he took his seat a - bove.   Lift up your
keys of death and hell are to our Sav - iour given.
bow to his com-mand and fall be - neath his feet.
take the faith - ful up to their e - ter - nal home. We soon shall

See also: Darwall's 148th 606 757

Words: Charles Wesley (1707–1788), alt Music: John Darwall (1731–1789); harmony, William Henry Monk (1823–1889); descant, Sydney H. Nicholson (1875–1947)

Words: public domain Music: descant, copyright © Hope Publishing Co.

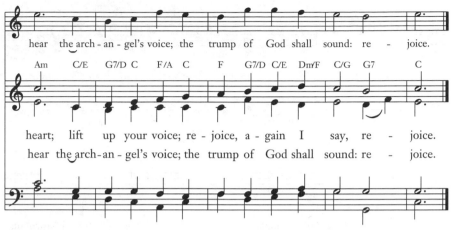

hear the arch-an-gel's voice; the trump of God shall sound: re - joice.

Am C/E G7/D C F/A C F G7/D C/E Dm/F C/G G7 C

heart; lift up your voice; re - joice, a - gain I say, re - joice.

hear the arch-an-gel's voice; the trump of God shall sound: re - joice.

French

1. Chrétien, réjouis-toi!
   tressaille d'allégresse,
   car ton Sauveur est roi:
   regarde à lui sans cesse.
   En son amour, chrétien,
   réjouis-toi, réjouis-toi toujours!

2. Exalte le Seigneur:
   il a sauvé ton âme!
   Dieu l'a comblé d'honneur
   après la croix infâme.
   En son amour, chrétien,
   réjouis-toi, réjouis-toi toujours!

3. Éclate en saints transports!
   Voici ton Dieu confie
   les portes de la mort
   au Prince de la vie.
   En son amour, chrétien,
   réjouis-toi, réjouis-toi toujours!

4. Espère, adore et crois!
   Jésus seul est le Maître.
   Au loin déjà je vois
   sa gloire enfin paraître.
   En son amour, chrétien,
   réjouis-toi, réjouis-toi toujours!

5. Christ règne dans le ciel
   au sein de la lumière,
   et son règne éternel
   bientôt viendra sur terre.
   En son amour, chrétien,
   réjouis-toi, réjouis-toi toujours!

268
All hail King Jesus
ALL HAIL, KING JESUS Irregular

Words: Dave Moody   Music: Dave Moody

Words: copyright © Glory Alleluia Music, 1979. Used by permission of Tempo Music Publications. Music: copyright © Glory Alleluia Music, 1979. Used by permission of Tempo Music Publications.

reign with you through-out e-ter-ni-ty.

269   Your kingdom come, O God

ST. CECILIA 6 6 6 6

1. Your king-dom come, O God! Your rule, O Christ, be - gin;
2. Where is your reign of peace and pu - ri - ty and love?
3. When comes the prom-ised time, the end of strife and war,
4. O Lord our God, a - rise and come in your great might!
5. Some scorn your sa - cred name, and wolves de - vour your fold;

break with your i - ron rod the tyr - an - nies of sin.
When shall all hat - red cease as in the realms a - bove?
when lust, op - pres-sion, crime and greed shall be no more?
Re - vive our long-ing eyes which lan - guish for your sight.
by man - y deeds of shame we learn that love grows cold.

6. On nations near and far
thick darkness gathers yet:
arise, O Morning Star;
arise and never set!

Words: Lewis Hensley (1824–1905), alt Music: Leighton George Hayne (1836–1883)

Words: public domain Music: public domain

270

The head that once was crowned with thorns

ST. MAGNUS 8 6 8 6 CM

1. The head that once was crowned with thorns is
2. The high-est place that heaven af-fords is
3. the joy of all who dwell a-bove, the
4. To them the cross, with all its shame, with
5. They suf-fer with their Lord be-low; they
6. The cross he bore is life and health, though

crowned with glo-ry now; a roy-al di-a-
his, is his by right, the King of kings, and
joy of all be-low to whom he man-i-
all its grace, is given, their name an ev-er-
reign with him a-bove, their prof-it and their
shame and death to him, his peo-ple's hope, his

dem a-dorns the might-y Vic-tor's brow.
Lord of lords, and heaven's e-ter-nal Light;
fests his love and grants his name to know.
last-ing name, their joy the joy of heaven.
joy to know the mys-tery of his love.
peo-ple's wealth, their ev-er-last-ing theme.

See also: St. Magnus 15 368 629

Words: Thomas Kelly (1769–1854/5)   Music: Jeremiah Clarke (c. 1674–1707), from Divine
Companion 1707; harmony, William Henry Monk (1823–1889) after John Pyke Hullah (19th cent.)

Words: public domain   Music: public domain

348

271   Let all the world in every corner sing

LUCKINGTON 10 4 6 6 6 6 10 4

1.–2. Let all the world in eve-ry cor-ner sing: my God and King!

The heavens are not too high, his praise may thith - er fly; the
The church with psalms must shout; no door can keep them out, but,

earth is not too low, his prais - es there may grow. Let all the
a - bove all, the heart must bear the long - est part. Let all the

world in eve - ry cor - ner sing: my God and King!

Words: George Herbert (1593–1633)   Music: Basil Harwood (1859–1949)

272

Christ is King!

ST. LEONARD 878787

1. Christ is King! Let earth-ly pow-ers, wealth, do-min-ion, state and crown, here be-fore the Ser-vant Sav-iour praise and wor-ship and kneel down. Je-sus reigns: a cross ex-alts him; suf-fering is the roy-al gown.

2. Christ is King! O saints be joy-ful; grace and jus-tice will be shown, weak-ness lift-ed in-to glo-ry, pride and greed cast from their throne. Je-sus reigns: the once-re-jec-ted has be-come the Cor-ner-stone.

3. Christ is King! Death's power is end-ed; now there is no need for fear. Love and love a-lone re-deems us, wipes a-way our guilt and tears. Je-sus reigns: the Lamb once-slaugh-tered in a-bun-dant life ap-pears.

Alternate tune: Regent Square

Words: Sylvia G. Dunstan (1955–1993)   Music: J.C. Bach (1642–1703)

Words: copyright © G.I.A. Publications Inc., 1991   Music: public domain

273

Jesus, our mighty Lord

MONKS GATE 11 11 12 11

1. Je - sus, our might-y Lord, our strength in sad-ness,
2. Good shep-herd of your sheep, your own de-fend-ing,
3. Glo - rious their life who sing, with glad thanks-giv-ing,

the Fa-ther's con-quering Word, true source of glad-ness—
in love your chil-dren keep to life un-end-ing.
true hymns to Christ the King in all their liv-ing:

your name we glo-ri-fy, O Je-sus, throned on high:
You are your-self the way: lead us then day by day
all who con-fess his name, come then with hearts a-flame,

you gave your-self to die for our sal-va-tion.
in your own steps, we pray, O Lord most ho-ly.
the God of peace ac-claim as Lord and Sav-iour.

Words: Greek, Clement of Alexandria (170?–220?), paraphrase, F. Bland Tucker (1895–1984)
Music: Sussex folk melody; arrangement, Ralph Vaughan Williams (1872–1958)

274 Crown him with many crowns

DIADEMATA 6 6 8 6 D SMD

Descant

5. Crown him the Lord of years, the end of time,

D   Bm   G   D/F♯ G   A7/E D   A

1. Crown him with ma-ny crowns, the Lamb up-on the throne: hark,
2. Crown him the Son of God, be-fore the worlds be-gan; let
3. Crown him the Lord of life, who tri-umphed o'er the grave, and
4. Crown him the Lord of peace whose king-dom is at hand; from
5. Crown him the Lord of years, the Source, the End of time, Cre-

Cre - a - tor of the spheres in maj - es - ty sub - lime.

D   A/C♯ Bm   /D   E   /D   A/C♯ E7/B A   D   Esus4-3   A   /G

how the heaven-ly an-them drowns all mu-sic but its own! A-
all who tread where he has trod, crown him the Son of Man, who
rose vic-to-rious in the strife for those he came to save. His
pole to pole let war-fare cease and Christ rule eve-ry land! A
a-tor of the roll-ing spheres in maj-es-ty sub-lime. All

Words: Matthew Bridges (1800–1893), Godfrey Thring (1823–1903), alt   Music: George Job
Elvey (1816–1893); descant, Richard Proulx (1937–)

Words: public domain   Music: descant, copyright © Richard Proulx

All hail, Re-deem-er, hail, for you have died for

D/F♯ D A7/E D/F♯ G B7/F♯ E D/F♯ E/G♯ A /G

wake, my soul, and sing of him who died to be your
eve-ry grief has known that wrings the hu-man breast, and
glo-ries now we sing who died and rose on high, who
ci-ty stands on high; Christ's glo-ry it dis-plays, and
hail, Re-deem-er, hail, for you have died for me; your

me; praise shall not fail through all e-ter-ni-ty.

D/F♯ G D/F♯ Em7 A D /F♯ G D Asus4–3 D

Sav-iour and your match-less King through all e-ter-ni-ty.
takes and bears them for his own, that all in him may rest.
died e-ter-nal life to bring, and lives that death may die.
there the na-tions "Ho-ly" cry in joy-ful hymns of praise.
praise shall nev-er, nev-er fail through all e-ter-ni-ty!

275

Jesus shall reign where're the sun

WARRINGTON 8888LM

Je - sus shall reign wher - e'er the sun does its suc - ces - sive
For him shall end - less prayer be made, and prais - es throng to
Peo - ple and realms of eve - ry tongue dwell on his love with
Bless - ings a - bound wher - e'er he reigns: the pris - oners leap to
Let eve - ry crea - ture rise and bring the hon - ours due our

jour - neys run; his king - dom stretch from shore to shore,
crown his head; his name like fra - grance sweet shall rise
sweet - est song, and in - fant voic - es shall pro - claim
lose their chains; the wea - ry find e - ter - nal rest,
glo - rious King; an - gels de - scend with songs a - gain,

till moons shall wax and wane no more.
with eve - ry morn - ing sac - ri - fice.
their ear - ly bless - ings on his name.
and all who suf - fer want are blest.
and earth re - peat the long A - men.

Alternate tune: Duke Street

Words: Psalm 72:17–20; paraphrase, Isaac Watts (1674–1748), alt Music: Ralph Harrison
(c.1748–1810)

Words: public domain Music: public domain

Hungarian

1. Úr lesz a Jézus mindenütt,
   Hol csak a naphak fénye süt,
   úr lesz a messze tengerig,
   Hol a hold nem fogy, s nem telik.

2. Őneki mondjunk hő imát,
   Díszítsük azzal homlokat,
   Jó illat légyen szent neve,
   Minden napon dícsérete.

3. Országok, népek és nyelvek,
   Ő dicsőségét zengjétek,
   Gyermekek hangja hirdesse:
   Áldott a Jézus szent neve!

4. Ő királysága bő áldás,
   Ott van a felszabadulás
   Fáradtak ott megnyugszanak,
   Ínségesek megáldatnak.

5. Minden teremtés dícsérje,
   A Király Krisztust tisztelje;
   Angyali ének zengjen fenn,
   S mind e föld mondja rá: Amen.

276 Come, O Spirit, with your sound

BOUNDLESS MERCY 7 6 7 6 D

1. Come, O Spir-it, with your sound like a wind, quick rush-ing;
2. Come, O Spir-it, with your flame, leap-ing tongues of fi - re;
3. Come, O Spir-it, fill your church, mak-ing strong our mis - sion;

come from heaven and stir our hearts, each dis - ci - ple touch-ing!
come, and with your glo-rious light all our thoughts in - spi - re!
fill your daugh-ters and your sons with a might-y vi - sion,

Mould our ac-tions to your will, you our serv-ice giv - ing;
Rest up-on each ser-vant's head till each one is speak-ing
till the great and glo-rious day when the whole cre - a - tion

move with-in our fel-low-ship; trans-form now our liv - ing!
of our Christ, the Ho-ly One all the earth is seek - ing!
sings your praise as Lord and King, giv-er of sal-va - tion!

Words: John A. Dalles (1954–) Music: Union Harmony 1837; harmony, Hilton Rufty (1909–)

Words: copyright © John A. Dalles, 1990 Music: harmony, copyright © J. Fischer and Bro., a division of Belwin–Mills Publishing Corp, 1934, 1962

277

On this assembled host

ST. MICHAEL 6 6 8 6 SM

1. On this as - sem - bled host, in this ac - cept - ed hour,
2. We meet with one ac - cord in our ap - point - ed place,
3. Like might - y rush - ing wind up - on the waves be - neath,
4. The young, the old in - spire with wis - dom from a - bove,
5. Spir - it of light, ex - plore and chase our gloom a - way,

O Spir - it, as at Pen - te - cost, de - scend in grace and power.
and wait the prom - ise of our Lord, the Spir - it of all grace.
move with one im - pulse eve - ry mind; one soul, one spir - it breathe.
and give us hearts and tongues of fire to pray and praise and love.
your splen - dour shin - ing more and more un - to God's per - fect day.

Words: James Montgomery (1771–1854), alt   Music: Genevan Psalter 1551;
harmony, William Henry Monk (1823–1889)

Words: public domain Music: public domain

That day in Jerusalem

TONGUES OF FIRE   Irregular

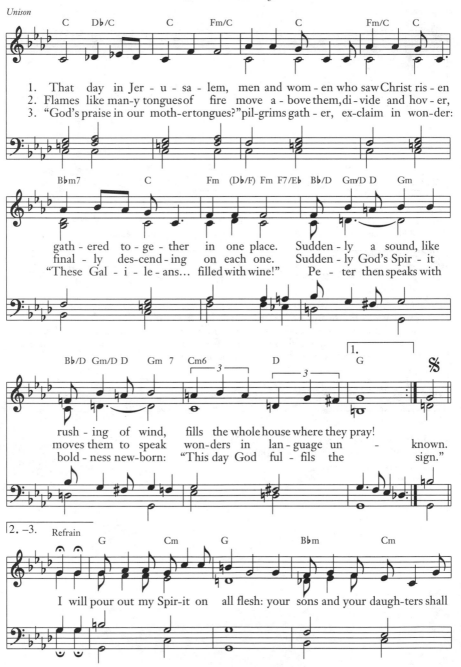

1. That day in Jer - u - sa - lem, men and wom - en who saw Christ ris - en
2. Flames like man-y tongues of fire move a - bove them, di - vide and hov - er,
3. "God's praise in our moth-er tongues?" pil-grims gath - er, ex-claim in won-der:

gath - ered to - ge - ther in one place. Sudden - ly a sound, like
final - ly des-cend-ing on each one. Sudden - ly God's Spir - it
"These Gal - i - le - ans... filled with wine!" Pe - ter then speaks with

rush - ing of wind, fills the whole house where they pray!
moves them to speak won-ders in lan - guage un - known.
bold - ness new-born: "This day God ful - fils the sign."

2. –3.   Refrain

I will pour out my Spir-it on all flesh: your sons and your daugh-ters shall

Words: Andrew Donaldson (1951–) Music: Andrew Donaldson (1951–)

Words: copyright © Andrew Donaldson, 1992 Music: copyright © Andrew Donaldson, 1992

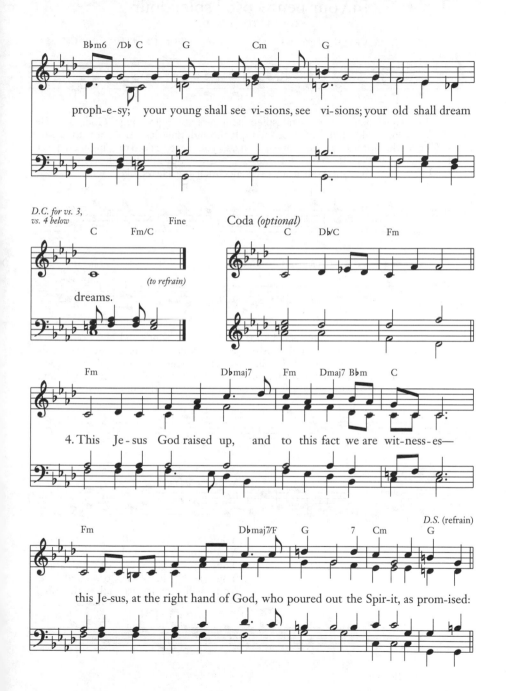

prophe-sy; your young shall see vi-sions, see vi-sions; your old shall dream

D.C. for vs. 3,
vs. 4 below

Fine

Coda *(optional)*

dreams.

(to refrain)

4. This Je-sus God raised up, and to this fact we are wit-ness-es—

D.S. (refrain)

this Je-sus, at the right hand of God, who poured out the Spir-it, as prom-ised:

Day of Pentecost

279

In your pentecostal splendour

TON Y BOTEL 8 7 8 7 D

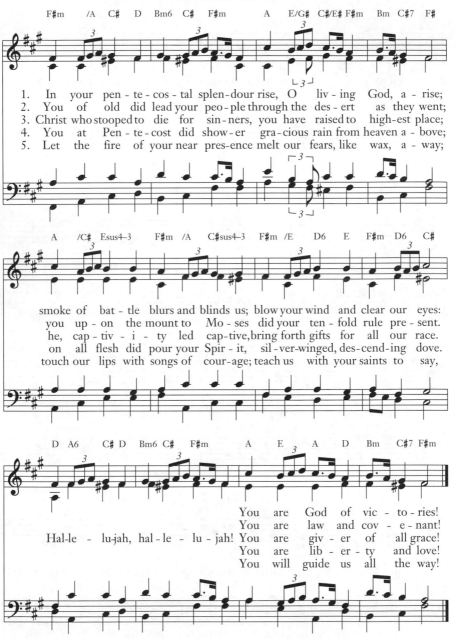

1. In your pen-te-cos-tal splen-dour rise, O liv-ing God, a-rise;
2. You of old did lead your peo-ple through the des-ert as they went;
3. Christ who stooped to die for sin-ners, you have raised to high-est place;
4. You at Pen-te-cost did show-er gra-cious rain from heaven a-bove;
5. Let the fire of your near pres-ence melt our fears, like wax, a-way;

smoke of bat-tle blurs and blinds us; blow your wind and clear our eyes:
you up-on the mount to Mo-ses did your ten-fold rule pre-sent.
he, cap-tiv-i-ty led cap-tive, bring forth gifts for all our race.
on all flesh did pour your Spir-it, sil-ver-winged, des-cend-ing dove.
touch our lips with songs of cour-age; teach us with your saints to say,

You are God of vic-to-ries!
You are law and cov-e-nant!
Hal-le - lu-jah, hal-le - lu-jah! You are giv-er of all grace!
You are lib-er-ty and love!
You will guide us all the way!

Alternate tune: Rhuddlan

See also: Ton Y Botel 429

Words: John Edward Speers (1916–) Music: Thomas John Williams (1869–1944)

Words: copyright © John Edward Speers Music: copyright © Concordia Publishing House, 1969. Used with permission.

280 O God, your love's undying flame

CAREY'S (SURREY) 888888

1. O God, your love's un-dy-ing flame was seen in des-ert bush a-blaze, when Mo-ses learned your sec-ret name, the Lord of past and fu-ture days: Lord, we would learn what you re-quire and burn for you with liv-ing fire.

2. O Lord of fire, your love a flame that longed to set the earth a-blaze, to bring the King-dom's joy you came and freed us, trapped in earth-bound ways: Lord, we would share your love's de-sire and burn for you with liv-ing fire.

3. O Ho-ly Spir-it, tongues of flame that set the new-born church a-blaze, to each be-liev-er then you came, and lives were filled with power and praise: O Spir-it, come, our lives in-spire to burn for you with liv-ing fire.

Alternate tune: Sussex Carol

Words: Basil E. Bridge (1927–) Music: Henry Carey (c. 1690–1743)

Words: copyright © Basil E. Bridge Music: public domain

281 Wind who makes all winds that blow

ARFON (MINOR) 7 7 7 7 D

1. Wind who makes all winds that blow— gusts that bend the sap - lings low,
   gales that heave the sea in waves, stir - ings in the mind's deep caves—
2. Fire who fuels all fires that burn— suns a - round which plan - ets turn,
   bea - cons mark-ing reefs and shoals, shin - ing truth to guide our souls—
3. Ho - ly Spir - it, Wind and Flame, move with - in our mor - tal frame.
   Make our hearts an al - tar pyre, kin - dle them with your own fire.

aim your breath with stead - y power on your church this day, this hour.
come to us as once you came: burst in tongues of sac - red flame!
Breathe and blow up - on that blaze till our lives, our deeds and ways,

Raise, re - new the life we've lost, Spir - it God of Pen - te - cost.
Light and Pow - er, Might and Strength, fill your church, its breadth and length.
speak that tongue which eve - ry land by your grace shall un - der - stand.

Alternate tune: Aberystwyth

Words: Thomas H. Troeger (1945–) Music: Welsh hymn

Words: copyright © Oxford University Press from New Hymns for the Lectionary, 1985 Music: public domain

282 Filled with the Spirit's power

FARLEY CASTLE 10 10 10 10

1. Filled with the Spir-it's power, with one ac-cord the in-fant
2. Now with the mind of Christ set us on fire, that u - ni -
3. Wid - en our love, good Spir - it, to em-brace in your strong

church con-fessed its ris - en Lord. O Ho - ly Spir - it, in the
ty may be our great de - sire. Give joy and peace; give faith to
care all those of eve - ry race. Like wind and fire with life a -

church to - day no less your power of fel - low-ship dis - play.
hear your call, and read - i - ness in each to work for all.
mong us move, till we are known as Christ's and Chris-tians prove.

Words: J.R. Peacey (1896–1971)   Music: Henry Lawes (1596–1662)

Words: copyright © 1978 by Hope Publishing Co.   Music: public domain

283
Let every Christian pray
LUDGATE 666666

1. Let eve-ry Chris - tian pray, this day and eve - ry day, come,
2. The Spir - it brought to birth the church of Christ on earth to
3. On - ly the Spir - it's power can fit us for this hour, come,

Ho - ly Spir - it, come! Was not the church we love com -
seek and save the lost: God ne - ver has with-drawn, since
Ho - ly Spir - it, come! U - nite, in-struct, in - spire and

mis - sioned from a - bove? Come, Ho - ly Spir - it, come!
that tre - men - dous dawn, the gifts of Pen - te - cost.
fill us with your fire: come, Ho - ly Spir - it, come!

Alternate tune: Laudes Domini

Words: Acts 2; paraphrase, Fred Pratt Green (1903–) Music: J. Dykes Bower (1905–1981)

Words: copyright © 1971 by Hope Publishing Co. Music: copyright © Royal School of Church Music

284
Revive your work, O Lord

CARLISLE 6 6 8 6 SM

6. Re-vive your work, O Lord: give pen-te-cos tal show-ers;

Eb Bb/D Cm Abmaj7 Bb Eb Ab/C Eb/Bb /G Ab 6 Eb/Bb Bb

1. Re-vive your work, O Lord: your might-y arm make bare;
2. Re-vive your work, O Lord: dis-turb this sleep of death;
3. Re-vive your work, O Lord: cre-ate soul-thirst for you,
4. Re-vive your work, O Lord: ex-alt your pre-cious name,

the glo-ry shall be all your own; the bless-ing, Lord, be ours.

Bb Eb Bb/Ab Eb/G Fm Bb Eb/G Ab/C Eb 7 Ab Fm6 Eb/G Ab Fm Eb/Bb Bb 7 Eb

speak with the voice which wakes the dead, and make your peo-ple hear.
ig-nite the smoul-dering em-bers now by your al-might-y breath.
and hun-ger for the bread of life, our spir-its to re-new.
and by the Ho-ly Spir-it come and set our love a-flame.

5. Revive your work, O Lord:
   give power unto your word;
   grant that your living gospel may
   in living faith be heard.

6. Revive your work, O Lord:
   give pentecostal showers;
   the glory shall be all your own;
   the blessing, Lord, be ours.

Words: Albert Midlane (1825–1909), alt Music: Charles Lockhart (1745–1815);
descant, Sydney H. Nicholson (1875–1947)

Words: public domain Music: descant, copyright © Oxford University Press

285
Our Lord, his passion ended

NAPHILL 7 7 7 7 D

1. Our Lord, his pas-sion end - ed, has glo-rious-ly asc - end - ed,
2. God's Spir - it is di - rect - ing; no more they sit ex - pect - ing,
3. O Lord of eve - ry na - tion, fill us with in - spir - a - tion!

yet though from him di - vid - ed, he leaves us not un - guid - ed;
but forth to all the na - tion they go with ex - ul - ta - tion;
We know our own un - fit - ness, yet would for you bear wit - ness.

all his ben - e - fits to crown he has sent his Spir - it down,
that which God in them has wrought fills their life and soul and thought,
By your Spir - it now we raise to the heav-enly Fa - ther praise:

burn-ing like a flame of fire, his dis - ci - ples to ins-pire.
so their wit - ness now can do work as great as oth - ers too.
Ho - ly Spir - it, Fa-ther, Son, make us know you, eve - ry one.

Words: F.C. Burkitt (1864–1935), alt   Music: Harold Darke (1888–1976)

Words: copyright © Society for Promoting Christian Knowlege   Music: copyright © 1983 by Hope Publishing Co.

286   Creator God, creating still

THIS ENDRYS NIGHT   8 6 8 6 CM

1. Cre - a - tor God, cre - a - ting still by   will   and word   and deed,
2. Re - deem-er God, re-deem-ing still with   o - ver-flow - ing grace,
3. Sus - tain-er God, sus-tain - ing still with strength for eve - ry day,
4. Great Trin - i - ty, for this   new day, we   need your pres - ence still.

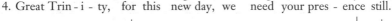

cre - ate   a new hu-man - i - ty   to meet the pres-ent   need.
pour out your love   on us, through us; make this   a   ho - ly   place.
em-power us now   to   do   your will; cor-rect us when we   stray.
Cre - ate,   re-deem, sus-tain   us   now   to   do your work and   will.

Alternate tune: Tallis' Canon

Words: Genesis 1:2, John 15:26, Titus 2:11–14; paraphrase, Jane Parker Huber (1926–)
Music: English carol tune, c.15th century

287
O God, whose fire lit the stars

HALIFAX 8 6 8 6 D CMD

Unison

1. O God, whose fire   lit   the stars   and   set them   in   their
2. O Christ, in whom God's ho - ly   fire   blazed forth   in   hu - man
3. O Spir - it,   as   at   Pen - te - cost   you   fell,   a   liv - ing
4. Praise God who makes   all   stars   to shine! Praise Christ who con-quered

course: you   are life's or - i - gin   and end,   the
form: in   you God's truth has touched   the earth   in
flame,   and   sent the cho - sen   twelve   a - broad the
night!   And   praise the Spir - it   by   whose gifts our

Words: Herman G. Stuempfle, Jr. (1923–)   Music: George Frideric Handel (1685–1759); arrangement, David Hurd (1950–)

Words: copyright © Herman G. Stuempfle Jr.   Music: arrangement, copyright © David Hurd, 1985

vast cre - a - tion's source. Come, touch us who were
love made cru - ci - form. May we, your liv - ing
gos - pel to pro - claim: de - scend on all you
faith will end in sight! Sing prais - es to the

formed from dust and set our hearts a - blaze that
bo - dy now, en - kin - dled by that flame, by
call to - day to serve a ser - vant Lord. Ig -
Trin - i - ty, cre - a - tion's life and light, one

life and breath may rise to you, a sac - ri - fice of praise.
glow-ing word and lov - ing deed make known your glo-rious name.
nite their pray - ing hearts till they are burn - ing with your word.
ho - ly fire, a three-fold flame for - ev - er burn-ing bright!

288 Creating God, your fingers trace

KILLIBEGS 8 8 8 8 LM

Unison

1. Cre - at - ing God, your fin - gers trace
2. Sus - tain - ing God, your hands up - hold
3. Re - deem - ing God, your arms em - brace
4. In - dwell - ing God, your gos - pel claims

the bold de - signs of far - thest space;
earth's mys - teries known or yet un - told;
all now des - pised for creed or race;
one fa - mi - ly with count - less names;

let sun and moon and stars and light and what lies
let wa - ter's frag - ile blend with air, en - a - bling
let peace, de - scend-ing like a dove, make known on
let eve - ry life be touched by grace un - til we

Words: Jeffery W. Rowthorn (1934–), alt   Music: William Davies (1921–)

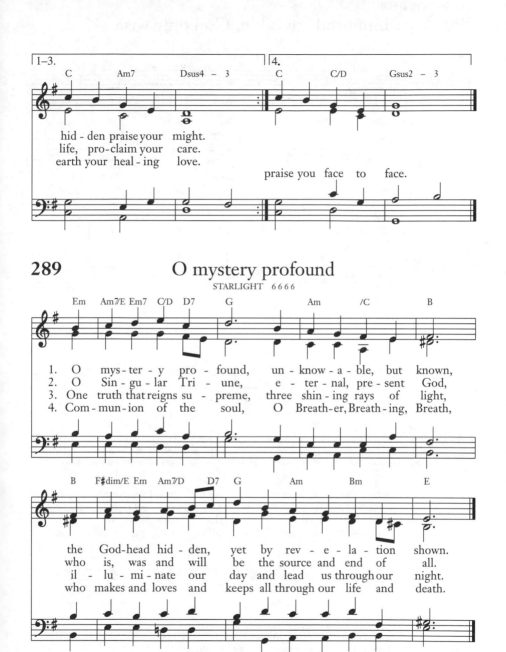

289

O mystery profound

STARLIGHT 6 6 6 6

1. O mys-ter-y pro-found, un-know-a-ble, but known,
the God-head hid-den, yet by rev-e-la-tion shown.

2. O Sin-gu-lar Tri-une, e-ter-nal, pre-sent God,
who is, was and will be the source and end of all.

3. One truth that reigns su-preme, three shin-ing rays of light,
il-lu-mi-nate our day and lead us through our night.

4. Com-mun-ion of the soul, O Breath-er, Breath-ing, Breath,
who makes and loves and keeps all through our life and death.

Words: Sylvia G. Dunstan (1955–1993)   Music: Anthony Hedges (1931–)

290 Immortal, invisible, God only wise

ST. DENIO 11 11 11 11

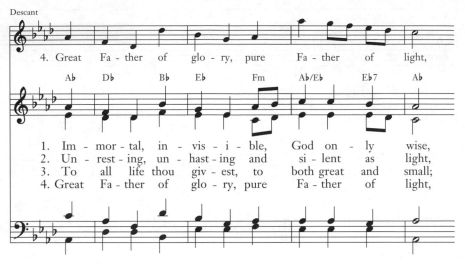

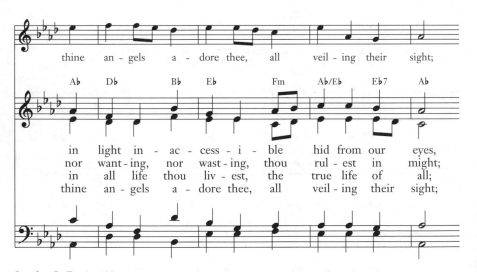

See also: St. Denio 685

Words: Walter Chalmers Smith (1824–1908)   Music: Welsh folk song from Caniadau y Cyssegr 1839;
arrangement, John Roberts (1822–1877); descant, C.S. Lang (1891–1971)

Words: public domain Music: descant, copyright © Novello & Co. Ltd.

all laud we would ren - der: oh help us to see

Ab   Eb/G Ab   /C   Ab Fm Ab/C   Eb

most bless - ed, most glo - rious, the An - cient of Days,
thy jus - tice like moun - tains high soar - ing a - bove
we blos - som and flour - ish like leaves on the tree,
all laud we would ren - der: oh help us to see

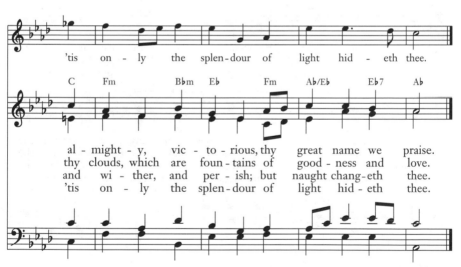

'tis on - ly the splen - dour of light hid - eth thee.

C Fm   Bbm Eb   Fm   Ab/Eb   Eb7   Ab

al - might - y, vic - to - rious, thy great name we praise.
thy clouds, which are foun - tains of good - ness and love.
and wi - ther, and per - ish; but naught chang - eth thee.
'tis on - ly the splen - dour of light hid - eth thee.

291 Thou whose almighty word

MOSCOW 6646664

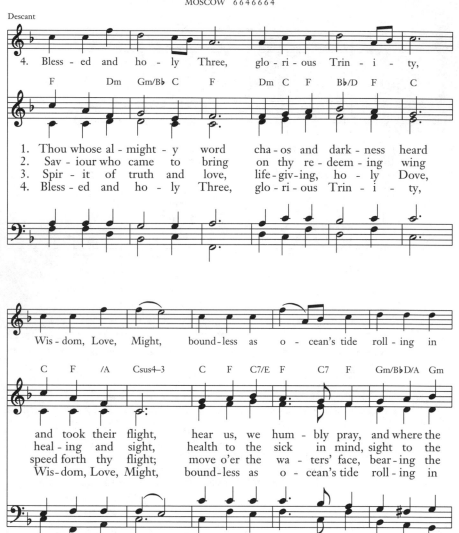

Descant

4. Bless - ed and ho - ly Three, glo - ri - ous Trin - i - ty,

1. Thou whose al - might - y word cha - os and dark - ness heard
2. Sav - iour who came to bring on thy re - deem - ing wing
3. Spir - it of truth and love, life - giv - ing, ho - ly Dove,
4. Bless - ed and ho - ly Three, glo - ri - ous Trin - i - ty,

Wis - dom, Love, Might, bound - less as o - cean's tide roll - ing in

and took their flight, hear us, we hum - bly pray, and where the
heal - ing and sight, health to the sick in mind, sight to the
speed forth thy flight; move o'er the wa - ters' face, bear - ing the
Wis - dom, Love, Might, bound - less as o - cean's tide roll - ing in

See also: Moscow 293

Words: John Marriott (1780–1825), alt   Music: Felice de Giardini (1716–1796);
descant, C.S. Lang (1891–1971)

Words: public domain Music: descant, copyright © Novello & Co. Ltd.

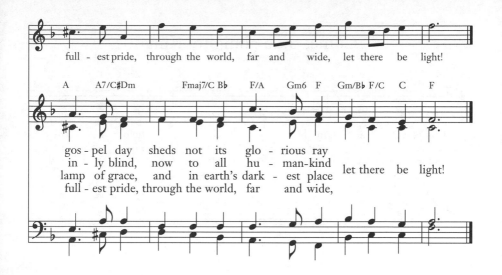

full - est pride, through the world, far and wide, let there be light!

A A7/C#Dm Fmaj7/C Bb F/A Gm6 F Gm/Bb F/C C F

gos - pel day sheds not its glo - rious ray
in - ly blind, now to all hu - man-kind let there be light!
lamp of grace, and in earth's dark - est place
full - est pride, through the world, far and wide,

292 Father, I adore you

FATHER, I ADORE YOU 674

Unison

F Gm/Bb C F Gm C F Gm C F

1. Fa - ther, I a - dore you, lay my life be - fore you. How I love you.
1. Pè - re, je t'a - do - re, je te donne ma vi - e. Comme je t'ai - me.

2. Jesus, I adore you…   3. Spirit, I adore you…
2. Jésus, je t'adore…   3. Esprit, je t'adore…

Words: Terrye Coelho–Strom (1952–)   Music: Terrye Coelho–Strom (1952–)

293 Come, thou almighty King

MOSCOW 6646664

1. Come, thou al - might - y King; help us thy name to sing; help us to praise. Fath - er, all glo - ri - ous, o'er all vic - to - ri - ous,
2. Come, thou in - car - nate Word; gird on thy might - y sword; our prayer at - tend: come, and thy peo - ple bless, and give thy word suc - cess;
3. Come, ho - ly Com - fort - er; thy sa - cred wit - ness bear in this glad hour! Thou who al - might - y art, now rule in eve - ry heart,
4. To the great One - in - Three e - ter - nal prais - es be hence ev - er - more! His sov - ereign maj - es - ty may we in glo - ry see,

See also: Moscow 291

Words: anonymous   Music: Felice de Giardini (1716–1796)

Words: public domain   Music: public domain

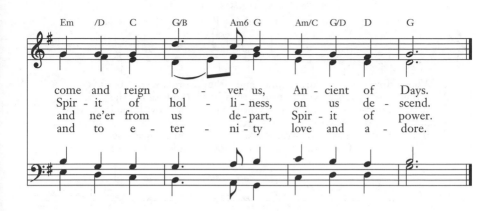

come and reign o - ver us, An - cient of Days.
Spir - it of hol - li - ness, on us de - scend.
and ne'er from us de - part, Spir - it of power.
and to e - ter - ni - ty love and a - dore.

294   Hallelujah (Sinclair)

HALLELUJAH (SINCLAIR) 4 4 4

Hal-le - lu - jah, hal-le - lu - jah, hal-le - lu - jah, hal-le - lu - jah,

hal-le - lu - jah, hal-le - lu - jah, hal-le - lu - jah, hal-le - lu - jah!

Words: traditional   Music: Jerry Sinclair (1943–1993)

God the Holy Trinity

295

When long before time

THE SINGER AND THE SONG   11 11 11 11

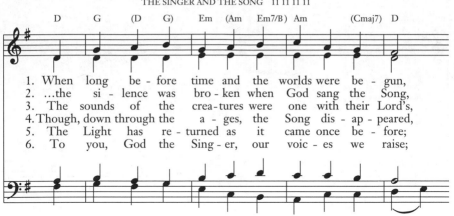

1. When long be - fore time and the worlds were be - gun,
2. ...the si - lence was bro - ken when God sang the Song,
3. The sounds of the crea-tures were one with their Lord's,
4. Though, down through the a - ges, the Song dis - ap - peared,
5. The Light has re - turned as it came once be - fore;
6. To you, God the Sing - er, our voic - es we raise;

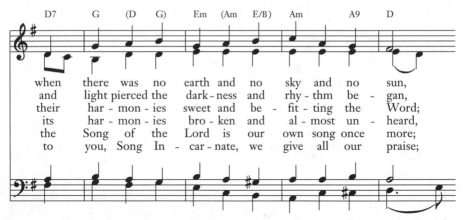

when there was no earth and no sky and no sun,
and light pierced the dark - ness and rhy - thm be - gan,
their har - mon - ies sweet and be - fit - ting the Word;
its har - mon - ies bro - ken and al - most un - heard,
the Song of the Lord is our own song once more;
to you, Song In - car - nate, we give all our praise;

Words: Peter Davison (1936–)   Music: Peter Davison (1936–); arrangement, George Black (1931–)

and   all   was   deep   si - lence and   night reigned su - preme,
and   with its   first birth-cries cre - a - tion was   born,
the   Sing - er   was   pleased as   the   earth sang the   song;
the   Sing - er   comes to   us   to   sing it   a - gain:
so   let   us   all   sing with one   heart and one   voice
to   you, Ho - ly   Spi - rit,   our   life and   our   breath,

and   e - ven   our   Mak - er   had   on - ly   a   dream...
and   crea - ture - ly   voi - ces   sang praise to   the   morn.
the   choir of   the   crea - tures   re - ech - oed   it   long.
our   God - is - with - us   in   the   world now   as   then.
the   song of   the   Sing - er   in   whom we   re - joice.
be   glo - ry   for - ev - er, through life and   through death.

God the Holy Trinity

296

The clay–stained hands of love

LITTLE MARLBOROUGH   6 6 8 6 SM

Unison

1. The clay-stained hands of love   cre - a - ted hu - man   form.
2. The heal - ing hands of love   gave speech and sight and   strength.
3. The wound-ed hands of love   showed life had con-quered   death.
4. The hid - den hands of love   are build-ing up the   church.
5. We sing our praise, O Love,   for your life - giv - ing   hands.

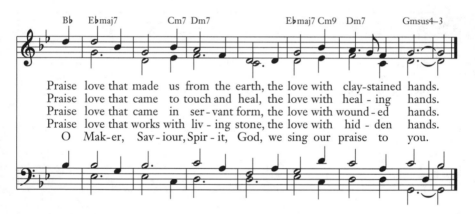

Praise love that made   us from the earth, the love with   clay-stained hands.
Praise love that came   to touch and heal, the love with   heal - ing   hands.
Praise love that came   in ser - vant form, the love with wound - ed   hands.
Praise love that works with liv - ing stone, the love with   hid - den   hands.
O   Mak - er,   Sav - iour, Spir - it, God, we sing our praise to   you.

Words: Richard D. Leach from Songs for the People of God 1980   Music: The Good Old Songs, alt, harmony, Jack Noble White

297

O love that casts out fear

MOSELEY 6 6 6 6

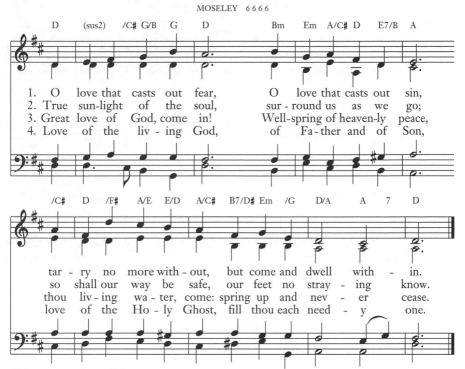

1. O love that casts out fear,   O love that casts out sin,
2. True sun-light of the soul,   sur - round us as we go;
3. Great love of God, come in!   Well-spring of heaven-ly peace,
4. Love of the liv - ing God,   of Fa-ther and of Son,

tar - ry no more with - out,   but come and dwell with - in.
so shall our way be safe,   our feet no stray - ing know.
thou liv - ing wa - ter, come: spring up and nev - er cease.
love of the Ho - ly Ghost,   fill thou each need - y one.

Alternate tune: Quam Dilecta

Words: Horatius Bonar (1808–1889)   Music: Henry T. Smart (1813–1879)

Words: public domain   Music: public domain

298

Glory be to God the Father

REGENT SQUARE 878787

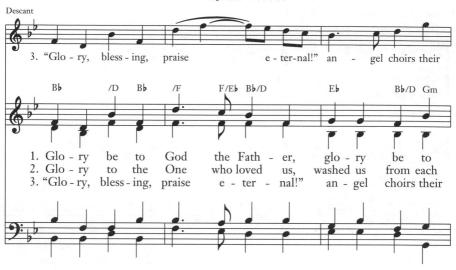

See also: Regent Square 146

Words: Horatius Bonar (1808–1889), alt   Music: Henry T. Smart (1813–1879);
descant, C.S. Lang (1891–1879)

Words: public domain   Music: descant, copyright © Novello & Co. Ltd.

echoes all creation's song. Glory, glory,

Gm D Gm/Bb Gm F/C C7 F F

God almighty, Three-in-One! Glory, glory,
raised us up to serve and reign. Glory, glory,
echoes all creation's song. Glory, glory,

Bb 7 Eb Cm Bb/D Cm/Eb Gm F 7 Bb

glory, glory, praises to our God belong.

glory, glory, while eternal ages run.
glory, glory, to the Lamb that once was slain.
glory, glory, praises to our God belong.

Optional Verse

1. Glory be to God our Maker,
God Redeemer, holy Son;
glory be to God the Spirit,
God almighty, Three-in-One!
Glory, glory, glory, glory,
while eternal ages run.

299

Holy, holy, holy

NICAEA 11 12 12 10

Descant

4. Ho - ly, ho - ly, ho - ly, Lord God al - might - y!

D Bm A 7 D G (A9/G) (A9/G) D

1. Ho - ly, ho - ly, ho - ly, Lord God al - might - y!
2. Ho - ly, ho - ly, ho - ly! all the saints a - dore thee,
3. Ho - ly, ho - ly, ho - ly! though the dark - ness hide thee,
4. Ho - ly, ho - ly, ho - ly, Lord God al - might - y!

all thy works shall praise thy name, in earth and sky and sea.

A/C# D A/C# Bm E/B A/C# D A/E E7 A 7

ear - ly in the morn - ing our song shall rise to thee.
cast - ing down their gold - en crowns a - round the glass - y sea,
though our eyes in sin - ful - ness thy glo - ry may not see,
all thy works shall praise thy name in earth and sky and sea.

French
1. Gloire, gloire, gloire, honneur et puissance;
   que ton nom soit exalté sur terre et dans les cieux!
   Gloire, gloire, gloire, force, obéissance,
   Pour ton amour, pour tes dons merveilleux!

2. Gloire, gloire, gloire, Dieu de toute grâce;
   pour nous tu livras ton Fils sur le bois de la croix!
   Gloire, gloire, gloire, prenant notre place,
   de nous il fit des prêtres et des rois.

Mandarin
Shèng zāi, shèng zāi, shèng zāi, quán néng dà zhǔ zǎi!
Qīng chén wǒ zhòng gē shēng huān shēng shàng dà tiān tīng.
Shèng zāi, shèng zāi, shèng zāi! Cí bēi quán néng zhǔ zǎi!
Zàn měi sān yī Shén, Fù, Zǐ yǔ Shèng Líng!

Words: Reginald Heber (1783–1826), Hymns Written and Adapted, 1827, alt., French translation,
H. Arnéra , revised R. Gerald Hobbs, 1996   Music: John Bacchus Dykes (1823–1876); descant,
C.S. Lang (1891–1971)

Words: public domain; French translation Music: descant, copyright © Novello & Co. Ltd.

Ho - ly, ho - ly, ho - ly, mer - ci - ful and might - y,

D   Bm   A - 7   D   G   D

Ho - ly, ho - ly, ho - ly, mer - ci - ful and might - y,
cher - u - bim and ser - a - phim fall - ing down be - fore thee,
on - ly thou art ho - ly; there is none be - side thee,
Ho - ly, ho - ly, ho - ly, mer - ci - ful and might - y,

God in three Per - sons, bless - ed Trin - i - ty!

Bm   D/F♯   D7/F♯   G   D   7   G   Em/G   A7   D

God in three Per - sons, bless - ed Trin - i - ty!
who wert and art and ev - er - more shalt be.
per - fect in power, in love and pu - ri - ty.
God in three Per - sons, bless - ed Trin - i - ty!

3. Gloire, gloire, gloire, victoire, espérance,
   les saints et les bienheureux proclament tous en choeur:
   gloire, gloire, gloire, et magnificence,
   au Père, au Fils, au Saint Consolateur.

4. Gloire, gloire, gloire, redisent les anges,
   joignant leurs sublimes voix au choeur mélodieux:
   gloire, gloire, gloire, des chants, des louanges,
   partout frémit l'immensité des cieux.

300

Father, we love you

GLORIFY THY NAME   12 9 10 9

1. Fa - ther, we love you, we wor - ship, we a - dore you,
1. Pè - re, nous t'ai - mons, te lou - ons et t'a - dor - ons,

glo - ri - fy your name in all the earth, glo - ri - fy your name,
glo - ri - fie ton nom sur toute la terre, glo - ri - fie ton nom,

glo - ri - fy your name, glo - ri - fy your name in all the earth.
glo - ri - fie ton nom, glo - ri - fie ton nom sur toute la terre.

2. Jesus... 3. Spirit...   2. Jésus... 3. Esprit...

Words: Donna Adkins (1940–)   Music: Donna Adkins (1940–); harmony, Dale Grotenhuis (1931–)

God Creator and Ruler

301   Many and great, O God, are your works

DAKOTA MELODY   Irregular

Unison

1. Man-y and great, O God, are your works, mak-er of
2. Grant un-to us com-mun-ion with you, O star-a-

earth and sky. Your hands have set the heav-ens with stars,
bid-ing One. Come un-to us and dwell with us,

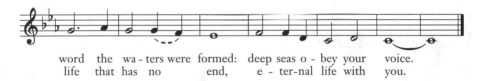

your fin-gers spread the moun-tains and plains. Lo, at your
with you are found the gifts of life. Bless us with

word the wa-ters were formed: deep seas o-bey your voice.
life that has no end, e-ter-nal life with you.

* May be accompanied by a drone part on C. Percussion ad lib.

Cree Words

1a. Ka-ti-pe-yi-ci-ket ki-si-pas-ka-mi-kaahk kii-me-kiw.
O-si-taw mi-na a-ca-ko-sak
Ma-ni-to o-to-te-na wii-ya.
Ciist wii-ya ka-pi-maa-cii-ko-yahk e-pe-mi-ci-wa-ki.

2a. O-pe-wii ce-wi-naan Ma-ni-to is-pi-mihk oh-ci. E-
ko-si wii-ci-tas-ke-mi-naan. Kih-
ci me-ki-wi-na maa-ka mii-yi-
naan kaa-ki- ke pi-maa-ti-si-win e-ko-te is-pi-mihk.

Words: Psalm 104:24–30, Jeremiah 10:12,13; paraphrase, Joseph R. Renville (1779–1846);
translation, Philip Frazier (1892–1964); Cree translation, Stan McKay (1941–)
Music: Native American; adaptation, Joseph R. Renville (1779–1846)

Words: translation, copyright © Dakota Conference, United Church of Christ; Cree translation, copyright © Stan McKay Music: public domain

387

302 O Lord of every shining constellation

HIGHWOOD 11 10 11 10

1. O Lord of eve - ry shin-ing con-stel - la - tion
2. You, Lord, have made the at-om's hid-den forc - es,
3. O Life, a - wak - ing life in cell and tis - sue,
4. You, Lord, have stamped your im-age on your crea - tures,

that wheels in splen - dour through the mid - night sky,
your laws its might - y en - er - gies ful - fil;
from flower to bird, from beast to hu - man brain,
and, though they mar that im - age, love them still;

grant us your Spir - it's true il - lu - mi - na - tion
teach us, to whom you give such rich re - sourc - es,
help us to trace, from birth to fi - nal is - sue,
lift up our eyes to Christ, that in his fea - tures

Words: Albert F. Bayly (1901–1984) Music: Richard Runciman Terry (1865–1938)

Words: copyright © Oxford University Press Music: copyright © Oxford University Press

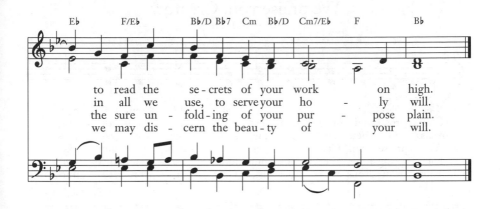

to read the se-crets of your work on high.
in all we use, to serve your ho - ly will.
the sure un - fold-ing of your pur - pose plain.
we may dis - cern the beau-ty of your will.

303 Holy, holy, holy
SANCTUS (ARGENTINA) Irregular

Ho - ly, ho - ly, ho - ly. My heart, my heart a - dores you!
San - to, san - to, san - to. ¡Mi cor - a - zón te a - do - ra!
Dieu saint, Dieu saint, Dieu saint: mon coeur, mon coeur t'a - do - re!

My heart is glad to say the words: you are ho - ly, Lord.
¡Mi cor - a - zón te sa - be de - cir: ¡San - to e - res Se - ñor!
Mon coeur le sait, mon coeur te le dit: sac - re est ton nom.

Words: Argentine traditional liturgical   Music: anonymous; arrangement, Pablo Sosa (1933),
Iona Community (Scotland)

304

Les cieux et la terre /
We praise you, Creator

LYONS 11 11 11 11

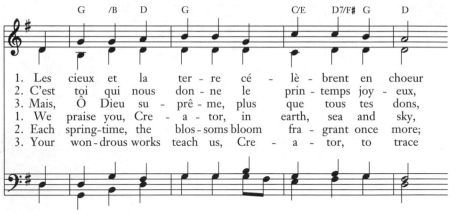

1. Les cieux et la ter - re cé - lè - brent en choeur
2. C'est toi qui nous don - ne le prin - temps joy - eux,
3. Mais, Ô Dieu su - prê - me, plus que tous tes dons,
1. We praise you, Cre - a - tor, in earth, sea and sky,
2. Each spring-time, the blos - soms bloom fra - grant once more;
3. Your won - drous works teach us, Cre - a - tor, to trace

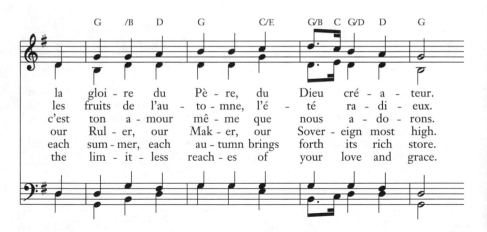

la gloi - re du Pè - re, du Dieu cré - a - teur.
les fruits de l'au - to - mne, l'é - té ra - di - eux.
c'est ton a - mour mê - me que nous a - do - rons.
our Rul - er, our Mak - er, our Sover - eign most high.
each sum - mer, each au - tumn brings forth its rich store.
the lim - it - less reach - es of your love and grace.

Words: French, Edmond L. Budry (1854–1932), alt; English translation, Andrew Donaldson (1951–)
Music: Johann Michael Haydn (1737–1806); arrangement, William Gardiner (1770–1853)

Words: French words, copyright © World Student Christian Federation from Cantate Domino; translation, copyright © Andrew Donaldson, 1995
Music: public domain

Ô Dieu re-dou-ta-ble dans ta ma-jes-té,
Lar-ges-se in-fi-nie que rien ne ta-rit!
Ô source é-ter-nel-le de grâce et de paix,
Each new gen-er-a-tion lifts voic-es in praise:
With wit-ness com-pel-ling our praise and our prayer,
Your grace dwells a-mong us, your love goes be-fore;

tu es ad-mi-ra-ble dans ta cha-ri-té!
Ta main ras-sa-si-e tout ê-tre qui vit.
ton peu-ple fi-dè-le te loue à ja-mais.
how good your cre-a-tion, how gra-cious your ways!
cre-a-tion is tell-ing of your faith-ful care.
from eld-est to young-est, we praise and a-dore.

305

God, who stretched

HOLY MANNA 8 7 8 7 D

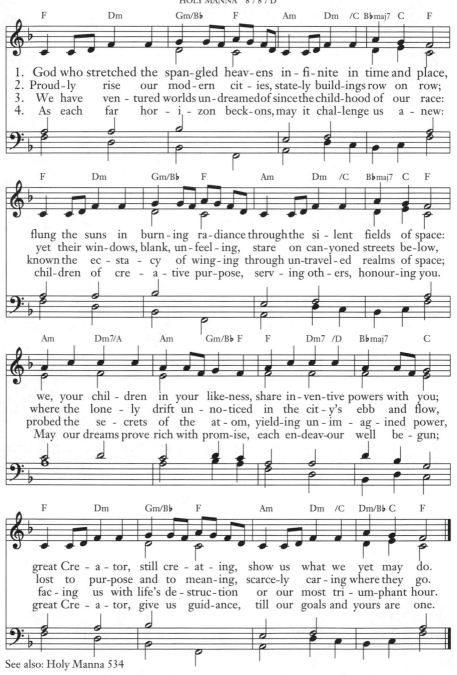

1. God who stretched the span-gled heav-ens in-fi-nite in time and place,
2. Proud-ly rise our mod-ern cit-ies, state-ly build-ings row on row;
3. We have ven-tured worlds un-dreamed of since the child-hood of our race:
4. As each far hor-i-zon beck-ons, may it chal-lenge us a-new:

flung the suns in burn-ing ra-diance through the si-lent fields of space:
yet their win-dows, blank, un-feel-ing, stare on can-yoned streets be-low,
known the ec-sta-cy of wing-ing through un-travel-ed realms of space;
chil-dren of cre-a-tive pur-pose, serv-ing oth-ers, honour-ing you.

we, your chil-dren in your like-ness, share in-ven-tive powers with you;
where the lone-ly drift un-no-ticed in the cit-y's ebb and flow,
probed the se-crets of the at-om, yield-ing un-im-ag-ined power,
May our dreams prove rich with prom-ise, each en-deav-our well be-gun;

great Cre-a-tor, still cre-at-ing, show us what we yet may do.
lost to pur-pose and to mean-ing, scarce-ly car-ing where they go.
fac-ing us with life's de-struc-tion or our most tri-um-phant hour.
great Cre-a-tor, give us guid-ance, till our goals and yours are one.

See also: Holy Manna 534

Words: Catherine Cameron (1927–)   Music: William Moore from Walker's Southern Harmony, 1835; harmony, Margaret Mealy (1922–) from Songs of the People of God 1980

306 Praise God from whom all blessings flow

OLD 100th 8 8 8 8 LM

Praise God from whom all bless - ings flow; praise
Gloire à Dieu, no - tre Cré - a - teur; gloire

God all crea - tures high and low; praise
à Christ, no - tre Ré - demp - teur; gloire

God in Je - sus ful - ly known: Cre -
à l'Es - prit con - so - la - teur! Lou -

a - tor, Word and Spir - it, One.
ange et gloire à Dieu Sau - veur!

Words: Brian A. Wren (1936–)   Music: Genevan Psalter, 1551, last line, Ravenscroft's Psalter, 1621
Words: copyright © 1989 by Hope Publishing Co.   Music: public domain

393

307 God of the sparrow, God of the whale

ROEDER 5 4 6 7 7

Unison

1. God of the spar - row God of the whale
2. God of the earth-quake God of the storm
3. God of the rain - bow God of the cross
4. God of the hun - gry God of the sick
5. God of the neigh-bour God of the foe
6. God of the ag - es God near at hand

God of the swirl - ing stars How does the crea-ture say
God of the trum - pet blast How does the crea-ture cry
God of the emp - ty grave How does the crea-ture say
God of the prod - i - gal How does the crea-ture say
God of the prun - ing hook How does the crea-ture say
God of the lov - ing heart How do your chil-dren say

Awe   How does the crea-ture say   Praise
Woe   How does the crea-ture cry   Save
Grace How does the crea-ture say   Thanks
Care   How does the crea-ture say   Life
Love   How does the crea-ture say   Peace
Joy   How do your chil-dren say   Home

Descant (Instrumental)

Words: Jaroslav J. Vajda (1919–)   Music: Carl F. Schalk (1929–)

308 Lord of all being, throned afar

ARIZONA 8 8 8 8 LM

1. Lord of all being, throned a - far, thy glo - ry
flames from sun and star, cen - tre and soul of
eve - ry sphere, yet to each lov - ing heart how near!

2. Sun of our life, thy quick - ening ray sheds on our
path the glow of day; star of our hope, thy
soft - ened light cheers the long watch - es of the night.

3. Our mid-night is thy smile with - drawn; our noon-tide
is thy gra - cious dawn; our rain-bow arch, thy
mer - cy's sign; all, save the clouds of sin, are thine.

4. Lord of all life, be - low, a - bove, whose light is
truth, whose warmth is love, be - fore thy ev - er -
blaz - ing throne we ask no lus - tre of our own.

5. Grant us thy truth to make us free, and kin - dling
hearts that burn for thee, till all thy liv - ing
al - tars claim one ho - ly light, one heaven - ly flame.

Words: Oliver Wendell Holmes (1809–1894)   Music: Robert Henry Earnshaw (1856–1929)

Words: public domain   Music: public domain

309

God of many names

MANY NAMES 10 8 8 10 8 8 with refrain (10 10 10 7)

Unison

1. God of man - y Names, gath - ered in - to One,
God of Hov - ering Wings, Womb and Birth of time,
2. God of Jew - ish faith, Ex - o - dus and Law,
God of Je - sus Christ, Rab - bi of the poor,
3. God of Wound - ed Hands, Web and Loom of love,
God of man - y Names, gath - ered in - to One,

in your glo - ry come and meet us, Mov - ing, end - less - ly Be - com - ing;
joy - ful - ly we sing your prais - es, Breath of life in eve - ry peo - ple—
in your glo - ry come and meet us, joy of Mir - i - am and Mo - ses;
joy - ful - ly we sing your prais - es, cru - ci - fied, a - live for - ev - er—
in your glo - ry come and meet us, Car - pen - ter of new cre - a - tion;
joy - ful - ly we sing your prais - es, Mov - ing, end - less - ly Be - com - ing—

Words: Brian A. Wren (1936–)   Music: William P. Rowan (1951–)

Words: copyright © 1986 by Hope Publishing Co.   Music: copyright © 1986 by Hope Publishing Co.

Refrain *(Harmony)*

Hush, hush, hal-le - lu-jah, hal-le-lu-jah! Shout, shout, hal-le - lu-jah, hal-le-lu-jah!

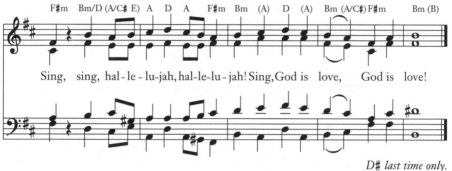

Sing, sing, hal-le - lu-jah, hal-le-lu - jah! Sing, God is love, God is love!

D♯ *last time only.*

310

Bring many names

WESTCHASE 9 10 11 9

Unison

1. Bring man-y names, beau-ti-ful and good:
2. Strong moth-er God, work-ing night and day,
3. Warm fath-er God, hug-ging eve-ry child,
4. Old, ach-ing God, grey with end-less care,
5. Young, grow-ing God, ea-ger, on the move,
6. Great, liv-ing God, nev-er ful-ly known,

cel-e-brate, in par-a-ble and sto-ry, ho-li-ness in
plan-ning all the won-ders of cre-a-tion, set-ting each e-
feel-ing all the strains of hu-man liv-ing, car-ing and for-
calm-ly pierc-ing e-vil's new dis-guis-es, glad of good sur-
say-ing no to false-hood and un-kind-ness, cry-ing our for
joy-ful dark-ness far bey-ond our see-ing, clos-er yet than

Words: Brian A. Wren (1936–)   Music: Carlton R. Young (1926–)

glo - ry,   liv - ing, lov - ing God:
qua - tion,   gen - i - us at play:
giv - ing   till we're re - con - ciled:
pris - es,   wis - er than de - spair: hail and ho -
just - ice,   giv - ing all you have:
breath - ing,   ev - er-last - ing home:

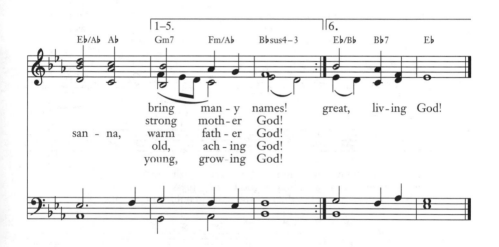

bring   man - y   names!   great, liv - ing God!
strong   moth - er God!
san - na,   warm fath - er God!
old,   ach - ing God!
young,   grow - ing God!

311

We worship God the Rock

ELING   10 10 10 10

1. We wor-ship God the Rock, un-moved, se - cure,
2. We wor-ship God the Riv - er, flow-ing fast,
3. We wor-ship God the Rock and Riv - er, one;

like moun-tains which from a - ges past en - dure,
with life - re - new-ing wa-ters sweep - ing past,
with - out the wa - ter, life had not be - gun;

a strong foun - da - tion for our faith and life,
a stream cre - a - ting good to bless the earth,
with - out the rock, the riv - er could not flow;

our rock of con - fi - dence in storm and strife.
and bring-ing beau - ty in new forms to birth.
we find both true, when God we ful - ly know.

Words: Albert F. Bayly (1901–1984)   Music: Godfrey Ridout (1918–1984)

312

Mothering God,
you gave me birth

ROCHESTER 8 8 8 8 8

Unison

1. Moth - er - ing God, you gave me birth in the bright
2. Moth - er - ing God, you took my form, of - fer - ing
3. Moth - er - ing Spir - it, nur - turing one, in arms of

morn - ing of this world. Cre - a - tor, source of
me your food of light, grain of life, and
pa - tience hold me close, so that in faith I

eve - ry breath, you are my rain, my wind, my sun.
grape of love, your ver-y bod - y for my peace.
root and grow un - til I flower, un - til I know.

Words: Jean Janzen (1933–), based on a Latin text by Julian of Norwich (d.c. 1417)
Music: David Ashley White (1944–)

Words: copyright © Jean Janzen Music: copyright © Selah Publishing Co., Inc., 1994

313

Oh worship the King

HANOVER 10 10 11 11

Descant
5. O meas-ure-less Might, un-change-a-ble Love, while an-gels de-

G   /B D   G   D/F♯ Em Am/C D   G   D   G   D/F♯ Em6

1. Oh wor-ship the King, all glor-ious a-bove; oh grate-ful-ly
2. Oh tell of God's might, oh sing of God's grace, whose robe is the
3. The earth, with its store of won-ders un-told, Al-migh-ty, thy
4. Thy boun-ti-ful care what tongue can re-cite? It breathes in the
5. O meas-ure-less Might, un-change-a-ble Love, while an-gels de-

light   to hymn thee   a - bove,   thy   ran-somed cre - a - tion, in

D   G/B D/F♯ Em /G A   D   B   Em   Am/C B   Em   D7/F♯

sing God's power and God's love,   our Shield and De-fend-er, the
light, whose can-o-py space; whose char-iots of wrath the deep
power hath found-ed of old, hath stab-lished it fast by a
air; it shines in the light; thy mer-cies, how ten-der, how
light to hymn thee a-bove, thy ran-somed cre-a-tion, in

Alternate tune: Lyons

Words: Psalm 104; paraphrase, Robert Grant (1779–1838), alt Music: William Croft (1678–1727);
descant, Alan Gray (1855–1935)

glo - ry a - blaze, in true ad - o - ra - tion shall sing to thy praise.

G   D/F# Em6   D   G/B   C   F/A G   D/F# Bm   G   C   Am   D   G

An - cient of   Days, pa - vil-ioned in splen-dour and gird- ed with praise.
thun - der-clouds form, and dark is God's path on the wings of the storm.
change-less de - cree, and round it hath cast, like a man-tle, the sea.
firm to   the end, our Ma - ker, De - fend - er, Re-deem-er and Friend.
glo - ry   a - blaze, in true ad - o - ra - tion shall sing to thy praise.

1. Anges du Très-Haut, louez le Seigneur,
   et du Saint des saints chantez la grandeur!
   Toujours enflammés d'une pure ardeur,
   bénissez le nom du Dieu créateur!

2. Saints glorifiés, choeurs des bienheureux,
   vous qui contemplez déjà dans les cieux
   du jour éternel l'éclat radieux,
   louez du Sauveur le nom glorieux.

3. Qu'ici-bas aussi, de nos coeurs fervents
   montent chaque jour nos voeux et nos chants,
   pour louer de Dieu la gloire en tous temps,
   et répondre aux voix des cieux triomphants.

314 God is love: come heaven, adoring

ABBOT'S LEIGH 87878787

1. God is love: come heaven, a-dor-ing; God is love: come
2. God is love, whose arms en-fold-ing all the world in
3. God is love, and though with blind-ness sin af-flicts all

earth, re-joice. Come cre-a-tion, voic-es soar-ing, sing ex-
one em-brace, with un-fail-ing grasp are hold-ing eve-ry
hu-man life, God's e-ter-nal lov-ing-kind-ness guides us

ult-ing with one voice. God who laid the earth's foun-
child of eve-ry race, and when hu-man hearts are
through all earth-ly strife. Sin and death and hell shall

Alternate tune: Hyfrydol

Words: Timothy Rees C.R. (1874–1939), alt   Music: Cyril Vincent Taylor (1907–1991)

Gsus 4–3   A (/G D6/F♯) A7/E (D6 A9/C♯) Bm/D F♯7   Bm   D/F♯ F♯m/A Bm   /D

da - tion, God who spread the heavens a - bove, God who breathes through
break-ing un - der sor - row's i - ron rod, all the sor - row,
nev- er o'er us fin - al tri- umph gain; God is love: so

C/E   D/F♯   Bm/A   Em/G B7/D♯ Em   A7/E D/F♯   G   D/A   A7   D

all cre - a - tion— God is love, e - ter - nal love.
all the ach - ing wrings with pain the heart of God.
love for - ev - er o'er the u - ni - verse must reign.

405

God Creator and Ruler

315

A mighty fortress is our God

EIN' FESTE BURG   8 7 8 7 6 6 6 6 7

1. A might-y for-tress is our God, a ref-uge nev-er
2. Did we in our own strength con-fide, our striv-ing would be
3. And though this world, with e-vil filled, should threat-en to un-
4. That Word a-bove all earth-ly powers—no thanks to them!—a-

fail - ing, our help-er sure a-mid the flood of mor-tal
los - ing, were not a Sav-iour on our side, the One of
do us, we will not fear, for God has willed the truth to
bid - ing, en-sures that all God's gifts are ours, through Christ in

ills pre - vail - ing. For still our an-cient foe yet
God's own choos - ing. Who is this Sav-iour, who? Christ
tri-umph through us: the powers of death and hell our
us re - sid - ing, whose sum-mons rings a-bove all

See also: Ein' Feste Burg 316

Words: Psalm 46; paraphrase, Martin Luther (1483–1546), translation, Frederick H. Hedge (1805–1890), alt
Music: Martin Luther (1483–1546); arrangement Hans Leo Hassler (1564–1612)

Words: this version, copyright © The Presbyterian Church in Canada, 1977   Music: public domain

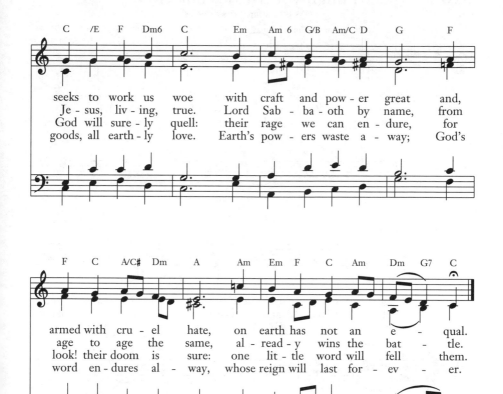

seeks to work us woe with craft and pow - er great and,
Je - sus, liv - ing, true. Lord Sab - ba - oth by name, from
God will sure - ly quell: their rage we can en - dure, for
goods, all earth - ly love. Earth's pow - ers waste a - way; God's

armed with cru - el hate, on earth has not an e - qual.
age to age the same, al - read - y wins the bat - tle.
look! their doom is sure: one lit - tle word will fell them.
word en - dures al - way, whose reign will last for - ev - er.

316 A mighty fortress is our God

EIN' FESTE BURG 8 7 8 7 6 6 6 6 7

1. A might - y for - tress is our God, a bul - wark
2. The wa - ters of God's good - ness flow through-out the
3. Be-hold what won-drous deeds of peace God does for

nev - er fail - ing, pro - tect - ing us with staff and rod,
ho - ly cit - ty, and glad - den hearts of those who know
our sal-va - tion; God knows our wars and makes them cease

and pow - er all - pre-vail - ing. What if the na - tions rage
God's ten-der - ness and pit - y. Though na - tions stand un - sure,
in eve - ry land and na - tion. The war - rior's spear and lance

See also: Ein' Feste Burg 315

Words: Psalm 46; v. 1 lines 1–2, Martin Luther (1483–1546), translation, Frederick H. Hedge
(1805–1890); v. 3, Omer Westendorf (1916–)   Music: Martin Luther (1483–1546)

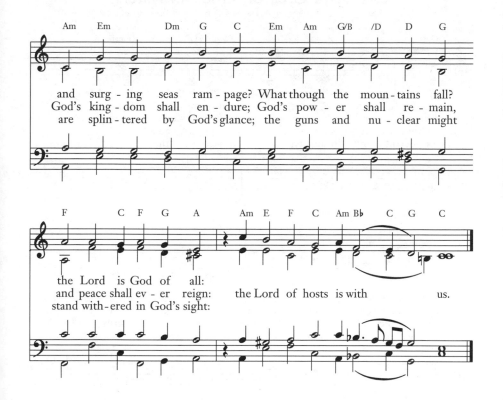

and surg - ing seas ram - page? What though the moun - tains fall?
God's king - dom shall en - dure; God's pow - er shall re - main,
are splin - tered by God's glance; the guns and nu - clear might

the Lord is God of all:
and peace shall ev - er reign: the Lord of hosts is with us.
stand with - ered in God's sight:

317 Colourful Creator, God of mystery

HOUGHTON 6 5 6 5 D

Unison

1. Col-our-ful Cre - a - tor, God of mys-ter - y,
2. Har-mo-ny of a - ges, God of lis-tening ear,
3. Au-thor of our jour - ney, God of near and far,
4. God of truth and beau - ty, Po-et of the Word,

thank you for the art - ist teach-ing us to see glimps-es of the
thank you for com - pos-ers tun-ing us to hear ech - oes of the
praise for tale and dra-ma tell-ing who we are, strip-ping to the
may we be cre - a - tors by the Spir - it stirred, o - pen to your

mean - ing of the com - mon - place, vi - sions of the
Gos - pel in the songs we sing, sounds of love and
es - sence strug-gles of our day, times of change and
pres - ence in our joy and strife, ves - sels of the

Words: Ruth Duck (1947–) Music: Carlton R. Young (1926–)

ho - ly in each hu - man face.
long - ing from the deep - est spring.
con - flict when we choose our way.
ho - ly cours-ing through our life.

318 Glory to God

GLORIA A DIOS 16 8 6 6 6

Rhythm:

First time-Leader(s); Repeat-All:

Glo - ry to God, glo - ry to God, glo - ry in the high - est!
Gloire au Sei - gneur, gloire au Sei - gneur dans les hauts-lieux, gloi - re!
Glo - ria a Dios, glo - ria a Dios, glo - ria en los cie - los!

All:

To God be glo - ry for - ev - er! Hal - le - lu-jah, a - men!
Gloire au Sei - gneur, al - lé - lu - ia! Al - lé - lu - ia, a - men!
A Dios la glo - ria por siem - pre! Al - le - lu - ya, a - men!

Hal - le - lu-jah, a - men! Hal - le - lu-jah, a - men!
Al - lé-lu - ia, a - men! Al - lé-lu - ia, a - men!
Al - le - lu - ya, a - men! Al - le - lu - ya, a - men!

Words: traditional   Music: Peruvian traditional

Words: public domain   Music: public domain

319
Wherever I may wander

NEW ENGLAND FOLK MELODY 7 6 8 6 D

1. Wher-ev-er I may wan-der, wher-ev-er I may be,
2. Through-out the whole cre-a-tion, I see God's lov-ing care

I'm cer-tain of my Mak-er's love; God's care is o-ver me.
for eve-ry-one in eve-ry land, God's chil-dren eve-ry-where.

God made the great high moun-tains, and made the wide blue sea;
Wher-ev-er I may wan-der, wher-ev-er I may be,

Words: Ann B. Snow (20th cent.)   Music: New England folk melody

Words: copyright © W.L. Jenkins, 1963. Used by permission of Westminister/John Knox Press Music: public domain

God made the sky where air-planes fly; God made the world, and me.
I'm cer-tain of my Mak-er's love; God's care is o - ver me.

320   There is a green hill far away

1. There is a green hill far away,
   without a city wall,
   where the dear Lord was crucified,
   who died to save us all.

2. We may not know, we cannot tell
   what pains he had to bear;
   but we believe it was for us
   he hung and suffered there.

3. He died that we might be forgiven;
   he died to make us good,
   that we might go at last to heaven,
   saved by his precious blood.

4. There was no other good enough
   to pay the price of sin;
   he only could unlock the gate
   of heaven, and let us in.

5. Oh dearly, dearly has he loved,
   and we must love him too,
   and trust in his redeeming blood,
   and try his works to do.

Words: Cecil Frances Alexander (1818–1895)
Words: public domain

321 Praise to the Lord, the Almighty

LOBE DEN HERREN 14 14 4 7 8

Descant

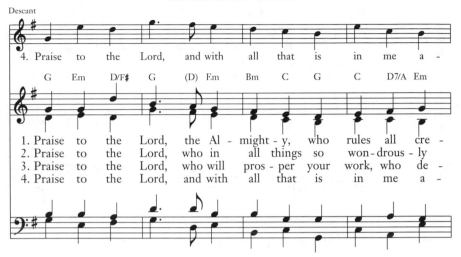

4. Praise to the Lord, and with all that is in me a -

G Em D/F# G (D) Em Bm C G C D7/A Em

1. Praise to the Lord, the Al - might - y, who rules all cre -
2. Praise to the Lord, who in all things so won - drous - ly
3. Praise to the Lord, who will pros - per your work, who de -
4. Praise to the Lord, and with all that is in me a -

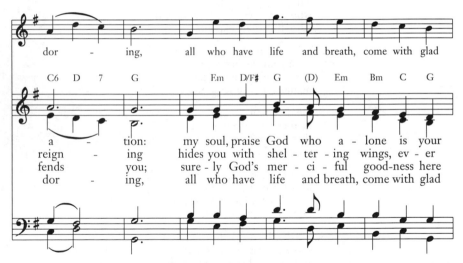

dor - ing, all who have life and breath, come with glad

C6 D 7 G Em D/F# G (D) Em Bm C G

a - tion: my soul, praise God who a - lone is your
reign - ing hides you with shel - ter - ing wings, ev - er
fends you; sure - ly God's mer - ci - ful good-ness here
dor - ing, all who have life and breath, come with glad

Words: German, Joachim Neander (1650–1680); translation, Catherine Winkworth (1827–1878); alt
Music: Stralsund Gesangbuch 1665; descant, C.S. Lang (1891–1971)

Hungarian

1. Áldjad én lelkem a dicsőség erös Királyát!
   Őnéki mennyei karokkal együtt zengj hálát!
   Zúgó harang, ének és orgonahang,
   Mind az ő szent nevét áldják!

2. Áldjad Őt, mert az Úr mindent oly szépen intézett!
   Sasszárnyon hordozott, vezérelt, bajodban védett.
   Nagy irgalmát naponként tölti ki rád:
   Áldását mindenben érzed.

3. Áldjad Őt, mert csodaképen megalkotott téged:
   Elkísér útadon, tőle van testi épséged.
   Sok baj között erőd volt és örömöd:
   Szárnyával takarva védett.

4. Áldjad az Úr nevét, Őt áldja minden énbennem!
   Őt áldjad, lelkem, és Róla tégy hitvallást nyelvem!
   El ne feledd: Napfényed Ő teneked!
   Őt áldjad örökké! Ámen.

322   Sing praise to God on mountain tops

THE VICAR OF BRAY   8 7 8 7 D

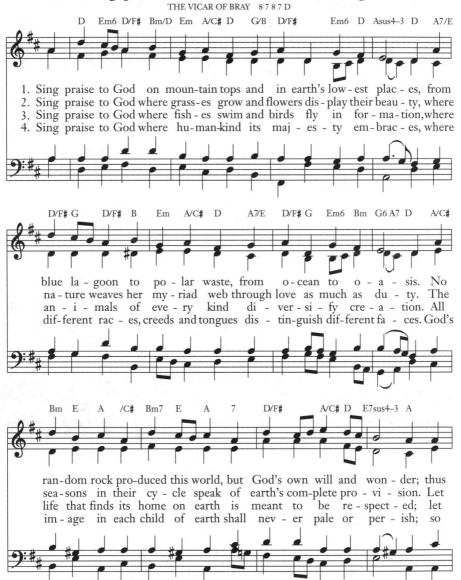

1. Sing praise to God on moun-tain tops and in earth's low-est plac-es, from
2. Sing praise to God where grass-es grow and flowers dis-play their beau-ty, where
3. Sing praise to God where fish-es swim and birds fly in for-ma-tion, where
4. Sing praise to God where hu-man-kind its maj-es-ty em-brac-es, where

blue la-goon to po-lar waste, from o-cean to o-a-sis. No
na-ture weaves her my-riad web through love as much as du-ty. The
an-i-mals of eve-ry kind di-ver-si-fy cre-a-tion. All
dif-ferent rac-es, creeds and tongues dis-tin-guish dif-ferent fa-ces. God's

ran-dom rock pro-duced this world, but God's own will and won-der; thus
sea-sons in their cy-cle speak of earth's com-plete pro-vi-sion. Let
life that finds its home on earth is meant to be re-spect-ed; let
im-age in each child of earth shall nev-er pale or per-ish; so

Words: Iona Community (Scotland)   Music: English traditional; arrangement, Stewart MacPherson
(1865–1941)

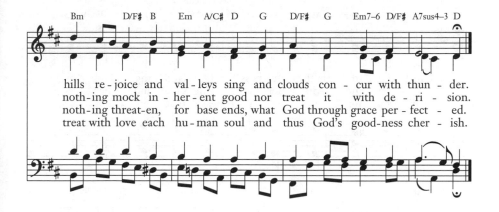

| Bm | D/F# B | Em A/C# D | G | D/F# | G | Em7-6 D/F# A7sus4-3 D |

hills re-joice and val-leys sing and clouds con - cur with thun - der.
noth-ing mock in - her - ent good nor treat it with de - ri - sion.
noth-ing threat-en, for base ends, what God through grace per - fect - ed.
treat with love each hu-man soul and thus God's good-ness cher - ish.

323   Praise the Lord, ye heavens, adore him

1. Praise the Lord, ye heavens, adore him;
   praise him, angels in the height;
   sun and moon, rejoice before him;
   praise him, all ye stars and light.
   Praise the Lord, for he hath spoken;
   worlds his mighty voice obeyed;
   laws which never shall be broken
   for their guidance hath he made.

2. Praise the Lord, for he is glorious;
   never shall his promise fail;
   God hath made his saints victorious;
   sin and death shall not prevail.
   Praise the God of our salvation;
   hosts on high, his power proclaim;
   heaven and earth and all creation
   laud and magnify his name.

Words: Anonymous, 1796
Words: public domain

324

Great is thy faithfulness

FAITHFULNESS 11 10 11 10 dactyllic

1. Great is thy faith - ful-ness, O God my Fath - er;
2. Sum - mer and win - ter and spring-time and har - vest,
3. Par - don for sin and a peace that en - dur - eth,

there is no shad - ow of turn - ing with thee;
sun, moon and stars in their cours - es a - bove,
thine own dear pres - ence to cheer and to guide,

thou chang - est not; thy com - pas - sions they fail not;
join with all na - ture in el - o - quent wit - ness
strength for to - day and bright hope for to - mor - row:

Words: Thomas O. Chisholm (1866–1960)   Music: William M. Runyan (1870–1957)

as thou hast been, thou for - ev - er wilt be.
to thy great faith - ful-ness, mer - cy and love.
bless - ings all mine, with ten thou - sand be - side!

Refrain

Great is thy faith - ful-ness; great is thy faith - ful-ness;

morn - ing by morn - ing new mer - cies I see;

all I have need - ed thy hand hath pro - vid - ed;

great is thy faith - ful-ness, Lord, un - to me.

325   Eternal Father, strong to save

MELITA 888888

1. E - ter - nal Fath - er, strong to save, whose arm hath bound the
2. O Christ, whose voice the wa - ters heard and hushed their rag - ing
3. O Ho - ly Spir - it, who did brood up - on the wa - ters
4. O Trin - i - ty of love and power, our kin - dred shield in

rest - less wave, who bade the might - y o - cean deep its
at thy word, who walked up - on the foam - ing deep and
dark and rude, and bade their an - gry tu - mult cease, and
dan - ger's hour; from rock and tem - pest, fire and foe, pro -

own ap - point - ed lim - its keep: oh hear us when we
calm a - mid the storm didst sleep: oh hear us when we
gave, for wild con - fu - sion, peace: oh hear us when we
tect them where - so - e'er they go; then ev - er - more shall

Words: William Whiting (1825–1878), alt   Music: John Bacchus Dykes (1823–1876)

Words: public domain   Music: public domain

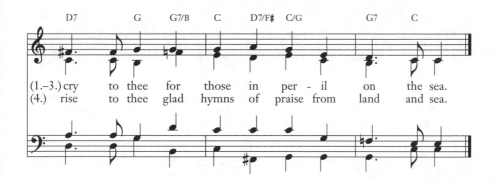

cry to thee for those in per - il on the sea.
(1.-3.)
rise to thee glad hymns of praise from land and sea.
(4.)

326   Give to the winds thy fears
ST. GEORGE   6 6 8 6 SM

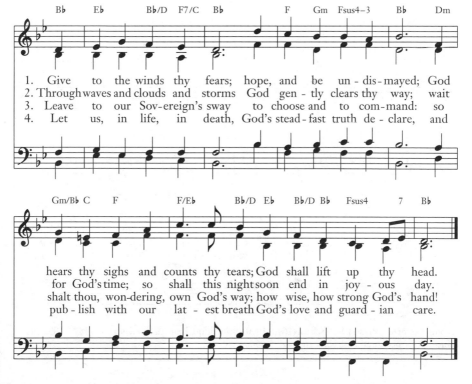

1. Give to the winds thy fears; hope, and be un - dis - mayed; God
2. Through waves and clouds and storms God gen - tly clears thy way; wait
3. Leave to our Sov-ereign's sway to choose and to com-mand: so
4. Let us, in life, in death, God's stead-fast truth de - clare, and

hears thy sighs and counts thy tears; God shall lift up thy head.
for God's time; so shall this night soon end in joy - ous day.
shalt thou, won-dering, own God's way; how wise, how strong God's hand!
pub - lish with our lat - est breath God's love and guard - ian care.

Words: German, Paul Gerhardt (1607–1676), translation, John Wesley (1703–1791), alt
Music: Henry John Gauntlett (1805–1876)

Words: public domain   Music: public domain

327 Sing praise to God who reigns above

MIT FREUDEN ZART 8 7 8 7 8 8 7

1. Sing praise to God who reigns a - bove, the God of all cre - a - tion, the God of power, the God of love, the God of our sal - va - tion; with
2. The an - gel host, O King of kings, your praise for - ev - er tell - ing, in earth and sky all liv - ing things be - neath your sha - dow dwell - ing, a -
3. What God's al - might - y power has made in mer - cy God is keep - ing; by morn - ing glow or eve - ning shade, nor slum - ber - ing nor sleep - ing. Wher -
4. Then all my glad - some way a - long I sing a - loud your prais - es, that all may hear the grate - ful song my voice un - wear - ied rais - es: be
5. All you that name Christ's ho - ly name, give God all praise and glo - ry: all who con - fess Christ's power, pro - claim a - loud the won - drous sto - ry. Cast

Words: German, Johann Jakob Schütz (1640–1690), translation, Frances Elizabeth Cox (1812–1897), alt
Music: Bohemian Brethren's Kirchengesänge 1566

Words: this version, copyright © The Presbyterian Church in Canada, 1997 Music: public domain

heal-ing balm my soul is filled, and eve - ry faith - less
dore the wis - dom which could span, and power which formed cre -
e'er God rules in sov - ereign might there all is just and
joy - ful in the Lord, my heart; both soul and bo - dy
eve - ry i - dol from its throne, for Christ is Lord and

mur-mur stilled:
a - tion's plan:
all is right: to God all praise and glo - ry!
bear your part:
Christ a - lone:

328 This is my Father's world

TERRA BEATA 6 6 8 6 D SMD Irregular

1. This is my Fath-er's world, and to my lis-tening
2. This is my Mak-er's world; the birds their car - ols
3. This is my Sav-iour's world; oh let me not for -

ears all na-ture sings, and round me rings the
raise; the morn-ing light, the li - ly white, de -
get that though the wrong seems oft so strong, God

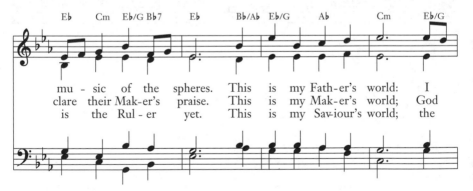

mu - sic of the spheres. This is my Fath-er's world: I
clare their Mak-er's praise. This is my Mak-er's world; God
is the Rul - er yet. This is my Sav-iour's world; the

Words: Maltbie D. Babcock (1858–1901); alt   Music: English traditional melody; arrangement, anonymous

Words: this version, copyright © The Presbyterian Church in Canada, 1997 Music: public domain

rest me in the thought; of rocks and trees, of
shines in all that's fair; in the rus - tling grass, God's
bat - tle is not done; Je - sus, who died, shall be

skies and seas God's hands the won - ders wrought.
foot - steps pass; God speaks to me eve - ry - where.
sat - is - fied, and earth and heaven be one.

Chinese (Mandarin)

Zhè shi Tian Fu shi jiè,
Wo mén cè er jing ting;
Yu zhòu ge chàng si wéi xiang ying
Xing chén zuò lè tong sheng.
Zhè shi Tian Fu shi jiè;
wo xin man you an ning,
huá cao shù mù,
qióng cang bi hai;
Shù shuo Tian Fu qi néng.

329 Thank you, O Lord of earth and heaven

LES COMMANDEMENTS DE DIEU 9 8 9 8

1. Thank you, O Lord of earth and heav - en, thank you for
   all your love has planned; thank you for food and dai - ly
   bless - ings, gifts from your ev - er - gra - cious hand.

2. Thank you for such a great sal - va - tion, mer - cy as
   bound-less as the sea; thank you for love which died to
   save us, love which gave all to set us free.

3. Thank you for means of grace and gui - dance, gifts of your
   Spir - it, strength di - vine; thank you for word and prayer and
   sym - bol, food for our souls in bread and wine.

4. Thank you for that blest hope of glo - ry, great day when
   Christ shall come a - gain, day when, in per - fect love and
   jus - tice, he in his maj - es - ty shall reign.

5. Grant us, be - cause of all your mer - cies, lips which pro -
   claim our thanks and praise; lives which, in lov - ing glad sur -
   ren - der, serve and a - dore you all their days.

6. Glory to God our heav - en - ly Fa - ther; glo - ry to
   Je - sus, God the Son; glo - ry to God the Ho - ly
   Spir - it; glo - ry to God the Three - in - One.

Words: after Edward Reynolds (1599–1676), James Seddon (1915–1983)
Music: Genevan Psalter 1549, Louis Bourgeois (c. 1510–1561)

330

O God, our help in ages past

ST. ANNE 8 6 8 6 CM

1. O God, our help in a - ges past, our hope for years to come,
2. Un - der the sha-dow of thy throne thy saints have dwelt se - cure;
3. Be - fore the hills in or - der stood, or earth re - ceived her frame,
4. A thou-sand a - ges in thy sight are like an eve-ning gone,
5. Time, like an ev - er - roll-ing stream, bears all our years a - way.
6. O God, our help in a - ges past, our hope for years to come,

our shel - ter from the storm-y blast, and our e - ter - nal home.
suf - fi - cient is thine arm a - lone, and our de-fence is sure.
from ev - er - last - ing thou art God, to end-less years the same.
short as the watch that ends the night be - fore the ris - ing sun.
They fly for - got - ten, as a dream dies at the open-ing day.
still be our guard while trou-bles last, and our e - ter - nal home.

Words: Isaac Watts (1674–1748), alt   Music: William Croft (1678–1727)

Words: public domain Music: public domain

331

The God of Abraham praise

LEONI 6684D

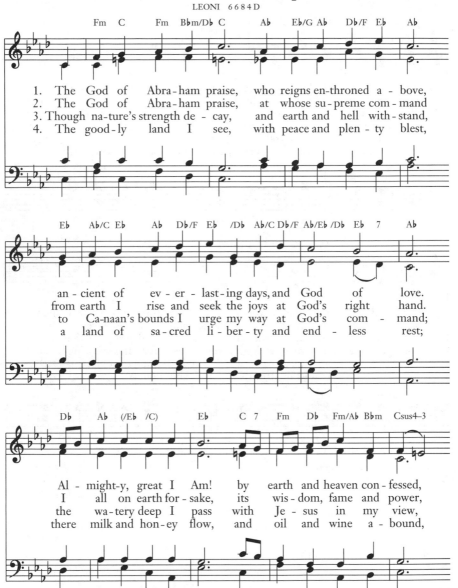

1. The God of Abra-ham praise, who reigns en-throned a - bove,
2. The God of Abra-ham praise, at whose su-preme com - mand
3. Though na-ture's strength de - cay, and earth and hell with-stand,
4. The good-ly land I see, with peace and plen - ty blest,

an - cient of ev - er - last-ing days, and God of love.
from earth I rise and seek the joys at God's right hand.
to Ca-naan's bounds I urge my way at God's com - mand;
a land of sa - cred li - ber - ty and end - less rest;

Al - might-y, great I Am! by earth and heaven con - fessed,
I all on earth for - sake, its wis - dom, fame and power,
the wa-tery deep I pass with Je - sus in my view,
there milk and hon-ey flow, and oil and wine a - bound,

Words: Hebrew, Yigdal; paraphrase, Thomas Olivers (1725–1799), alt   Music: Jewish traditional melody c.1770; arrangement, anonymous

Words: public domain   Music: public domain

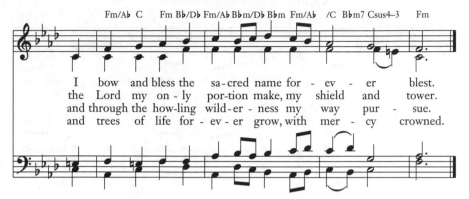

I bow and bless the sa-cred name for - ev - er blest.
the Lord my on - ly por-tion make, my shield and tower.
and through the how-ling wild-er - ness my way pur - sue.
and trees of life for - ev-er grow, with mer - cy crowned.

5. There dwells the Lord our King,
the Lord our Righteousness;
triumphant o'er the world and sin,
the Prince of Peace
on Zion's sacred height
God's kingdom still maintains,
and glorious with the saints in light
forever reigns.

6. The whole triumphant host
give thanks to God on high;
"hail, Father, Son and Holy Ghost"
they ever cry.
Hail Abraham's God, and mine!
I join the heavenly lays;
all might and majesty are thine,
and endless praise.

God Creator and Ruler

332   O Lord my God! / How great thou art

O STORE GUD   11 10 11 10 with refrain (10 8 10 8)

1. O Lord my God! when I in awe-some won-der con-sid-er
2. When through the woods and for-est glades I wan-der and hear the
3. And when I think that God, his Son not spar-ing, sent him to
4. When Christ shall come with shout of ac-cla-ma-tion and take me

all the worlds thy hands have made, I see the stars, I
birds sing sweet-ly in the trees, when I look down from
die, I scarce can take it in, that on the cross, my
home, what joy shall fill my heart! Then I shall bow in

hear the roll-ing thun-der, thy power through-out the u-ni-verse dis-
loft-y moun-tain gran-deur and hear the brook, and feel the gen-tle
bur-den glad-ly bear-ing, he bled and died to take a-way my
hum-ble ad-o-ra-tion, and there pro-claim, my God, how great thou

Words: Carl Gustav Boberg; translation, Stuart K. Hine (1899–1989); Korean, Myung Ja Yue;
Ojibway, Stanley Williams (1918–); Mohawk, Josephine S. (Konwenne) Day (1905–)   Music:
Swedish folk melody; harmony, Stuart K. Hine (1899–1989)

Hungarian

1. Nagy Istenem, ha nézem a világot,
   Melyet teremtett szent legyen szavad
   Ha itt a földön millió lényt látok,
   Kiket igazgatsz, táplálsz egymagad,
   Refrain:

   Szívem feléd ujjong örömtele:
   Mily nagy vagy Te, Mily nagy vagy Te!
   Szívem feléd ujjong örömtele
   Mily nagy vagy Te, Mily nagy vagy Te!

2. Uram, Igédben, hogyha megtalállak,
   Ha látom ott kegyelmes tetteid,
   Választott néped amint egyre áldod,
   Türelmesen viselve bneit,
   Refrain:

3. Ha Jézust látom itt a földön járva,
   Alázatos, türelmes szolgaként,
   Látom, hogy áldást áraszt a világra,
   S kereszthalálra adja életét,
   Refrain:

4. Ha majd az Úr elszólít e világból,
   És szinrl szinre láthatom meg Őt,
   Ha majd felém dicső arca világol,
   S én térdre hullok szent szine előtt,
   Refrain:

Korean

1. Choo haw-naw-neem chee-oo-sheen moh-dun seh-geh
   Neh maw-um soh-geh ku-ree-uh pohl-teh
   Haw-nul-eh pyuhl ool-yuh puh-jee-nun nweh-sung
   Choo-neem-eh kwuhn-nung oo-joo-eh chawt-neh

   Refrain:
   Choo-neem-eh nohp-goh wee-deh haw-sheem-ul
   neh yung-hohn-ee chawn-yawng haw-neh
   Choo-neem-eh nohp-goh wee-deh haw-sheem-ul
   neh yung-hohn-ee chawn-yawng haw-neh

2. Soop-soh-gee naw hum-hawn sawn kohl-jawk-eh-suh
   Chee-juh-gwee-nun chuh seh soh-ree-dul gwaw
   Koh-yoh haw-geh hu-ru-nun shee-net-mool-un
   Choo-neem-eh sohm-shee noh-reh haw-doh-daw
   Refrain:

3. Choo haw-naw-neem tohk-seng-jaw aw-keem uhp-shee
   Oo-ree-rul wee-heh poh-neh choo-shut-neh
   Sheep-jaw-gaw-eh pee-hul-yuh choo-gu-sheen joo
   Neh moh-dun chweh-rul koo-sohk haw-shut-neh
   Refrain:

4. Neh choo yeh-soo seh-sawng-eh taw-shee ohl-teh
   Chuh chun-gook-u-roh nawl een-doh haw-ree
   Naw kyum-sohn-ee uhp-du-ryuh kyung-beh haw-myuh
   Yung-wun-ee choo-rul chawn-yawng haw-ree-raw
   Refrain:

Cree

1. Kisemantoo katipey ihcikeyan
   Emamaskatey itaman taapwe
   Kaositayan kahkiyaw askiiya
   Kisokaatsiwin misiwe nokwan.

Refrain:
Ninikamon emamicimitan
Kikicaayiwin, kikicaayiwin.
Ninikamon emamicimitan
Kikicaayiwin, kikicaayiwin.

2. Ispi sakaahk mekwac epimoteyan
   Nipetawaw piyesiis nikamot
   Miina wacihk ohci etapiyane
   Niwaapahten siipii pimiciwahk.
   Refrain:

3. Kikoosis nama kikiimanicihaw
   Maaka nikiinipoostamakonan
   Asiteyaatikohk mihko kiimekiw
   Poonatamakoyahk maciihtiwin.
   Refrain:

4. Karayst takoteci ispimihk ohci
   Nikamiyowaten kiiwetahit
   Nikapatapatey imototawaw
   Nikawiiten ekicaayiwiyan.
   Refrain:

Ojibway:

1. N'ge zha Mun e doom, pe che me quain duh mon suh,
   Nahg duh waind mon, a zhe kwa taum gooz yun;
   Nuh wob mog nung oog, noond wog nim keeg bah shkoom wod,
   Wob je gah daig, A zhe kwa taum gooz yun.

Refrain:
Mee suh n'guh mood, n'je chog nuh kwa mah gad,
A zhe Q'taum gooz yun, A zhe Q'taum gooz yun;
Mee suh n'guh mood, n'je chog nuh kwa mah gad,
A zhe Q'taum gooz yun, A zhe Q'taum gooz yun.

2. Pah yuh zha uon, o de ba bah yuh nah kwog,
   Noon dwog p'na sheen sug, ewh me no maunz wod;
   Oon zah be yon, o de a d'she yuh shpaub kog,
   Noon don zee beens, n'moosh toon ewh b'guh mon muk.
   Refrain:

3. Pe suh ewh m'quand mon, ke be zhe nonzh wod niwh Gwe Sun,
   Che o gooj goz nid, mah suh auzh da yah t'goong;
   K'che naind moowh ning, ke zhe dah p'non wees ge too win,
   Neen je zhob we zhid, mah suh bah toz win ing.
   Refrain:

4. Pe be yod owh Christ, ka gait we q'taum gwa waim gud,
   Pe suh kee wa we zhid, ka gait n'guh moo je gain dum;
   Me suh ewh uh pe, Ge Mah ka noo kwa twung suh,
   Weend mah gah yung, A peech e shpan dahg zid.
   Refrain:

Mohawk

1. Se wen niio, no nen ka non ton nion kwas,
   Se snon sa ke tsi niio ie ron ni,
   iah kwat ka thos tsi tes kwas wah the ten ni
   sa sats ten se ra te ioh re ni on.

Refrain:
A kwa tonn hets ten sa ri wah kwa se
Tsi ni sa ia, tah ne ra kwa.
A kwa tonn hets ten sa ri wah kwa se
Tsi ni sa ia, tah ne ra kwa.

2. Non nen tho non I ke tsi ioh non te nion,
   ent kat ka tho, tsi niio ne ra kwa,
   ioh kwi ro ton tsi tha kon ti ren no ton
   wa ka thon te, oh neh kah tsi kon neh.
   Refrain:

3. No nen ke hia ras shon kwa wi ro ien ha,
   tho ten nie ton ken tho na renn he ie
   ro nek kwa on o ni son kwen he iah se,
   so ra ke wen, ion kwa ri wa ne ren.
   Refrain:

4. No nen ten tre ien ses ha tsia ten ha we,
   en ka na neh na tonn ha ra tse ra
   tsi nien hen we en hi sen na ien he ke,
   Se wen niio, sa ia tah ne ra kwa.
   Refrain:

333   I sing the almighty power of God

FOREST GREEN   8 6 8 6 CM

1. I sing the al-might-y power of God that made the moun-tains rise,
2. I sing the good-ness of the Lord, that filled the earth with food;
3. There's not a plant or flower be - low but makes thy glo - ries known,

that spread the flow - ing seas a - broad and built the lof - ty skies.
God formed the crea-tures with a word, and then pro-nounced them good.
and clouds a - rise and tem-pests blow by or - der from thy throne,

I sing the wis - dom that or-dained the sun to rule the day;
Lord, how thy won - ders are dis-played, wher - e'er I turn my eyes,
while all that bor - rows life from thee is ev - er in thy care,

the moon shines full at God's com-mand, and all the stars o - bey.
if I sur - vey the ground I tread, or gaze up - on the skies!
and eve - ry-where that I could be, thou, God, art pres-ent there.

Words: Isaac Watts (1674–1748), alt   Music: English traditional; arrangement Ralph Vaughan
Williams (1872–1958)

Words: public domain   Music: arrangement, copyright © Oxford University Press

334 God who gives to life its goodness

HERMON 8787D

1. God who gives to life its good-ness, God cre-a-tor of all joy,
2. God who fills the earth with beau-ty, God who binds each friend to friend,

God who gives to us our free-dom God who bless-es tool and toy:
God who names us co-cre-a-tors, God who wills that cha-os end:

teach us now to laugh and praise you deep with-in, or shout-ed loud,
grant us now cre-a-tive spi-rits, minds re-spon-sive to your mind,

till the whole cre-a-tion danc-es for your good-ness, ho-ly God.
hearts and wills your rule ex-tend-ing, all our acts by Love re-fined.

Words: Walter Henry Farquharson (1936–)   Music: Charles Venn Pilcher (1879–1961);
harmony, Walter MacNutt (1910–1996)

335 Give us, O God, the grace to see

JORDAN 8 8 8 8 LM

1. Give us, O God, the grace to see your smile with-in the morning light, your sig-na-ture up-on the sea, your
2. Give us, O God, the grace to hear your word when mar-ble turns to clay, your voice when thun-der-clouds ap-pear, your
3. Give us, O God, the grace to feel your breath up-on the winds of change, your kiss in sac-ra-ments that heal, your
4. Give us, O God, the grace to be con-vinced when mir-a-cles are rare, your truth when stars turn eb-o-ny, your

Words: Roger Kronmann   Music: Jordon Cho–Tung Tang

Words: copyright © Chinese Christian Literature Council Ltd., 1977   Music: copyright © Chinese Christian Literature Council Ltd., 1977

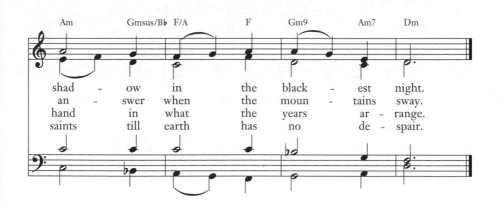

shad - ow in the black - est night.
an - swer when the moun - tains sway.
hand in what the years ar - range.
saints till earth has no de - spair.

336 Lord, have mercy

KYRIE (RUSSIAN) Irregular

Ky - ri - e e - lei - son. Ky - ri - e e - lei - son.
Lord have mer - cy, Lord have mer - cy,
Sei - gneur aie pi - tié, Sei - gneur aie pi - tié,

Ky - ri - e e - le - i - son.
Lord have mer - cy on us.
Sei - gneur aie pi - tié de nous.

Words: traditional liturgical   Music: Russian Orthodox Liturgy

337

Eternal, Unchanging,
we sing to your praise

ST. BASIL 11 11 11 11

1. E - ter - nal, Un - chang-ing, we sing to your praise:
2. A - gain we re - joice in the world you have made,
3. We praise you for Je - sus, our Sav - iour and Lord,

your mer - cies are end - less, and right-eous your ways;
your might - y cre - a - tion in beau - ty ar - rayed;
the might of his Spir - it, the truth of his word;

your ser - vants pro - claim the re - nown of your name,
we thank you for life, and we praise you for joy,
give com - fort in sor - row and pa - tience in pain,

O Sov - ereign om - ni - po - tent, ev - er the same.
for love and for hope that no power can de - stroy.
the faith sure and stead - fast that Je - sus shall reign.

Alternate tune: St. Denio

Words: Robert B.Y. Scott (1899–1987)   Music: Healey Willan (1880–1968)

338 Let all things now living

ASH GROVE   12 11 12 11 D with repeat

Words: Katherine K. Davis (1892–1980)   Music: Welsh traditional; harmony, Gerald H. Knight (1908–1979)

claim God di - vine. Re - joice, re -

F/C   C7   F   F/A   F   F/A   C7/E   F   C7/G   /E   /G

end of our days. God's ban - ners are o'er us; pure light goes be -
claim God di - vine. We, too, should be voic-ing our love and re -

joice! with glad ad - o - ra - tion a song let us

C7/G   F   C   F   A7/C♯   Dm   C/G   G

fore us, a pil - lar of fire shin - ing forth in the
joic - ing; with glad ad - o - ra - tion a song let us

raise. Ah,

C   /E   F   C/E   F   Dm   B♭6   Gm   /B♭

night, till shad - ows have van - ished and dark - ness is
raise, till all things now liv - ing u - nite in thanks -

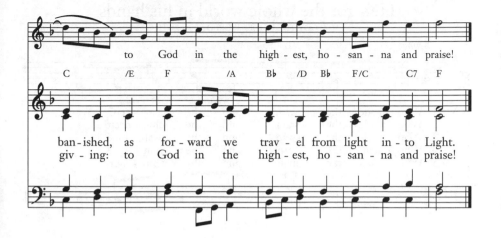

to God in the high - est, ho - san - na and praise!

C   /E   F   /A   Bb   /D   Bb   F/C   C7   F

ban - ished,   as   for - ward   we   trav - el from light   in - to   Light.
giv - ing: to   God   in   the   high - est, ho - san - na and praise!

339   Who made the earth and the heaven /
He's got the whole world in his hands

HE'S GOT THE WHOLE WORLD   8 3 8 3 8 3 8

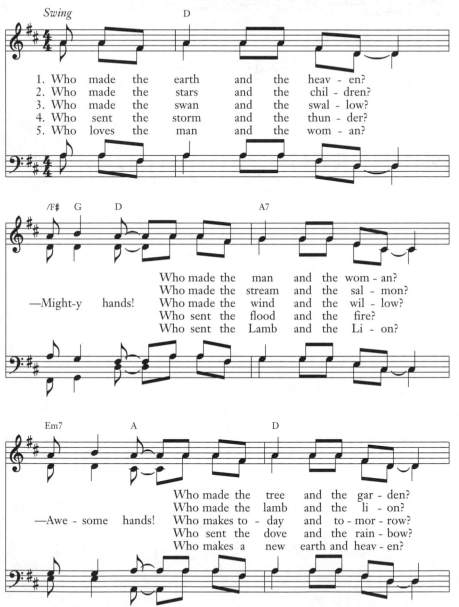

1. Who made the earth and the heav - en?
2. Who made the stars and the chil - dren?
3. Who made the swan and the swal - low?
4. Who sent the storm and the thun - der?
5. Who loves the man and the wom - an?

—Might-y hands! Who made the man and the wom - an?
Who made the stream and the sal - mon?
Who made the wind and the wil - low?
Who sent the flood and the fire?
Who sent the Lamb and the Li - on?

—Awe - some hands! Who made the tree and the gar - den?
Who made the lamb and the li - on?
Who makes to - day and to - mor - row?
Who sent the dove and the rain - bow?
Who makes a new earth and heav - en?

Words: Andrew Donaldson (1951–); traditional words, African-American spiritual
Music: African-American spiritual; arrangement, Andrew Donaldson (1951–)

Words: this version, copyright © Andrew Donaldson, 1997   Music: arrangement, copyright © Andrew Donaldson, 1996

—Lov-ing hands! Who's got the world in might-y hands?

6. You've got the whole world— Mighty God!
   You've got the whole world— Awesome God!
   You've got the whole world— Loving God!
   You've got the whole world in your hands!

Traditional Version

1. He's got the whole world in his hands (3x)
   He's got the whole world in his hands.

2. He's got the sun and the moon in his hands...
   He's got the whole world in his hands.

3. He's got the wind and the rain...

4. He's got the tiny little baby...

5. He's got you and me, brother,...
   he's got you and me, sister,...
   he's got you and me, brother...

6. He's got the whole world...

340

At the name of Jesus

KING'S WESTON   6 5 6 5 D

1. At the name of Je - sus eve - ry knee shall bow,
2. Hum - bled for a sea - son to re - ceive a name
3. Name him, Chris - tians, name him, with love strong as death,
4. In your hearts en - throne him; there let him sub - due
5. Chris - tians, this Lord Je - sus shall re - turn a - gain,

eve - ry tongue con - fess him King of glo - ry now;
from the lips of sin - ners un - to whom he came.
name with awe and won - der, and with bat - ed breath;
all that is not ho - ly, all that is not true,
with his Fa - ther's glo - ry and an an - gel train,

Words: Caroline Maria Noel (1817–1877)   Music: Ralph Vaughan Williams (1872–1958)

Words: public domain   Music: copyright © Oxford University Press

'tis our God's good pleas - ure we should call him Lord,
Faith - ful, Je - sus bore it spot - less to the last,
this is God the Sav - iour; this is Christ the Lord,
Crown him as your cap - tain in temp - ta - tion's hour;
for all wreaths of em - pire meet up - on his brow,

who from the be - gin - ning was the might - y Word.
brought it back vic - to - rious when from death he passed.
ev - er to be wor-shipped, trust - ed and a - dored.
let his will en - fold you in its light and power.
and our hearts con - fess him King of glo - ry now.

God in Christ

341

Before the world began

INCARNATION 64646664

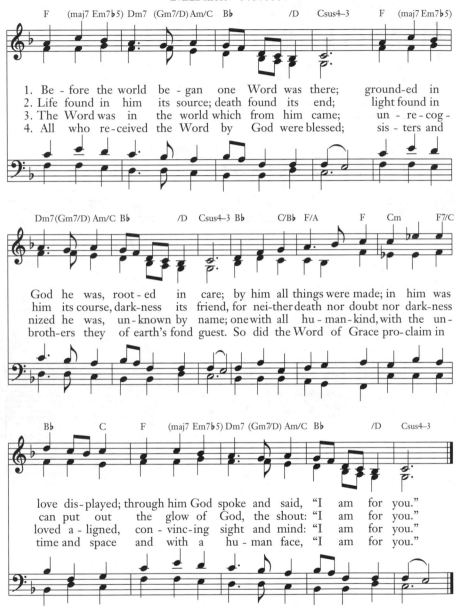

1. Be - fore the world be - gan one Word was there; ground-ed in
2. Life found in him its source; death found its end; light found in
3. The Word was in the world which from him came; un - re - cog -
4. All who re-ceived the Word by God were blessed; sis - ters and

God he was, root - ed in care; by him all things were made; in him was
him its course, dark-ness its friend, for nei-ther death nor doubt nor dark-ness
nized he was, un-known by name; one with all hu - man-kind, with the un -
broth-ers they of earth's fond guest. So did the Word of Grace pro-claim in

love dis-played; through him God spoke and said, "I am for you."
can put out the glow of God, the shout: "I am for you."
loved a - ligned, con - vinc-ing sight and mind: "I am for you."
time and space and with a hu - man face, "I am for you."

Words: John 1:1–13; paraphrase, Iona Community (Scotland)   Music: Iona Community (Scotland)

342
All who the name of Jesus bear

ST. STEPHEN (NEWINGTON) 8 6 8 6 CM

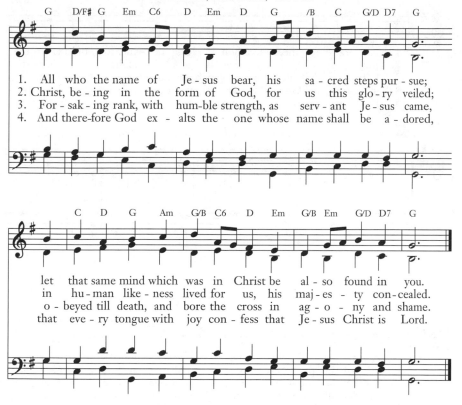

1. All who the name of Je - sus bear, his sa - cred steps pur - sue;
2. Christ, be - ing in the form of God, for us this glo - ry veiled;
3. For - sak - ing rank, with hum-ble strength, as serv - ant Je - sus came,
4. And there-fore God ex - alts the one whose name shall be a - dored,

let that same mind which was in Christ be al - so found in you.
in hu - man like - ness lived for us, his maj - es - ty con-cealed.
o - beyed till death, and bore the cross in ag - o - ny and shame.
that eve - ry tongue with joy con - fess that Je - sus Christ is Lord.

Words: Scottish Paraphrase 1781, alt   Music: William Jones (1726–1800)

Words: this version, copyright © The Presbyterian Church in Canada, 1997 Music: public domain

343

All praise to thee

ENGELBERG   10 10 10 4

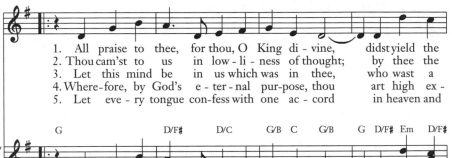

1. All praise to thee, for thou, O King di - vine, didst yield the
2. Thou cam'st to us in low - li - ness of thought; by thee the
3. Let this mind be in us which was in thee, who wast a
4. Where-fore, by God's e - ter - nal pur-pose, thou art high ex -
5. Let eve - ry tongue con-fess with one ac - cord in heaven and

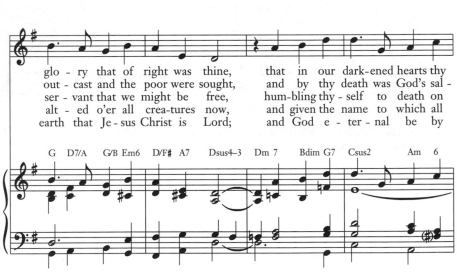

glo - ry that of right was thine, that in our dark-ened hearts thy
out - cast and the poor were sought, and by thy death was God's sal -
ser - vant that we might be free, hum-bling thy - self to death on
alt - ed o'er all crea-tures now, and given the name to which all
earth that Je - sus Christ is Lord; and God e - ter - nal be by

See also: Engelberg 522 439

Words: F. Bland Tucker (1895–1984)   Music: C.V. Stanford (1852–1924)

grace might shine:
va - tion wrought:
Cal - va - ry: Hal - le - lu - jah.   Hal - le - lu - jah.
knees shall bow:
all   a - dored:

Em   /D   Am9   Am6 G C/ED7   Am9   Am7 G(C6/G)G

344   The wise may bring their learning

1. The wise may bring their learning,
   the rich may bring their wealth,
   and some may bring their greatness,
   and some bring strength and health;
   we, too, would bring our treasures
   to offer to the King;
   we have no wealth or learning:
   what shall we children bring?

2. We'll bring him hearts that love him;
   we'll bring him thankful praise,
   and young souls meekly striving
   to walk in holy ways:
   and these shall be the treasures
   we offer to the King,
   and these are gifts that even
   a little child may bring.

3. We'll bring the little duties
   we have to do each day;
   we'll try our best to please him,
   at home, at school, at play:
   and better are these treasures
   to offer to our King
   than richest gifts without them;
   yet these a child may bring.

Words: Anonymous

Words: public domain

345

A holy baby

BAWKU   13 13 13 13 with refrain (9 8)

1. A ho - ly ba - by is born in Ju-dah's Beth-le - hem.
2. The work-ing shep-herds left all their sheep to search for him.
3. The ma - gi came to of - fer gifts and wor-ship him.
4. To E - gypt land his par-ents flew from Her - od's wrath.
5. He grew in wis-dom in Naz-a - reth of Gal - i - lee.
6. He taught the teach-ers in the tem-ple of Je - ru - sa - lem.

He is

Je - su, the son of Ma - ry; he is Je - su, the son of Ma - ry.

7.   In Jordan River the Holy Spirit came to him. He is…

8.   He brought the new way of life to all believers. He is…

9.   Our sins and failings have nailed him to the cross to die. He is…

10.   God raised him up and brought him back to life again. He is…

11.   Jesu our Saviour forgives our sins and gives us life. He is…

12.   Our Saviour's Spirit will be with us forevermore. He is…

Words: Tom Colvin (1925–)   Music: Northern Ghana Folk Song; adaptation, Tom Colvin (1925–)

Words: copyright © 1969 by Hope Publishing Co.   Music: adaptation, copyright © 1969 by Hope Publishing Co.

346 Jesus the Christ said: I am the bread

YISU NE KAHA   9 9 9 9 with repeats

1. Je-sus the Christ said: "I am the bread, the bread of life for the world am I.
1. Il nous a dit: Je suis le vrai pain, le pain pour la vie é - ter - nel - le.

The bread of life for the world am I, the bread of life for the world am I."
Le pain pour la vie é-ter-nel - le, le pain pour la vie é-ter-nel - le.

2. Jesus the Christ said: I am the shepherd,
   the one good shepherd of the sheep am I...

3. Jesus the Christ said: I am the door,
   the way and the door for the poor am I...

4. Jesus the Christ said: I am the life,
   the resurrection and the life am I...

French

2. Il nous a dit: Je suis le berger,
   l'unique berger qui vous guide...

3. Il nous a dit: Je suis le chemin,
   le chemin et la porte des pauvres...

4. Il nous a dit: Je suis la vraie vie,
   la vie qui renaît éternelle...

Words: Dermott Monahan, French translation, Joseph Gélineau   Music: Urdu melody;
arrangement, Andrew Donaldson (1951–)

God in Christ

347

There were ninety and nine

THE NINETY AND NINE   Irregular

1. There were nine - ty and nine that safe - ly lay
2. "Lord, thou hast here thy ninety and nine:
3. But none of the ran - somed ev - er knew
4. And all through the moun - tains, thun - der - riven,

in the shel - ter of the fold, but one was out
are they not e-nough for thee?" But the Shepherd made an -
how deep were the wa - ters crossed, nor how dark was the night
and up from the rock - y steep, there rose a cry

on the hills a - way, far off from the gates of gold,
swer, "This of mine has wan-dered a - way from me,
that the Lord passed through, ere he found his sheep that was lost.
to the gate of heaven, "Re - joice, I have found my sheep."

Words: Elizabeth Cecilia Clephane (1830–1869)   Music: Ira David Sankey (1840–1908)

Words: public domain   Music: public domain

452

a - way on the moun - tains wild and bare,
and al - though the road be rough and steep,
Out in the des - ert he heard its cry,
And the an - gels echoed a - round the throne,

a - way from the ten - der Shep - herd's care,
I go to the des - ert to find my sheep;
sick and help - less and read - y to die,
"Re - joice, for the Lord brings back his own;

a - way from the ten - der Shep - herd's care.
I go to the des - ert to find my sheep."
sick and help - less and read - y to die.
re - joice, for the Lord brings back his own."

Tell me the stories of Jesus

STORIES OF JESUS 8 4 8 4 5 4 5 4

Unison (Optional S.A.)

1. Tell me the sto-ries of Je - sus I love to hear,
2. First, let me hear how the chil - dren stood round his knee,
3. Tell me a-bout the dis - ci - ples from far and near,
4. Tell me, in ac-cents of won - der, how rolled the sea,
5. In - to the ci - ty I'd fol - low the chil-dren's band,

things I would ask him to tell me if he were here:
and I shall fan - cy his bless - ing rest - ing on me:
and I will lis - ten a - mong them ea - ger to hear.
toss-ing the boat in a tem - pest on Gal - i - lee,
wav-ing a branch of the palm tree high in my hand;

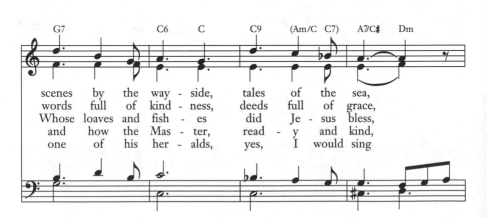

scenes by the way - side, tales of the sea,
words full of kind - ness, deeds full of grace,
Whose loaves and fish - es did Je - sus bless,
and how the Mas - ter, read - y and kind,
one of his her - alds, yes, I would sing

Words: William Henry Parker (1845–1929), alt   Music: Frederick Arthur Challinor (1860–1952)

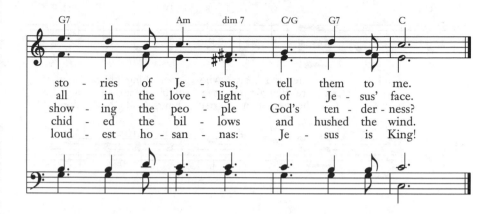

			Am	dim 7	C/G	G7	C

sto	-	ries	of	Je	-	sus,	tell	them	to	me.
all		in	the	love	-	light	of	Je	-	sus'	face.
show	-	ing	the	peo	-	ple	God's	ten	-	der -	ness?
chid	-	ed	the	bil	-	lows	and	hushed	the	wind.
loud	-	est	ho -	san	-	nas:	Je	-	sus	is	King!

349 My hope is built on nothing less

1. My hope is built on nothing less
than Jesus' blood and righteousness;
I dare not trust the sweetest frame,
but wholly lean on Jesus' name.
Refrain:
On Christ, the solid rock, I stand;
all other ground is sinking sand.

2. When darkness hides his lovely face,
I rest on his unchanging grace;
in every high and stormy gale
my anchor holds within the veil.
Refrain:

3. His oath, his covenant, his blood
support me in the whelming flood;
when all around my soul gives way,
he then is all my hope and stay.
Refrain:

4. When he shall come with trumpet sound,
oh, may I then in him be found
clothed in his righteousness alone,
faultless to stand before the throne!
Refrain:

Words: Edward Mote (1797–1874)
Words: public domain

350

To God be the glory

TO GOD BE THE GLORY 11 11 11 11

1. To God be the glo - ry, who great things has done!
2. Oh per - fect re - demp - tion, the pur - chase of blood,
3. Great things God has taught us, great things God has done

God so loved the world!—free - ly send - ing the Son,
to eve - ry be - liev - er the pro - mise of God,
and great our re - joic - ing through Je - sus the Son,

who yield - ed his life an a - tone - ment for sin,
that when the of - fen - der, re - pent - ing, be - lieves,
but pur - er and high - er and great - er will be

Words: Fanny J. Crosby (1820–1915), alt   Music: William H. Doane (1832–1916)

Words: this version, copyright © The Presbyterian Church in Canada, 1995   Music: public domain

and o - pened the life - gate that all may go in.
through Je - sus' a - tone-ment, full par - don re - ceives!
our won - der, our glad - ness, when Je - sus we see!

Refrain
Praise the Lord! Praise the Lord! Let the earth hear God's voice!

Praise the Lord! Praise the Lord! Let the peo - ple re - joice!

Oh come to the Fa - ther through Je - sus the Son,

and give God the glo - ry, who great things has done.

To God be the Glory
Original Words

1. To God be the glory! great things he hath done!
   So loved he the world that he gave us his Son,
   who yielded his life an atonement for sin,
   and opened the lifegate that all may go in.

   Refrain:
   Praise the Lord, praise the Lord, let the earth hear his voice;
   praise the Lord, praise the Lord, let the people rejoice.
   Oh come to the Father through Jesus the Son,
   and give him the glory; great things he hath done!

2. Oh perfect redemption, the purchase of blood,
   to every believer the promise of God;
   the vilest offender who truly believes,
   that moment from Jesus a pardon receives!
   Refrain:

3. Great things he hath taught us, great things he hath done,
   and great our rejoicing through Jesus the Son;
   but purer and higher and greater will be
   our wonder, our transport, when Jesus we see!
   Refrain:

351

There is a fountain opened wide

BELMONT 8 6 8 6 CM

1. There is a foun - tain o - pened wide where
2. The dy - ing thief re - joiced to see that
3. O Lamb of God, your pre - cious blood shall
4. And since, by faith, I saw the stream your
5. When this poor, halt - ing, stam - mering tongue lies

life and hope be - gin, for Christ the Lord was
foun - tain in his day, and there have I, as
nev - er lose its power, till all the ran - somed
flow - ing wounds sup - ply, re - deem - ing love has
si - lent in the grave, then in a no - bler,

cru - ci - fied to cleanse us from our sin.
vile as he, washed all my sins a - way.
church of God be saved to sin no more.
been my theme, and shall be till I die.
sweet - er song I'll sing your power to save.

Words: William Cowper (1731–1800); revision, Hymns for Today's Church
Music: William Gardiner (1770–1853)

352 And can it be that I should gain

SAGINA 888888

1. And can it be that I should gain God's rich - es
2. 'Tis mys-tery all! the Im-mor - tal dies: who can ex -
3. He left his Fath - er's throne a - bove, so free, so
4. Long my im - pris - oned spir - it lay fast bound in
5. No con-dem - na - tion now I dread; Je - sus, and

through the Sav-iour's blood? Died he for me, who caused his pain? For
plore his strange de - sign? In vain the first - born ser - aph tries to
in - fi - nite his grace, emp-tied him - self of all but love, and
sin and na - ture's night; thine eye dif - fused a quick-ening ray; I
all in him, is mine; a - live in him, my liv - ing head, and

me, who him to death pur - sued? A - maz-ing love! how
sound the depths of love di - vine. 'Tis mer - cy all! let
bled for A - dam's help - less race. 'Tis mer - cy all, im -
woke, the dun - geon flamed with light; my chains fell off; my
clothed in right - eous - ness di - vine, bold I ap-proach the e -

Words: Charles Wesley (1707–1788), alt   Music: Thomas Campbell (1825–1876)

Words: public domain Music: public domain

353   Hail, our once-rejected Jesus

BLAENWERN 8 7 8 7 D

1. Hail, our once - re - ject - ed Je - sus! Hail, our Gal - i -
2. Lamb of God, for us ap-point - ed, all our sin on
3. Je - sus, heaven - ly hosts a - dore you, where in glo - ry

le - an King! Once you suf - fered to re-lease us, all God's
you was laid; by Al-might - y Love a-noint-ed, full a -
you a - bide; eve - ry knee shall bow be-fore you, reign - ing

sav - ing grace to bring. Faith-ful ser - vant, ho - ly Sav-iour,
tone - ment you have made. Now your peo - ple are for-giv - en
at your Fa-ther's side. There for sin - ners you are plead-ing;

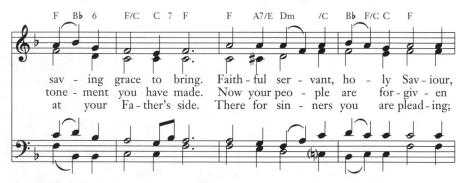

See also: Blaenwern 799

Words: John Bakewell (1721–1819), alt   Music: William P. Rowlands (1860–1937)

Words: this version, copyright © The Presbyterian Church in Canada, 1997 Music: copyright © T.H. Rowlands

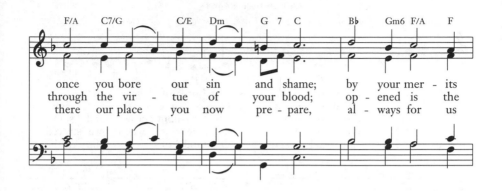

once you bore our sin and shame; by your mer - its
through the vir - tue of your blood; op - ened is the
there our place you now pre - pare, al - ways for us

we find fa - vour; life is giv - en through your name.
gate of heav - en; you are now our peace with God.
in - ter - ced - ing till in glo - ry we ap - pear.

O living Word of God

CROFT'S 136th   6 6 6 6 8 8

1. O liv-ing Word of God, strong Lord of heaven and earth,
2. O sov-ereign Word of power, O all-cre-at-ing might,
3. O ho-ly Word of truth, all wis-dom's crown and sum,
4. O match-less Word of love who sought us when we strayed,
5. O Lord of life and power, O God of love and truth,

whose might-y voice rang out, and light and life had birth,
in-vade our in-most souls, trans-form our na-ture's night,
to you with all our guests, our hopes, our fears, we come;
in whom we call our God our Fa-ther, un-dis-mayed,
to you we bring our hearts, our free-dom, strength and youth,

one Source a-lone our be-ing knows—from you our soul and sub-stance flows.
till all we are and all we do af-firms our Sav-iour's claims are true.
in you a-lone true an-swer find, and rest of soul and peace of mind.
where sin and woe de-spoil their prey, make us your word of love to-day!
your life to know, your will to do, to serve our world for love of you!

Words: Margaret Clarkson (1915–)   Music: George Frideric Handel (1685–1759)

God in Christ

355

Light of the minds that know him

MEIRIONYDD 7 6 7 6 D

1. Light of the minds that know him, may Christ be light to mine!
2. Life of the souls that love him, may Christ be ours in - deed!
3. Strength of the wills that serve him, may Christ be strength to me,
4. May it be ours to know him that we may tru - ly love,

My sun in ris - en splen - dour, my light of truth di - vine,
The liv - ing bread from heav - en on whom our spir - its feed,
who stilled the storm and tem - pest, who calmed the toss - ing sea,
and lov - ing, ful - ly serve him as serve the saints a - bove,

my guide in doubt and dark - ness, my true and liv - ing way,
who died for love of sin - ners to bear our guilt - y load,
his Spir - it's power to move me, his will to mas - ter mine,
till in that home of glo - ry with fade - less splen - dour bright,

my clear light ev - er shin - ing, my dawn of heav - en's day.
and make of life's brief jour - ney a new Em - ma - us road.
his cross to car - ry dai - ly and con - quer in his sign.
we serve in per - fect free - dom our strength, our life, our light.

Words: Timothy Dudley–Smith (1926–) from a prayer of Augustine of Hippo (354–430)
Music: W. Lloyd (1785–1852); arrangement as in Caniadau Seion 1840

356 You, Lord, are both lamb and shepherd

PARADOX 878787

1. You, Lord, are both lamb and shep-herd. You, Lord, are both
2. Clothed in light up - on the moun-tain, stripped of might up -
3. You, who walk each day be - side us, sit in pow - er
4. Wor - thy is our earth - ly Je - sus! Wor - thy is our

prince and slave, you, peace - mak - er and sword - bring - er
on the cross, shin - ing in e - ter - nal glo - ry,
at God's side. You, who preach a way that's nar - row,
cos - mic Christ! Wor - thy your de - feat and vic - tory.

of the way you took and gave, you, the ev - er -
beg - gared by a sol - dier's toss, you, the ev - er -
have a love that reach - es wide, you, the ev - er -
Wor - thy still your peace and strife. You, the ev - er -

Alternate tune: Picardy

Words: Sylvia G. Dunstan (1955–1993)   Music: John Van Maanen (1958–)

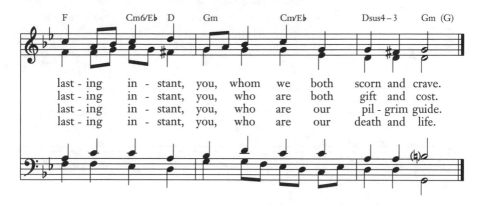

last - ing   in - stant,   you,   whom   we   both   scorn and crave.
last - ing   in - stant,   you,   who   are   both   gift and cost.
last - ing   in - stant,   you,   who   are   our   pil - grim guide.
last - ing   in - stant,   you,   who   are   our   death and life.

357   How sweet the name of Jesus sounds

ST. PETER   8 6 8 6 CM

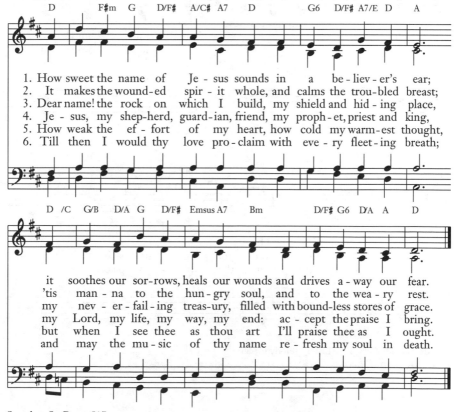

1. How sweet the name of   Je - sus sounds in   a   be - liev - er's   ear;
2. It makes the wound-ed   spir - it whole, and calms the trou-bled breast;
3. Dear name! the rock on   which I   build, my   shield and hid - ing   place,
4. Je - sus, my shep-herd, guard-ian, friend, my proph - et, priest and king,
5. How weak the ef - fort   of   my heart, how cold my warm-est thought,
6. Till then I would thy   love pro - claim with eve - ry fleet-ing breath;

it   soothes our sor-rows, heals our wounds and drives a - way our   fear.
'tis   man - na to the   hun - gry soul, and   to the wea - ry   rest.
my   nev - er - fail-ing   treas-ury, filled with bound-less stores of   grace.
my   Lord, my life, my   way, my   end: ac - cept the praise I   bring.
but   when I   see thee   as   thou art   I'll praise thee as   I   ought.
and   may the mu - sic   of   thy name   re - fresh my soul in   death.

See also: St. Peter 517

Words: John Newton (1725–1807), alt   Music: Alexander Robert Reinagle (1799–1877)

358

There is a redeemer

THERE IS A REDEEMER   Irregular

Unison

1. There is a re-deem - er, Je - sus, God's own
2. Je - sus my Re-deem - er, name a - bove all
3. When I stand in glo - ry, I will see his

Son,   pre - cious Lamb of
names,   pre - cious Lamb of
face,   and there I'll serve my

God, Mes-si - ah, Ho - ly one.
God, Mes-si - ah, oh for sin - ners slain.
King for-ev - er, in that ho - ly place.

Words: Melody Green   Music: Melody Green

Refrain

Thank you, O my Fa - ther, for giv-ing us your

Son, and leav - ing your Spir - it till your

work on earth is done. done.

469

359

The great Physician now is near

SYMPATHY 8 7 8 7 Iambic with Refrain

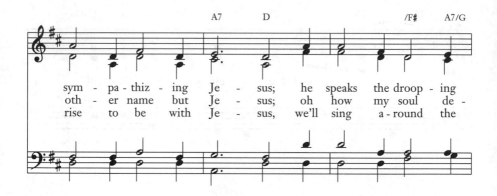

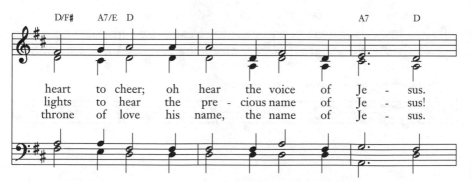

1. The great Phy-si-cian now is near, the sym-pa-thiz-ing Je-sus; he speaks the droop-ing heart to cheer; oh hear the voice of Je-sus.

2. His name dis-pels my guilt and fear, no oth-er name but Je-sus; oh how my soul de-lights to hear the pre-cious name of Je-sus!

3. And when to that bright world a-bove we rise to be with Je-sus, we'll sing a-round the throne of love his name, the name of Je-sus.

Words: William Hunter (1812–1877)   Music: John H. Stockton (1813–1877)

Words: public domain   Music: public domain

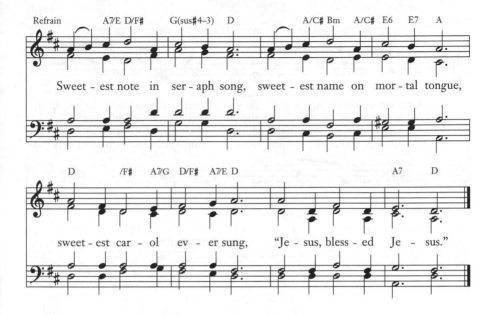

Refrain

Sweet-est note in ser-aph song, sweet-est name on mor-tal tongue,

sweet-est car-ol ev-er sung, "Je-sus, bless-ed Je-sus."

360   Jesus, thy blood and righteousness

1. Jesus, thy blood and righteousness
   my beauty are, my glorious dress;
   'midst flaming worlds, in these arrayed,
   with joy shall I lift up my head.

2. Bold shall I stand in thy great day;
   for who aught to my charge shall lay?
   Fully absolved through these I am
   from sin and fear, from guilt and shame.

3. When from the dust of death I rise
   to claim my mansion in the skies,
   even then this shall be all my plea,
   Jesus hath lived, hath died for me.

4. Jesus, be endless praise to thee,
   whose boundless mercy hath for me,
   for me a full atonement made,
   an everlasting ransom paid.

5. Oh let the dead now hear thy voice;
   now bid thy banished ones rejoice;
   their beauty this, their glorious dress,
   Jesus, thy blood and righteousness.

Words: Nicolaus Ludwig von Zinzendorf (1700–1760); translation, John Wesley (1703–1791)
Words: public domain

361

A Stranger, knocking on a door

CASAD 888888

Unison

1. A Strang-er, knock-ing on a door that o - pens on - ly from in -
2. A Shep-herd, dy - ing for the sheep, will gath-er oth - ers to the
3. A Sav-iour, ris - en from the dead, with marks of pain in hands and
4. The Spir - it makes an o - pen door and calls us, gath-ered here to -

side, our with-ered spir - its can re - store if
fold with love un - stint-ing, wide and deep, and
feet, is known to us in break-ing bread, and
day, to praise the past that's gone be - fore, then

on - ly we will o - pen wide our hearts, our-selves, and give the
tales of faith as yet un - told. Each lamb, em-braced, shall taste and
draws us clos - er when we meet: ma - jes - tic love most hum - bly
go a-long our pil-grim way: with Christ a - live, and at our

Alternate tune: Sussex Carol

Words: Brian A. Wren (1936–)   Music: Laurence Wareing

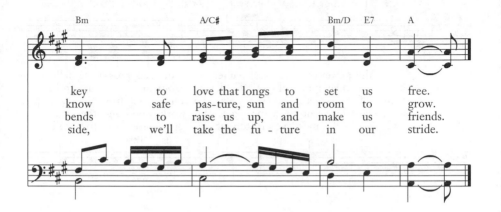

key | to | love that longs to | set | us | free.
know | safe | pas-ture, sun and | room | to | grow.
bends | to | raise us up, and | make | us | friends.
side, | we'll | take the fu - ture | in | our | stride.

362   Jesus, good above all other
QUEM PASTORES 8 8 8 7

1. Je - sus, good a - bove all oth - er, hum - ble child of faith - ful moth - er,
2. Je - sus, cra - dled in a man - ger, keep us free from sin and dan - ger,
3. Je - sus, for your peo - ple dy - ing, ris - en Sav - iour, death de - fy - ing,
4. Lord, in all our do - ings guide us; pride and hate shall not di - vide us;

in a sta - ble born our broth - er, whom the an - gel hosts a - dore.
and to all, both friend and stran - ger, give your bless - ing ev - er more.
Lord in heaven, your grace sup - ply - ing, come to us, be pres - ent here.
we'll go on with you be - side us, and with joy we'll per - se - vere.

Words: Percy Dearmer (1867–1936), based on John Mason Neale (1818–1866) Music: German carol, 14th century; harmony, Ralph Vaughan Williams (1872–1958)

God in Christ

363   All hail the power of Jesus' name

MILES LANE   8 6 8 6 with repeat

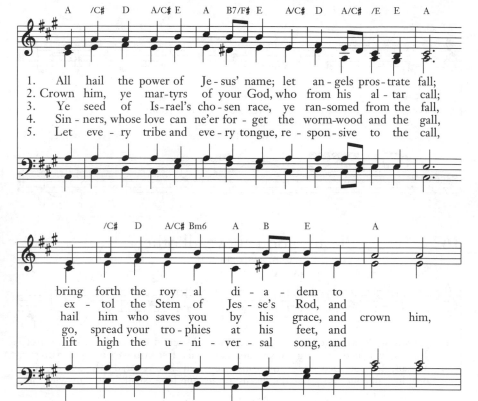

1. All hail the power of Je-sus' name; let an-gels pros-trate fall;
2. Crown him, ye mar-tyrs of your God, who from his al-tar call;
3. Ye seed of Is-rael's cho-sen race, ye ran-somed from the fall,
4. Sin-ners, whose love can ne'er for-get the worm-wood and the gall,
5. Let eve-ry tribe and eve-ry tongue, re-spon-sive to the call,

bring forth the roy-al di-a-dem to
ex-tol the Stem of Jes-se's Rod, and
hail him who saves you by his grace, and crown him,
go, spread your tro-phies at his feet, and
lift high the u-ni-ver-sal song, and

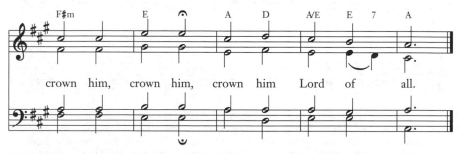

crown him, crown him, crown him Lord of all.

Words: anonymous; Edward Perronet (1726–1792)   Music: William Shrubsole (1760–1806);
fauxbourdon, Edgar C. Robinson

Words: public domain   Music: fauxbourdon, copyright © Oxford University Press, 1931

Alternate instrumental or choral accompaniment

God in Christ

364

Approach, my soul, the mercy–seat

BALERMA 8 6 8 6 CM

1. Ap-proach, my soul, the mer - cy seat, where Je - sus an - swers prayer;
2. Thy prom - ise is my on - ly plea, with this I ven - ture nigh;
3. Bowed down be - neath a load of sin, by Sa - tan sore - ly pressed,
4. Be thou my shield and hid - ing-place, that, shel-tered near thy side,
5. O won-drous love! to bleed and die, to bear the cross and shame,

there hum-bly fall be - fore his feet, for none can per - ish there.
thou call - est bur-dened souls to thee, and such, O Lord, am I.
by war with-out and fears with-in, I come to thee for rest.
I may my fierce ac - cus - er face, and tell him thou hast died.
that guilt - y sin-ners, such as I, might plead thy gra - cious name.

Words: John Newton (1725–1807)   Music: attributed to François Barthélémon (1741–1808)

Words: public domain   Music: public domain

365 This is the threefold truth

ACCLAMATIONS 12 12 12

1. This is the three-fold truth on which our faith de - pends,
2. On this we fix our minds as, pray-ing side by side,
3. By this we are up - held when doubt or grief as - sails
4. This is the three-fold truth which, if we hold it fast,

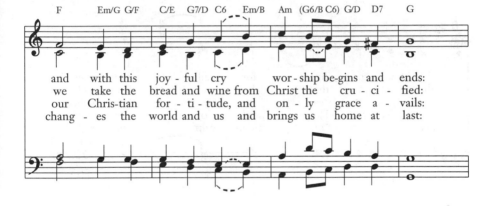

and with this joy - ful cry wor - ship be-gins and ends:
we take the bread and wine from Christ the cru - ci - fied:
our Chris-tian for - ti - tude, and on - ly grace a - vails:
chang - es the world and us and brings us home at last:

Christ has died! Christ is ris - en! Christ will come a - gain!

Words: Fred Pratt Green (1903–)   Music: Jack Schrader

Words: copyright © 1980 by Hope Publishing Co.   Music: copyright © 1980 by Hope Publishing Co.

366

Jesus, thou joy of loving hearts

MARYTON 8 8 8 8 LM

1. Je - sus, thou joy of lov - ing hearts,
2. Thy truth un - changed hath ev - er stood;
3. We taste thee, O thou liv - ing bread,
4. For thee our rest - less spir - its yearn
5. O Je - sus, al - ways with us stay;

thou fount, thou light for all to see:
thou sav - est those that on thee call;
and long to feast up - on thee still;
wher - e'er our change - ful lot is cast,
make all our mo - ments calm and bright;

from the best bliss that earth im - parts
to those who seek thee thou art good;
we drink of thee, the foun - tain - head,
glad when thy grac - ious smile we see,
chase the dark night of sin a - way;

See also: Maryton 642

Words: Latin, medieval; translation, Ray Palmer (1808–1887), alt Music: Henry Percy Smith (1825–1898); harmony, Eric H. Thiman (1900–1975) from Anglican Hymnal 1965

Words: public domain Music: harmony, copyright © the estate of Eric Thiman

478

Chords: D A7 Bm Em 6 D G6 A D

we turn un - filled a - gain to thee.
to those who find thee, all in all.
and thirst our souls from thee to fill.
blest when our faith can hold thee fast.
shed o'er the world thy ho - ly light.

367 Jesus, the very thought of thee

ST. AGNES, DURHAM 8 6 8 6 CM

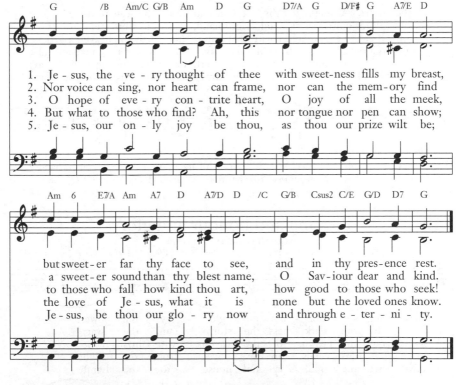

Chords: G /B Am/C G/B Am D G D7/A G D/F# G A7/E D

1. Je - sus, the ve - ry thought of thee with sweet-ness fills my breast,
2. Nor voice can sing, nor heart can frame, nor can the mem - ory find
3. O hope of eve - ry con - trite heart, O joy of all the meek,
4. But what to those who find? Ah, this nor tongue nor pen can show;
5. Je - sus, our on - ly joy be thou, as thou our prize wilt be;

Chords: Am 6 E7/A Am A7 D A7/D D /C G/B Csus2 C/E G/D D7 G

but sweet - er far thy face to see, and in thy pres - ence rest.
a sweet - er sound than thy blest name, O Sav - iour dear and kind.
to those who fall how kind thou art, how good to those who seek!
the love of Je - sus, what it is none but the loved ones know.
Je - sus, be thou our glo - ry now and through e - ter - ni - ty.

Alternate tune: St. Botolph

Words: Latin, medieval, translation, Edward Caswell (1814–1878) Music: John Bacchus Dykes (1823–1876)

368 Let Christian faith and hope dispel

ST. MAGNUS 8 6 8 6 CM

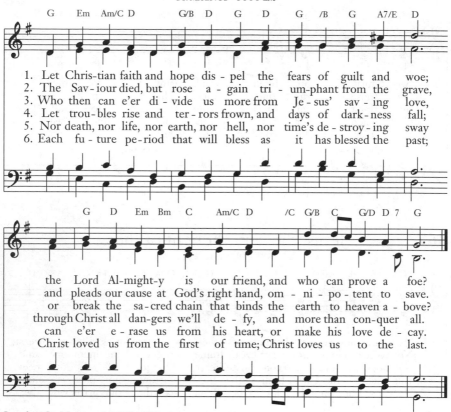

1. Let Chris-tian faith and hope dis-pel the fears of guilt and woe;
2. The Sav-iour died, but rose a-gain tri-um-phant from the grave,
3. Who then can e'er di-vide us more from Je-sus' sav-ing love,
4. Let trou-bles rise and ter-rors frown, and days of dark-ness fall;
5. Nor death, nor life, nor earth, nor hell, nor time's de-stroy-ing sway
6. Each fu-ture pe-riod that will bless as it has blessed the past;

the Lord Al-might-y is our friend, and who can prove a foe?
and pleads our cause at God's right hand, om-ni-po-tent to save.
or break the sa-cred chain that binds the earth to heaven a-bove?
through Christ all dan-gers we'll de-fy, and more than con-quer all.
can e'er e-rase us from his heart, or make his love de-cay.
Christ loved us from the first of time; Christ loves us to the last.

See also: St. Magnus 15 270 629

Words: anonymous, John Logan (1748–1788), Scottish Paraphrase   Music: Jeremiah Clarke
(c.1674–1707), from Divine Companion 1707; harmony, William Henry Monk (1823–1889)
after John Pyke Hullah (19th cent.)

Words: public domain   Music: public domain

369 Blessing and honour and glory

O QUANTA QUALIA 10 10 10 10

1. Bless-ing and hon-our and glo-ry and power,
2. Past are the dark-ness, the storm and the war;
3. Sounds now the heaven of the heavens with Christ's name,
4. Ev-er des-cends ho-ly love from on high;
5. Give we the glo-ry and praise to the Lamb;

See also: O Quanta Qualia 608

Words: Horatius Bonar (1808–1889), alt   Music: Melody from Paris Antiphoner 1681;
harmony, John Bacchus Dykes (1823–1876)

Words: public domain Music: public domain

370

Hallelujah! sing to Jesus

HYFRYDOL 8787D

1. Hal - le - lu - jah! sing to Je - sus!
his the tri - umph,
his the scep - tre, his the throne;
his the vic - to - ry a - lone.

2. Hal - le - lu - jah! not as or - phans
he is near us,
are we left in sor - row now;
faith be - lieves, nor ques - tions how.

3. Hal - le - lu - jah! King e - ter - nal,
born of Ma - ry,
thee the Lord of lords we own:
earth thy foot - stool, heaven thy throne.

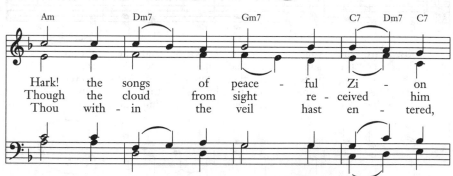

Hark! the songs of peace - ful Zi - on
Though the cloud from sight re - ceived him
Thou with - in the veil hast en - tered,

Words: William Chatterton Dix (1837–1898)   Music: Rowland Hugh Pritchard (1812–1887);
harmony, Ralph Vaughan Williams (1872–1958)

Words: public domain   Music: arrangement, copyright © Oxford University Press

thun - der like a might - y flood;
when the for - ty days were o'er,
robed in flesh, our great High Priest,

Je - sus out of eve - ry na - tion
shall our hearts for - get his prom - ise,
thou on earth both priest and vic - tim

has re - deemed us by his blood.
"I am with you ev - er - more"?
in the eu - cha - ris - tic feast.

371 Love divine, all loves excelling

HYFRYDOL 8 7 8 7 D

1. Love di-vine, all loves ex - cel - ling, joy of heaven, to
2. Breathe, oh breathe thy lov - ing Spir - it in - to eve - ry
3. Come, al - migh - ty to de - liv - er, let us all thy
4. Fin - ish then thy new cre - a - tion; pure and spot - less

earth come down; fix in us thy hum - ble dwell - ing,
troub - led breast! Let us all in thee in - her - it,
grace re - ceive; sud - den - ly re - turn and nev - er,
let us be; let us see thy great sal - va - tion

all thy faith - ful mer - cies crown. Je - sus, thou art
let us find the prom - ised rest; take a - way our
nev - er more thy tem - ples leave. Thee we would be
per - fect - ly re - stored in thee, changed from glo - ry

Hungarian

1. Isten testbe szállt szerelme
   Mennyből földre jött öröm.
   Téged hívuak esdekelve,
   És újjongunk jöttödön.
   Jézus teljes jóság vagy Te,
   Mert megszántál és szeretsz;
   Szállást venni jer szívünkbe,
   Megtartónk csak úgy lehetsz.

2. Ó, leheld rám áldott Lelked,
   Nyughatatlan, lásd, szívem,
   Mindaddig, mig csendességet
   Nyervén, Benned nem pihen.
   Oltsd el bennem a bűn vágyát,
   Kezdet légy Te és a Vég;
   Add meg lelkem szabadságát,
   Melyben hit van s békesség.

Words: Charles Wesley (1707–1788)   Music: Rowland Hugh Pritchard (1812–1887);

Words: public domain   Music: public domain

	Gm		C7 Dm C7/E	F	/E	Dm Bb6 Am Gmsus4–3 Bbmaj7 C7sus4–3

all com - pas - sion, pure, un-bound - ed love thou art;
love of sin - ning; Al - pha and O - me - ga be;
al - ways bless - ing, serve thee as thy hosts a - bove,
in - to glo - ry till in heaven we take our place,

F	Am	Gm	C7	F	/A	C	Bb	C

vis - it us with thy sal - va - tion;
end of faith as its be - gin - ning,
pray and praise thee, with - out ceas - ing,
till we cast our crowns be - fore thee,

F/A	Bb	/D	F/C	C7	F

en - ter eve - ry trem - bling heart.
set our hearts at lib - er - ty.
glo - ry in thy per - fect love.
lost in won - der, love and praise.

3. Ó, jöjj vissza, Szabadító,
   Tőled nyerjünk életet;
   Jöjj sietve s immár többé
   El ne hagyjad gyermeked!
   Téged áldunk minden órán,
   És szolgálunk, szens Urunk,
   Mindig Hozzád óhajtozván,
   Áldunk és magasztalunk.

4. Végezd új teremtő munkád,
   Tiszták, szentek hadd legyünk.
   Add, hogy vágyva váyjunk Hozzád,
   Míg tart földi életünk.
   Vigy a mennybe, hol Elődbe
   Mind lerakjuk koronánk,
   Áldva zengi nagy szerelmed
   Mindörökké szivünk, szánk.

372

Praise him, praise him,
Jesus our blessed Redeemer

ALLEN   12 10 12 10 11 10 with refrain (4 8 4 6)

1. Praise him, praise him, Je-sus, our bless-ed Re-deem - er!
2. Praise him, praise him, Je-sus, our bless-ed Re-deem - er!
3. Praise him, praise him, Je-sus, our bless-ed Re-deem - er!

Sing, O earth, his won-der-ful love pro-claim!
For our sins he suf-fered and bled and died;
Heaven - ly por - tals loud with ho-san - nas ring!

Hail him, hail him, high-est arch-an-gels in glo - ry;
he, our Rock, our hope of e - ter-nal sal - va - tion,
Je - sus Sav - iour, reign-eth for-ev-er and ev - er;

strength and hon - our give to his ho - ly name!
hail him, hail him! Je - sus the Cru - ci - fied.
crown him, crown him, Pro-phet and Priest and King!

Words: Fanny J. Crosby (1820–1915)   Music: Chester G. Allen (1838–1878)

373

Jesus loves me, this I know

JESUS LOVES ME   7 7 7 7 with refrain

1. Je - sus loves me, this I know, for the Bi - ble tells me so,
2. Je - sus loves me, this I know, as he loved so long a - go,
3. Je - sus loves me still to - day, walk-ing with me on my way,

lit - tle ones to him be - long, they are weak but he is strong.
tak - ing chil - dren on his knee, say - ing, "Let them come to me."
want - ing as a friend to give light and love to all who live.

Refrain

Yes, Je - sus loves me! Yes, Je - sus loves me!

Yes, Je - sus loves me! The Bi - ble tells me so.

Words: Anna Bartlett (1821–1910); revisions, v.2,3, David Rutherford McGuire (1929–1971)
Music: William Batchelder Bradbury (1816–1868)

374 Oh for a thousand tongues to sing

RICHMOND 8 6 8 6 CM

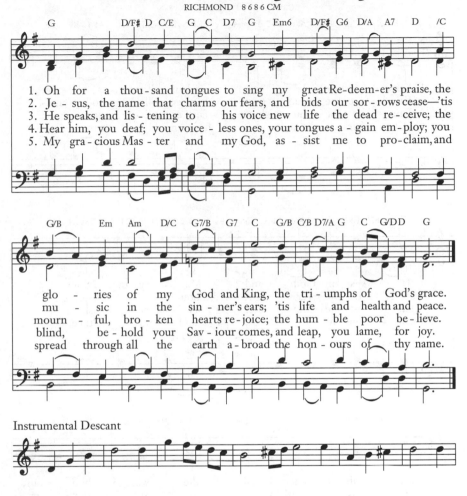

1. Oh for a thou-sand tongues to sing my great Re-deem-er's praise, the
2. Je - sus, the name that charms our fears, and bids our sor - rows cease—'tis
3. He speaks, and lis - tening to his voice new life the dead re - ceive; the
4. Hear him, you deaf; you voice - less ones, your tongues a - gain em - ploy; you
5. My gra - cious Mas - ter and my God, as - sist me to pro-claim, and

glo - ries of my God and King, the tri - umphs of God's grace.
mu - sic in the sin - ner's ears; 'tis life and health and peace.
mourn - ful, bro - ken hearts re-joice; the hum - ble poor be - lieve.
blind, be - hold your Sav - iour comes, and leap, you lame, for joy.
spread through all the earth a - broad the hon - ours of thy name.

Instrumental Descant

Alternate tune: Azmon See also: Richmond 118

Words: Charles Wesley (1707–1788), alt Music: Thomas Haweis (1734–1820);
arrangement, Samuel Webbe, the younger (1770–1843); descant, C.S. Lang (1891–1971)

God in Christ

375

Fairest Lord Jesus

CRUSADER'S HYMN 569558

1. Fair - est Lord Je - sus, Lord of all cre - a - tion,
2. Fair are the mead - ows, fair - er still the wood - lands,
3. Fair is the sun - shine, fair - er still the moon - light,
4. All fair-est beau - ty heav-en - ly and earth - ly,

Je - sus, of God and Ma - ry the Son:
robed in the ver - dure and bloom of spring.
fair is the shim - mer-ing, star - ry sky:
won - drous-ly, Je - sus, is found in thee;

thee will I cher - ish, thee will I hon - our,
Je - sus is fair - er, Je - sus is pur - er,
Je - sus shines bright - er, Je - sus shines clear - er,
none can be near - er, fair - er or dear - er

Words: German, anonymous 1677; translation, Lilian Stevenson (1871–1960)   Music: Silesian folk song;
arrangement, James Hopkirk (1908–1972)

Words: translation, copyright © Oxford University Press   Music: arrangement, copyright © the estate of James Hopkirk

490

O	thou	my	soul's	de -	light	and		crown.
he	makes	the	sad -	dest	heart	to		sing.
than	all	the	heaven -	ly	host	on		high.
than	thou,	my	Sav -	iour,	art	to		me.

God in Christ

376 Lord, the light of your love is shining

SHINE, JESUS, SHINE 9 9 10 10 6 with refrain (13 9 13 10)

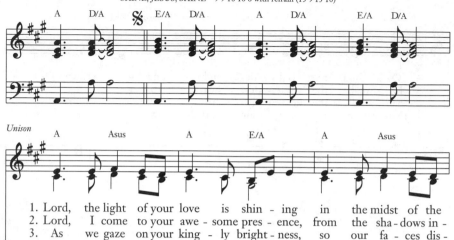

Unison

1. Lord, the light of your love is shin - ing in the midst of the
2. Lord, I come to your awe - some pres - ence, from the sha - dows in -
3. As we gaze on your king - ly bright - ness, so our fa - ces dis -

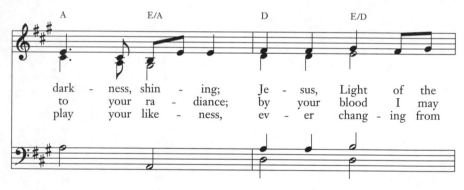

dark - ness, shin - ing; Je - sus, Light of the
to your ra - diance; by your blood I may
play your like - ness, ev - er chang - ing from

World, shine up - on us. Set us free by the
en - ter your bright - ness. Search me, try me, con -
glo - ry to glo - ry: mir - rored here may our

Words: Graham Kendrick (1950–)   Music: Graham Kendrick (1950–)

377

Come, children, join to sing

MADRID 6666D

1. Come, chil-dren, join to sing—
2. Come, lift your hearts on high— hal - le - lu - jah, a - men—
3. Loud now our voic - es raise—

praise to our Ser-vant King,
let prais - es fill the sky— hal - le - lu - jah, a - men!
no power can still our praise—

Let all with heart and voice saved by God's gra-cious choice,
Christ calls his peo - ple friends; lost, out-cast he de - fends
On heav-en's bles - sed shore, God's good-ness we'll a - dore

now in this place re - joice—
with love that nev - er ends— hal - le - lu - jah, a - men!
sing - ing for - ev - er-more—

Words: Christian Henry Bateman (1831–1889), alt   Music: Anonymous

Words: this version, copyright © The Presbyterian Church in Canada, 1997   Music: public domain

494

378
Jesus, Jesus, Jesus in the morning

JESUS IN THE MORNING 4 12 4 7

Je - sus, Je - sus, Je-sus in the morn-ing, Je-sus in the noon-time;

Je - sus, Je - sus, Je-sus when the sun goes down!

2. Love him...
3. Serve him...
4. Thank him...
5. Praise him...
6. Jesus...

Words: African–American folk song   Music: African–American folk song; arrangement, Andrew Donaldson (1951–)

Words: public domain   Music: arrangement, copyright © The Presbyterian Church in Canada, 1997

From heaven you came, helpless babe

THE SERVANT KING   8 8 7 8 with refrain

1. From heaven you came, help-less babe, en-tered our world, your
2. There in the gard - en of tears, my hea - vy load he
3. Come see his hands and his feet, the scars that speak of
4. So let us learn how to serve, and in our lives en -

glo - ry veiled, not to be served but to serve,
chose to bear; his heart with sor - row was torn:
sac - ri - fice, hands that flung stars in - to space
throne him, each oth - er's needs to pre - fer,

and give your life that we might live.
"Yet not my will but yours," he said.
to cru - el nails sur - ren - dered.
for it is Christ we're serv - ing.

Words: Graham Kendrick (1950–)   Music: Graham Kendrick (1950–)

This is our God, the Ser-vant King, he calls us now to fol-low him, to bring our lives as a dai-ly of-fer-ing of wor-ship to the Ser-vant King. King.

380 Spirit, come, dispel our sadness

GENEVAN 42   8 7 8 7 7 7 8 8

1. Spir-it, come, dis-pel our sad-ness; pierce the clouds of sin-ful night; come, thou source of sweet-est glad-ness, breathe thy life and spread thy light. Lov-ing Spir-it, God of peace, great dis-tri-bu-ter of grace, rest up-on this

2. From that height which knows no meas-ure, as a gra-cious shower de-scend, bring-ing down the rich-est treas-ure we can wish or God can send. O thou glo-ry, shin-ing down from the Fath-er and the Son, grant us thine il-

3. Come, O best of all do-na-tions God can give, or we im-plore; hav-ing thy sweet con-so-la-tions we need wish for noth-ing more. Come, a-noint us now with power; on our souls thy grac-es shower; auth-or of the

Words: German, Paul Gerhardt (1607–1676); translation, John Christian Jacobi (1670–1750),
Augustus Montague Toplady (1740–1778), alt   Music: Louis Bourgeois (c. 1510–1561)

Words: public domain   Music: public domain

Em C6 Bsus4-3   Em   E   Am   G/B   C6   Em   D   G

con - gre - ga - tion; hear, oh hear our sup - pli - ca - tion.
lum - in - a - tion; rest up - on this con - gre - ga - tion.
new cre - a - tion, make our hearts thy hab - i - ta - tion.

381   Holy Spirit, hear us
GLENFINLAS 6 5 6 5

F   C   F   Gm   Am   Bb   6   F   C/E   Dm   Csus4-2 - 3

1. Ho - ly Spir - it, hear us; help us while we sing;
2. Ho - ly Spir - it, prompt us when we bow to pray;
3. Ho - ly Spir - it, speak now through this book we read;
4. Ho - ly Spir - it, give us Je - sus' heart and mind;
5. Ho - ly Spir - it, help us dai - ly by your might,

F/A   Bbsus2 C6   Dmsus4-3   F/A   Bb6   7   C   Bb   6   F

breathe in - to the mu - sic of the praise we bring.
near - er come and teach us what we ought to say.
on its liv - ing pag - es shine the light we need.
make us as our Teach - er: lov - ing, strong and kind.
what is wrong, to con - quer, and to choose the right.

Words: William Henry Parker (1845–1929), alt   Music: Kenneth G. Finlay (1882–1974)

382 Spirit of God, descend upon my heart

MORECAMBE 10 10 10 10

1. Spir - it of God, de - scend up - on my heart; wean it from
2. I ask no dream, no proph-et ec - sta - sies, no sud-den
3. Hast thou not bid me love thee, God and King? All, all thine
4. Teach me to feel that thou art al-ways nigh; teach me the
5. Teach me to love thee as thine an-gels love, one ho - ly

earth; through all its puls - es move. Stoop to my weak - ness,
rend - ing of the veil of clay, no an - gel mes - sen -
own, soul, heart and strength and mind; I see thy cross; there
strug - gles of the soul to bear, to face the ris - ing
pas - sion fill - ing all my frame: the bap-tism of the

migh - ty as thou art, and make me love thee as I ought to love.
ger, no o-pening skies, but take the dim-ness of my soul a - way.
teach my heart to cling: oh let me seek thee and oh let me find.
doubt, the reb - el sigh; teach me the pa-tience of un - an-swered prayer.
heaven de-scend-ed Dove, my heart an al - tar and thy love the flame.

Words: George Croly (1780–1860), alt   Music: ascribed to Frederick Cook Atkinson (1841–1860)

Words: public domain Music: public domain

383 Come, holy spirit / Veni Sancte Spiritus

VENI SANCTE SPIRITUS   Irregular

All*

Ve - ni San - cte Spi - ri - tus.

Leader(s)

1. Come, Ho - ly Spir - it; from heav - en shine forth with your glo - rious light. *Refrain* Ve - ni San - cte Spi - ri - tus. 2. Come from the four winds, O Spir - it; come, breath of God; dis - perse the shad - ows o - ver us; re - new and strength - en your peo - ple. *Refrain* Ve - ni San - cte Spi - ri - tus. 3. Fath - er of the poor, come to our pov - er - ty. Show - er up - on us the sev - en gifts of your grace. Be the light of our lives. O come! *Refrain* Ve - ni San - cte Spi - ri - tus.

* **Note:** *The choral accompaniment is sung continuously throughout, while the leader(s) may pause for an even number of measures between verses.*

Words: Latin, anonymous, paraphrase, Jacques Berthier (1923–1994)   Music: Jacques Berthier (1923–1994)

384   O Breath of life, come sweeping through us

SPIRITUS VITAE   9 8 9 8

1. O Breath of life, come sweep-ing through us; re - vive your
2. O Wind of God, come bend us, break us, till hum-bly
3. O Breath of love, come breathe with - in us, re - new-ing
4. O Tongues of fire, come rest up - on us, so we may

church with life and power.   O Breath of life, come cleanse, re -
we con - fess our need;   then in your ten - der - ness re -
thought and will and heart: come, Love of Christ, a - fresh to
speak your word a - right;   kin - dle the flame of love a -

new us, and fit your church to meet this hour.
make us, re - vive, re - store, for this we plead.
win us, re - vive your church in eve - ry part.
mong us; e - quip your church to spread the light.

Words: Bessie Porter Head (1850–1936), alt; v.4, Iona Maclean (1954–)
Music: Mary J. Hammond (1878–1964)

385 Like the murmur of the dove's song

BRIDEGROOM 87876

Like the mur-mur of the dove's song, like the chal-lenge of her
To the mem-bers of Christ's bod - y, to the branch-es of the
With the heal - ing of di - vi - sion, with the cease-less voice of

flight, like the vig - our of the wind's rush, like the
Vine, to the church in faith as - sem - bled, to her
prayer, with the power to love and wit - ness, with the

new flame's ea - ger might: come, Ho - ly Spir - it, come.
midst as gift and sign: come, Ho - ly Spir - it, come.
peace be - yond com - pare:

Words: Carl P. Daw, Jr. (1944–) Music: Peter Cutts (1937–)

Words: copyright © 1982 by Hope Publishing Co. Music: copyright © 1969 by Hope Publishing Co.

386

Come down, O Love divine

DOWN AMPNEY 6 6 11 D

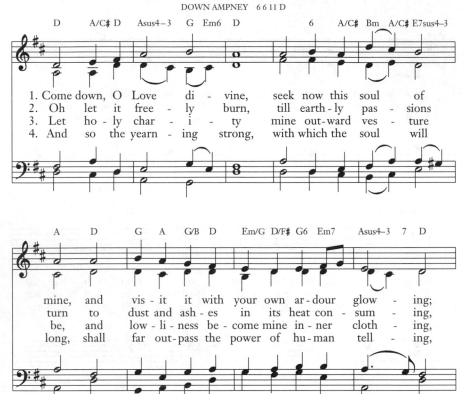

1. Come down, O Love di - vine, seek now this soul of
2. Oh let it free - ly burn, till earth - ly pas - sions
3. Let ho - ly char - i - ty mine out - ward ves - ture
4. And so the yearn - ing strong, with which the soul will

mine, and vis - it it with your own ar - dour glow - ing;
turn to dust and ash - es in its heat con - sum - ing,
be, and low - li - ness be - come mine in - ner cloth - ing,
long, shall far out - pass the power of hu - man tell - ing,

O Com - fort - er, draw near, with - in my heart ap - pear,
and let your glo - rious light shine ev - er on my sight,
true low - li - ness of heart, which takes the hum - bler part,
for none can guess its grace, till we be - come the place

Words: Italian, Bianco da Siena (13??–1434); translation, R.F. Littledale (1833–1890), alt
Music: Ralph Vaughan Williams (1872–1958)

and kin-dle it, your ho-ly flame be-stow - ing.
and clothe me round, the while my path il - lum - ing.
and pride in earth-ly glo-ry scorns with loath - ing.
where - in the Ho-ly Spir-it makes a dwell - ing.

387   Holy Spirit, come, confirm us

DRAKE'S BROUGHTON   8 7 8 7

1. Ho-ly Spir-it, come, con-firm us   in   the truth that Christ makes known;
2. Ho-ly Spir-it, come, con-sole us; come as Ad-vo-cate   to   plead;
3. Ho-ly Spir-it, come, re-new us; come your-self to make us live,
4. Ho-ly Spir-it, come, pos-sess us, you the love of Three-in-One,

we have faith and un-der-stand-ing through your help-ing gifts a-lone.
lov-ing Spir-it from the Fa-ther, grant in Christ the help we need.
ho-ly through your lov-ing pres-ence, ho-ly through the gifts you give.
Ho-ly Spir-it of the Fa-ther, Ho-ly Spir-it of the Son.

Words: Brian Foley (1919–)   Music: Edward Elgar (1857–1934)

388

Come, O Holy Spirit

WA WA WA 6 7 3

Come, O Ho-ly Spir-it, come.
Wa wa wa É - mi - mi - mo.
Ho-ly Spir-it, come.
E - mi - o - lo - ye.

Come, Al-might-y Spir-it,
Wa wa wa A - lag - ba -

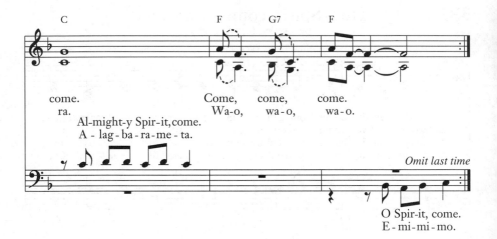

come.
ra.
Al-might-y Spir-it, come.
A - lag - ba - ra - me - ta.

Come, come, come.
Wa-o, wa-o, wa-o.

Omit last time

O Spir-it, come.
E - mi - mi - mo.

Viens Esprit, Esprit de Dieu,
Viens, ô Saint-Esprit.
Viens, puissant Esprit de Dieu,
Viens, puissant Créateur.
Viens, viens, viens, ô Esprit, viens.

Words: Church of the Lord (Aladura), Nigeria; English, I-to Loh (1936–); French, R. Gerald Hobbs (1941–)
Music: Church of the Lord (Aladura), Nigeria; transcription, I-to Loh (1936–), as taught by Samuel Solanke.

389 Breathe on me, breath of God

TRENTHAM 6686SM

1. Breathe on me, breath of God; fill me with life a - new, that I may
2. Breathe on me, breath of God, un - til my heart is pure, un - til with
3. Breathe on me, breath of God, till I am whol - ly thine, un - til this
4. Breathe on me, breath of God, so shall I nev - er die, but live with

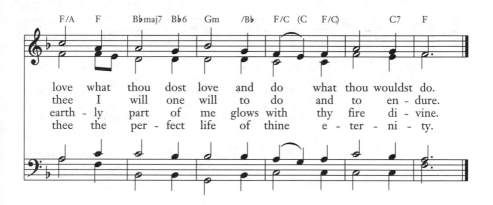

love what thou dost love and do what thou wouldst do.
thee I will one will to do and to en - dure.
earth - ly part of me glows with thy fire di - vine.
thee the per - fect life of thine e - ter - ni - ty.

Words: Edwin Hatch (1835–1889) Music: Robert Jackson (1840–1914)

390

Spirit divine, attend our prayers

GRÄFENBERG   8 6 8 6 CM

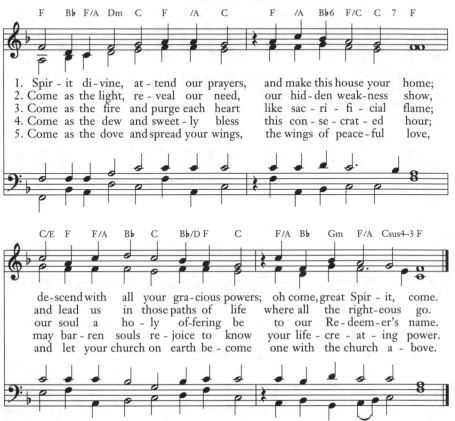

1. Spir - it di - vine, at - tend our prayers, and make this house your home;
2. Come as the light, re - veal our need, our hid - den weak - ness show,
3. Come as the fire and purge each heart like sac - ri - fi - cial flame;
4. Come as the dew and sweet - ly bless this con - se - crat - ed hour;
5. Come as the dove and spread your wings, the wings of peace - ful love,

de - scend with all your gra - cious powers; oh come, great Spir - it, come.
and lead us in those paths of life where all the right - eous go.
our soul a ho - ly of - fering be to our Re - deem - er's name.
may bar - ren souls re - joice to know your life - cre - at - ing power.
and let your church on earth be - come one with the church a - bove.

6. Come as the wind, with rushing sound
   and pentecostal grace,
   that all of woman born may see
   the glory of your face.

7. Spirit divine, attend our prayers;
   make our lost world your home;
   descend with all your gracious powers;
   oh come, great Spirit, come.

See also: Grafenberg 511

Words: Andrew Reed (1787–1862), alt   Music: Johann Crüger (1598–1662), from Praxis pietatis melica 1647

Words: public domain   Music: public domain

391

O Holy Spirit, root of life

OTTERSPOOR 8 8 8 8 LM

Alternate tune: Conditor Alme Siderum

Words: Jean Janzen (1933–), based on a Latin text by Hildegard of Bingen (1098–1179)
Music: Ron Klusmeier (1946–)

Words: copyright © Jean Janzen, 1991 Music: copyright © WorshipArts

392 O holy Dove of God descending

LOIS 9996

1. O ho - ly Dove of God de - scend - ing,
2. O ho - ly Wind of God now blow - ing,
3. O ho - ly Rain of God now fall - ing,
4. O ho - ly Flame of God now burn - ing,

C (G/B) Am (G6) Fmaj7 (Dm) G

you are the love that knows no end - ing; all of our shat - tered
you are the seed that God is sow - ing; you are the life that
you make the word of God en - thrall - ing; you are that in - ner
you are the power of Christ re - turn - ing; you are the an - swer

C (G/B) Am (G6) Fmaj7 (Dm) G (C/B) F (Dm) Em7 (Am)

Words: Bryan Jeffrey Leech (1931–)   Music: Bryan Jeffery Leech (1931–)

Words: copyright © Fred Bock Music Co., 1976   Music: copyright © Fred Bock Music Co., 1976

dreams   you're mend - ing:
starts   us   grow - ing: Spir - it, now live   in   me.
voice   now   call   - ing:
to   our   yearn - ing:

Dm   (G/B) C   Dm7   F   G7   C

393   I'm not ashamed to own my Lord

1. I'm not ashamed to own my Lord,
   or to defend his cause,
   maintain the glory of his cross,
   and honour all his laws.

2. Jesus, my Lord! I know his name;
   his name is all my boast;
   nor will he put my soul to shame,
   nor let my hope be lost.

3. I know that safe with him remains,
   protected by his power,
   what I've committed to his trust
   till the decisive hour.

4. Then will he own his servant's name
   before his Father's face,
   and in the new Jerusalem
   appoint my soul a place.

Words: Isaac Watts (1674–1748), from Scottish Paraphrases

Words: public domain

394

Holy Spirit, truth divine

SONG 13   7 7 7 7

1. Ho - ly Spir - it, truth di - vine, dawn u - pon this soul of mine;
2. Ho - ly Spir - it, love di - vine, glow with - in this heart of mine;
3. Ho - ly Spir - it, power di - vine, fill and nerve this will of mine;
4. Ho - ly Spir - it, right di - vine, reign with - in this soul of mine;

Word of God and in - ward light, wake my spir - it; clear my sight.
kin - dle eve - ry high de - sire; per - ish self in thy pure fire.
by thy strength I strong - ly live, brave - ly serve and glad - ly give.
be my law and I shall be firm - ly bound, for - ev - er free.

5. Holy Spirit, peace divine,
   still this restless heart of mine;
   speak to calm this tossing sea
   stayed on thy tranquillity.

6. Holy Spirit, joy divine,
   gladden now this heart of mine;
   in the desert ways I sing,
   "Spring, O well, forever spring."

Words: Samuel Longfellow (1819–1892), alt   Music: adapted from Orlando Gibbons (1583–1625)

395

Fire of God, O sacred flame

GOTT SEI DANK 7 7 7 7

1. Fire of God, O sa - cred flame, Spir - it
2. Breath of God that swept in power in the
3. Strength of God, your might with - in con - quers
4. Truth of God, your pierc - ing rays pen - e -
5. Love of God, your grace pro - found nei - ther

who in splen - dour came, let your heat my
pen - te - cos - tal hour; ho - ly breath, be
sor - row, pain and sin; for - ti - fy from
trate my se - cret ways. May the light that
a - ges, nor is bound; come, my heart's own

soul re - fine till it glows with love di - vine.
now in me source of vi - tal en - er - gy.
e - vil's art all the gate - ways of my heart.
shames my sin guide me, ho - lier paths to win.
guest to be, dwell for - ev - er - more in me.

Words: Albert F. Bayly (1901–1984)   Music: Freylinghausen's Geistreiches Gesangbuch 1704

Words: copyright © Oxford University Press, 1988   Music: public domain

396

As comes the breath of spring

DENBY 6666D

1. As comes the breath of spring, with light and mirth and song,
2. You come like dawn-ing day, with flam-ing truth and love,
3. You come like songs at morn that fill the earth with joy,
4. You breathe, and there is health; you move, and there is power;

so does your Spir - it bring new days, brave, free and strong.
to chase all glooms a - way, to brace our wills to prove
till we in Christ new-born new strength in praise em - ploy.
you whis-per, there is wealth of love, your rich - est dower.

You come with thrill of life to chase hence win-ter's breath,
how wise, how good to choose the truth and its brave fight;
You come to rouse the heart from drift - ing to de - spair,
Your pres-ence is to us like sum - mer in the soul;

Alternate tune: Leoni

Words: David Lakie Ritchie (1865–1951)   Music: Charles J. Dale (c. 1860–1920)

Words: public domain   Music: public domain

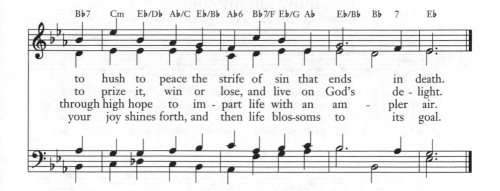

| Bb7 | Cm | Eb/Db | Ab/C | Eb/Bb | Ab6 | Bb7/F | Eb/G | Ab | | Eb/Bb | Bb | 7 | | Eb |

to   hush   to   peace the   strife of   sin that   ends   in   death.
to   prize it,   win   or   lose, and   live on   God's   de - light.
through high hope   to   im - part   life with   an   am   -   pler   air.
your   joy shines forth, and   then   life blos-soms   to   its   goal.

397

From the cowardice that
dares not face new truth

From the cowardice that dares not face new truth,
from the laziness that is contented with half-truth,
from the arrogance that thinks it knows all truth,
Good Lord, deliver me. Amen.

Words: Kenyan, anonymous
Words: public domain

398

When the spirit of the Lord
moves in my soul

LIKE DAVID THE SHEPHERD   11 8 with repeats and refrain (4 8 4 8)

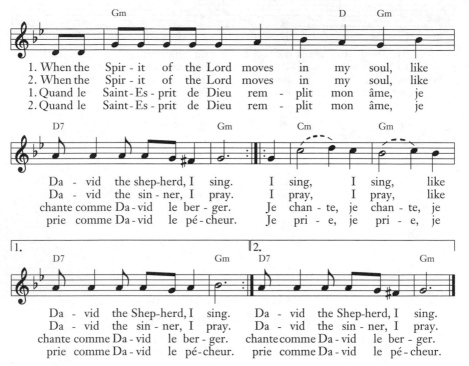

1. When the Spir - it of the Lord moves in my soul, like
2. When the Spir - it of the Lord moves in my soul, like
1. Quand le Saint - Es - prit de Dieu rem - plit mon âme, je
2. Quand le Saint - Es - prit de Dieu rem - plit mon âme, je

Da - vid the shep-herd, I sing. I sing, I sing, like
Da - vid the sin - ner, I pray. I pray, I pray, like
chante comme Da - vid le ber - ger. Je chan - te, je chan - te, je
prie comme Da - vid le pé - cheur. Je pri - e, je pri - e, je

1.

Da - vid the Shep-herd, I sing.
Da - vid the sin - ner, I pray.
chante comme Da - vid le ber - ger.
prie comme Da - vid le pé - cheur.

2.

Da - vid the Shep-herd, I sing.
Da - vid the sin - ner, I pray.
chante comme Da - vid le ber - ger.
prie comme Da - vid le pé - cheur.

3. When the Spirit of the Lord moves in my soul,
   like David the victor, I dance.
   I dance, I dance, like David the victor, I dance.

4. When the Spirit of the Lord moves in my soul,
   like David the poet, I praise.
   I praise, I praise, like David the poet, I praise.

3. Quand le Saint–Esprit de Dieu remplit mon âme,
   je danse comme David le vainqueur.
   Je danse, je danse, je danse comme David le vainqueur.

4. Quand le Saint–Esprit de Dieu remplit mon âme,
   j'exalte comme David le poète.
   J'exalte, j'exalte, j'exalte comme David le poète.

Words: traditional Spanish; translation, the editors of International Songbook, 1990;
French translation, Andrew J. Donaldson (1951–)   Music: traditional

399

Spirit, Spirit of gentleness

SPIRIT, SPIRIT OF GENTLENESS   Irregular

Spir - it,   Spir - it of gen-tle-ness,   blow through the
Souf - fle,   vent doux du Saint-Es-prit;   ta grâ - ce

wil - der-ness,   call - ing and free.
me con-duit   hors du dé - sert.

Spir - it,   Spir - it of rest-less-ness,   stir me from
Souf - fle,   grand vent du Saint-Es-prit,   se-coue notre

pla - cid-ness,   Wind,   Wind on the sea.
a - pa-thie,   vent,   vent sur la mer.

Words: James K. Manley (1940–); French translation, Andrew Donaldson (1951–)   Music: James K.
Manley (1940–)

Words: copyright © James K. Manley; translation, copyright © Andrew Donaldson, 1995   Music: copyright © James K. Manley

517

Verses

1. You moved on the wa - ters; you called to the deep; then you coaxed up the moun - tains from the val - leys of sleep, and o - ver the ae - ons you called to each thing: —

2. You swept through the des - ert, you stung with the sand, and you goad - ed your peo - ple with a law and a land, and when they were blind - ed with their i - dols and lies, then you

3. You sang in a sta - ble; you cried from a hill; then you whis-pered in si - lence when the whole world was still, and down in the ci - ty you called once a - gain, when you

4. You call from to - mor - row; you break an - cient schemes; from the bond - age of sor - row the cap - tives dream dreams; our wom - en see vi - sions, our men clear their eyes; with

518

wake from your slum - bers
spoke through your proph - ets
blew through your peo - ple
bold new de - ci - sions

and rise on your wings.
to o - pen their eyes.
on the rush of the wind.
your peo - ple a - rise.

1. Tu formas la terre,
   Esprit créateur;
   tu dressas les montagnes
   en gloire et splendeur.
   À travers les âges,
   tu crias à tous vents:
   «Déployez vos ailes,
   sortez du néant.»
   Refrain:

2. Tu choisis un peuple;
   poussé par ta voix,
   il quitta l'esclavage
   vers une terre et une loi.
   Et quand il fut trompé
   par des illusions,
   tu donnas aux prophètes
   tes saintes visions.
   Refrain:

3. Tu chantas dans l'étable,
   tu gémis sur la croix;
   tu rompis le silence,
   par un souffle de joie.
   Et puis, dans les villes,
   tu nous envoyas
   le vent d'une tempête
   qui nous ranima.
   Refrain:

4. Esprit, tu écrases
   l'ancien désespoir;
   tu dévoiles à l'esclave
   le chemin de l'espoir.
   Les femmes et les hommes
   reçoivent ta vision,
   ton peuple se lève,
   avec décision.
   Refrain:

400

Spirit of the living God

SPIRIT OF THE LIVING GOD   12 12 8 12

1. Spir - it of the liv-ing God, fall a-fresh on me. Spir - it of the liv - ing God, fall a-fresh on me. Melt me, mould me, fill me, use me. Spir - it of the liv-ing God, fall a-fresh on me!

2. Spir - it of the liv-ing God, move a-mong us all; make us one in heart and mind; make us one in love: hum-ble, car - ing, self-less, shar - ing. Spir - it of the liv-ing God, fill our lives with love!

Words: v.1, Daniel Iverson (1890–1977); v.2, Michael Baughen (1930–)   Music: Daniel Iverson (1890–1977)

401 O Spirit of the living God

MELCOMBE 8 8 8 8 LM

1. O Spir - it of the liv - ing God, in
2. Give tongues of fire and hearts of love, to
3. Be dark - ness, at thy com - ing, light, con -
4. O Spir - it of the Lord, pre - pare all
5. Bap - tize the na - tions: far and nigh the

all the full - ness of thy grace, where - ev - er hu - man
preach the rec - on - cil - ing word; give power and unc - tion
fu - sion or - der, in thy path; souls with - out strength in -
the round earth its God to meet; breathe thou a - broad like
tri - umphs of the cross re - cord; the name of Je - sus

foot hath trod, de - scend on our re - bel - lious race.
from a - bove, when - e'er the joy - ful sound is heard.
spire with might; bid mer - cy tri - umph o - ver wrath.
morn - ing air, till hearts of stone be - gin to beat.
glo - ri - fy, till eve - ry kin - dred call him Lord.

Words: James Montgomery (1771–1854) Music: Samuel Webbe, the elder (1740–1816)
Words: public domain Music: public domain

402
O Holy Spirit, by whose breath

VENI CREATOR   8 8 8 8 with coda

1. O Ho - ly Spir - it, by whose breath life ris - es vi -
brant out of death: come to cre - ate, re - new, in - spire;

2. You are the seek - er's sure re - source, of burn - ing love
the liv - ing source, pro - tec - tor in the midst of strife,

3. In you God's en - er - gy is shown, to us your var -
ied gifts made known. Teach us to speak; teach us to hear;

4. Flood our dull sens - es with your light; in mu - tual love
our hearts u - nite. Your power the whole cre - a - tion fills;

5. From in - ner strife grant us re - lease; turn na - tions to
the ways of peace. To full - er life your peo - ple bring

Words: Latin, 9th century; translation, John Webster Grant (1919–)   Music: Mechlin Plainsong;
harmony, Healey Willan (1880–1968)

come, kin - dle in our hearts your fire.
the giv - er and the Lord of life.
yours is the tongue and yours the ear.
con - firm our weak, un - cer - tain wills.
that as one bo - dy we may sing:

D.C.

V. 5 to Coda

Coda (after last verse)

praise to the Fa - ther, Christ the Word,

and to the Spir - it, God the Lord. A - men.

403 She comes sailing on the wind

SHE FLIES ON   Irregular

Refrain
Unison

She comes sail-ing on the wind, her wings flash-ing in the sun; on a journ-ey just be-gun, she flies on.

And in the pas-sage of her flight, her song rings out through the night, full of laugh-ter, full of light, she flies on.

(3. To a)

5. Long after the deep darkness that fell upon the world,
   after dawn returned in flame of rising sun,
   the Spirit touched the earth again, again her wings unfurled,
   bringing life in wind and fire as she flew on. Refrain

Words: Gordon Light (1944–)   Music: Gordon Light (1944–); arrangement, Andrew Donaldson (1951–)

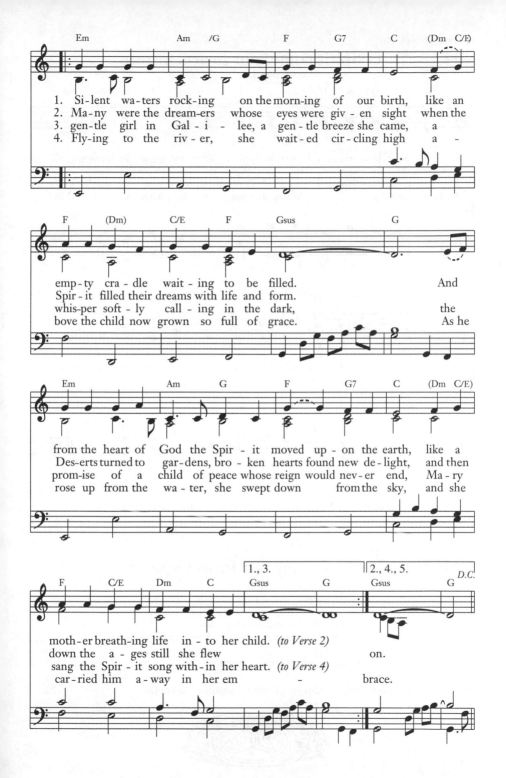

1. Si-lent wa-ters rock-ing on the morn-ing of our birth, like an
2. Ma-ny were the dream-ers whose eyes were giv-en sight when the
3. gen-tle girl in Gal-i-lee, a gen-tle breeze she came, a
4. Fly-ing to the riv-er, she wait-ed cir-cling high a -

emp-ty cra-dle wait-ing to be filled. And
Spir-it filled their dreams with life and form.
whis-per soft-ly call-ing in the dark, the
bove the child now grown so full of grace. As he

from the heart of God the Spir-it moved up-on the earth, like a
Des-erts turned to gar-dens, bro-ken hearts found new de-light, and then
prom-ise of a child of peace whose reign would nev-er end, Ma-ry
rose up from the wa-ter, she swept down from the sky, and she

1., 3.

moth-er breath-ing life in-to her child. *(to Verse 2)*
down the a-ges still she flew *(to Verse 4)*
sang the Spir-it song with-in her heart. *(to Verse 4)*
car-ried him a-way in her em - brace.

2., 4., 5.

on.

525

404 O Spirit come, our hearts inspire

TALLIS' ORDINAL 8 6 8 6 CM

1. O Spir-it, come; our hearts in - spire; let us thine in-fluence prove,
2. Come, Ho - ly Spir - it, for in thee thy pro-phets wrote and spoke.
3. Ex - pand thy wings, cel - es - tial Dove; brood o'er our na-ture's night;
4. God's ver - y self we then shall know, if thou with - in us shine,

source of the old pro - phet - ic fire and fount of life and love.
Un - lock the truth, thy - self the key; un - seal the sa - cred book.
on our dis - or-dered spir - its move, and let there now be light.
and sound, with all thy saints be - low the depths of love di - vine.

See also: Tallis' Ordinal 1

Words: Charles Wesley (1707–1788), alt   Music: Thomas Tallis (c. 1505–1585)

Words: public domain   Music: public domain

405 Lord, we pray not for tranquillity

Lord, we pray not for tranquillity,
nor that our tribulations may cease;
we pray for thy spirit and thy love,
that thou grant us strength and grace to overcome
adversity;
through Jesus Christ. Amen.

Words: Girolamo Savonarola (1452–1498), English translation, unknown

Words: public domain

406

Jump with joy

NJO NJO NJO Irregular

Leader(s) (E♭)

1. Jump with joy for Je-sus' life ev - er-last-ing, hal-le-lu - jah!
   for Je - sus binds us to geth-er,
1. Njo, njo, njo mwa Ye - su m - ku - li moy - o, hal-le-lu - jah!
   mwa Ye - su mu - li u - mo - dzi,

All E♭ (B♭7) E♭ B♭7/D E♭

Jump with joy for Je-sus' life ev - er-last-ing, hal-le-lu - jah!
for Je - sus binds us to-geth-er,
Njo, njo, njo mwa Ye - su m - ku - li moy - o, hal-le-lu - jah!
mwa Ye - su mu - li u - mo - dzi,

Leader(s) *All* E♭ (B♭7) E♭ B♭7 E♭

Sing now with glad-ness, hal-le-lu-jah! Sing now with glad-ness, hal-le-lu-jah!
Joy - ful - ly prais-ing, Joy - ful - ly prais-ing,
Ti - kon-dwe - re - re, hal-le-lu-jah! Ti - kon-dwe - re - re, hal-le-lu-jah!
Ti - san - ga - la - le, Ti - san - ga - la - le,

2. Jump with joy, for Jesus' love is eternal, hallelujah!
   Jump with joy, for Jesus' love is eternal, hallelujah!
   Jump with joy, for we are one now in Jesus, hallelujah!
   Jump with joy, for we are one now in Jesus, hallelujah!
   Dancing our praises, hallelujah! Dancing our praises, hallelujah!
   Shouting with laughter, hallelujah! Shouting with laughter, hallelujah!

2. Njo, njo, njo, mwa Yesu muli chikondi, hallelujah!
   Njo, njo, njo, mwa Yesu muli chikondi, hallelujah!
   Njo, njo, njo, mwa Yesu muli kumvana, hallelujah!
   Njo, njo, njo, mwa Yesu muli kumvana, hallelujah!
   Tibvine bvine, hallelujah! Tibvine bvine, hallelujah!
   Tisekerere, hallelujah! Tisekerere hallelujah!

Words: Chichewa chorus; translation, Clara Henderson (1955–) Music: Chichewa chorus transcribed as sung in the Blantyre Synod of the Church of Central Africa Presbyterian; harmony, All Africa Congress of Churches Assembly Choir

Words: translation, copyright © The Presbyterian Church in Canada, 1994 Music: public domain

Praise, my soul, the King of heaven

PRAISE, MY SOUL 878787

1. Praise, my soul, the King of heav - en; to his feet thy trib-ute bring;

ran-somed, healed, re - stored, for - giv - en, who like me his praise should sing?

Praise him, praise him, praise him, praise him, praise the ev-er-last-ing King.

2. Praise him for his grace and fa - vour to our fath-ers in dis-tress;
4. Frail as sum-mer's flower we flour - ish; blows the wind and it is gone,

Words: Psalm 103; paraphrase, Henry Francis Lyte (1793–1847) Music: John Goss (1800–1880)

Words: public domain Music: public domain

praise him, still the same for ev - er, slow to chide and swift to bless;
but, while mor-tals rise and per-ish, God en-dures un - chang-ing on:

praise him, praise him, praise him, praise him, glo-rious in his faith-ful-ness.
praise him, praise him, praise him, praise him, praise the high e - ter-nal One.

Unison

3. Fath-er-like he tends and spares us; well our fee-ble frame he knows;

in his hands he gent-ly bears us, res-cues us from all our foes:

praise him, praise him, praise him, praise him, wide-ly as his mer-cy flows.

V. 4 is under V.2

Unison

5. An-gels, help us to a-dore him, ye be-hold him face to face;

sun and moon, bow down be - fore him, dwell - ers all in time and space,

praise him, praise him, praise him, praise him, praise with us the God of grace.

I will call upon the Lord

I WILL CALL UPON THE LORD Irregular

Medium tempo

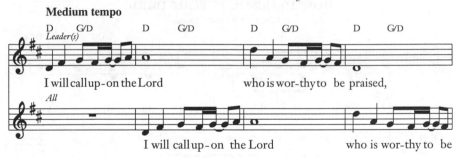

I will call up-on the Lord who is wor-thy to be praised,

I will call up-on the Lord who is wor-thy to be

so shall I be saved from my en-e-mies. The

praised, so shall I be saved from my en-e-mies. The

Lord liv-eth and bless-ed be the Rock and may the

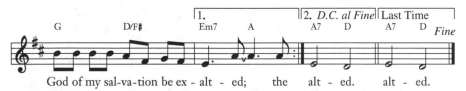

God of my sal-va-tion be ex-alt-ed; the alt-ed. alt-ed.

Words: Michael O'Shields Music: Michael O'Shields

O Lord, our Lord,
how majestic is your name

O LORD, OUR LORD   Irregular

Words: Michael W. Smith (1957–)   Music: Michael W. Smith (1957–)

name. Prince of Peace, might-y God, O

Lord God Al - might - y.

1.

2.

D.C.

410 Joyful, joyful we adore you

HYMN TO JOY 8 7 8 7 D

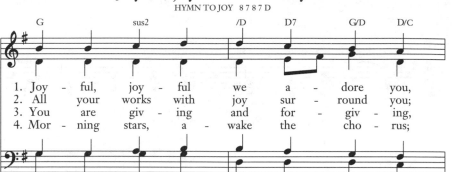

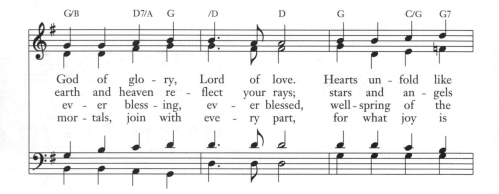

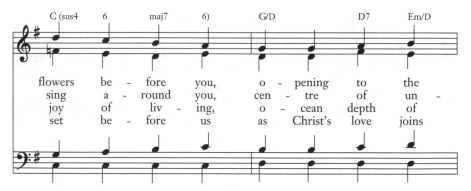

1. Joy - ful, joy - ful we a - dore you,
2. All your works with joy sur - round you;
3. You are giv - ing and for - giv - ing,
4. Mor - ning stars, a - wake the cho - rus;

God of glo - ry, Lord of love. Hearts un - fold like
earth and heaven re - flect your rays; stars and an - gels
ev - er bless - ing, ev - er blessed, well - spring of the
mor - tals, join with eve - ry part, for what joy is

flowers be - fore you, o - pening to the
sing a - round you, cen - tre of un -
joy of liv - ing, o - cean depth of
set be - fore us as Christ's love joins

Words: Henry Van Dyke (1852–1933), alt   Music: Ludwig van Beethoven (1770–1827);
arrangement, Edward Hodges (1796–1867)

Words: public domain   Music: public domain

sun a - bove. Melt the clouds of sin and sad - ness;
bro - ken praise. Field and for - est, vale and moun - tain,
hap - py rest. God Cre - a - tor, Christ our Sav - iour,
heart to heart! Ev - er sing - ing, march we on - ward,

drive the dark of doubt a - way; giv - er of im -
flower - y mead - ow, flash - ing sea, chant - ing bird and
all are yours who live in love. Teach us how to
vic - tors in the midst of strife; joy - ful mu - sic

mor - tal glad - ness, fill us with the light of day.
flow - ing foun - tain, join to praise you joy - ful - ly.
love our neigh - bour; lift us to your joy a - bove.
leads us sun - ward in the tri - umph song of life.

Stand up and bless the Lord

ST. THOMAS 6 6 8 6 SM

1. Stand up and bless the Lord; God's people now re-joice; stand up and bless the Lord your God with heart and soul and voice.
2. Though high a-bove all praise, a-bove all bless-ing high, who would not fear God's ho-ly name, and praise and mag-ni-fy?
3. Oh for the liv-ing flame from God's own al-tar brought, to touch our lips, our minds in-spire, and wing to heaven our thought.
4. God is our strength and song; now is sal-va-tion ours. God's love in Christ we now pro-claim with all our ran-somed powers.
5. Stand up and bless the Lord; the Lord your God a-dore; stand up and bless God's glo-rious name hence-forth for-ev-er-more.

Words: James Montgomery (1771–1854), alt   Music: Williams' Psalmody 1770

412 Come, let us sing to the Lord our song

FORNEY 9889

1. Come, let us sing to the Lord our song:
2. O thirs-ty soul, come drink at the well;
3. You dwell a-mong us and cause us to pray, and
4. Des-erts shall bloom and moun-tains shall sing

we have stood si - lent - ly too long;
God's liv-ing wa - ters will nev-er fail.
walk with each oth - er fol - lowing your way;
to the de - sire of all liv-ing things.

sure-ly the Lord de - serves our praise, so
Sure-ly the Lord will help you to stand,
our prec-ious bro - thers and sis - ters will grow
Come, all you crea - tures, high and low;

joy - ful - ly thank God for our days.
strength-ened and com - for-ted by God's hand.
in the ful-fill - ing love they know.
let your prais - es end - less-ly flow.

Words: Jim Strathdee (1941–) Music: Jim Strathdee (1941–); arrangement, Jean Strathdee (1944–)

413 Come let us join our cheerful songs

NATIVITY 8 6 8 6 CM

1. Come, let us join our cheer-ful songs with an-gels round the throne;
2. "Wor-thy the Lamb that died," they cry, "to be ex-alt-ed thus."
3. Je-sus is wor-thy to re-ceive hon-our and power div-ine;
4. The whole cre-a-tion joins in one to bless the sac-red name

ten thou-sand thou-sand are their tongues, but all their joys are one.
"Wor-thy the Lamb," our lips re-ply, "for he was slain for us."
may bless-ings, more than we can give, be, Lord, for-ev-er thine.
of him that sits up-on the throne, and to a-dore the Lamb.

Alternate tune: Richmond

Words: Revelation 5; paraphrase, Isaac Watts (1674–1748) Music: Henry Lahee (1826–1912)

Words: public domain Music: public domain

414 God, reveal your presence

ARNSBERG (REVERENCE) 6 6 8 D 3 3 6 6

1. God, re-veal your pres-ence: glad-ly we a-dore you,
   Ho-ly is your tem-ple: all with-in keep si-lence,
2. In God's ho-ly pres-ence: hear the harps re-sound-ing;
   "Ho-ly, ho-ly, ho-ly!" hear the hymn as-cend-ing,
3. Foun-tain of all bless-ing, pur-i-fy my spir-it;
   Like the ho-ly an-gels on your glo-ry gaz-ing,

Words: German, Gerhard Tersteegen (1697–1769); translation, Frederick William Foster (1760–1835), and John Miller (1756–1790); alterations, William Mercer (1811–1873), alt
Music: Joachim Neander (1650–1680)

Words: this version, copyright © The Presbyterian Church in Canada, 1997 Music: public domain

538

and with awe ap - pear be - fore you. You a - lone now we own,
hum - bly bow with deep - est rev - erence.
see the crowds the throne sur - round - ing; Turn your ear to us here;
an - gels, saints, their voic - es blend - ing.
all my trust is in your mer - it. Let your will ev - er still
we a - dore, ho - san - nas rais - ing.

as our God and Sav - iour: praise your name for - ev - er!
hear, O Christ, the prais - es that your church now rais - es.
rule your church ter - res - trial, as the hosts ce - les - tial.

Hungarian
1. Itt van Isten köztünk: Jertek Öt imádni,
   Hódolattal elé állni.
   Itt van a középen: Minden csendre térve
   Öelötte hulljon térdre.
   Az, aki hirdeti
   S hallja itt az Igét: Adja néki szívét!

2. Itt van Isten köztünk: Ö, kit éjjel-nappal
   Angyalsereg áld s magasztal.
   Szent, szent, szent az Isten! Néki énekelnek
   A mennyei fényes lelkek.
   Halld, Urunk, szózatunk,
   Ha mi, semmiségek Áldozunk Tenéked!

3. Jöjj és lakozz bennem: Hadd legyen már itt lenn
   Templomoddá szívem-lelkem!
   Mindig közellévö: jelentsd Magad nékem,
   Ne lakhasson más e szívben;
   Már itt lenn Mindenben
   Csakis Téged lásson, Leborulva áldjon!

Children of Jerusalem

INFANT PRAISE 7 7 7 7 with refrain

1. Chil-dren of Je - ru - sa - lem sang the praise of
2. Teach us now to love you, Lord; teach us how to
3. Par - ents, teach - ers, old and young, all u - nite to

Je - sus' name: chil - dren now, in eve - ry place join to
read your word; teach us all the ways of heaven. Joy - ful
swell the song, high - er and yet high - er rise, till ho -

sing the Sav-iour's praise.
praise to God be given. Hark! hark! hark! the children's voices sing.
san - nas fill the skies.

Hark! hark! hark! the chil-dren's voic-es sing loud ho - san-nas,

Words: John Henley (1800–1842), alt Music: Curwen's Tune Book 1842

Words: public domain Music: public domain

loud ho - san - nas, loud ho - san - nas to our King.

416 Blessed Jesus, at your word

LIEBSTER JESU 787888

1. Bless - ed Je - sus, at your word we are gath-ered all to hear you;
   let our minds and wills be stirred now to love you and re - vere you;
2. All our knowledge, sense and sight lie in deep - est dark-ness shroud - ed,
   till your Spir - it breaks our night with the beams of truth un-cloud - ed;
3. Glo-rious Lord, your-self im - part, light of light, from God pro-ceed - ing,
   o - pen now each mind and heart; help us by the Spir - it's plead - ing.

by your teachings true and ho - ly drawn from earth to love you sole - ly.
you a - lone to God can win us; you must work all good with - in us.
Hear the cry your church now rais-es; Lord, ac - cept our prayers and prais-es.

Words: Tobias Clausnitzer (1619–1684); translation, Catherine Winkworth (1827–1878), alt
Music: Johann Rudolph Ahle (1625–1673); harmony, J.S. Bach (1685–1750)

Words: public domain Music: public domain

Come, rejoice in God

JUBILATE SERVITE Irregular

May be sung as a round.

Words: Psalm 100; paraphrase, Jacques Berthier (1923–1994), Taizé Community (France)
Music: Jacques Berthier (1923–1994), Taizé Community (France)

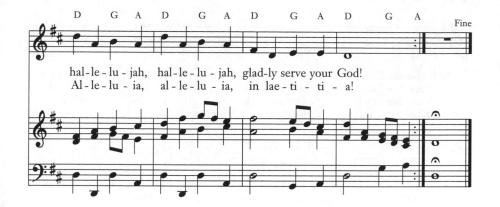

hal-le-lu-jah, hal-le-lu-jah, glad-ly serve your God!
Al-le-lu-ia, al-le-lu-ia, in lae-ti-ti-a!

Praise the Lord

LAUDATE PUERI Irregular

Unison

1. Praise the Lord! Praise, you ser-vants of the Lord, praise the
2. Praise the Lord! Thanks and prais-es sing to God, day by
3. Praise the Lord! Praise and glo-ry give to God; who is
4. Praise the Lord! Praise, you ser-vants of the Lord, praise the

name of the Lord! Bless-ed be the name of the Lord!
day to the Lord! High a-bove the na-tions is God,
like God the Lord? Rais-ing up the poor from the dust,
love of the Lord! Giv-ing to the home-less a home,

Bless-ed be the name of the Lord from this time
high a-bove the na-tions is God, in glo-ry
rais-ing up the poor from the dust, God makes them
giv-ing to the home-less a home, God fills their

Words: Psalm 113; v. 3, 4, Marjorie Jillson (1931–) Music: Heinz Werner Zimmerman (1930–)

forth and for - ev - er - more!
high o - ver earth and sky.
dwell in pros - per - i - ty.
hearts with new hope and joy.

Praise the Lord!   Praise the Lord!

419   You are medicine for me

You are medicine for me when I am sick.
You are my strength when I need help.
You are life itself when I fear death.
You are the way when I long for heaven.
You are light when all is dark.
You are my food when I need nourishment. Amen.

Words: Ambrose of Milan (339–397), English translation, unknown
Words: public domain

420 Je louerai l'Éternel / Praise, I will praise

JE LOUERAI L'ETERNEL Irregular

Words: French, Claude Fraysse (1941–) Psalm 9: 2–3; translation, Kenneth I. Morse (1913–)
Music: Claude Fraysse (1941–); vocal arrangement, Alain Bergèse

Rejoice in the Lord

REJOICE 14 14 11 11

May be sung as a round.

① Re - joice in the Lord al - ways, and a - gain I say, Re - joice!

② Re - joice in the Lord al - ways, and a - gain I say, Re - joice!

③ Re - joice! Re - joice! and a - gain I say, Re - joice!

④ Re - joice! Re - joice! and a - gain I say, Re - joice!

Words: Philippians 4:4 Music: Traditional; arrangement, Dale Grotenhuis (1931–)

Sing a new song unto the Lord

SING A NEW SONG   7 6 9 6 with refrain (8 9 8 6)

Unison
Refrain

Sing a new song un-to the Lord; let your song be sung from moun-tain's height. Sing a new song un-to the Lord, sing-ing hal - le - lu - jah!

Words: Psalm 98; paraphrase, Daniel L. Schutte   Music: Daniel L. Schutte (1947–), arrangement
Sr. Theophane Hytrek, OSF (1915–1992)

| G | D7/A | Am/G | D/F# | Em | /D | C6 | G6/B |

1. For God's peo-ple dance for joy. Oh come be-fore the
2. Rise, O chil-dren, from your sleep; your Sav-iour now has
3. Glad my soul for I have seen the glo-ry of the

| D7/A G | D7/F# | G | D7/A | Am/G | /E | D |

Lord,   play for the Lord on glad tam-bou-rines, and
come.   He has turned your sor-row to joy, and
Lord.   The trum-pet sounds; the dead shall be raised I

| C | Am7 | Dsus4– 2–   3 | *D.C. al Fine* |

let your trum - pet sound.
filled your soul with song.
know my Sav - iour lives.

Sing your praise to God eternal

ARFON (MAJOR) 8 7 8 7 D

1. Sing your praise to God e - ter - nal, sing your praise to God the Son,
2. Join the praise of eve - ry crea - ture; sing with sing - ing birds at dawn;
3. Praise God on our days of glad-ness for the sum-mons to re - joice;

sing your praise to God, the Spir - it, liv - ing and for - ev - er One.
when the stars shine forth at night-fall, hear their heaven-ly an - ti - phon.
praise God in our times of sad-ness, for the calm, con - sol - ing voice.

God has made us, God has blessed us, God has called us to be true;
Praise God for the light of sum - mer, au - tumn glo - ries, win - ter snows,
God our Mak - er, strong and lov - ing, Christ our Sav-iour, Lead-er, Lord,

Words: Robert B.Y. Scott (1899–1987)   Music: Welsh melody; arrangement, Stanley Osborne (1907–)

Words: copyright © Emmanuel College   Music: arrangement, copyright © Anglican Church of Canada and United Church of Canada, 1971

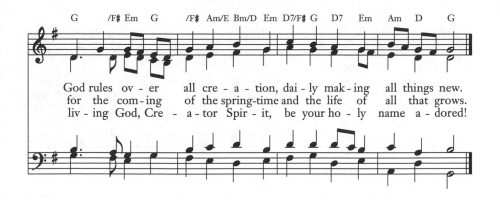

God rules ov - er   all cre - a - tion, dai - ly mak - ing   all things new.
for the com - ing   of the spring-time and the life of   all that grows.
liv - ing God, Cre - a - tor Spir - it,   be your ho - ly   name a - dored!

424   Sing, praise and bless the Lord

LAUDATE DOMINUM 6 6 4 4 with hallelujahs

Sing, praise and   bless the Lord.   Sing, praise and   bless the Lord,
Lau - da - te   Do - mi - num,   lau - da - te   Do - mi - num

peo - ples,   na - tions,   hal - le - lu - jah!   hal - le - lu - jah!
om - nes   gen - tes,   al - le - lu - ia!   al - le - lu - ia!

Words: Psalm 100 Music: Taizé Community (France)

We praise you, O God

KREMSER 12 11 12 11

1. We praise you, O God, our Re- deem- er, Cre- a - tor; in
grate - ful de - vo - tion our trib - ute we bring. We
lay it be - fore you; we kneel and a - dore you; we
bless your ho - ly name; glad prais- es we sing.

2. We wor- ship you; God ev - er- faith - ful, we bless you; through
life's storm and tem - pest our guide you have been. When
per - ils o'er - take us, you will not for - sake us, and
with your help, O Lord, life's bat - tles we win.

3. With voic- es u - ni - ted our prais- es we of - fer, and
glad - ly our songs of true wor - ship we raise. Our
sins now con - fess - ing, we pray for your bless-ing; to
you, our great Re - deem - er, for - ev - er be praise.

Words: Dutch, anonymous, 1626, translation, Julia Bulkley Cady Cory (1882–1963); alt
Music: Netherlands folk song, 1626; arrangement, Edward Kremser (1838–1914)

Words: public domain   Music: public domain

Holy, holy, holy

SANCTUS (CABENA) Irregular

Ho - ly, ho - ly, ho - ly Lord, God of power and might, heav-en and earth are full of your glo-ry. Ho - san - na in the high - est. Blest is the one* who comes in the name of the Lord. Ho - san - na in the high - est.

* alternate: Bless-ed is he

Words: traditional   Music: Barrie Cabena (1933–)

Words: public domain   Music: copyright © Barrie Cabena

427

In the presence of your people

CELEBRATION Irregular

Descant (2nd time)

Lei, lei, lei…

In the pres-ence of your peo-ple I will praise your name, for a-lone you are ho-ly, en-throned on the prais-es of Is-ra-el.

Let us cel-e-brate your good-ness and your stead-fast love;

Words: Brent Chambers (1948–)   Music: Brent Chambers (1948–)

may your name be ex-alt-ed here on earth and in heaven a-bove.

428   We love your house, O God

QUAM DILECTA 6 6 6 6

1. We love your house, O God, the place where hon - our dwells;
2. We love the house of prayer, where you your ser - vants greet,
3. We love the word of life, the word that tells of peace,
4. We love to sing be - low of mer - cies free - ly given,
5. Lord Je - sus, give us grace on earth to love you more,

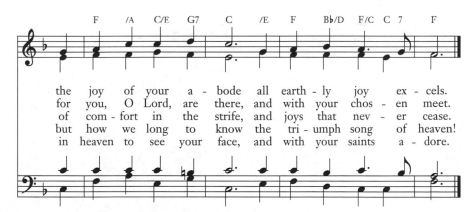

the joy of your a - bode all earth - ly joy ex - cels.
for you, O Lord, are there, and with your chos - en meet.
of com - fort in the strife, and joys that nev - er cease.
but how we long to know the tri - umph song of heaven!
in heaven to see your face, and with your saints a - dore.

Words: Henry Williams Baker (1821–1877), William Bullock (1798–1874), alt
Music: Henry Lascelles Jenner (1820–1898)

Words: public domain Music: public domain

Your strong word once cleaved the darkness

TON Y BOTEL 8 7 8 7 D

1. Your strong word once cleaved the dark - ness; at your
2. Now on those who dwelt in dark - ness, dark as
3. Your strong word de - clares us right - eous; bright with
4. God the Fa - ther, Light - Cre - a - tor, praise to

speak - ing it was done; for cre - a - ted
night and deep as death, broke the light of
your own ho - li - ness, glo - rious now, we
you and hon - our be; to you, Light of

light we thank you, while your or - dered sea - sons run:
your sal - va - tion, breathed your own life - giv - ing breath:
press to glo - ry, and our lives our hopes con - fess,
Light be - got - ten, praise be sung e - ter - nal - ly;

See also: Ton Y Botel 279

Words: Martin H. Franzmann (1907–1976)   Music: Thomas John Williams (1869–1944)

430 You are Author

SARA SHRISTE   10 10 6 11 with hallelujas

Unison

You are Au-thor and Lord of cre - a - tion; you are Mak- er of
Sa - ra shri-ste ko ma-lik ta - paiy-lay; sa-ra shri-ste ko
L'É ter - nel est l'Au-teur de la vi - e, Cré-a - teur, Sou - ve -

Note: lower voices may vocalize parts on "Ah" for choral performance.

life and of liv - ing, and from deep in our hearts,
ra - jah ta - paiy-lay. Ham-bro rhe-day s'a - me-ta-le
rain de l'his-toir - e: nous te lou-ons, Seig-neur,

won - der and love in - spire our wor-ship and praise.
ad - har pra - nam; s'ad - aiy-bahns ta - paiy-ko gun - gan.
du fond des coeurs rem - plis de joie et d'a - mour.

Words: Nepalese traditional, taught by Elisabeth Padillo–Oleson; translation, Iona Community (Scotland);
French translation, Andrew Donaldson (1951–)   Music: probably of European origin, taught by Elisabeth
Padillo–Oleson; arrangement, Iona Community (Scotland)

431

Jesus, where'er thy people meet

WARRINGTON 8888 LM

1. Je - sus, wher - e'er thy peo - ple meet, there they be - hold thy
2. Here may we prove the power of prayer to strength-en faith and
3. Lord, we are few, but thou art near, nor short thine arm, nor

mer - cy seat; where'-er they seek thee thou art found,
sweet - en care, to teach our faint de - sires to rise,
deaf thine ear; oh rend the heavens, come quick - ly down

and eve - ry place is hal - lowed ground.
and bring all heaven be - fore our eyes.
and make a thou - sand hearts thine own.

Words: William Cowper (1731–1800) Music: Ralph Harrison (1748–1810)

Words: public domain Music: public domain

432   O Lord of heaven and earth and sea

ES IST KEIN TAG 8 8 8 4

1. O Lord of heaven and earth and sea, to thee all praise and glory be; how shall we show our love to thee who givest all?
2. The golden sunshine, sweet spring air, sweet flowers and fruit, thy love declare; where harvests ripen thou art there, who givest all.
3. For peaceful homes and healthful days, for all the blessings earth displays, we owe thee thankfulness and praise, who givest all.
4. Thou didst not spare thine only Son, but gav'st him for a world undone and freely with that Blessed One thou givest all.
5. Thou giv'st the Spirit's blessed dower, Spirit of life and love and power, and dost thy sevenfold graces shower upon us all.

6. For souls redeemed, for sins forgiven,
   for means of grace and hopes of heaven,
   O Lord, what can to thee be given,
   —who givest all?—

7. to thee from whom we all derive
   our life, our gifts, our power to give?
   Oh may we ever with thee live,
   who givest all.

Alternate tune: Almsgiving

Words: Christopher Wordsworth (1807–1885) Music: J.D. Meyer in *Geistliche Seelenfreud*, Ulm 1692

All creatures of our God and King

LASST UNS ERFREUEN 8 8 4 4 8 8 with hallelujahs

Descant

Let all things their Cre - a - tor bless, and

Unison

1. All crea-tures of our God and King lift
2. Wild rush - ing wind, un - bound - ed, strong, high
3. Deep flow - ing wa - ter, pure and clear, make
4. Dear moth - er earth, who day by day brings
5. Let eve - ry - one of ten - der heart, for -
6. Let all things their Cre - a - tor bless, and

wor - ship God: sing   prais - es,   hal - le -

Harmony

up your voice and with us sing:
clouds that sail in heaven a - long:
mu - sic for your God to hear: sing   prais - es,   hal - le -
forth your bless-ings on our way:
giv - ing oth - ers, take their part:
wor - ship God in hum - ble - ness:

Words: based on Francis of Assisi's "Canticle of the Sun" (1182–1226), translation, William H. Draper
(1855–1933), alt Music: Church Song 1623; harmony, Ralph Vaughan Williams (1872–1958); descant,
Christopher Gower (1939–)

lu - jah! *Unison* Fa - ther, praise the Son,

Eb6 F Bb Eb/G Eb /D Cm7 Bb7/D Eb Ab/C Bbsus4 – 3 /Ab

O broth - er sun with gold - en beam,
New ris - ing dawn in praise re - joice,
Fierce fire, so mas - ter - ful and bright,
lu - jah! All flowers and fruit that in you grow,
All who long pain and sor - row bear,
Praise, praise the Fa - ther, praise the Son,

Spir - it, Three-in - One: sing prais - es sing

Harmony

Eb/G Bb7 /F Eb Ab/C Eb/Bb Ab Eb/G Eb Ab/C Ab6 Bb/Ab Eb/G Fm7 Eb/G

O sis - ter moon with sil - ver gleam,
kind lights of eve - ning, find a voice:
pierce now the dark with heat and light:
let them God's glo - ry al - so show: sing prais - es, sing
give God your bur - dens and your care:
and praise the Spir - it, Three-in - One:

prais - es, hal-le - lu - jah, hal-le - lu - jah, hal-le - lu - jah!

Unison

Ab6 Bb7 Cm Bb/D Eb6 F Bb Cm7 Eb6 Fm Bb7/D C7 Fm Eb/G Ab6 Bb 7 Eb

prais - es, hal-le - lu - jah, hal-le - lu - jah, hal-le - lu - jah!

563

434

For the beauty of the earth

DIX 777777

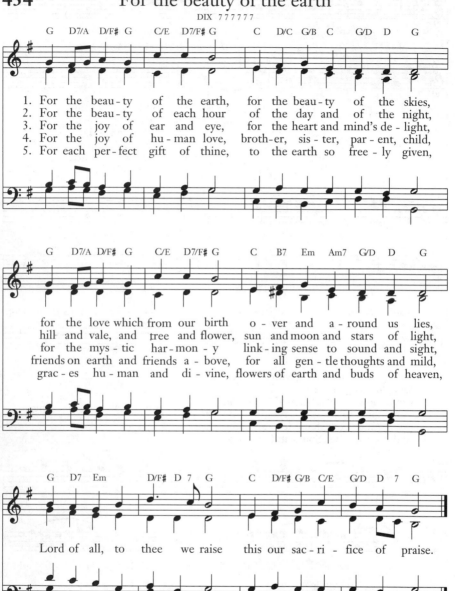

For the beauty of the earth, for the beauty of the skies,
For the beauty of each hour of the day and of the night,
For the joy of ear and eye, for the heart and mind's de-light,
For the joy of hu-man love, broth-er, sis-ter, par-ent, child,
For each per-fect gift of thine, to the earth so free-ly given,

for the love which from our birth o-ver and a-round us lies,
hill and vale, and tree and flower, sun and moon and stars of light,
for the mys-tic har-mon-y link-ing sense to sound and sight,
friends on earth and friends a-bove, for all gen-tle thoughts and mild,
grac-es hu-man and di-vine, flowers of earth and buds of heaven,

Lord of all, to thee we raise this our sac-ri-fice of praise.

See also: Dix 39 172

Words: Folliott Sandford Pierpoint (1835–1917), alt Music: Adapted from a Chorale by Conrad Kocher (1786–1872); harmony, William Henry Monk (1823–1889), Carman H. Milligan (1909–)

Words: public domain Music: harmony, copyright © Carman H. Milligan

435

All things bright and beautiful

ROYAL OAK 7 6 7 6 with refrain

Refrain

All things bright and beau-ti-ful, all crea-tures great and small,

all things wise and won-der-ful, in love God made them all.

Fine

1. Each lit-tle flower that o-pens, each lit-tle bird that sings,
2. The cold wind in the win-ter, the pleas-ant sum-mer sun,
3. The rock-y moun-tain splen-dour, the haunt-ing cur-lew's call,
4. God gave us eyes to see them, and lips that we might tell

D.C.

God made their glow-ing col-ours; God made their ti-ny wings.
the ripe fruits in the gar-den, God made them, eve-ry one.
the great lakes and the prai-ries, the for-ests in the fall,
how great is God al-might - who has made all things well.

Words: Cecil Frances Alexander (1818–1895), alt Music: English folk melody;
arrangement, Martin Shaw (1875–1958)

God, we praise you for the morning

DICKEY 8786

1. God, we praise you for the morn - ing; hope springs forth with each new day, new be - gin - ning, prayer and prom - ise, joy in work and in play.
2. God, we praise you for cre - a - tion, moun - tains, seas and prai - rie land. Wak - ing souls find joy and heal - ing in your boun - ti - ful hand.
3. God, we praise you for com - pas - sion, all the lov - ing that you show; hu - man touch - ing, tears and laugh - ter, help your chil - dren to grow.
4. God, we praise you for your Spir - it, Com - fort - er and dai - ly friend; rest - less search - er, gen - tle teach - er, strength and cour - age you send.
5. God, we praise you for the Sav - iour, come that we may know your ways. In his lov - ing, dy - ing, ris - ing, Christ is Lord of our days.
6. Hal - le - lu - jah, hal - le - lu - jah, hal - le - lu - jah, hal - le - lu - jah, hal - le - lu - jah! Christ is Lord of our days!

Words: Jim Strathdee (1941–), Jean Strathdee (1944–)   Music: Jim Strathdee (1941–)

437 First of the week and finest day

CANNOCK 8 8 8 8 LM

1. First of the week and fin - est day, when God com -
2. First of the week was East - er morn when Christ the
3. First of the week the Spir - it came to fill the
4. First of the week we set a - side to meet, to

mand - ed light to shine: cast dark - ness and its
Lord from death was raised; new life, fresh hope that
church with grace and power; the rush - ing wind and
learn, to give, to pray, to spread Christ's gos - pel

works a - way to ce - le - brate with bread and wine!
day was born and God in heaven and earth was praised.
tongues of flame, were her - alds of that prom - ised hour.
far and wide — in truth, this is the Lord's own day!

Words: David Mowbray (1938–) Music: P. Armes (1836–1908)

438 When morning gilds the skies

LAUDES DOMINI 6 6 6 6 6 6

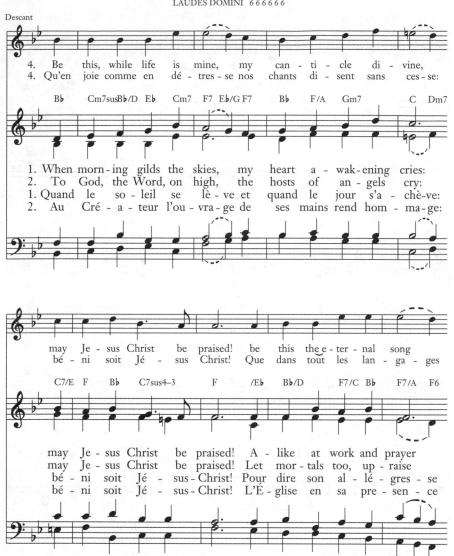

Descant

4. Be this, while life is mine, my can - ti - cle di - vine,
4. Qu'en joie comme en dé - tres - se nos chants di - sent sans ces - se:

1. When morn-ing gilds the skies, my heart a - wak-ening cries:
2. To God, the Word, on high, the hosts of an - gels cry:
1. Quand le so - leil se lè - ve et quand le jour s'a - chè-ve:
2. Au Cré - a - teur l'ou - vra-ge de ses mains rend hom - ma-ge:

may Je - sus Christ be praised! be this the e - ter - nal song
bé - ni soit Jé - sus Christ! Que dans tout les lan - ga - ges

may Je - sus Christ be praised! A - like at work and prayer
may Je - sus Christ be praised! Let mor - tals too, up - raise
bé - ni soit Jé - sus - Christ! Pour dire son al - lé - gres - se
bé - ni soit Jé - sus - Christ! L'É - glise en sa pre - sen - ce

Words: German anonymous, 19th century; English, Edward Caswall (1814–1878),
French, Jacques Beaudon (1913–1985), revised R. Gerald Hobbs (1941–)
Music: Joseph Barnby (1838–1896); descant, Reginald S. Thatcher (1888–1957)

Words: French, copyright © Londa Ann Beaudon Music: descant, copyright © Oxford University Press

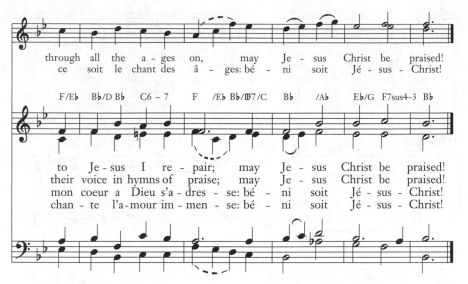

through all the a - ges on, may Je - sus Christ be praised!
ce soit le chant des â - ges: bé - ni soit Jé - sus - Christ!

to Je - sus I re - pair; may Je - sus Christ be praised!
their voice in hymns of praise; may Je - sus Christ be praised!
mon coeur a Dieu s'a - dres - se: bé - ni soit Jé - sus - Christ!
chan - te l'a-mour im - men - se: bé - ni soit Jé - sus - Christ!

3. Let earth's wide circle round
   in joyful notes resound:
   may Jesus Christ be praised!
   Let earth and sea and sky,
   from depth to height reply:
   may Jesus Christ be praised!

4. Be this, while life is mine,
   my canticle divine:
   may Jesus Christ be praised!
   be this the eternal song
   through all the ages on:
   may Jesus Christ be praised!

3. C'est le choeur des louanges
   qu'entonnent tous les anges:
   béni soit Jésus-Christ!
   Et que la terre entière
   répète la prière:
   béni soit Jésus-Christ!

4. Qu'en joie comme en détresse
   nos chants disent sans cesse:
   béni soit Jésus-Christ!
   Que dans tous les langages
   ce soit le chant des âges:
   béni soit Jésus-Christ!

When in our music God is glorified

ENGELBERG 10 10 10 4

1. When in our mu - sic God is glo - ri - fied,
2. How of - ten, mak - ing mu - sic, we have found
3. So has the church, in lit - ur - gy and song,
4. And did not Je - sus sing a Psalm that night
5. Let eve - ry in - stru-ment be tuned for praise!

and a - do - ra - tion leaves no room for pride, it is as
a new di - men - sion in the world of sound, as wor-ship
in faith and love, through cen - tu - ries of wrong, borne wit - ness
when ut - most e - vil strove a - gainst the Light? Then let us
Let all re - joice who have a voice to raise! And may God

Words: Fred Pratt Green (1903–) Music: C.V. Stanford (1852–1924)

Words: copyright © 1972 by Hope Publishing Co. Music: public domain

| 1.–4. |

though the whole cre - a - tion cried,
moved us to a more pro - found
to the truth in eve - ry tongue: Hal - le - lu - jah!
sing, for whom he won the fight:
give us faith to sing al - ways:

Csus2 Am7 Am6 Em Am6 Em /D   /C Am7   D7/A G C/E D7sus4–3

| 5.

Hal - le - lu - jah!   A - men.

Cmaj7   Am   /C   G   Am7/G G   C   (6) /C   G

For all the love

STARS 10 10 10 4

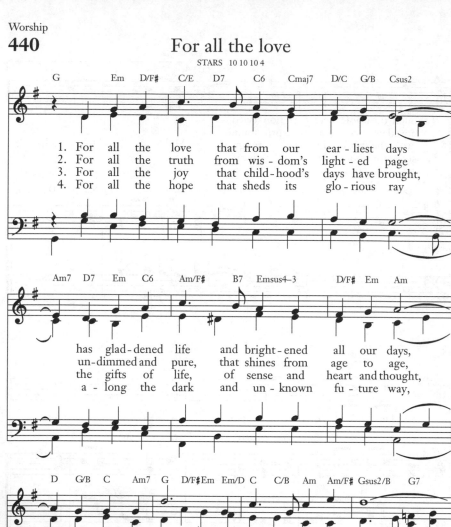

1. For all the love that from our ear-liest days
2. For all the truth from wis-dom's light-ed page
3. For all the joy that child-hood's days have brought,
4. For all the hope that sheds its glo-rious ray

has glad-dened life and bright-ened all our days,
un-dimmed and pure, that shines from age to age,
the gifts of life, of sense and heart and thought,
a-long the dark and un-known fu-ture way,

we bring you, Lord, our song of grate-ful praise,
God's ho-ly word, our price-less her-i-tage,
of life's deep mean - ing to our spir-its taught,
and lights the path to God's e-ter-nal day,

Alternate tune: Sine Nomine

Words: L.J. Egerton Smith (1879–1958), alt   Music: Carl F. Schalk (1929–)

Words: public domain   Music: copyright © Carl F. Schalk, 1993

5. For all the strength that we have gained through prayer,
   to face life's tasks, its eager quests to share,
   till ampler powers fulfil its promise fair,
   hallelujah!

6. For Christ the Lord, our Saviour and our friend,
   upon whose love and truth our souls depend,
   our hope, our strength, our joy that knows no end,
   hallelujah!

441

Can a little child like me

THANKSGIVING 7 7 7 7 7 7 with refrain

1. Can a lit - tle child like me thank the Fath - er
2. For our play - ing, for our rest, for the earth in
3. For the laugh - ter, for the tear, for the love that

fit - ting - ly? Yes, oh yes! be good and true,
beau - ty dressed, for the moon and sun so bright,
meets us here, for the les - sons of our youth—

pa - tient, kind in all we do; love the Lord and
for the day and for the night, for your pa - tient,
hon - our, grat - i - tude and truth— for the great gift

do our part; learn to say with all our heart:
lov - ing care, for your boun - ty eve - ry - where:
of your Son, for your work in us be - gun:

Words: Mary Mapes Dodge (1831–1905), alt   Music: W.K. Basswood (19th cent.)

Words: this version copyright © The Presbyterian Church in Canada, 1997   Music: public domain

Refrain

Sav - iour, we thank you, Spir - it, we thank you,

Great God our Mak - er, we thank you!

442 Speak, Lord, in the stillness

CASWALL (BEMERTON) 6 5 6 5

1. Speak, Lord, in the still - ness speak your word to me;
2. Speak, O gra - cious Mas - ter, in this qui - et hour;
3. For the words you give me they are life in - deed;
4. Speak, your ser - vant lis - tens, be not si - lent, Lord;
5. Fill me with the know - ledge of your glo - rious will;

hushed my heart to lis - ten in ex - pect - an - cy.
let me see your face, Lord, feel your touch of power.
liv - ing bread from heav - en, now my spir - it feed.
let me know your pres - ence; let your voice be heard.
all your own good pleas - ure in my life ful - fill.

Words: Emily M. Crawford (1868–1927), alt   Music: Friedrich Filitz (1804–1878)
Words: public domain   Music: public domain

443 When all thy mercies, O my God

BELGRAVE 8 6 8 6 CM

1. When all thy mer - cies, O my God, my ris - ing
2. Oh how shall words with e - qual warmth the grat - i -
3. Ten thou - sand thou - sand pre - cious gifts my dai - ly
4. Through eve - ry sea - son of my life thy good - ness

soul sur - veys, trans - port - ed with the view, I'm
tude de - clare that glows with - in my en - rap - tured
thanks em - ploy, nor is the least a cheer - ful
I'll pur - sue, and af - ter death, in dis - tant

lost in won - der, love and praise.
heart? But thou canst read it there.
heart that tastes these gifts with joy.
worlds, the glo - rious theme re - new.

5. When nature fails, and day and night
   divide thy works no more,
   my ever-grateful heart, O Lord,
   thy mercy shall adore.

6. Through all eternity to thee
   a joyful song I'll raise,
   for oh! eternity's too short
   to utter all thy praise.

Alternate tunes: St. Stephen (Newington) Winchester Old

Words: Joseph Addison (1672–1719), alt   Music: William Horsley (1774–1858)

Words: public domain   Music: public domain

444

Sweet is the solemn voice

HAMBURG (VOICE DIVINE) 8 8 8 8 LM

1. Sweet is the sol - emn voice that calls the Chris-tian
2. I love to walk with - in the courts where two or
3. How good to raise our com - mon song! Join - ing in
4. With - in these walls may peace a - bound; may all our

to the house of prayer; I love to stand with -
three for wor - ship meet, for it is there that
ho - ly praise and love, we im - i - tate the
hearts in one a - gree, and where we meet, where

in its walls, for you, O Lord, are pres - ent there.
Christ re - sorts to make their ho - ly bond com - plete.
bless - ed throng, u - nit - ing hearts and songs a - bove.
Christ is found, may peace and con - cord ev - er be.

Words: Henry Francis Lyte (1793–1847)   Music: Gregorian plainsong;
arrangement, Lowell Mason (1792–1872)

Words: public domain   Music: public domain

Open our eyes, Lord

OPEN OUR EYES   Irregular

Unison

1. O-pen our eyes, Lord, we want to see
2. O-pen our ears, Lord, and help us to

Je - sus, to reach out and touch
lis - ten. O-pen our eyes,

1.
him, and say that we love him.
Lord,

2.
we want to see Je - sus.

Words: Bob Cull   Music: Bob Cull

446

O Lord, hear my prayer /
The Lord is my song

O LORD, HEAR MY PRAYER 5 5 6 D

*
A. O Lord, hear my prayer; O Lord, hear my prayer. When I call an - swer me. O
B. The Lord is my song; the Lord is my praise: all my hope comes from God. The

* Note: two alternate texts, not to be sung in succession.

Lord, hear my prayer; O Lord, hear my prayer. Come and lis - ten to me. O
Lord is my song; the Lord is my praise: God, the well-spring of life. The

Words: Taizé Community (France)   Music: Taizé Community (France)

447

O Great Spirit

O GREAT SPIRIT Irregular

O   Great   Spir - it,   1. how   I long to
                                         2. how   I long to

hear your   name.   How   I long to see your face.   A
touch your hands.

way hi ho, a way hi ho, a way hi hi   ho.

Words: Doreen Clellamin (1941–) Music: Doreen Clellamin (1941–)

O God beyond all praising

THAXTED 7 6 7 6 Triple

1. O God be-yond all prais - ing, we wor-ship you to -
day and sing the love a - maz - ing that
songs can-not re - pay, for we can on - ly won - der at
eve - ry gift you send, at bless-ings with - out num-ber and

2. Then hear, O gra - cious Sav - iour; ac - cept the love we
bring, that we who know your fa - vour may
serve you as our king, and wheth - er our to - mor-rows be
filled with good or ill, we'll tri - umph through our sor - rows and

Words: Michael Perry (1942–1996) Music: Gustav T. Holst (1874–1934)

mer - cies with - out end. We lift our hearts be -
rise to bless you still: to mar - vel at your

fore you and wait up - on your word; we
beau - ty and glo - ry in your ways, and

hon - our and a - dore you, our great and might - y Lord.
make a joy - ful du - ty our sac - ri - fice of praise.

449
Lord, listen to your children praying
CHILDREN PRAYING 9 8 9 9

Lord, lis-ten to your chil-dren pray - ing;

Lord, send your Spir - it in this place;

Lord, lis-ten to your chil-dren pray - ing, send us

love; send us power; send us grace!

Words: Ken Medema (1943–) Music: Ken Medema (1943–)

Words: copyright © 1970, 1971 by Hope Publishing Co. Music: copyright © 1973 by Hope Publishing Co.

450

Great Shepherd of your people, hear

BERFORD 8 6 8 6 CM

1. Great Shepherd of your people, hear! Your
2. Within these walls let holy peace and
3. May we in faith receive your word, in
4. The hearing ear, the seeing eye, the

presence now display; as you have given a
love and friendship dwell; here give the troubled
faith present our prayers, and in the presence
contrite heart bestow, and shine upon us

place for prayer, so give us hearts to pray.
conscience ease; the wounded spirit heal.
of our Lord unburden all our cares.
from on high, that we in grace may grow.

Alternate tune: Abridge

Words: John Newton (1725–1807)   Music: A Book of Psalmody 1718

Words: public domain   Music: public domain

451 Dear Father, Lord of humankind

REST 86886

Alternate tune: Repton (last line of each verse must be repeated)

Words: John Greenleaf Whittier (1807–1892), alt   Music: Frederick Charles Maker (1844–1927)

Words: public domain   Music: public domain

5. Drop thy still dews of quietness,
   till all our strivings cease;
   take from our souls the strain and stress,
   and let our ordered lives confess
   the beauty of thy peace.

6. Breathe through the heats of our desire
   thy coolness and thy balm;
   let sense be dumb, let flesh retire;
   speak through the earthquake, wind and fire,
   O still small voice of calm.

452   Jesus, stand among us

CASWALL (BEMERTON) 6 5 6 5

1. Je-sus, stand a-mong us in your ris-en power;
2. Breathe the Ho-ly Spir - it in - to eve-ry heart;
3. Thus with quick-ened foot - steps we pur-sue our way,

let this time of wor - ship be a hal-lowed hour.
bid the fears and sor - rows from each soul de - part.
watch-ing for the dawn - ing of e - ter - nal day.

Words: William Pennefather (1816–1873), alt   Music: Friedrich Filitz (1804–1876)

Words: public domain   Music: public domain

Oh sing to our God

CANTAD AL SEÑOR 11 11 11 10

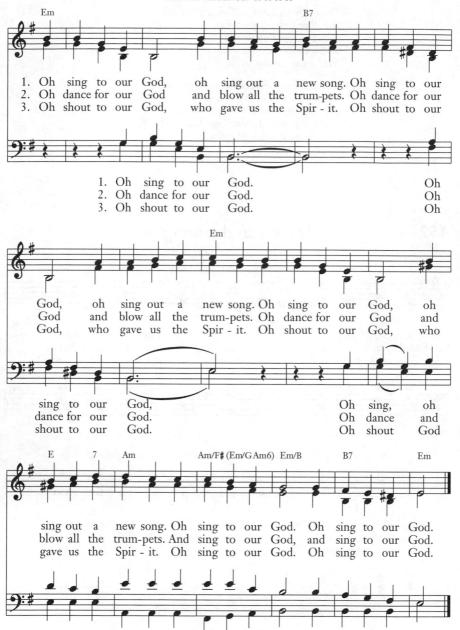

1. Oh sing to our God, oh sing out a new song. Oh sing to our
2. Oh dance for our God and blow all the trum-pets. Oh dance for our
3. Oh shout to our God, who gave us the Spir - it. Oh shout to our

1. Oh sing to our God. Oh
2. Oh dance for our God. Oh
3. Oh shout to our God. Oh

God, oh sing out a new song. Oh sing to our God, oh
God and blow all the trum-pets. Oh dance for our God and
God, who gave us the Spir - it. Oh shout to our God, who

sing to our God, Oh sing, oh
dance for our God. Oh dance and
shout to our God. Oh shout God

sing out a new song. Oh sing to our God. Oh sing to our God.
blow all the trum-pets. And sing to our God, and sing to our God.
gave us the Spir - it. Oh sing to our God. Oh sing to our God.

Words: Psalm 98; Brazilian folk song, translation, Gerhard Cartford (1923–), alt;
French, Daniel Forget (1956–) Music: Brazilian folk melody

Words: English, copyright © Gerhard Cartford; French, copyright © Daniel Forget, 1997 Music: public domain

French

1. Oh chantons à Dieu un chant d'allégresse;
   oh chantons à Dieu un chant d'espérance;
   oh chantons à Dieu un chant nouveau du coeur;
   oh chantons à Dieu; oh chantons à Dieu.

2. Oh dansons pour Dieu au son des trompettes,
   oh dansons pour Dieu au son de la harpe;
   oh dansons pour Dieu au son du tambourin;
   et chantons à Dieu; et chantons à Dieu.

3. Louons notre Dieu, pour l'Esprit de grâce,
   louons notre Dieu, car Dieu est merveilleux;
   louons notre Dieu, d'un seul coeur tous uni;
   et chantons à Dieu; et chantons à Dieu.

454   Blest be the everlasting God

ABRIDGE 8 6 8 6 CM

1. Blest be the ev - er - last - ing God, the Fa - ther of our Lord;
2. When God raised Je - sus from the dead, when Christ a - rose on high,
3. To an in - her - i - tance di - vine God taught our hearts to rise:
4. Saints by the power of God are kept un - til sal - va - tion come;

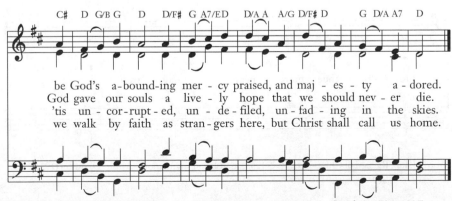

be God's a - bound - ing mer - cy praised, and maj - es - ty a - dored.
God gave our souls a live - ly hope that we should nev - er die.
'tis un - cor - rupt - ed, un - de - filed, un - fad - ing in the skies.
we walk by faith as stran - gers here, but Christ shall call us home.

Words: Isaac Watts (1674–1748), alt Scottish Paraphrases Music: Isaac Smith (c.1734–1805)

Words: public domain Music: public domain

587

Day by day

DAY BY DAY 11 12 10

Day by day, dear Lord, of thee three things I

pray: to see thee more

clear - ly, to love thee more dear - ly, to

fol - low thee more near - ly, day by day.

Words: Latin, Richard of Chicester (c.1197–1253), translation, anonymous Music: D. Austin (1932–)

Words: public domain Music: copyright © D. Austin

456

Be present at our table

TALLIS' CANON   8 8 8 8 LM

Be pres-ent at our ta - ble, Lord; be here and eve - ry - where a-dored.

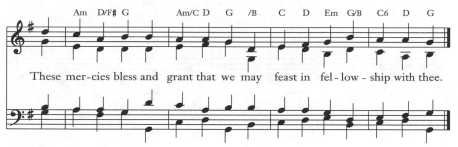

These mer-cies bless and grant that we may feast in fel - low - ship with thee.

Note: May be sung as a round.

Alternate tune: Old 100th

Words: traditional   Music: Thomas Tallis (c.1505–1585)

Words: public domain   Music: public domain

Now thank we all our God

NUN DANKET 6 7 6 7 6 6 6 6

1. Now thank we all our God with heart and hands and voic - es,
2. Oh may this boun-teous God through all our life be near us,
3. All praise and thanks to God who reigns in high - est heav - en,

who won-drous things has done, in whom God's world re - joic - es,
with ev - er - joy - ful hearts and bless - ed peace to cheer us,
the Fa - ther and the Son and Spir - it now be giv - en,

who from our moth - er's arms has blessed us on our way
and keep us all with grace, and guide us when per - plexed,
the one e - ter - nal God, whom heaven and earth a - dore,

Words: German, Martin Rinckart (1586–1649); translation, Catherine Winkworth (1829–1878), alt
Music: Johann Crüger (1598–1662)

Words: public domain   Music: public domain

with   count-less gifts of   love, and   still   is   ours to - day.
and   free   us   from all ills   in   this world and the   next.
for   thus   it   was, is   now   and   shall be   ev - er - more.

458   God, of your goodness give me yourself

God, of your goodness give me yourself;
for you are sufficient for me. I cannot
properly ask anything less, to be worthy of you.
If I were to ask less, I should always be in want.
In you alone do I have all. Amen.

Words: Julian of Norwich (1342–after 1416)
Words: public domain

O servants of God

LAUDATE DOMINUM 10 10 11 11

1. O serv - ants of God, your Mas - ter pro - claim, and
2. God rules from on high, al - migh - ty to save; yet
3. Sal - va - tion to God, who sits on the throne! Let
4. Then let us a - dore, give God what is right: all

pub - lish a - broad that won - der - ful name: the
ev - er is nigh, whose pres - ence we have. The
all cry a - loud, and hon - our the Son. The
glo - ry and power, all wis - dom and might, and

name all - vic - to - rious of Je - sus ex - tol, whose
great con - gre - ga - tion God's tri - umph shall sing, a -
prais - es of Je - sus the an - gels pro - claim, fall
hon - our and bless - ing, with an - gels a - bove, and

Words: Charles Wesley (1707–1788), alt Music: Charles Hubert Hastings Parry (1848–1918)
Words: public domain Music: public domain

reign, ev - er glo - rious, shall rule o - ver all,
scrib - ing sal - va - tion to Je - sus our King.
down on their fac - es, and wor - ship the Lamb.
thanks nev - er ceas - ing, and in - fi - nite love.

460   Teach us, good Lord, to serve you

Teach us, good Lord,
to serve you as you deserve;
to give and not to count the cost;
to fight and not to heed the wounds;
to toil and not to seek for rest;
to labour and not to ask for any reward,
except for that of knowing that we do your will;
through Jesus Christ our Lord. Amen.

Words: Ignatius of Loyola (1491–1556); translation, unknown
Words: public domain

Be thou my vision

SLANE 10 10 10 10

Descant

5. High King of heav - en, when the bat - tle is done,

Unison   Eb   /G   Ab   Bb   /Ab   Eb/G   Ab   Fm6   Eb

1. Be thou my vi - sion, O Lord of my heart;
2. Be thou my wis - dom; be thou my true word,
3. Be thou my breast-plate, my sword for the fight;
4. Rich - es I heed not, nor vain earth - ly praise,
5. High King of heav - en, when the bat - tle is done,

grant heav - en's joy to me, O bright heaven's Sun;

Bb   Fm (/Eb)   Bb/D   Eb   /G   Ab   Eb/G   Eb6   Bb   /Ab   Eb/G

naught be all else to me, save that thou art,
I ev - er with thee and thou with me, Lord;
be thou my ar - and be thou my might;
thou my in - her - it - ance, through all my days;
grant heav - en's joy to me, O bright heaven's Sun;

Words: Irish anonymous, 8th century, translation, Mary Byrne (1880–1931), paraphrase, Eleanor Hull (1860–1935), alt Music: Irish traditional; harmony, Erik Routley (1917–1982); descant, John Wilson (1905–1992)

Words: translation, paraphrase, copyright © Chatto and Windus Ltd. Music: harmony copyright © 1975 and descant © 1983 by Hope Publishing Co.

heart of my own heart, what - ev - er be - fall,

thou my best thought in the day and the night,
thou my great Fath - er, thine own may I be,
thou my soul's shel - ter and thou my high tower,
thou and thou on - ly, the first in my heart,
heart of my own heart, what - ev - er be - fall,

still be my vi - sion, O rul - er of all.

wak - ing or sleep - ing, thy pres - ence my light.
thou in me dwell - ing, and I one with thee.
raise thou me heaven - ward, O Power of my power.
high King of heav - en, my treas - ure thou art!
still be my vi - sion, O rul - er of all.

462 All my hope on God is founded

MICHAEL 8 7 8 7 3 3 7

1. All my hope on God is found - ed who does still my
2. Hu - man pride and earth - ly glo - ry, sword and crown, be -
3. God's great good-ness reigns e - ter - nal, deep in wis - dom,
4. Dai - ly does Al - might - y Giv - er boun - teous gifts on
5. Still from earth to God e - ter - nal sac - ri - fice of

trust re - new; through all change and chance God guides me,
tray all trust; what our care and toil es - tab - lish,
pass - ing thought; light and life are all God's splen-dour
us be - stow, God's de - sire our soul de - light - ing,
praise be done, high a - bove all prais - es prais - ing

on - ly good and on - ly true. Love un - known,
tower and tem - ple, fall to dust, but God's power,
bring - ing beau - ty out of naught. Ev - er - more
plea - sure lead - ing where we go. Love will stand
for the gift of Christ, the Son. Hear Christ call

Words: German, Joachim Neander (1650–1680), translation, Robert Bridges (1944–1930), alt
Music: Herbert Howells (1892–1983)

Words: this version copyright © The Presbyterian Church in Canada, 1997 Music: copyright © Novello & Company Ltd.

| CmᐧA | Daug | Gm | Aaug/C♯ A7 | Dm | (7) | G6 | | C | 9 | F |

God's   a -   lone,   calls my   heart to   be   God's   own.
hour   by   hour,   is   my   tem - ple   and   my   tower.
from   God's store   new-born worlds rise   and   a   -   dore.
at   God's hand;   joy   will wait   on   God's   com -   mand.
one   and   all: you   that fol - low   shall   not   fall.

463   O burning mountain, O chosen sun

O burning mountain, O chosen sun,
O perfect moon, O fathomless well,
O unattainable height, O clearness beyond measure,
O wisdom without end, O mercy without limit,
O strength beyond resistance, O crown beyond all majesty:
the humblest thing you created sings your praise. Amen.

Words: Mechthild of Magdeburg (1212–1283)

Words: public domain

Worship
464

Oh that I had a thousand voices

O DASS ICH TAUSEND ZUNGEN HÄTTE 989888

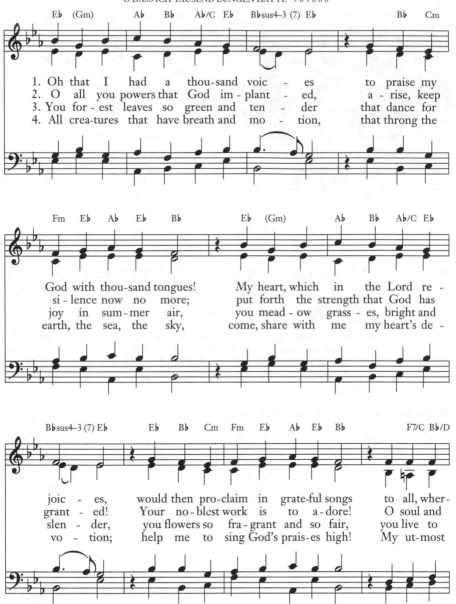

1. Oh that I had a thou-sand voic - es to praise my God with thou-sand tongues! My heart, which in the Lord re - joic - es, would then pro-claim in grate-ful songs to all, wher -
2. O all you powers that God im - plant - ed, a - rise, keep si - lence now no more; put forth the strength that God has grant - ed! Your no - blest work is to a - dore! O soul and
3. You for - est leaves so green and ten - der that dance for joy in sum - mer air, you mead - ow grass - es, bright and slen - der, you flowers so fra - grant and so fair, you live to
4. All crea-tures that have breath and mo - tion, that throng the earth, the sea, the sky, come, share with me my heart's de - vo - tion; help me to sing God's prais-es high! My ut-most

Words: German, Johann Mentzer (1658–1734); translation, The Lutheran Hymnal, 1941
Music: König's Harmonischer Liederschatz 1738

Words: English translation, copyright © Concordia Publishing House, 1941. Used and adapted with permission. Music: public domain

598

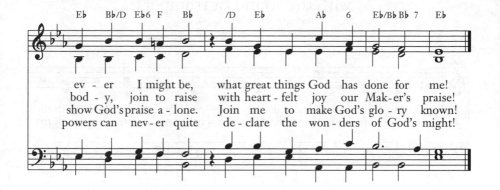

| Eb | Bb/D | Eb6 | F | Bb | | /D | Eb | | Ab | 6 | Eb/Bb | Bb | 7 | Eb |

ev - er   I might be,   what great things God   has   done for   me!
bod - y,   join to raise   with heart - felt   joy   our Mak - er's   praise!
show God's praise a - lone.   Join me   to   make God's glo - ry   known!
powers can   nev - er quite   de - clare   the   won - ders   of God's might!

465   The things, good Lord, that we pray for

The things, good Lord, that we pray for, give us the
grace to labour for.

Words: Thomas More (1478–1535)

Words: public domain

Praise the Lord
with the sound of trumpet

PRAISE THE LORD Irregular

1. Praise the Lord with the sound of trum-pet, praise the Lord with the
2. Praise the Lord with the crash-ing cym-bal, praise the Lord with the

harp and lute, praise the Lord with the gen-tle-sound-ing flute.
pipe and string, praise the Lord with the joy-ful songs you sing.

Praise the Lord in the field and for-est, praise the Lord in the
Praise the Lord on a week-day morn-ing, praise the Lord on a

cit-y square, praise the Lord an-y-time and an-y-where.
Sun-day noon, praise the Lord by the light of sun or moon.

Note: May be sung as a round

Words: Natalie Sleeth (1930–1992) Music: Natalie Sleeth (1930–1992)

Praise the Lord in the wind and sun-shine, praise the Lord in the
Praise the Lord in the time of sor-row, praise the Lord in the

dark of night, praise the Lord in the rain or snow or in the morn-ing light.
time of joy, praise the Lord eve-ry mo-ment; noth-ing let your praise de-stroy.

Praise the Lord in the deep-est val-ley, praise the Lord on the high-est hill,
Praise the Lord in the peace and qui-et, praise the Lord in your work or play,

1.
praise the Lord; nev-er let your voice be still.
praise the Lord eve-ry-where in eve-ry

2.
way!

467 Praise, my soul, the God who crowns you

PRAISE, MY SOUL 878787

1. Praise, my soul, the God who crowns you, crowns with mer - cy
4. Praise the Lord in high - est heav - ens, might - y ones who

all your days; bless the God whose good sur - rounds you,
do God's will; an - gels, cry through all do - min - ions,

res - cues, heals, for - gives, re - claims. Hal - le - lu - jah,
God is sov - ereign o - ver all. Hal - le - lu - jah,

hal - le - lu - jah, all with - in me, bless and praise.
hal - le - lu - jah, praise your Mak - er, O my soul.

Words: Psalm 103; paraphrase, Andrew J. Donaldson (1951–) Music: John Goss (1800–1880)

Words: paraphrase, copyright © The Presbyterian Church of Canada, 1995 Music: public domain

Lord, dismiss us with your blessing

TANTUM ERGO 8 7 8 7 8 7

1. Lord, dis-miss us with your bless-ing; fill our hearts with
2. We give thanks and ad-o - ra - tion for your gos-pel's
3. so that when your love shall call us, Sav - iour, from the

joy and peace; let us each, your love pos - sess - ing,
joy - ful sound; may the fruits of your sal - va - tion
world a - way, fear of death shall not ap - pall us,

tri - umph in re - deem - ing grace. Oh re - fresh us,
in our hearts and lives a - bound. May your pres - ence,
glad your sum - mons to o - bey. May we ev - er,

oh re - fresh us, trav - eling through life's wil - der - ness.
may your pres - ence with us ev - er - more be found,
may we ev - er live in you in end - less day.

Words: John Fawcett (1740–1817) Music: melody from Samuel Webbe's Antiphona, 1792

Words: public domain Music: public domain

Our Father in heaven

PATER NOSTER (NIXON)

Our Fath-er in hea-ven, hal-lowed be your name; your king-dom come;

your will be done, on earth as in heav-en. Give us to-day

our dai-ly bread. For-give us our sins as we for-give those who sin a-

gainst us. Save us from the time of tri-al and de-liv-er us from

Words: Matthew 6:9–13; translation, English Language Liturgical Consultation, 1988
Music: Darryl Nixon (1952–)

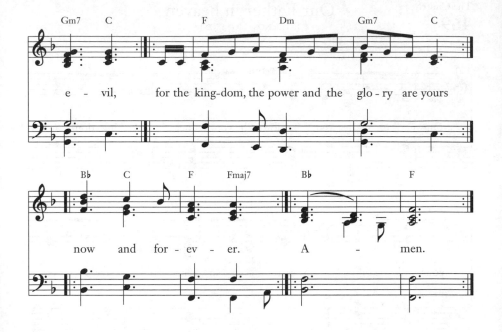

e - vil, for the king-dom, the power and the glo - ry are yours

now and for - ev - er. A - men.

470   You that know the Lord is gracious

ABBOT'S LEIGH 8 7 8 7 D

Descant

Tell the praise of God who called you

1. You that know the Lord is gra - cious,
2. Liv - ing stones, by God ap - point - ed
3. Tell the praise of God who called you

Words: Cyril A. Alington (1872–1955), alt   Music: Cyril Vincent Taylor (1907–1991)

Words: copyright © 1950 by Hope Publishing Co.   Music: copyright © 1942, renewal 1970 by Hope Publishing Co.

out of dark - ness in - to light,

Bm (/D)   Em   7   6   D/F♯   G6   Gmaj7   Asus4 – 3   /G

you   for   whom   a   cor - ner - stone
each   to   its   al - lot - ted   place,
out   of   dark - ness   in - to   light,

broke   the   fet - ters   that   en - thralled you,

D/F♯   A6   Bm   /A   G   A   G/B (/C♯)   G/D   D   /C♯

stands,   of   God   e - lect   and   pre - cious,
roy - al   priests,   by   God   a - noint - ed,
broke   the   fet - ters   that   en - thralled you,

gave   you   free - dom,   peace   and   sight.

Bm (/D)   Em   7   6   D/F♯   G6   Gmaj7   A

laid   that   you   may   build   there - on,
will   you   not   de - clare   God's grace?
gave   you   free - dom,   peace   and   sight.

praise and mag - ni - fy the Lord.

Em   D/F#   G   D/F# /A A7   D

walls   that may   re - e - cho praise.
to   an   old   and wea - ry earth.
praise   and mag -   ni - fy the Lord.

471

We are one in the Spirit

WE ARE ONE IN THE SPIRIT Irregular with refrain

1. We are one in the Spir - it, we are
2. We will walk with each oth - er, we will
3. We will work with each oth - er, we will
4. All praise to the Fath - er, from

one in the Lord, we are one in the
walk hand in hand, we will walk with each
work side by side, we will work with each
whom all things come, and all praise to Christ

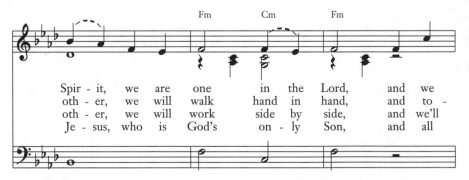

Spir - it, we are one in the Lord, and we
oth - er, we will walk hand in hand, and to -
oth - er, we will work side by side, and we'll
Je - sus, who is God's on - ly Son, and all

Words: Peter Scholtes (1938–) Music: Peter Scholtes (1938–); harmony, Richard D. Wetzel (1935–)

pray that all u - ni - ty will one day be re -
geth - er we'll spread the news that God is in our
guard each one's dig - ni - ty and save each one's
praise to the Spir - it, who makes us

stored,
land,
pride, and they'll know we are Chris-tians by our
one,

love, by our love, and they'll know we are

Chris - tians by our love.

472

We are God's people

SYMPHONY 11 11 14 8 9

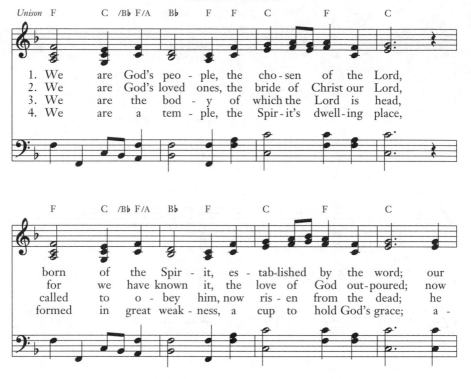

Unison

1. We are God's peo-ple, the cho-sen of the Lord,
2. We are God's loved ones, the bride of Christ our Lord,
3. We are the bod-y of which the Lord is head,
4. We are a tem-ple, the Spir-it's dwell-ing place,

born of the Spir - it, es - tab-lished by the word; our
for we have known it, the love of God out-poured; now
called to o - bey him, now ris - en from the dead; he
formed in great weak - ness, a cup to hold God's grace; a -

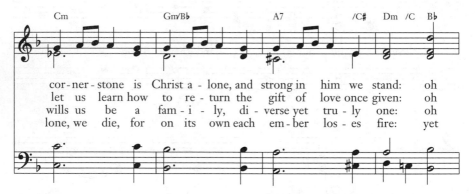

cor - ner - stone is Christ a - lone, and strong in him we stand: oh
let us learn how to re - turn the gift of love once given: oh
wills us be a fam - i - ly, di - verse yet tru - ly one: oh
lone, we die, for on its own each em - ber los - es fire: yet

Words: Bryan Jeffery Leech (1931–) Music: Johannes Brahms (1833–1897);
arrangement, Fred Bock (1939–)

Words: copyright © Fred Bock Music Co., 1976 Music: arrangement, copyright © Fred Bock Music Co., 1976

let us live trans-par-ent-ly, and walk heart to heart and hand in hand.
let us share each joy and care and live with a zeal that pleas-es heaven.
let us free-ly give our gifts, and so shall God's work on earth be done.
joined in one the flame burns on to give warmth and light, and to in-spire.

473   We love your kingdom, Lord

HOLYROOD 6 6 8 6 SM

1. We love your king-dom, Lord, the place of your a-bode,
2. We love your church, O God, whose saints be-fore you stand,
3. For them our tears shall fall, for them our prayers as-cend;
4. O Je-sus, Sav-iour, Guide, our Sov-ereign and our Friend,

the church our blest Re-deem-er saved with his own pre-cious blood.
dear as the ap-ple of your eye, and writ-ten on your hand.
for them our cares and toils be given, till toils and cares shall end.
from eve-ry snare and foe, your hand shall great de-liv-erance send.

Words: Timothy Dwight (1752–1817), alt   Music: James Watson (1816–1880)

Words: public domain   Music: public domain

474

The love of God comes close

RHOSYMEDRE 7 6 6 6 8 8 8

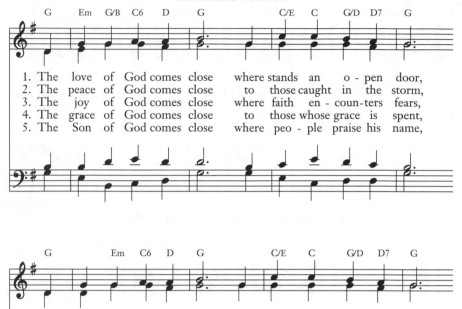

1. The love of God comes close where stands an o - pen door,
2. The peace of God comes close to those caught in the storm,
3. The joy of God comes close where faith en - coun-ters fears,
4. The grace of God comes close to those whose grace is spent,
5. The Son of God comes close where peo - ple praise his name,

to let the stran-ger in, to min - gle rich and poor.
for - go - ing lives of ease to ease the lives for - lorn.
where heights and depths of life are found through smiles and tears.
when hearts are tired or sore and hope is bruised and bent.
where bread and wine are blest and shared as when he came.

Words: John L. Bell (1949–), Graham Maule (1958–) Music: John David Edwards (1805–1885)

The love
The peace
The joy of God is here to stay, em - brac-ing those who
The grace
The Son

walk the Way; the

love
peace
joy of God is here to stay.
grace
Son

475 I am the church! You are the church!

PORT JERVIS   7 7 8 6 with refrain

Words: Richard Avery (1934–), and Donald Marsh (1923–)   Music: Richard Avery (1934–),
Donald Marsh (1923–)

Words: copyright © 1972 by Hope Publishing Co.   Music: copyright © 1972 by Hope Publishing Co.

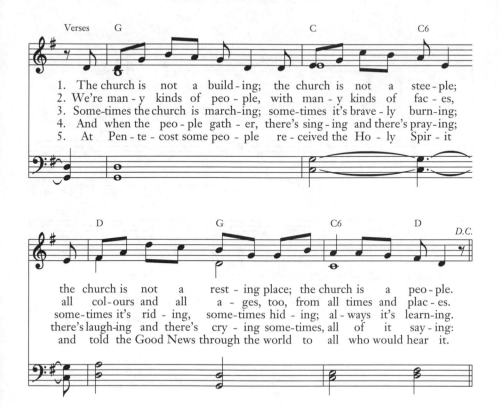

1. The church is not a build - ing; the church is not a stee - ple;
2. We're man - y kinds of peo - ple, with man - y kinds of fac - es,
3. Some-times the church is march-ing; some-times it's brave - ly burn-ing;
4. And when the peo - ple gath - er, there's sing - ing and there's pray-ing;
5. At Pen - te - cost some peo - ple re - ceived the Ho - ly Spir - it

the church is not a rest - ing place; the church is a peo - ple.
all col - ours and all a - ges, too, from all times and plac - es.
some-times it's rid - ing, some-times hid - ing; al - ways it's learn-ing.
there's laugh-ing and there's cry - ing some-times, all of it say - ing:
and told the Good News through the world to all who would hear it.

617

476 Amigos de Cristo / Friends of the Lord

AMIGOS DE CRISTO   Irregular with refrain

Refrain

A - mi - gos   de Cris-to;   we're friends   of   the Lord;
we've been   for - giv - en,   and we've   been   re-stored;   a -

mi-gos   de Cris-to;   we're friends of   the Lord.   For Lord.   Lord.

Fine
Last time

1. Friends   of   the   cov - e-nant re - newed   each   morn;
2. Born   of   a   fam - i - ly, the   young   and   old,

bap - tized and   lov - ing it, we've been   re - born.
we'll   be   on   hand   to see new   life   un - fold.

Words: Latin American traditional   Music: Traditional

Words: public domain   Music: public domain

Gift of the dove is ours for - ev - er - more. A -
We un - der - stand the need to be made whole.

mi - gos de Cris-to; we're friends of the Lord. A -

The Church

477

Your hand, O God, has guided

THORNBURY 7 6 7 6 D

1. Your hand, O God, has guid - ed your flock from age to age;
2. Your her-alds brought glad ti - dings to great-est, as to least;
3. And we, shall we be faith - less? Shall hearts fail, hands hang down?
4. Your mer-cy will not fail us, nor leave your work un - done;

the won-drous tale is writ - ten full clear on eve - ry page;
they sum-moned all to has - ten to share the great King's feast,
Shall we e - vade the con - flict, and cast a - way our crown?
with your right hand to help us, the vic - tory shall be won,

our fore - bears knew your good - ness, and we their deeds re -
and this was all their teach - ing, in eve - ry deed and
Not so; in God's deep coun - sels some bet - ter thing is
and then by earth and heav - en your name shall be a -

See also : Thornbury 478

Words: Edward Hayes Plumptre (1821–1891), alt Music: Basil Harwood (1859–1949)

Words: public domain Music: copyright © the executors of Dr. Basil Harwood. Used by permission.

cord, and both of this bear wit - -ness,
word, to all a - like pro - claim - ing, "One
stored: we will main - tain, un - flinch - ing,
dored, and this shall be their an - -them,

church, one faith, one Lord."

478

To Abraham and Sarah

THORNBURY 7 6 7 6 D

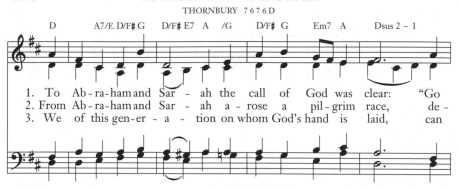

1. To Ab - ra - ham and Sar - ah the call of God was clear: "Go
2. From Ab - ra - ham and Sar - ah a - rose a pil - grim race, de -
3. We of this gen - er - a - tion on whom God's hand is laid, can

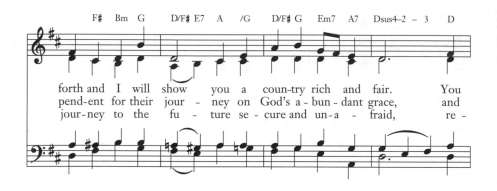

forth and I will show you a coun-try rich and fair. You
pend-ent for their jour - ney on God's a - bun - dant grace, and
jour-ney to the fu - ture se - cure and un - a - fraid, re -

need not fear the jour - ney for I have pledged my
in their heart was writ - ten by God this sav - ing
joic - ing in God's good - ness and trust - ing in this

See also: Thornbury 477

Words: Judith Fetter (1937–)   Music: Basil Harwood (1859–1949)

word:
word: "that you shall be my peo - ple and
word:

I will be your God."

Organ

479

The church's one foundation

AURELIA 7 6 7 6 D

1. The chur-ch's one foun - da - tion is Je - sus Christ our Lord;
2. Called forth from eve - ry na - tion, yet one o'er all the earth,
3. Though with a scorn-ful won - der the world sees us op - pressed,
1. L'é - glise u - ni - ver - sel - le a pour roc Jé - sus - Christ;
2. L'é - glise en sa pri - èr - e u - nit à leur Sau - veur

we are his new cre - a - tion by wa - ter and the word;
our char - ter of sal - va - tion, one Lord, one faith, one birth,
by schi - sms rent a - sun - der, by her - e - sies dis - tressed,
elle est l'oeu-vre nou - vel - le que sa pa - ro - le fit.
les peu-ples de la ter - re, sou - mis au seul Sei - gneur.

from heaven he came and sought us that we might ev - er be
one ho - ly name pro - fess - ing and at one ta - ble fed,
yet saints their watch are keep - ing; their cry goes up, "How long?"
Ha - bi - tant le ciel mê - me, il vint se l'at - ta - cher,
C'est son nom qu'elle ac - cla - me, son pain qui la nour - rit;

Words: Samuel John Stone (1839–1900) alt French translation, Fernand Barth (1923–)
Music: Samuel Sebastian Wesley (1810–1876)

Words: public domain   Music: public domain

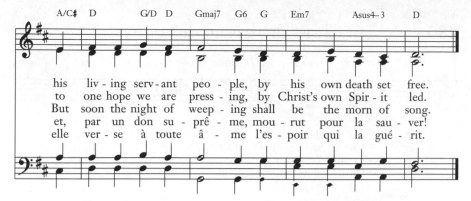

his	liv - ing	serv - ant	peo -	ple,	by	his	own	death	set	free.
to	one hope	we are	press -	ing,	by	Christ's	own	Spir -	it	led.
But	soon the	night of	weep -	ing	shall	be	the	morn	of	song.
et,	par un	don su -	prê -	me,	mou -	rut	pour	la	sau -	ver!
elle	ver - se	à toute	â -	me	l'es -	poir	qui	la	gué -	rit.

4. 'Mid toil and tribulation,
   and tumult of our war,
   we wait the consummation
   of peace forevermore;
   till with the vision glorious
   our longing eyes are blest,
   and the great church victorious
   shall be the church at rest.

5. We now on earth have union
   with God the Three-in-One,
   and share, through faith, communion
   with those whose rest is won,—
   O happy ones and holy!
   Lord, give us grace that we,
   like them, the meek and lowly,
   on high may dwell with thee.

3. Honnie et méconnue,
   menant de durs combats,
   elle attend la venue
   de la paix ici–bas.
   Contemplant par avance
   la fin de son tourment,
   la grande délivrance,
   le repos permanent.

4. Aujourd'hui, sur la terre,
   elle est unie à Dieu,
   et, par un saint mystère,
   aux élus du saint lieu.
   Rends–nous, comme eux, fidèles,
   et reçois–nous, Seigneur,
   dans la vie éternelle,
   dans l'éternel bonheur!

Hungarian

1. Az egyháznak a Jézus a fundámentoma,
   A szent Igére épült fel lelki temploma.
   Leszállt a mennybl hívni és eljegyezni őt,
   Megváltva drága vérén a váltságban hívot.

2. Kihívott mínden néphől egy lelki népet itt,
   Kit egy úr, egy keresztség és egy hit egyesít.
   Csak egy nevet magasztal, csak egy cél vonja őt,
   és egy terített asztal ád néki új erőt.

3. A világ fejedelme feltámad ellene,
   Vagy hamis tudománytól gyaláztatik neve,
   S míg egykor felderl majd az Úrnak hajnala,
   Csak virrasztói kérdik: Meddig az éjszaka?

4. Sok bajban, küzdelemben meghajszolt, megvetett,
   De szent megújulásért és békéért eped,
   Míg látomása egykor dicsőn beteljesl
   S a győzedelmes egyház Urával egyesül.

5. A három-egy Istennel már itt a földön egy,
   S az üdvözült sereggel egy nép és egy sereg
   Ó mily áldott reménység: Ha itt időnk lejár,
   Te boldog szenteiddel fenn Nálad béke vár!

480 In Christ there is no east or west

MCKEE 8 6 8 6 CM

1. In Christ there is no east or west, in him no south or north, but one great fellow-ship of love through-out the whole wide earth.

2. In Christ shall true hearts eve-ry-where their high com-mun-ion find; his serv-ice is the gold-en cord close bind-ing hu-man-kind.

3. Join hands, com-pan-ions in the faith, what-e'er your race may be! Who loves and serves the liv-ing God is sure-ly kin to me.

4. In Christ now meet both east and west; in him meet south and north; all Christ-ly souls are one in him, through-out the whole wide earth.

Alternate tune: Flight of the Earls

Words: John Oxenham (1852–1941), alt   Music: Harry T. Burleigh (1866–1949); harmony, Francis B. Westbrook (1903–1975)

Words: public domain   Music: harmony, copyright © Oxford University Press

481

Blest be the tie that binds

DENNIS 6 6 8 6 SM

1. Blest be the tie that binds our hearts in Chris - tian love;
2. Be - fore our Mak - er's throne we pour our ar - dent prayers;
3. We share each oth - er's woes, each oth - er's bur - dens bear,
1. Bé - ni soit le li - en qui nous u - nit en Christ,
2. Au ciel, vers no - tre Dieu, a - vec joie et fer - veur,

the fel - low - ship of kin - dred minds is like to that a - bove.
our fears, our hopes, our aims are one, our com - forts and our cares.
and of - ten for each oth - er flows the sym - pa - thiz - ing tear.
le saint a - mour, l'a - mour di - vin que verse en nous l'Es - prit!
s'é - lè - vent nos chants et nos voeux, par - fum doux au Sei - gneur.

4. When we asunder part,
   it gives us keenest pain,
   but we shall still be joined in heart,
   and hope to meet again.

5. This glorious hope revives
   our courage on the way:
   in perfect friendship we shall live
   in God's eternal day.

3. Nous mettons en commun
   nos fardeaux, nos labeurs;
   en Jésus nous ne sommes qu'un
   dans la joie et les pleurs!

4. Si nous devons bientôt
   quitter ces lieux bénis,
   nous nous retrouverons là–haut,
   pour toujours réunis.

Words: John Fawcett (1740–1817), alt; French translation, Edmond L. Budry (1854–1932)
Music: Johann Georg Nägeli (1773–1836); arrangement, Lowell Mason (1792–1872)

Words: public domain   Music: public domain

482 Christ is made the sure foundation

WESTMINSTER ABBEY 878787

Descant

5. Laud and hon-our to the Fa - ther, laud and hon - our

G   D/F♯   G   C/E   C6   D   /C   G/B   D7/A   G   (D)   A7/E

1. Christ is made the sure foun - da - tion, Christ the head and
2. All with - in that ho - ly ci - ty, dear - ly loved of
3. To this tem - ple, where we call thee, come, O Lord of
4. Here be - stow on all thy serv-ants what they ask of
5. Laud and hon - our to the Fa-ther, laud and hon - our

to the Son, laud and hon - our to the Spir - it,

D   Asus4–3   D   A/C♯   D   /C   G/B   D7/A   G

cor - ner - stone, cho - sen of the Lord, and pre - cious,
God on high, in ex - ult - ant ju - bi - la - tion
hosts, to - day: with thy faith - ful lov - ing - kind - ness,
thee to gain, what they gain from thee for - ev - er
to the Son, laud and hon - our to the Spir - it,

See also: Westminister Abbey 595

Words: anonymous, 7th-8th cent.; translation, John Mason Neale (1818–1866)
Music: Henry Purcell (1659–1695), alt; descant, James Gillespie (1929–)

Words: public domain Music: descant, copyright © Church Society, London

ev - er Three, and ev - er One, one in might and

C/E   D6   C6   Baug Am7 Bsus4–3 Em   E   /D   A/C#

bind - ing all the church in one, ho - ly Zi - ion's
pour per - pet - ual mel - o - dy, God the One - in -
hear thy serv - ants as they pray, and thy full - est
with the bless - ed to re - tain, and here - af - ter
ev - er Three, and ev - er One, one in might and

one in glo - ry, while un - end - ing ag - es run.

D   /C   G/B   C   Am   D   G   Dsus4 – 3   G

help for - ev - er, and her con - fi - dence a - lone.
Three a - dor - ing in glad hymns e - ter - nal - ly.
ben - e - dic - tion shed with - in its walls al - way.
in thy glo - ry ev - er - more with thee to reign.
one in glo - ry, while un - end - ing ag - es run.

*F♮ in Purcell's original.

483 Glorious things of thee are spoken

AUSTRIA 8 7 8 7 D

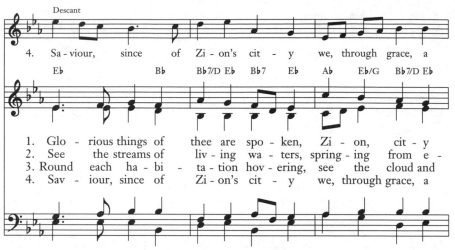

Descant

4. Sa - viour, since of Zi - on's cit - y we, through grace, a

Eb   Bb   Bb7/D Eb   Bb7   Eb   Ab   Eb/G   Bb7/D Eb

1. Glo - rious things of thee are spo - ken, Zi - on, cit - y
2. See the streams of liv - ing wa - ters, spring - ing from e -
3. Round each ha - bi - ta - tion hov - ering, see the cloud and
4. Sav - iour, since of Zi - on's cit - y we, through grace, a

part may claim, let the world de - ride or

Fm/Ab CmA   Bb   Eb   Bb   Bb7/D Eb

of our God; One whose word can - not be
ter - nal love, well sup - ply thy sons and
fire ap - pear, for a glo - ry and a
part may claim, let the world de - ride or

See also: Austria 497

Words: John Newton (1725–1807), alt   Music: Franz Joseph Haydn (1732–1809); descant, T.H. Ingham (1873–1948)

Words: public domain   Music: descant, copyright © Oxford University Press

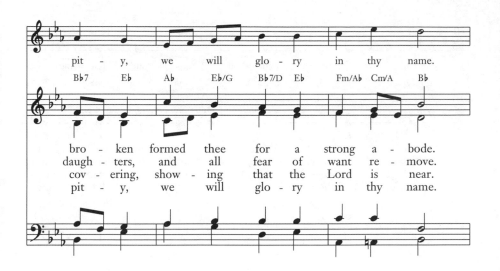

pit - y, we will glo - ry in thy name.

Bb7   Eb   Ab   Eb/G   Bb7/D   Eb   Fm/Ab   Cm/A   Bb

bro - ken formed thee for a strong a - bode.
daugh - ters, and all fear of want re - move.
cov - ering, show - ing that the Lord is near.
pit - y, we will glo - ry in thy name.

Fad - ing is all world - ly pleas - ure, all its boast - ed

Bb   Eb/Bb   Bb   Bb7/D   Eb   Bb   Eb/G   Ab6   Cm

On the Rock of A - ges found - ed, what can shake thy
Who can faint while such a riv - er ev - er will their
Thus they march, the pil - lar lead - ing— light by night and
Fad - ing is all world - ly pleas - ure, all its boast - ed

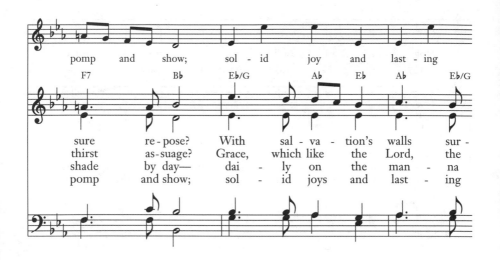

pomp and show; sol - id joy and last - ing

F7   B♭   E♭/G   A♭   E♭   A♭   E♭/G

sure   re - pose?   With   sal - va - tion's   walls   sur -
thirst   as - suage?   Grace,   which like   the   Lord,   the
shade   by day—   dai - ly   on   the   man - na
pomp   and show;   sol - id   joys   and   last - ing

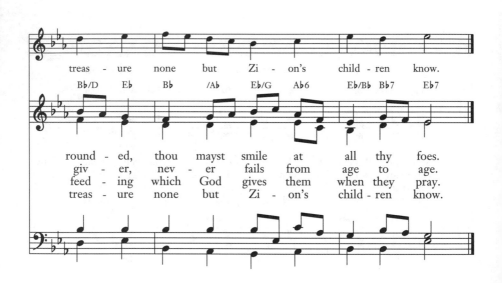

treas - ure none but Zi - on's child - ren know.

B♭/D   E♭   B♭   /A♭   E♭/G   A♭6   E♭/B♭ B♭7   E♭7

round - ed,   thou   mayst   smile   at   all   thy   foes.
giv - er,   nev - er   fails   from   age   to   age.
feed - ing   which   God   gives   them   when they   pray.
treas - ure   none   but   Zi - on's   child - ren   know.

The Church

484   The church is wherever God's people

CORNYSH CAROL 12 10 12 11

1. The church is wher-ev-er God's peo-ple are prais-ing,
2. The church is wher-ev-er God's peo-ple are help-ing,

sing-ing God's good-ness for joy on this day. The
car-ing for neigh-bours in sick-ness and need. The

church is wher-ev-er dis-ci-ples of Je-sus re-
church is wher-ev-er God's peo-ple are shar-ing the

mem-ber his sto-ry and walk in his way.
words of the Bi-ble in gift and in deed.

Words: Carol Rose Ikeler (1920–), alt   Music: Robert J.B. Fleming (1921–1976)

485 Saviour, like a shepherd lead us

BRADBURY 878787

1. Sav-iour like a shep-herd lead us: much we need your ten-der care;
2. We are yours; in love be-friend us; be the guard-ian of our way;
3. Let us al-ways seek your fa - vour; let us al - ways do your will.

in your pleas-ant pas-tures feed us, for our use your folds pre-pare:
keep your flock from sin, de-fend us; seek us when we go a-stray:
Je - sus Christ our on-ly Sav - iour, with your-self our spir-its fill:

bless-ed Je-sus; bless-ed Je-sus! you have bought us; yours we are.
bless-ed Je-sus, bless-ed Je-sus! hear your child-ren when we pray.
bless-ed Je-sus, bless-ed Je-sus! you have loved us; love us still.

Bless-ed Je-sus, bless-ed Je-sus! you have bought us, yours we are.
Bless-ed Je-sus, bless-ed Je-sus! hear your chil-dren when we pray.
Bless-ed Je-sus, bless-ed Je-sus! you have loved us; love us still.

Words: Dorothy A. Thrupp (1779–1847), alt Music: William Batchelder Bradbury (1816–1868);
harmony, V. Earle Copes (1921–)

Words: public domain Music: harmony, copyright © Abingdon Press, 1964

486 The church of Christ, in every age

DICKINSON COLLEGE 8 8 8 8 LM

1. The church of Christ, in eve - ry age, be - set by
2. A - cross the world, a - cross the street, the vic - tims
3. Then let the ser - vant church a - rise, a car - ing
4. For he a - lone, whose blood was shed, can cure the
5. We have no mis - sion but to serve in full o -

change but Spir - it - led, must claim and test
of in - jus - tice cry for shel - ter and
church that longs to be a part - ner in
fev - er in our blood, and teach us how
be - dience to our Lord, to care for all,

its her - i - tage and keep on ris - ing from the dead.
for bread to eat, and nev - er live un - til they die.
Christ's sac - ri - fice, and clothed in Christ's hu - man - i - ty.
to share our bread and feed the starv - ing mul - ti - tude.
with - out re - serve, and spread his lib - er - at - ing Word.

Words: Fred Pratt Green (1903–)   Music: Lee Hastings Bristol Jr. (1923–1979)

487 Onward, Christian soldiers

ST. GERTRUDE 6 5 6 5 D

1. On - ward, Chris - tian sol - diers, march-ing as to war,
2. Crowns and thrones may per - ish, king-doms rise and wane,
3. On - ward, then, ye peo - ple! join our hap - py throng;

with the cross of Je - sus go - ing on be - fore!
but the Church of Je - sus con - stant will re - main;
blend with ours your voic - es in the tri - umph song:

Christ the roy - al Mas - ter, leads a - gainst the foe;
gates of hell can nev - er 'gainst that church pre - vail;
"Glo - ry, laud and hon - our un - to Christ the King!"

Words: Sabine Baring-Gould (1834–1924), alt   Music: Arthur Seymour Sullivan (1842–1900)

Words: public domain   Music: public domain

for - ward in - to bat - tle, see his ban-ners go.
we have Christ's own prom - ise, and that can-not fail.
This through count - less a - ges we with an - gels sing.

Refrain

On-ward, Chris-tian sol - diers, march-ing as to war,

with the cross of Je - sus go - ing on be - fore!

488 O God, in whom we live and move

ALBANO 8 6 8 6 CM

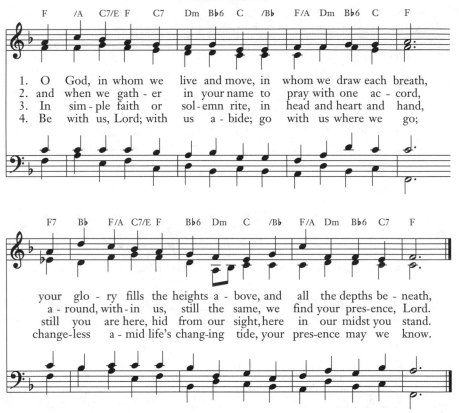

1. O God, in whom we live and move, in whom we draw each breath,
2. and when we gath - er in your name to pray with one ac - cord,
3. In sim - ple faith or sol - emn rite, in head and heart and hand,
4. Be with us, Lord; with us a - bide; go with us where we go;

your glo - ry fills the heights a - bove, and all the depths be - neath,
a - round, with - in us, still the same, we find your pres - ence, Lord.
still you are here, hid from our sight, here in our midst you stand.
change - less a - mid life's chang - ing tide, your pres - ence may we know.

Alternate tune: Gräfenberg

Words: George Wallace Briggs (1875–1959)   Music: Vincent Novello (1781–1861)

489
Help us to help each other, Lord

DUNFERMLINE 8 6 8 6 CM

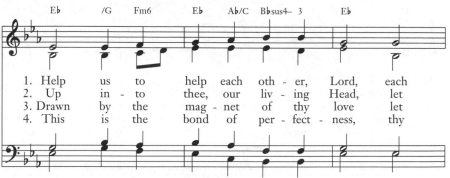

1. Help us to help each oth - er, Lord, each
2. Up in - to thee, our liv - ing Head, let
3. Drawn by the mag - net of thy love let
4. This is the bond of per - fect - ness, thy

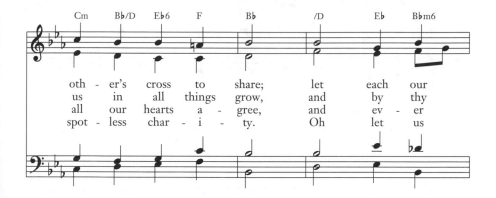

oth - er's cross to share; let each our
us in all things grow, and by thy
all our hearts a - gree, and ev - er
spot - less char - i - ty. Oh let us

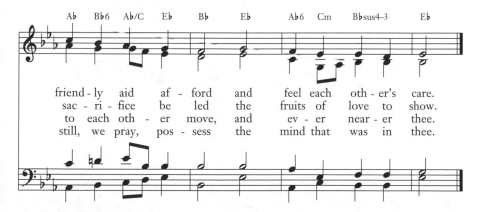

friend - ly aid af - ford and feel each oth - er's care.
sac - ri - fice be led the fruits of love to show.
to each oth - er move, and ev - er near - er thee.
still, we pray, pos - sess the mind that was in thee.

See also: Dunfermline 43 171 221

Words: Charles Wesley (1707–1788), alt Music: Scottish Psalter 1615

Words: public domain Music: public domain

490

God of grace and God of glory

CWM RHONDDA 8 7 8 7 4 4 7 7

1. God of grace and God of glory, on thy peo - ple
2. Lo! the hosts of e - vil round us, scorn thy Christ, as -
3. Cure thy chil - dren's war - ring mad - ness, bend our pride to
4. Set our feet on loft - y plac - es; gird our lives that
5. Save us from weak res - ig - na - tion to the e - vils

pour thy power; crown thine an - cient chur - ch's sto - ry;
sail his ways! From the fears that long have bound us,
thy con - trol; shame our wan - ton, self - ish glad - ness,
they may be ar - moured with all Christ - like grac - es,
we de - plore; let the search for thy sal - va - tion

bring its bud to glo - rious flower.
free our hearts to love and praise.
rich in things and poor in soul. Grant us wis - dom,
pledged to set all cap - tives free.
be our glo - ry ev - er - more.

See also: Cwm Rhondda 651

Words: Harry Emerson Fosdick (1878–1969), alt   Music: John Hughes (1873–1932);
descant, Malcolm Archer (1952–)

Words: public domain   Music: descant, copyright © Kevin Mayhew Ltd., 1990

for the fac - ing of this
for the liv - ing of these
grant us cour - age, lest we miss thy king-dom's
that we fail not them nor
serv - ing thee whom we a -

hour, for the fac - ing of this hour.
days, for the liv - ing of these days.
goal, lest we miss thy king-dom's goal.
thee, that we fail not them nor thee!
dore, serv - ing thee whom we a - dore.

of this hour,
of these days,
king-dom's goal,
them nor thee,
we a - dore

Descant

5. Save us from weak res - ig - na-tion to the e - vils we de-plore; let the search for

thy sal - va - tion be our glo-ry ev - er-more. Grant us wis-dom, grant us cour-age,

serv - ing thee whom we a - dore, serv - ing thee whom we a - dore.

The Church

491　God bless your church with strength

ICH HALTE TREULICH STILL　6 6 8 6 D SMD

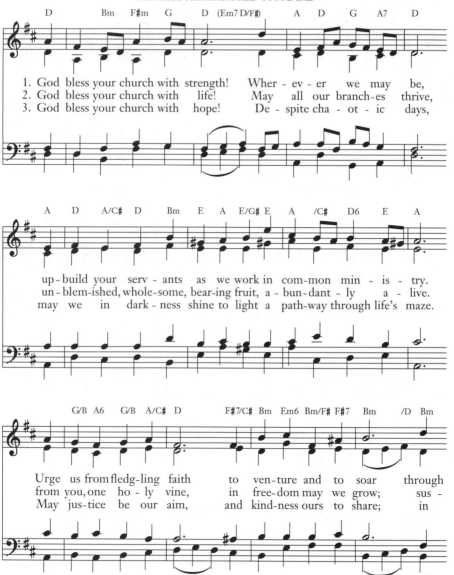

1. God bless your church with strength! Wher - ev - er　we may　be,
2. God bless your church with　life!　May　all our branch-es　thrive,
3. God bless your church with　hope!　De - spite cha - ot - ic　days,

up - build your serv - ants　as we work in com - mon min - is - try.
un - blem-ished, whole-some, bear-ing fruit, a - bun-dant - ly　a - live.
may we　in　dark - ness shine to light a　path-way through life's maze.

Urge　us from fledg-ling faith　to　ven-ture and　to　soar　through
from you, one ho - ly vine,　in　free-dom may we grow;　sus -
May jus-tice be　our aim,　and kind-ness ours to share;　in

Alternate tunes: Diademata　St. Thomas
Words: John A. Dalles (1954–)　Music: J.S. Bach (1685–1750)
Words: copyright © John A. Dalles, 1990　Music: public domain

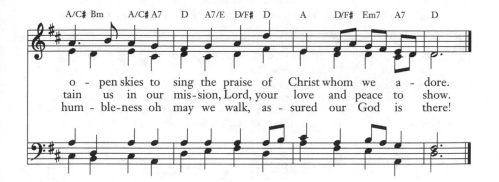

o - pen skies to sing the praise of Christ whom we a - dore.
tain us in our mis-sion, Lord, your love and peace to show.
hum - ble-ness oh may we walk, as - sured our God is there!

492   Lord Jesus Christ, lover of all

LOVER OF ALL   8 8 5

Lord Je - sus Christ, lov - er of all, trail wide the hem of your gar - ment. Bring heal-ing, bring peace.

Words: Iona Community (Scotland)   Music: Iona Community (Scotland)

493 How blessed are the ones who hear

CREDITON 8 6 8 6 CM

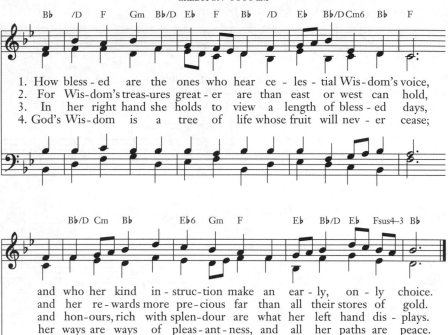

1. How bless - ed   are the ones who hear ce - les - tial Wis - dom's voice,
2. For Wis-dom's treas-ures great - er are than east or west can hold,
3. In   her right hand she holds to view a length of bless - ed days,
4. God's Wis-dom is   a   tree of life whose fruit will nev - er cease;

and who her kind in - struc-tion make an ear - ly, on - ly choice.
and her re - wards more pre - cious far than all their stores of gold.
and hon-ours, rich with splen-dour are what her left hand dis - plays.
her ways are ways of pleas - ant - ness, and all her paths are peace.

Alternate tune: St. Stephen (Newington)

Words: Michael Bruce (1746–1767), Scottish Paraphrases, alt Music: Thomas Clark (1775–1859);
harmony, Martin Shaw (1875–1958)

Words: this version, copyright © The Presbyterian Church in Canada, 1997 Music: harmony, copyright © Dr. Martin Shaw

494
Lord, be thy word
IBSTONE 6 6 6 6

1. Lord, be thy word my rule; in it may I re - joice,
2. thy prom - is - es my hope, thy prov - i - dence my guard,

thy glo - ry be my aim, thy ho - ly will, my choice,
thine arm my strong sup - port, thy self my great re - ward.

Alternate tune: Quam dilecta

Words: Christopher Wordsworth (1807–1885) Music: Maria Tiddeman (c. 1837–1915)

Words: public domain Music: public domain

495 The heavens declare your glory, Lord

CHURCH TRIUMPHANT 8 8 8 8 LM

1. The heavens de - clare your glo - ry, Lord! In
2. Sun, moon and stars con - vey your praise to
3. Nor shall your spread - ing gos - pel rest till
4. Great sun of right - eous - ness, a - rise and
5. Your no - blest won - ders here we view in

eve - ry star your wis - dom shines, but when our eyes be -
all the earth, and nev - er stand, so when your truth be -
through the world your truth has run, till Christ has all the
bless the world with heaven - ly light! Your gos - pel makes the
souls re - newed and sins for - given! Lord, cleanse my sins, my

hold your word, we read your name in clear - er lines.
gan its race, it touched and glanced on eve - ry land.
na - tions blest who see the light or feel the sun.
sim - ple wise; your laws are pure, your judge - ments right.
soul re - new, and make your word my guide to heaven.

See also: Church Triumphant 77

Words: Isaac Watts (1674–1748), alt   Music: J.W. Elliott (1833–1915)

Words: public domain   Music: public domain

496 Thy word is a lamp unto my feet

THY WORD Irregular

Thy word is a lamp un-to my feet and a light un-to my path.

1. When I feel a-fraid, think I've lost my way, still you're there right be-side
2. I will not for-get your love for me, and yet my heart for - ev - er is wan-

me, and no-thing will I fear as long as you are near.
dering. Je - sus, be my guide and hold me to your side, and

Please be near me to the end.
I will love you to the end.

Words: Amy Grant (1960–) Music: Amy Grant (1960–)

497

Word of God, across the ages

AUSTRIA 8 7 8 7 D

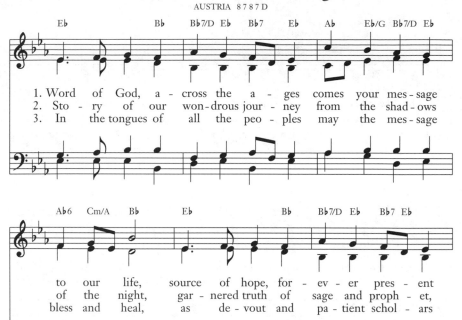

1. Word of God, a - cross the a - ges comes your mes - sage
2. Sto - ry of our won - drous jour - ney from the shad - ows
3. In the tongues of all the peo - ples may the mes - sage

to our life, source of hope, for - ev - er pres - ent
of the night, gar - nered truth of sage and proph - et,
bless and heal, as de - vout and pa - tient schol - ars

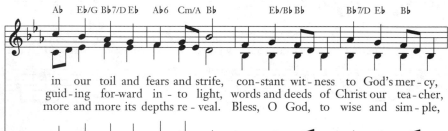

in our toil and fears and strife, con - stant wit - ness to God's mer - cy,
guid - ing for - ward in - to light, words and deeds of Christ our tea - cher,
more and more its depths re - veal. Bless, O God, to wise and sim - ple,

See also: Austria 483

Words: Ferdinand Q. Blanchard (1876–1968), alt   Music: Franz Joseph Haydn (1732–1809)

still our grace, what-e'er be-fall, guide un-fail - ing,
point-ing to the life and way, still ap-peal - ing,
all your truth of age - less worth, till all lands re -

strength e - ter - nal, of - fered free - ly to us all.
still in-spir - ing, in the strug - gles of to - day.
ceive the wit - ness and your know - ledge fills the earth.

498 Sing them over again to me

WORDS OF LIFE 8 6 8 6 6 6 with refrain

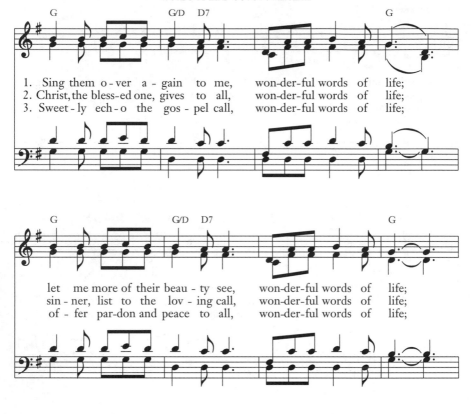

1. Sing them o-ver a-gain to me, won-der-ful words of life;
2. Christ, the bless-ed one, gives to all, won-der-ful words of life;
3. Sweet-ly ech-o the gos-pel call, won-der-ful words of life;

let me more of their beau-ty see, won-der-ful words of life;
sin-ner, list to the lov-ing call, won-der-ful words of life;
of-fer par-don and peace to all, won-der-ful words of life;

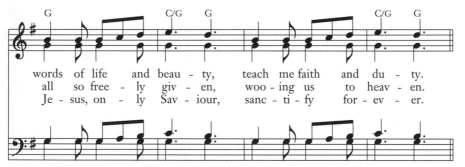

words of life and beau-ty, teach me faith and du-ty.
all so free-ly giv-en, woo-ing us to heav-en.
Je-sus, on-ly Sav-iour, sanc-ti-fy for-ev-er.

Words: Philip Bliss (1838–1876) Music: Philip Bliss (1838–1876)

Words: public domain Music: public domain

Refrain

Beau-ti-ful words, won-der-ful words, won-der-ful words of life,

beau-ti-ful words, won-der-ful words, won-der-ful words of life.

499

Tell me the old, old story

EVANGEL 7 6 7 6 D with refrain

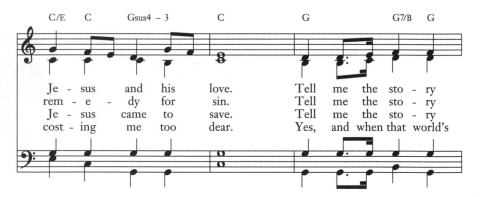

1. Tell me the old, old sto - ry of un - seen things a -
2. Tell me the sto - ry slow - ly, that I may take it
3. Tell me the sto - ry soft - ly, with ear - nest tones and
4. Tell me the same old sto - ry, when you have cause to

bove, of Je - sus and his glo - ry, of
in, that won - der - ful re - demp - tion, God's
grave; re - mem - ber I'm the sin - ner whom
fear that this world's emp - ty glo - ry is

Je - sus and his love. Tell me the sto - ry
rem - e - dy for sin. Tell me the sto - ry
Je - sus came to save. Tell me the sto - ry
cost - ing me too dear. Yes, and when that world's

Words: Katherine Hankey (1834–1911) Music: William H. Doane (1832–1916)

Words: public domain Music: public domain

sim - ply, as to a lit - tle child, for
of - ten, for I for - get so soon; the
al - ways, if you would real - ly be, in
glo - ry is dawn - ing on my soul, tell

I am weak and wea - ry, and help-less and de - filed.
ear - ly dew of morn - ing has passed a - way at noon.
an - y time of trou - ble, a com-fort - er to me.
me the old, old sto - ry: Christ Je - sus makes thee whole.

Refrain

Tell me the old, old sto - ry; tell me the old, old sto - ry;

tell me the old, old sto - ry of Je - sus and his love.

500

Open my eyes, that I may see

OPEN MY EYES 8 8 9 8 with refrain

1. O-pen my eyes, that I may see glimps-es of truth thou hast for me;
2. O-pen my ears, that I may hear voic - es of truth thou send-est clear,
3. O-pen my mouth, and let me bear glad - ly the warm truth eve - ry-where;

place in my hands the won-der-ful key that shall un-clasp and set me free.
and while the wave-notes fall on my ear, eve - ry-thing false will dis-ap-pear.
o - pen my heart and let me pre-pare love with thy chil-dren thus to share.

Refrain

Si-lent-ly now I wait for thee, read-y, my God, thy will to see;

o - pen my eyes:
o - pen my ears: il - lu-mine me, Spir - it di - vine!
o - pen my heart:

Words: Clara H. Scott (1841–1897) Music: Clara H. Scott (1841–1897)

Words: public domain Music: public domain

501

Live in charity

UBI CARITAS 9 10

Live in char - i - ty and stead - fast love;
U - bi ca - ri - tas et a - mor,

live in char - i - ty: God will dwell with you.
u - bi ca - ri - tas De - us i - bi est.

Words: traditional; translation, Taizé Community (France)   Music: Taizé Community (France)

The Bible

502

Lord, thy word abideth

RAVENSHAW 6 6 6 6

1. Lord, thy word a - bid - eth, and our foot-steps guid - eth;
2. When our foes are near us, then thy word doth cheer us,
3. When the storms are o'er us, and dark clouds be - fore us,
4. Who can tell the pleas - ure, who re - count the treas - ure,

who its truth be - liev - eth light and joy re - ceiv - eth.
word of con - so - la - tion, mes-sage of sal - va - tion.
then its light di - rect - eth, and our way pro - tect - eth.
by thy word im - part - ed to the sim - ple - heart - ed:

5. word of mercy, giving
   help unto the living;
   word of life, supplying
   comfort to the dying!

6. Oh that we, discerning
   its most holy learning,
   Lord, may love and fear thee,
   evermore be near thee.

Words: Henry Williams Baker (1821–1877)   Music: Hymn Book of the Bohemian Brethren 1531;
arrangement William Henry Monk (1823–1889)

Words: public domain   Music: public domain

503

Not far beyond the sea

CORNWALL 886D

1. Not far be-yond the sea, nor high a - bove the heavens, but
2. The young in Christ your scrip-tures feed with milk suf - fi - cient
3. Root-ed and ground-ed in your love, with saints on earth and
4. Help us to press on toward that mark, and, though our vi - sion

ver - y nigh your voice, O God, is heard. For
for their need, the nur - ture of the Lord. Be -
saints a - bove we join in full ac - cord: to
now is dark, to live by what we see. So,

each new step of faith we take you have more truth and
neath life's bur - den and its heat the ful - ly grown find
know the breadth, length, depth and height, the cru - ci - fied and
when we see you face to face, your truth and light our

light to break forth from your ho - ly word.
strong - er meat in your un - fail - ing word.
ris - en might of Christ, the in - car - nate Word.
dwell - ing - place for - ev - er - more shall be.

Words: George B. Caird (1917–1984), alt Music: Samuel Sebastian Wesley (1810–1876)

Words: copyright © George B. Caird, 1982. Used by permission of Viola M.Caird. Music: public domain

504

This is a story full of love

TIMOTHY 8 6 8 6 CM with repeat

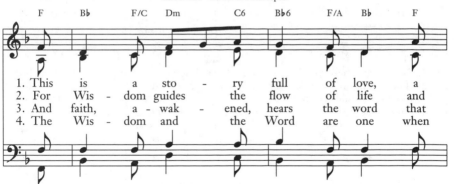

1. This is a sto - ry full of love, a
2. For Wis - dom guides the flow of life, and
3. And faith, a - wak - ened, hears the word that
4. The Wis - dom and the Word are one when

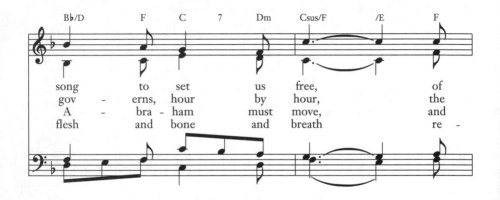

song to set us free, of
gov - erns, hour by hour, the
A - bra - ham must move, and
flesh and bone and breath re -

God, the Wis - dom and the Word, the
forc - es of the u - ni - verse, the
slaves of Phar - aoh take the road to
veal the hu - man face of God, the

Words: Brian A. Wren (1936–) Music: William P. Rowan (1951–)

Words: copyright © 1986 by Hope Publishing Co. Music: copyright © 1986 by Hope Publishing Co.

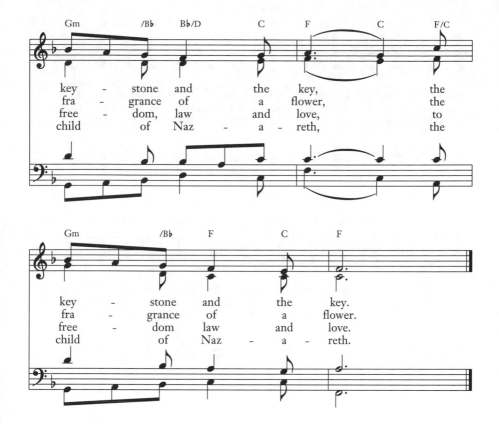

key - stone and the key, the
fra - grance of a flower, the
free - dom, law and love, to
child of Naz - a - reth, the

key - stone and the key.
fra - grance of a flower.
free - dom law and love.
child of Naz - a - reth.

5. Arising over earthly powers,
   our Saviour has begun
   to catch them in a web of love
   and weave them into one,
   and weave them into one.

6. Praise God, the Wisdom and the Word,
   till all the world can see
   that Jesus is the first and last,
   the keystone and the key,
   the keystone and the key.

505

O Christ, the Word, incarnate

CHENIES 7 6 7 6 D

1. O Christ, the Word in - car - nate, O Wis-dom from on high,
2. Your peo - ple hold this treas - ure from you, its source di - vine,
3. Oh make your church, dear Sav - iour, a lamp of pur - est gold,

O Truth un-changed, un-chang - ing, O Light of our dark sky:
a light that to all a - ges through-out the earth will shine;
to bear be - fore the na - tions your true light as of old;

we praise you for the ra - diance that from the hal-lowed page,
it is the chart and com - pass that all life's voy-age through,
oh teach your wan-dering pil - grims by this their path to trace,

Words: William Walsham How (1823–1897), alt   Music: Timothy Richard Matthews (1826–1910)

Words: public domain   Music: public domain

506   The Spirit breathes upon the word

HORSLEY 8 6 8 6 CM

1. The Spir - it breathes up - on the word, and brings the truth to sight;
2. The hand that gave it still sup - plies the gra-cious light and heat;
3. Let ev - er - last - ing thanks be thine for such a bright dis - play,
4. My soul re - joic - es to pur - sue the steps of One I love,

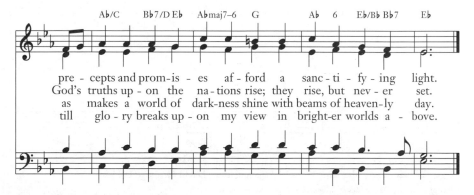

pre - cepts and prom-is - es af - ford a sanc - ti - fy - ing light.
God's truths up - on the na - tions rise; they rise, but nev - er set.
as makes a world of dark-ness shine with beams of heaven-ly day.
till glo - ry breaks up - on my view in bright-er worlds a - bove.

Words: William Cowper (1731–1800), alt Music: William Horsley (1774–1858)

Words: public domain Music: public domain

507

Break now the bread of life

LATHBURY 10 10 10 10

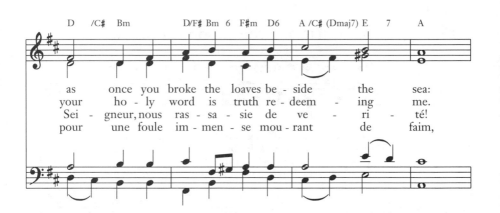

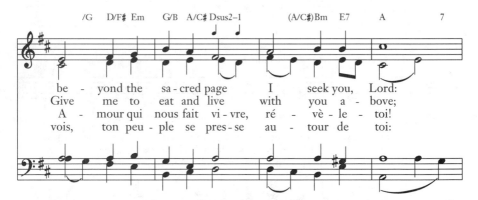

1. Break now the bread of life, dear Lord, to me,
2. You are the bread of life, dear Lord, to me;
1. Romps - nous le pain de vie! Que ta bon - té,
2. Ô toi, dont la clé - mence cré - a du pain

as once you broke the loaves be - side the sea:
your ho - ly word is truth re - deem - ing me.
Sei - gneur, nous ras - sa - sie de ve - ri - té!
pour une foule im - men - se mou - rant de faim,

be - yond the sa - cred page I seek you, Lord:
Give me to eat and live with you a - bove;
A - mour qui nous fait vi - vre, ré - vè - le - toi!
vois, ton peu - ple se pres - se au - tour de toi:

Words: Alexander Groves (1842–1909), Mary A. Lathbury (1841–1913), alt
Music: William Fiske Sherwin (1826–1888); adaptation, David Grundy (1934–)

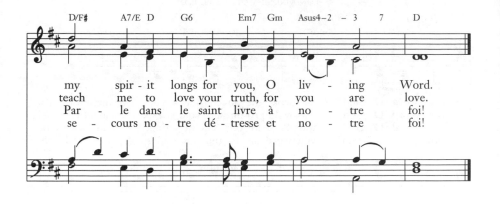

my spir-it longs for you, O liv - ing Word.
teach me to love your truth, for you are love.
Par - le dans le saint livre à no - tre foi!
se - cours no - tre dé - tresse et no - tre foi!

3. Oh send your Spirit now, dear Lord, to me;
touch now my blinded eyes and make me see:
then shall all bondage cease, all fetters fall,
and I shall find my peace, my all in all.

3. C'est toi, le pain de vie, Verbe puissant!
C'est de ta chair meurtrie, c'est de ton sang,
que notre âme doit vivre. Ah! donne-toi
par l'Esprit et le livre à notre foi!

4. Tu bénis tes apôtres, puis, à leur tour,
ils protèrent à d'autres ton grand amour.
Ô parole féconde, que notre foi
t'offre à ce pauvre monde qui meurt sans toi!

508 Your word, O God, awoke the uncreated

LONDONDERRY AIR 11 10 11 10 D

Unison

1. Your word, O God, a-woke the un-cre-at-ed; brought form from cha-os, out of dark-ness, light, till life, by si-lent a-ges longa-wait-ed, dis-played its grow-ing beau-ty in your sight. In field and

2. Your word, O God, a-woke pro-phe-tic voic-es on Car-mel's height, and Ju-dah's rock-y hills; the great I-sa-iah's ar-dent soul re-joic-es, and Jer-e-mi-ah's tor-tured bos-om thrills. To sage and

3. Your word, O God, took flesh for our sal-va-tion, and we be-held his glo-ry, truth and grace; he brings the gos-pel of our lib-er-a-tion, the tid-ings of your mer-cy light his face. In heal-ing

4. Now speak a-gain your word un-to the na-tions, in all the full-ness of your Spir-it's power, and as your voice woke for-mer gen-er-a-tions, de-clare your pur-pose for this pre-sent hour. Oh speak to

Words: Albert F. Bayly (1901–1984) Music: Irish traditional; arrangement, Donald Davison

Words: copyright © Oxford University Press Music: arrangement, copyright © W.D. Davison

for - est, o - cean, air and riv - er, our eyes be - held your crea - tures ver - y
psalm - ist comes your in - spi - ra - tion, in song sub - lime and wis - dom's sub - tle
deeds of love and ho - ly sto - ry we hear the mu - sic of your gra - cious
smite, to cleanse and to re - new us; your church a - waits the judge - ment of your

good, and, quick - ened by your breath, al - might - y
page, and in the law and re - cords of a
name: still more, his Cross and res - ur - rec - tion
sword, un - til with power your Spir - it shall en -

giv - er, your hu - man im - age in your pres - ence stood.
na - tion, your word, O God, speaks on from age to age.
glo - ry the sov - ereign tri - umphs of your love pro - claim.
due us to give the world the Gos - pel of our Lord.

509 Thanks to God whose word was spoken

WYLDE GREEN 878747

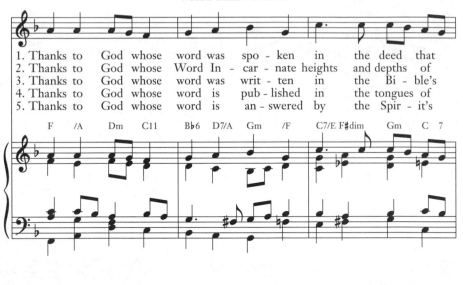

1. Thanks to God whose word was spo - ken in the deed that
2. Thanks to God whose Word In - car - nate heights and depths of
3. Thanks to God whose word was writ - ten in the Bi - ble's
4. Thanks to God whose word is pub - lished in the tongues of
5. Thanks to God whose word is an - swered by the Spir - it's

made the earth. God's the voice that called a na - tion;
life did share. Deeds and words and death and ris - ing,
sa - cred page, rec - ord of the rev - e - la - tion
eve - ry race. See its glo - ry un - di - mi - nished
voice with - in. Here we drink of joy un - mea - sured,

Words: R.T. Brooks (1918–1985), Music: Peter Cutts (1937–)

God's the fires that tried its worth.
grace in hu - man form de - clare.
show - ing God to eve - ry age. God has spo - ken:
by the change of time or place.
life re-deemed from death and sin. God is speak - ing:

A7/C♯   A 7   B♭   F6   Gm6   A 7   Dmsus4–3   F/A   Dm/B   C   /B♭

praise God for the liv - ing word.

F/A   F7   D7(/G/F♯   /E   /D   /B♭)   Gm   C11   C7   F

510 Deep in the shadows of the past

KINGSFOLD 8 6 8 6 D CMD

1. Deep in the shad-ows of the past, far out from set-tled
2. While oth-ers bowed to change-less gods, they met a mys-ter-
3. From Ex-o-dus to Pen-te-cost the prom-ise changed and
4. For all the writ-ings that sur-vived, for lead-ers long a-

lands, some no-mads trav-eled with their God a-
y, in-vis-i-ble, with-out a name, "I
grew, while some, re-mem-ber-ing the past, re-
go, who sift-ed, cop-ied and pre-served the

cross the des-ert sands. The dawn-ing hope of hu-man-kind
AM WHAT I WILL BE"; and by their tents, a-round their fires,
cord-ed what they knew, or with their let-ters and la-ments,
Bi-ble that we know, give thanks, and find its sto-ry yet

Words: Brian A. Wren (1936–) Music: English traditional; arranged by Ralph Vaughan Williams (1872–1958)

by them was sensed and shown: a prom - ise call - ing
in sto - ry, song and law, they praised, re - mem - bered,
their proph - e - cy and praise, re - cov - ered, kin - dled
our prom - ise, strength and call, the mod - el of e -

them a - head, a fu - ture yet un - known.
hand - ed on a past that prom - ised more.
and ex - pressed new hope for chang - ing days.
merg - ing faith, a - live with hope for all.

511

Lamp of our feet

GRÄFENBERG 8 6 8 6 CM

1. Lamp of our feet where - by we trace / our path when wont to stray,
2. bread of our souls where - on we feed, / true man - na from on high,
3. pil - lar of fire through watch-es dark / or ra - diant cloud by day,
4. word of the ev - er - liv - ing God, / will of God's glo - rious Son:
5. Lord, grant that we a - right may learn / the wis - dom it im - parts,

stream from the fount of heaven-ly grace, / brook by the trav - eler's way,
our guide and chart where-in we read / of realms be-yond the sky,
when waves would whelm our toss-ing bark, / our an - chor and our stay,
with - out thee how could earth be trod, / or heaven it - self be won?
and to its heaven - ly teach-ing turn / with sim - ple, child - like hearts.

See also: Gräfenberg 390

Words: Bernard Barton (1784–1849)   Music: Johann Crüger (1598–1662)

Words: public domain   Music: public domain

512 At the dawning of creation

SHIPSTON 8 7 8 7

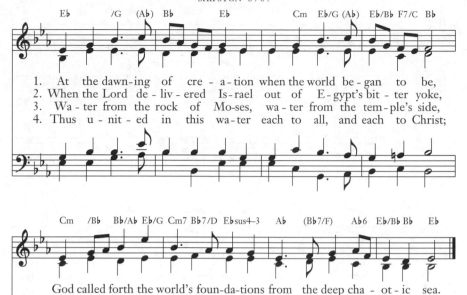

1. At the dawn-ing of cre - a-tion when the world be-gan to be,
2. When the Lord de - liv - ered Is-rael out of E-gypt's bit - ter yoke,
3. Wa - ter from the rock of Mo-ses, wa - ter from the tem-ple's side,
4. Thus u - nit - ed in this wa-ter each to all, and each to Christ;

God called forth the world's foun-da-tions from the deep cha - ot - ic sea.
then the part-ing of the wa-ters of the Liv-ing Wa-ter spoke.
wa - ter from the heart of Je-sus, flow in this bap - tis-mal tide.
to his life of love he calls us by his to - tal sac - ri - fice.

Alternate tune: Stuttgart

Words: David Fox (1956–) Music: English traditional; harmony, Ralph Vaughan Williams (1872–1958)

513 Now there is no male or female

OMNI DIE (LUXEMBOURG) 8 7 8 7 D

1. Now there is no male or fe-male; now there is no free or slave; now there
2. Cru - ci-fied with Christ the Sav-iour, bap-tized in his ho - ly death, and as
3. Death has no do - min-ion over him, so for us death holds no power; life's own

is no Jew or Gen - tile in the earth Christ died to save. Christ has
Christ was raised to glo - ry we have new life on this earth. Power of
wa - ters now have marked us born to God this ver - y hour. From this

set us free for free-dom: we no more sing slav-ery's creed; old sub -
wa - ter and God's nam-ing turns from dark-ness to the light, joins us
mo-ment and for - ev - er dead to sin, a - live in Christ, born of

See also: Omni Die (Luxembourg) 754

Words: Lynette Miller (20th cent.)   Music: Anonymous German Catholic, 17th century

Words: copyright © Lynette Miller, 1986   Music: public domain

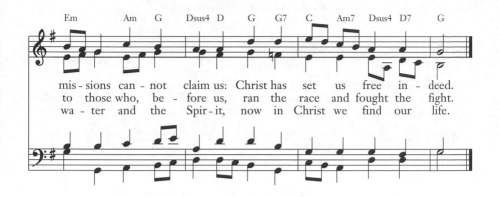

mis - sions can - not claim us: Christ has set us free in - deed.
to those who, be - fore us, ran the race and fought the fight.
wa - ter and the Spir - it, now in Christ we find our life.

514 Jesus, we are gathered / Jesu, tawa pano

JESU TAWA PANO Irregular

Je - sus, we are gath-ered; Je - sus, we are gath-ered; Je - sus,
Je - su, ta-wa pa - no; Je - su, ta-wa pa - no; Je - su,

Leader(s):   (Omit last time)
O Lord Je-sus
Mam-bo Je-su.

we are gath-ered; we are gath-ered to - geth-er with you.
ta - wa pa - no; ta - wa pa - no, mu zi - ta re - nyu.

Words: Patrick Matsikenyiri (20th cent.) Music: Patrick Matsikenyiri (20th cent.)

Words: copyright © Patrick Matsikenyiri, 1990 Music: copyright © Patrick Matsikenyiri, 1990

515 Out of deep, unordered water

BALGEMANN 8 7 8 7 with refrain (8 7 8 7)

1. Out of deep,   un-or-dered wa-ter   God cre-
2. Wa-ter on   the hu-man fore-head,   -   birth-mark
3. Stand-ing round   the font re-minds us   of the

a - ted life and land,   world of bird   and beast   and,
of   the love of God,   is the sign   of death   and
Heb - rews' climb a-shore.   Life is hal - lowed by   the

la - ter,   two-some peo   -   ple: wom-an, man.
ris - ing;   through the sea   there runs a road.
knowl-edge   God   has been   this way be-fore.

There is wa   -   ter in the riv-er   bring-ing life

Words: Fred Kaan (1929–) Music: Ron Klusmeier (1946–)

Words: copyright © 1968 by Hope Publishing Co. Music: copyright © WorshipArts

to tree and plant. Let cre - a - tion praise its

giv - er: there is wa - ter in the font.

516

A little child the Saviour came

ANGELUS 8 8 8 8 LM

1. A lit - tle child the Sav - iour came; the migh - ty
God was still his name, and an - gels wor-shipped
as he lay the help - less in - fant of a day.

2. Christ Je - sus, as a child, did show the way of
life for all to know; now Christ pro - claims the
mes - sage free, "Let lit - tle chil - dren come to me."

3. We bring them, Lord, and, with the sign of sprink - led
wa - ter, name them thine: their souls with sav - ing
grace en - dow; bap - tize them with thy Spir - it now.

4. Oh give thine angels charge, good Lord,
them safely in thy way to guard;
thy blessing on their lives command,
and write their names upon thy hand.

5. O thou, who by an infant's tongue
dost hear thy perfect glory sung;
may these, with all the heavenly host,
praise Father, Son and Holy Ghost.

Alternate tune: Puer Nobis Nascitur

Words: William Robertson (1820–1864) Music: Cantica Spiritualia 1847, from a melody by
Georg Joseph (d.1668)

Words: public domain Music: public domain

517

See Israel's gentle Shepherd stand

ST. PETER   8 6 8 6 CM

1. See   Is - rael's   gen - tle   Shep - herd   stand   with
2. "Per - mit   them   to   ap - proach," he   cries,   "nor
3. We   bring   them,   Lord,   in   thank - ful   hands,   and

all - en - gag - ing   charms;   hark   how   he   calls   the
scorn   their   hum - ble   name,   for   'twas   to   bless   such
yield   them   up   to   thee;   joy - ful   that   we   our -

ten - der   lambs,   and   folds   them   in   his   arms."
souls   as   these   the   Lord   of   an - gels   came."
selves   are   thine;   thine   let   our   chil - dren   be.

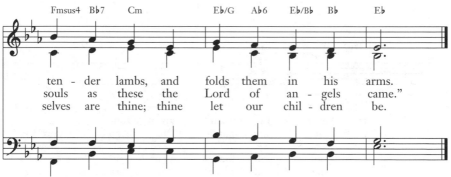

Words: Philip Doddridge (1702–1751)   Music: Alexander Robert Reinagle (1799–1877)

Words: public domain   Music: public domain

518 O God eternal, sovereign Lord

ALMSGIVING 8 8 8 4

1. O God e - ter - nal, sov - ereign Lord,
2. Through a - ges long your cov - enant stands,
3. Great God, from whom all bless - ings spring,
4. By word and wa - ter we con - fess
5. Bap - tize this child with eve - ry grace,

we gath - er now with one ac - cord, in mem-ory
our names are writ - ten on your hands, and for this
whose eyes see eve - ry pre - cious thing, this child in
the great-ness of your faith - ful - ness, in that our
that s/he might al - ways seek your face, and choose in

of your faith - ful word, given long a - go.
child your love com - mands this sign we show.
faith and love we bring, with hearts a - glow.
chil - dren you will bless: your love they know.
eve - ry time and place with Christ to go.

Words: William Fitch (1911–1984), alt   Music: John Bacchus Dykes (1823–1876)

Words: copyright © the estate of William Fitch   Music: public domain

519

Jesus, friend so kind and gentle

ROUSSEAU 878787

1. Je - sus, friend so kind and gen - tle, bring we these be -
2. You re - ceived the lit - tle chil - dren to your - self so
3. Grant to us a deep com - pas - sion for your chil - dren

lov - ed ones; may they know your kind - est bless - ing;
ten - der - ly; give to us who teach and guide them,
ev - ery - where; may we see our hu - man fam - ily

now en - fold them in your arms; may your good - ness
wis - dom and hu - mi - li - ty, vi - sion true, with
free from sor - row and de - spair, may your reign of

be a - round them; keep them free from all that harms.
joy and pa - tience, love to serve them faith - ful - ly.
love and glo - ry dwell a - mong us, bright and fair.

Words: Philip E. Gregory (1886–), alt   Music: J.J. Rousseau (1712–1778)

Baptism
520
Servants of the Saviour
WHITWORTH 6 5 6 5 D

1. Ser - vants of the Sav - iour, marked as Je - sus' own,
2. Ser - vants of the Sav - iour, cap - tive hearts re - leased,

o - ver sin vic - to - rious, by a new name known.
chil - dren of cre - a - tion, come and keep the feast!

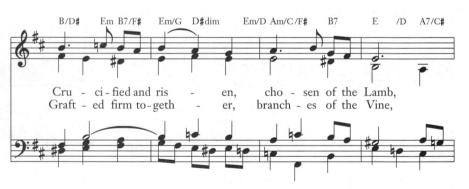

Cru - ci - fied and ris - en, cho - sen of the Lamb,
Graft - ed firm to-geth - er, branch - es of the Vine,

See also: St. Gertrude 487

Words: Sylvia G. Dunstan (1955–1993)   Music: Walter MacNutt (1910–1996)

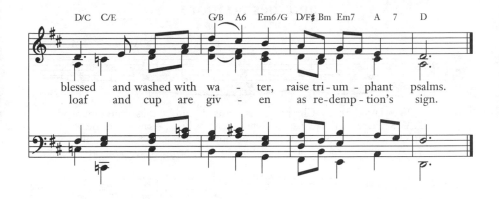

blessed and washed with wa - ter, raise tri - um - phant psalms.
loaf and cup are giv - en as re-demp - tion's sign.

521   Child of blessing, child of promise
STUTTGART 8 7 8 7

1. Child of bless-ing, child of prom-ise, bap-tized with the Spir-it's sign,
2. Child of love, our love's ex-pres-sion, love's cre - a - tion, loved in-deed!
3. Child of joy, our dear-est treas-ure, God's you are; from God you came.
4. Child of God, your lov-ing Par-ent, learn to know whose child you are;

with this wa - ter God has sealed you un - to love and grace di - vine.
Fresh from God, re - fresh our spir - its, in - to joy and laugh - ter lead.
Back to God we hum - bly give you; live as one who bears Christ's name.
grow to laugh and sing and wor-ship, trust and love God more than all.

Words: Ronald S. Cole-Turner (1948–) Music: Psalmodia Sacra, oder Andächtige und Schöne Gesänge 1715; harmony, William Henry Havergal (1793–1870)

Words: copyright © Ronald S. Cole-Turner, 1981 Music: public domain

522

We know that Christ is raised
and dies no more

ENGELBERG 10 10 10 4

1. We know that Christ is raised and dies no more;
   em-braced by fu - tile death, he broke its hold,
   and our de - spair he turned to blaz - ing joy:

2. We share by wa - ter in his sav - ing death;
   this un - ion brings to be - ing one new cell,
   a liv - ing and or - gan - ic part of Christ:

3. The Fa - ther's splen - dour clothes the Son with life,
   the Spir - it's fis - sion shakes the church of God;
   bap - tized we live with God the Three - in - One:

4. A new cre - a - tion comes to life and grows
   as Christ's new bod - y takes on flesh and blood;
   the u - ni - verse re - stored and whole will sing:

Words: John Brownlow Geyer (1932–)   Music: C.V. Stanford (1852–1924)

hal - le - lu - jah!   hal - le - lu - jah!

523   Christ has died; Christ is risen

ACCLAMATION (KRIEWALD)

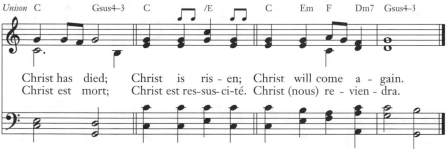

Christ has died; Christ is ris - en; Christ will come a - gain.
Christ est mort; Christ est res-sus- ci-té. Christ (nous) re - vien - dra.

Each phrase may be repeated

Words: traditional liturgical   Music: James A. Kriewald (1940–)

Words: public domain   Music: copyright © James A. Kriewald, 1985

Words: public domain   Music: copyright © James A. Kriewald, 1985

524

We come as guests invited

NYLAND 7 6 7 6 D

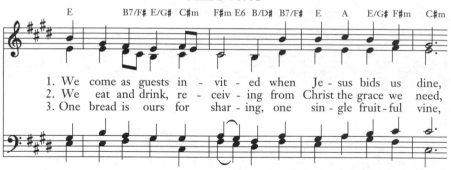

1. We come as guests in - vit - ed when Je - sus bids us dine,
2. We eat and drink, re - ceiv - ing from Christ the grace we need,
3. One bread is ours for shar - ing, one sin - gle fruit - ful vine,

his friends on earth u - nit - ed to share the bread and wine;
and in our hearts be - liev - ing on him by faith we feed;
our fel - low - ship de - clar - ing re - newed in bread and wine .

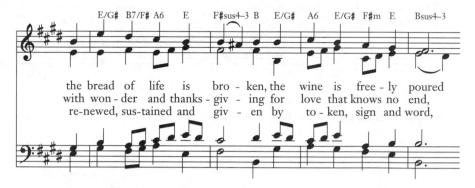

the bread of life is bro - ken, the wine is free - ly poured
with won - der and thanks - giv - ing for love that knows no end,
re - newed, sus - tained and giv - en by to - ken, sign and word,

Words: Timothy Dudley–Smith (1926–) Music: Finnish hymn melody;
arrangement, David Evans (1874–1948)

for us, in sol-emn to - ken of Christ our dy - ing Lord.
we find in Je - sus liv - ing our ev - er - pres - ent friend.
the pledge and seal of heav - en, the love of Christ our Lord.

525   Behold the Lamb of God

LAMB OF GOD 6 6 6 5

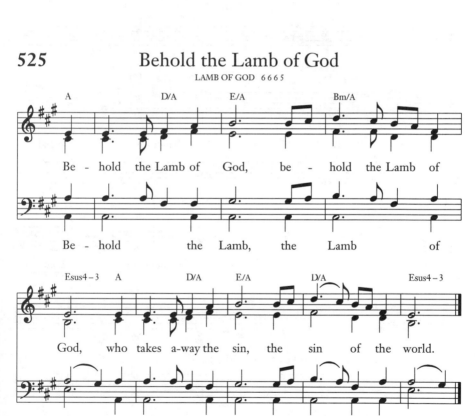

Be - hold the Lamb of God, be - hold the Lamb of
Be - hold the Lamb, the Lamb of

God, who takes a-way the sin, the sin of the world.
God, who takes a - way the sin of the world.

Words: traditional liturgical   Music: Iona Community (Scotland)

526 Lift up your hearts / Sing Hallelujah

SING ALLELUIA 8 5 8

(Lord!) 1. Lift up your hearts un-to the Lord.

1. Lift up your hearts un-to the Lord; lift up your

Sing hal-le-lu-jah, hal - le - lu -

hearts un-to the Lord. Sing hal-le-lu - jah, sing hal-le-

jah; lift up your hearts un-to the Lord!

lu - jah; lift up your hearts un-to the Lord!

2. In Christ the world has been redeemed…
3. His resurrection sets us free…
4. Therefore we celebrate the feast…
5. Sing hallelujah to the Lord…

Words: early Christian liturgy Music: Linda Stassen (1951–); harmony, Dale Grotenhuis (1931–)

527

Eat this bread

EAT THIS BREAD 6 9 6 9

Eat this bread, drink this cup; come to me and nev-er be hun-gry.

Eat this bread, drink this cup; trust in me and you will not thirst.

Descants for melody instrument(s)

Words: John 6:35; paraphrase, Robert J. Batastini (1942–), and Taizé Community (France)
Music: Jacques Berthier (1923–1994)

528

Jesus calls us here to meet him

JESUS CALLS US 8 7 8 7 D

1. Je - sus calls us here to meet him as, through word and song and prayer, we af - firm God's prom - ised pres - ence where his peo - ple live and care.
2. Je - sus calls us to con - fess him Word of Life and Lord of all, shar - er of our flesh and frail - ness sav - ing all who fail or fall.
3. Je - sus calls us to each oth - er: found in him are no di - vides. Race and class and sex and lan - guage: such are bar - riers he de - rides.
4. Je - sus calls us to his ta - ble root - ed firm in time and space, where the church in earth and heav - en finds a com - mon meet - ing place.

Words: Iona Community (Scotland)   Music: Gaelic melody; adaptation, Iona Community (Scotland)

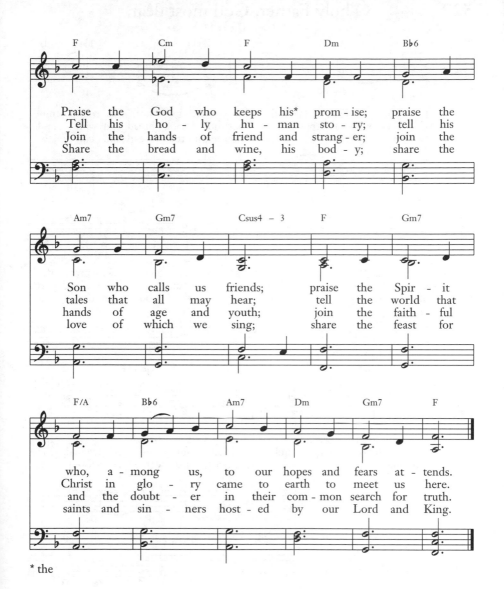

Praise the God who keeps his* prom - ise; praise the
Tell his ho - ly hu - man sto - ry; tell his
Join the hands of friend and strang - er; join the
Share the bread and wine, his bod - y; share the

Son who calls us friends; praise the Spir - it
tales that all may hear; tell the world that
hands of age and youth; join the faith - ful
love of which we sing; share the feast for

who, a - mong us, to our hopes and fears at - tends.
Christ in glo - ry came to earth to meet us here.
and the doubt - er in their com - mon search for truth.
saints and sin - ners host - ed by our Lord and King.

* the

Communion

529

O holy Father, God most dear

SUSSEX CAROL 888888

1. O ho-ly Fath-er, God most dear, be-hold us round thine al-tar here; ac-cept for sac-ri-fice, we pray, the com-mon food we here dis-play. For bread set forth, for wine out-poured, we bless thee, all-cre-at-ing Lord.

2. O Christ, who at the sup-per board took bread and wine and spoke the word, and, in that sol-emn pas-chal meal, gave flesh and blood our wound to heal, for us re-deemed, for life re-stored, we bless thee, all-cre-at-ing Word.

3. O Ho-ly Spir-it, be thou nigh this bread and cup to sanc-ti-fy, that, eat-ing of the food un-priced, we form one bo-dy, one in Christ. Re-deemed, re-stored in u-ni-ty, we bless thee, Ho-ly Trin-i-ty.

Words: G.A. Tomlinson (1906–) Music: English traditional;
harmony, Ralph Vaughan Williams (1872–1958)

530

I come with joy

DOVE OF PEACE 8 6 8 6 6

1. I come with joy, a child of God, for - giv - en,
2. I come with Chris - tians far and near to find, as
3. As Christ breaks bread and bids us share, each proud di -
4. The Spir - it of the ris - en Christ, un - seen, but
5. To - geth - er met, to - geth - er bound by all that

loved and free, the life of Je - sus to re - call in
all are fed, the new com - mun - i - ty of love in
vi - sion ends. The love that made us, makes us one, and
ev - er near, is in such friend - ship bet - ter known, a -
God has done, we'll go with joy, to give the world the

love laid down for me, in love laid down for me.
Christ's com - mun - ion bread, in Christ's com - mun - ion bread.
strang - ers now are friends, and strang - ers now are friends.
live a - mong us here, a - live a - mong us here.
love that makes us one, the love that makes us one.

Words: Brian A. Wren (1936–) Music: Walker's Southern Harmony 1835; harmony, Charles H. Webb
(1933–)

Words: copyright © 1971, 1995 by Hope Publishing Co. Music: harmony, copyright © United Methodist Publishing House, 1989

531

Draw us in the Spirit's tether

UNION SEMINARY 8 7 8 7 8 7

1. Draw us in the Spir-it's te - ther, for when hum - bly in your name, two or three are met to-geth - er, you are in the midst of them.

2. As dis - ci - ples used to gath - er in the name of Christ to sup, then with thanks to God the Fa - ther break the bread and bless the cup: Hal-le - lu - jah,

3. All our meals and all our liv - ing make as sac - ra - ments of you, that by car - ing, help-ing, giv - ing, we would be dis - ci - ples true.

Words: Matthew 18:20; paraphrase, Percy Dearmer (1867–1936) Music: Harold Friedell (1905–1958)

Words: paraphrase, copyright © Oxford University Press Music: copyright © The H.W. Gray Co., 1957, 1985

Touch we now your gar - ment's hem.
hal - le - lu - jah! So now bind our friend - ship up.
Live, O Christ in all we do.

532 Hallelujah

HALLELUJAH (IONA) Irregular

Hal - le - lu - jah, hal - le - lu - jah, hal - le - lu - jah,

Hal - le - lu - jah! Hal - le - lu - jah, hal - le - lu - jah,

hal - le - lu - jah, hal - le - lu - jah!

Words: traditional   Music: Iona Community (Scotland)

533 Deck thyself, my soul, with gladness

SCHMÜCKE DICH 8 8 8 8 D LMD

1. Deck thy - self, my soul, with glad - ness;
   come in - to the day - light's splen - dour:
2. Sun, who all my life dost bright - en;
   Joy, the sweet - est heart e'er know - eth;
3. Je - sus, Bread of Life, I pray thee,
   nev - er to my hurt in - vit - ed,

leave the gloom - y haunts of sad - ness;
there with joy thy prais - es ren - der
Light, who dost my soul en - light - en;
Fount, whence all my be - ing flow - eth:
let me glad - ly here o - bey thee;
be thy love with love re - quit - ed.

to the One whose grace un - bound - ed
at thy feet I cry, my Mak - er,
From this ban - quet let me meas - ure,

Words: Johann Franck (1618–1677); translation, Catherine Winkworth (1827–1878), alt
Music: Johann Crüger (1598–1662)

Words: public domain Music: public domain

hath this won - drous ban - quet found - ed,
let me be a fit par - tak - er
Lord, how vast and deep its treas - ure,

high o'er all the heav - ens reign - eth,
of this bless - ed food from heav - en,
through the gifts thou here dost give me,

yet to dwell a - mong us deign - eth.
for our good, thy glo - ry giv - en.
as thy guest in heaven re - ceive me.

534

All who hunger, gather gladly

HOLY MANNA 8 7 8 7 D

Unison

1. All who hung-er, gath-er glad-ly; ho-ly man-na is our bread. Come from wil-der-ness and wan-dering. Here, in truth, we will be fed. You that yearn for
2. All who hung-er, nev-er strang-ers, seek-er, be a wel-come guest. Come from rest-less-ness and roam-ing. Here, in joy, we keep the feast. We that once were
3. All who hung-er, sing to-geth-er; Je-sus Christ is liv-ing bread. Come from lone-li-ness and long-ing. Here, in peace, we have been led. Blest are those who

See also: Holy Manna 305

Words: Sylvia G. Dunstan (1955–1993)   Music: attributed to William Moore (fl.1825); harmony, Charles Anders (1929–)

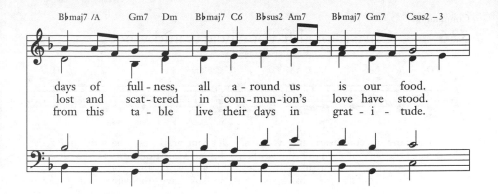

days of full-ness, all a-round us is our food.
lost and scat-tered in com-mun-ion's love have stood.
from this ta-ble live their days in grat-i-tude.

Taste and see the grace e-ter-nal. Taste and see that God is good.

535   The Lord's Prayer

Our Father in heaven,
hallowed be your name,
your kingdom come,
your will be done,
on earth as in heaven.
Give us today our daily bread.
Forgive us our sins
as we forgive those who sin against us.
Save us from the time of trial
and deliver us from evil.
For the kingdom, the power
and the glory are yours
now and forever. Amen

Words: Mattew 6:9–13; translation, English language Liturgical Consultation

Communion
536 Christians, lift your hearts and voices
PANIS VITAE 878787

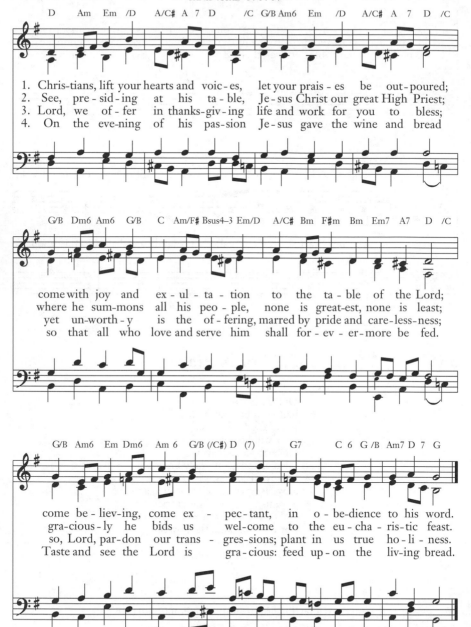

1. Chris-tians, lift your hearts and voic-es, let your prais-es be out-poured;
2. See, pre-sid-ing at his ta-ble, Je-sus Christ our great High Priest;
3. Lord, we of-fer in thanks-giv-ing life and work for you to bless;
4. On the eve-ning of his pas-sion Je-sus gave the wine and bread

come with joy and ex-ul-ta-tion to the ta-ble of the Lord;
where he sum-mons all his peo-ple, none is great-est, none is least;
yet un-worth-y is the of-fering, marred by pride and care-less-ness;
so that all who love and serve him shall for-ev-er-more be fed.

come be-liev-ing, come ex-pec-tant, in o-be-dience to his word.
gra-cious-ly he bids us wel-come to the eu-cha-ris-tic feast.
so, Lord, par-don our trans-gres-sions; plant in us true ho-li-ness.
Taste and see the Lord is gra-cious: feed up-on the liv-ing bread.

Words: John E. Bowers (1923–) Music: Walter MacNutt (1910–1996)

537

'Twas on that night

ROCKINGHAM 8 8 8 8 LM

1. 'Twas on that night when doomed to know the ea - ger
2. and af - ter thanks and glo - ry given to God who
3. "My bro - ken bo - dy thus I give for you, for
4. Then in his hands the cup he raised and God a -

rage of eve - ry foe, that night in which he
rules in earth and heaven, that sym - bol of his
all; take, eat and live; and oft the sa - cred
new he thanked and praised; the full - ness of God's

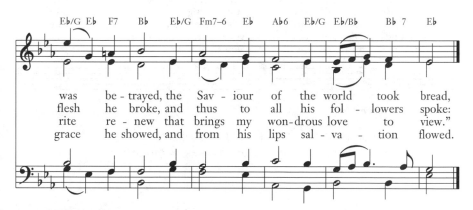

was be - trayed, the Sav - iour of the world took bread,
flesh he broke, and thus to all his fol - lowers spoke:
rite re - new that brings my won-drous love to view."
grace he showed, and from his lips sal - va - tion flowed.

5. "My blood I thus pour forth," he cries,
   "to cleanse the soul in sin that lies;
   in this the covenant is sealed,
   and heaven's eternal grace revealed.

See also: Rockingham 231

6. "With suffering love this cup is given;
   let all partake the wine of heaven,
   and when you gather, let it pour
   in living memory of this hour."

Words: ascribed to John Morison (1750–1798), Scottish Paraphrases, alt
Music: Psalmody in Miniature, Second Supplement, c. 1780; adaptation, Edward Miller (1731–1807)

Communion
538
You satisfy the hungry heart
FINEST WHEAT   8 6 8 6 CM with Refrain (8 6 8 6)

Unison
Refrain

You sat-is-fy the hun-gry heart with gift of fin-est wheat;

come give to us, O sav-ing Lord, the bread of life to eat.

1. As when the shep - herd calls the sheep, they
2. With joy - ful lips we sing to you our
3. Is not the cup we bless and share the
4. The mys - tery of your pres-ence here, no
5. In gra - cious love you give your - self; then

May be played in D major

Words: Omer Westendorf (1916–)   Music: Robert E. Kreutz (1922–)

Words: copyright © Archdiocese of Philadelphia, 1976   Music: copyright © Archdiocese of Philadelphia, 1976

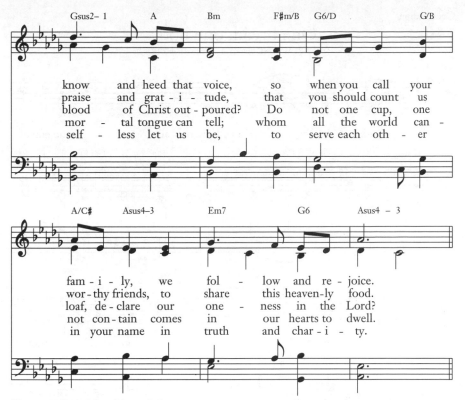

know   and heed that voice,   so   when you call   your
praise   and grat - i - tude,   that   you should count   us
blood   of Christ out - poured?   Do   not one   cup,   one
mor -   tal tongue can tell;   whom   all the   world   can -
self -   less let us   be,   to   serve each oth - er

fam - i - ly,   we   fol -   low and re - joice.
wor-thy friends,   to   share   this heaven-ly food.
loaf, de - clare   our   one -   ness in the Lord?
not con-tain comes in   our hearts to dwell.
in your name in truth   and char - i - ty.

Verses may be sung by soloist or choir

539   The Apostles' Creed

I believe in God, the Father almighty,
creator of heaven and earth.

I believe in Jesus Christ, God's only Son, our Lord,
who was conceived by the Holy Spirit,
born of the Virgin Mary,
suffered under Pontius Pilate,
was crucified, died, and was buried; he descended to the dead.
On the third day he rose again; he ascended into heaven,
he is seated at the right hand of the Father,
and he will come to judge the living and the dead.

I believe in the Holy Spirit,
the holy catholic Church,
the communion of saints,
the forgiveness of sins,
the resurrection of the body,
and the life everlasting. Amen

Words: traditional liturgical text; translation, English Language Liturgical Consultation

Communion
540
One bread, one body
ONE BREAD, ONE BODY 4 4 6 with refrain (9 8 8 9)

Refrain

One bread, one bo-dy, one Lord of all, one cup of

bless - ing which we bless, and we, though

ma-ny through-out the earth, we are one

Words: John B. Foley (20th cent.); v.4, Judee Archer Green (1953–) Music: John B. Foley (20th cent.);
arrangement, Gary Alan Smith (1947–)

bo - dy in this one   Lord.

1. Gen - tile   or   Jew,   ser - vant   or   free,
2. Man - y   the   gifts,   man - y   the   works,
3. Grain   for   the fields,   scat - tered and   grown,
4. Fruit   of   the vine,   gath - ered and crushed,

wom - an   or   man,   no   more.
one   in   the   Lord   of   all.
gath - ered   to   one,   for   all.
poured out   and   blest   for   all.

541 Lord, enthroned in heavenly splendour

ST. OSMUND 878747

1. Lord, en-throned in heaven-ly splen-dour, first be-got-ten from the dead,
2. Here our hum-blest hom-age pay we; here in lov-ing rev-erence bow;
3. Though the low-liest form doth veil thee as of old in Beth-le-hem,
4. Pas-chal Lamb, thine of-fering fin-ished once for all when thou wast slain,
5. Life-im-part-ing heaven-ly man-na, strick-en rock with stream-ing side,

thou a-lone, our strong de-fend-er, lift-est up thy peo-ple's head.
here for faith's dis-cern-ment pray we, lest we fail to know thee now.
here as there thine an-gels hail thee, branch and flower of Jes-se's stem.
in its full-ness un-di-min-ished shall for-ev-er-more re-main,
heaven and earth with loud ho-san-na wor-ship thee, the Lamb who died.

Hal-le-lu-jah,

Je-sus, true and liv-ing bread!
thou art here: we ask not how.
we in wor-ship join with them.
cleans-ing souls from eve-ry stain.
risen, as-cend-ed, glo-ri-fied!

Words: George Hugh Bourne (1840–1925) Music: Healey Willan (1880–1968)

542
Let all mortal flesh keep silence

PICARDY 878787

1. Let all mor-tal flesh keep si - lence, and with fear and
2. King of kings, yet born of Ma - ry, as of old on
3. Rank on rank the host of heav - en spreads its van-guard
4. At his feet the six-winged Ser - aph; Cher - u - bim with

trem - bling stand; pon-der noth-ing earth - ly mind - ed,
earth he stood, Lord of all, in hu - man vest - ure,
on the way, as the Light of Light, de - scend - ing
sleep - less eye veil their fac - es to the Pre - sence

for with bless - ing in his hand Christ our God to earth de-
in the bo - dy and the blood, Christ will give to all the
from the realms of end - less day, comes the powers of hell to
as with cease-less voice they cry, "Hal - le - lu - jah, hal - le -

scend - eth our full hom - age to de - mand.
faith - ful, his own self for heaven-ly food.
van - quish as the dark - ness clears a - way.
lu - jah, hal - le - lu - jah, Lord most high."

Words: Liturgy of St. James; English translation, Gerard Moultrie (1829–1885), alt
Music: French traditional carol

Words: public domain Music: public domain

705

Here, O my Lord, I see thee

LANGRAN 10 10 10 10

1. Here, O my Lord, I see thee face to face;
2. Here would we feed up - on the bread of God,
3. This is the hour of ban - quet and of song;
4. Too soon we rise; the sym - bols dis - ap - pear.
5. We have no help but thine, nor do we need

here would I touch and han - dle things un - seen,
here drink with thee the roy - al wine of heaven;
this is the heaven - ly ta - ble for us spread;
The feast, though not the love, is past and gone;
an - oth - er arm but thine to lean up - on;

here grasp with firm - er hand e - ter - nal grace,
here would we lay a - side each earth - ly load,
here let us feast, and, feast - ing, still pro - long
the bread and wine re - move, but thou art here,
it is e - nough, my Lord, e - nough in - deed;

Words: Horatius Bonar (1808–1889), alt   Music: James Langran (1835–1909)

Words: public domain   Music: public domain

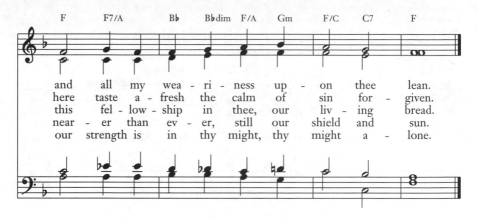

and   all   my   wea - ri - ness   up - on   thee   lean.
here   taste   a - fresh   the   calm   of   sin   for - given.
this   fel - low - ship   in   thee,   our   liv - ing   bread.
near - er   than   ev - er,   still   our   shield   and   sun.
our   strength is   in   thy   might,   thy   might   a - lone.

6. Mine is the sin, but thine the righteousness;
   mine is the guilt, but thine the cleansing blood.
   Here is my robe, my refuge and my peace,
   thy blood, thy righteousness, O Lord, my God.

7. Feast after feast thus comes and passes by,
   yet, passing, points to that glad feast above,
   giving sweet foretaste of the festal joy,
   the Lamb's great bridal feast of bliss and love.

544   Lord, have mercy

KYRIE (KRIEWALD)   Irregular

Unison

Lord,   have mer - cy.   Christ,   have
Ky - ri - e   e - lei - son.   Chris - te   e -
Sei - gneur, aie   pi - tié.   Christ,   aie

mer - cy.   Lord,   have mer - cy.
lei - son.   Ky - ri - e   e - lei - son.
pi - tié.   Sei - gneur, aie   pi - tié.

Words: traditional liturgical   Music: James A. Kriewald (1940–)

Words: public domain   Music: copyright © James A. Kriewald, 1985

707

545

Jesus, Lamb of God

AGNUS DEI (DONALDSON) 10 12 11

Je-sus, Lamb of God, have mer-cy on us. Je-sus, bear-er of our sin, have

mer-cy

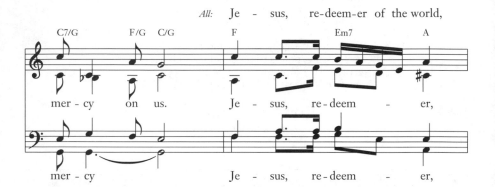

All: Je - sus, re-deem-er of the world,

mer-cy on us. Je - sus, re-deem - er,

mer - cy Je - sus, re-deem - er,

Je - sus, re-deem-er of the world, grant us peace.

Je - sus, re-deem - er, grant us peace.

Je - sus re-deem - er, grant us peace.

Words: traditional liturgical   Music: Andrew Donaldson (1951–)

Words: public domain   Music: copyright © Andrew Donaldson, 1994

Here is bread: here is wine

HERE IS BREAD 6 8 6 5 with refrain

1. Here is bread; here is wine:
2. Here is grace; here is peace:

Christ is with us: he is with us. Break the bread; taste the wine:
Know his grace; find his peace:

Christ is with us here.
feast on Je-sus
here. In this bread

Words: Graham Kendrick (1950–) Music: Graham Kendrick (1950–)

there is heal - ing; in this cup there's life for - ev - er. In this mo-ment

by the Spir - it Christ is with us here. 3. Here we are,

joined in one: Christ is with us; he is with us. We'll pro-claim

till he comes Je-sus cru-ci - fied. In this bread

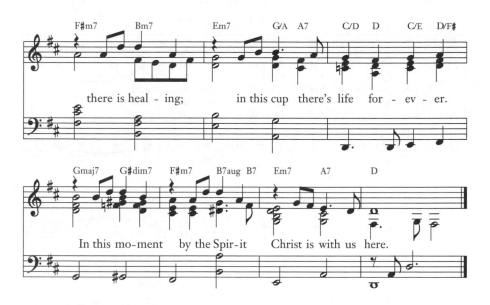

there is heal - ing; in this cup there's life for - ev - er.

In this mo - ment by the Spir - it Christ is with us here.

547 Lord, have mercy upon us

KYRIE (MERBECKE) 7 7 7

Lord, have mer-cy up-on us. Christ, have mer-cy up-on us.

Lord, have mer - cy up - on us.

Words: traditional Music: John Merbecke (c. 1510–c.1585); arrangement, Healey Willan (1880–1968)

Let us break bread together

LET US BREAK BREAD 10 10 14 7

1. Let us break bread to-geth-er on our knees;
2. Let us drink wine to-geth-er on our knees;
3. Let us praise God to-geth-er on our knees;

let us break bread to-geth-er on our knees;
let us drink wine to-geth-er on our knees;
let us praise God to-geth-er on our knees;

when I fall down on my knees with my face to the ris - ing sun,

O Lord, have mer-cy on me.

Words: African-American spiritual   Music: African-American spiritual;
arrangement, F.R.C. Clarke (1931–)

Words: public domain   Music: arrangement, copyright © Anglican Church of Canada and United Church of Canada, 1971

549

For the bread which you have broken

OMNI DIE 8 7 8 7

1. For the bread which you have bro - ken, for the
2. By this prom - ise that you love us, by your
3. With the ho - ly ones be - fore you, feast - ing
4. In your serv - ice, Lord, de - fend us; in our

wine which you have poured, for the words which you have
gift of peace re - stored, by the call to heaven a -
on your grace out - poured, may the church now wait - ing
hearts keep watch and ward; in the world where now you

spo - ken, now we give you thanks, O Lord.
bove us, hal - low all our lives, O Lord.
for you keep love's tie un - bro - ken, Lord.
send us, may your king - dom come, O Lord.

Words: Louis Fitzgerald Benson (1855–1930), alt   Music: Corner's Gesangbuch 1631;
arrangement, W.S. Rockstro (1823–1895)

Words: public domain   Music: public domain

550

Broken for me

BROKEN FOR ME Irregular

Bro-ken for me, bro-ken for you,

the bo-dy of Je - sus, bro-ken for you.

Words: Janet Lunt (20th cent.)   Music: Janet Lunt (20th cent.); arrangement, Andrew Maries

E   maj7 Asus2 – 1 E/G♯ F♯m7   Bsus4 – 3

1. He of - fered his bo - dy; he poured out his soul;
2. Come to my ta - ble and with me dine;
3. This is my bo - dy giv - en for you;
4. This is my blood I shed for you,

E   maj7 Asus2 – 1 E/G♯ F♯m7   Bsus4 – 3

Je - sus was bro - ken that we might be whole.
eat of my bread and drink of my wine.
eat it, re - mem - bering I died for you.
for your for - give - ness, mak - ing you new.

E   /B Amaj7 Emaj7/G♯ F♯m7 B7sus   E

the bo - dy of Je - sus, bro - ken for you.

Communion

551

Bread of the world

RENDEZ À DIEU 9 8 9 8 D

Bread of the world, in mer-cy bro-ken, wine of the
Pain vi-vant don-né pour nos â - mes, vin pour nos

soul, in mer-cy shed, by whom the words of life were spo-ken,
ê-tres ré-pan - du, pa - ro-les d'a-mour et de flam - mes,

and in whose death our sins are dead: look on the heart by sor-row
mort où l'es-poir nous est ren - du; vois no-tre des - tin mi-sé -

bro - ken, look on the tears by sin - ners shed, and be thy
ra - ble, les pleurs ver-sés sur nos mal - heurs, nour-ris-nous

See also: Rendez à Dieu 62

Words: Reginald Heber (1783–1826) Music: Louis Bourgeois (c.1510–1561)

Words: public domain Music: public domain

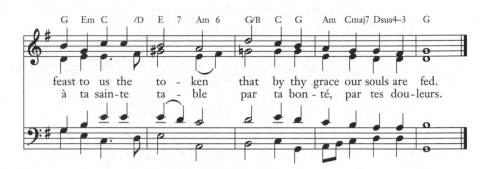

feast to us the to - ken that by thy grace our souls are fed.
à ta sain-te ta - ble par ta bon - té, par tes dou-leurs.

552   Lord, have mercy upon us

KYRIE (WILLAN) 7 7 7

Lord, have mer - cy up - on us. Christ, have mer - cy up -

on us. Lord, have mer - cy up - on us.

Words: traditional liturgical   Music: Healey Willan (1880–1968) from *Missa de Sancta Maria Magdalene*

553

May the Lord bless you, may the Lord keep you

MAY THE LORD BLESS YOU   10 11 10 11

May the Lord bless you, may the Lord keep you;

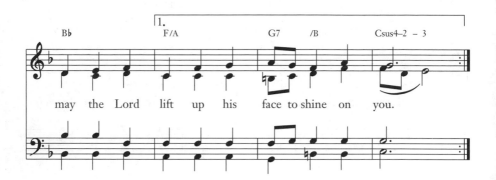

may the Lord lift up his face to shine on you.

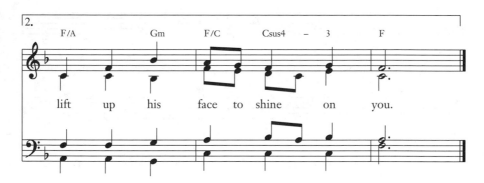

lift up his face to shine on you.

Words: traditional   Music: Judy Hunnicutt (20th cent.)

Words: public domain   Music: copyright © The Sacred Music Press, 1985

554

Now to Christ who loved us

TRIUMPH 878787

Now to Christ who loved us, gave us eve - ry pledge that love could give, free - ly shed his blood to save us, gave his life that we might live, be the pow - er and do - min - ion, and the glo - ry, ev - er-more.

Words: Samuel Miller Waring (1792–1827), alt   Music: Henry John Gauntlett (1805–1876)
Words: public domain   Music: public domain

Worship the Lord

WORSHIP THE LORD   11 11 12 7 with refrain (4 10 4 9)

Worship the Lord, (Worship the Lord) worship the Father, the
Lou-ange à Dieu, (lou-ange à Dieu), lou-ange à Dieu, au

Spir-it, the Son, rais-ing our hands (Rais-ing our hands) in de-
Christ, à l'Es-prit! Dieu soit lou-é (Dieu soit loué) par nos

vo-tion to God who is one!
deux mains ten-dues vers sa vie.

Words: Fred Kaan (1929–); French, Nicole Berthet (20th cent.); revision to French, R. Gerald Hobbs (1941–)   Music: Ron Klusmeier (1946–)

Words: copyright © 1974 by Hope Publishing Co.   Music: copyright © WorshipArts

F   Bb/F   F

1. Rais-ing our hands as a sign of re - joic - ing,
2. Pray-ing and train-ing that we be a bless - ing,
1. Vers toi, ô Dieu, vois nos mains qui s'é - lè - vent,
2. Vers toi, ô Dieu, nos pri - è - res s'é - lan - cent;

F   Bb/F   F

and with our lips our to - geth - er - ness voic - ing,
and by our hand - i - work dai - ly con - fess - ing,
un chant joy - eux jail - lis - sant de nos lè - vres;
trans - forme nos mains en un chant de lou - an - ge:

Gm7   C   Gm   C

giv - ing our - selves to a life of cre - a - tive - ness,
we are com - mit - ted to serv - ing hu - man - i - ty,
re - çois nos jours de tra - vail et de fê - te,
en ser - vant nos pro - chains c'est toi qu'elles chan - tent,

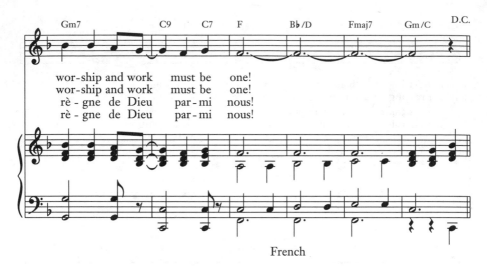

wor-ship and work   must be   one!
wor-ship and work   must be   one!
rè - gne de Dieu   par - mi   nous!
rè - gne de Dieu   par - mi   nous!

French

3.Called to be partners with God in creation,
honouring Christ as the Lord of the nation,
we must be ready for risk and for sacrifice,
worship and work must be one.
Refrain:

4.Bringing the bread and the wine to the table,
asking that we may be led and enabled,
truly united, to build new communities,
worship and work must be one.
Refrain:

5.Now in response to the life you are giving,
help us, Creator, to offer our living,
seeking a just and a healing society,
worship and work must be one.
Refrain:

3. Voici un monde soumis aux souffrances,
voici nos mains pour aider sa naissance;
remplis de ta force d'amour nos gestes,
règne de Dieu parmi nous!
Refrain:

4. Voici le pain et le vin sur la table;
fais de nous, Dieu, le ferment dans la
pâte,
le sel d'une vie solidaire, amicale,
règne de Dieu parmi nous!
Refrain:

5. Prends-nous la main quand nos forces
s'épuisent;
Dieu, que ta main aujourd'hui nous
conduise
là où nous verrons se lever ta justice,
règne de Dieu parmi nous!
Refrain:

556
Now let us from this table rise

SOLOTHURN 8 8 8 8 LM

1. Now let us from this ta - ble rise re -
newed in bo - dy, mind and soul; with Christ we die and
live a - gain, whose self - less love has made us whole.

2. With minds a - lert, up - held by grace, to
spread the Word in speech and deed, we fol - low in the
steps of Christ, at one with all in hope and need.

3. To fill each hu - man house with love, it
is the sac - ra - ment of care; the work that Christ be -
gan to do we hum - bly pledge our - selves to share.

4. Then give us grace, com - pan - ion - God, to
choose a - gain the pil - grim way, and help us to ac -
cept with joy the chal - lenge of to - mor - row's day.

Words: Fred Kaan (1929–)   Music: Swiss traditional; arrangement, C.H. Kitson (1874–1944)

Words: copyright © 1968 by Hope Publishing Co.   Music: arrangement, copyright © Association for Promoting Christian Knowledge

Communion

557 Shout for joy! The Lord has let us feast

LANSDOWNE 9 9 9 9

1. Shout for joy! The Lord has let us feast;
2. No more doubt - ing, no more sense-less dread:
3. Cel - e - brate with saints who dine on high,
4. Praise the Mak - er, praise the Mak-er's Son,

heaven's own fare has fed the last and least;
God's good self has graced our wine and bread;
wit - ness - es that love can nev - er die.
praise the Spir - it— Three yet ev - er One;

Christ's own peace is shared a - gain on earth;
all the won - der heaven has kept in store
"Hal - le - lu - jah!"—thus their voic - es ring:
praise the God whose food and friends a - vow

is shared on earth;
has kept in store
voice, their voic - es ring,
whose friends a - vow,

Words: Iona Community (Scotland) Music: John L. Bell (1949–)

Words: copyright © Iona Community (Scotland), 1989. Used by permission of G.I.A. Publications Inc. Music: copyright © G.I.A. Publications Inc., 1989. All rights reserved.

724

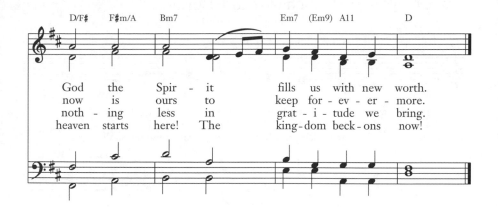

God   the   Spir - it   fills   us   with   new   worth.
now   is   ours   to   keep for - ev - er - more.
noth - ing   less   in   grat - i - tude we   bring.
heaven   starts   here! The   king-dom beck-ons   now!

558 The Son of God proclaim

FESTAL SONG 6 6 8 6 SM

1. The Son of God pro - claim, the Lord of time and space; the
2. Be - hold his out-stretched hands! Though all was in his power, he
3. He, God's cre - a - tive Word, the chur - ch's Lord and head, here
4. The Lord of life and death with won-dering praise we sing; we
5. We take this cup in hope; for he, who glad - ly bore the

God who bade the light break forth now shines in Je - sus' face.
took the towel and ba - sin then, and serves us in this hour.
bids us gath - er as his friends and share his wine and bread.
break the bread at his com-mand and name him God and King.
shame-ful cross, is risen a - gain and reigns for - ev - er - more.

Words: Basil E. Bridge (1927–)   Music: W.H. Walter (1825–1893)

Thou, who at thy first eucharist didst pray

SONG 1   10 10 10 10 10 10

1. Thou, who at thy first eu - char - ist didst pray
2. For all thy church, O Lord, we in - ter - cede;
3. So, Lord, at length when sac - ra - ments shall cease,

that all thy church might be for - ev - er one,
make thou our sad di - vi - sions soon to cease;
may we be one with all thy church a - bove,

grant us at eve - ry eu - char - ist to say
draw us the near - er each to each, we plead,
one with thy saints in one un - bro - ken peace,

Words: William Henry Turton (1856–1938)   Music: Orlando Gibbons (1583–1625)

Words: copyright © 1983 by Hope Publishing Co.   Music: public domain

with long-ing heart and soul, thy will be done.
by draw-ing all to thee, O Prince of Peace;
one with thy saints in one un-bound-ed love:

Oh may we all one bread, one bo-dy be,
thus may we all one bread, one bo-dy be,
more bless-ed still, in peace and love to be

through this blest sac-ra-ment of u-ni-ty.
through this blest sac-ra-ment of u-ni-ty.
one with the Trin-i-ty in u-ni-ty.

560

Put peace into each other's hands

ST. COLUMBA 8 7 8 7

1. Put peace in - to each oth - er's hands,
2. Put peace in - to each oth - er's hands
3. Put peace in - to each oth - er's hands
4. As at com - mun - ion, shape your hands
5. Put Christ in - to each oth - er's hands,

and like a treas - ure hold it;
with lov - ing ex - pec - ta - tion;
like bread we break for shar - ing;
in - to a wait - ing cra - dle;
he is love's deep - est meas - ure;

pro - tect it like a can - dle - flame;
be gen - tle in your words and ways
look peo - ple warm - ly in the eye:
the gift of Christ re - ceive, re - vere,
in love make peace, give peace a chance,

Words: Fred Kaan (1929–)   Music: Ancient Irish hymn melody; harmony, Eric H. Thiman (1900–1975)

Words: copyright © Oxford University Press from Planting Trees and Sowing Seeds   Music: harmony, copyright © United Reformed Church in the UK/Oxford University Press

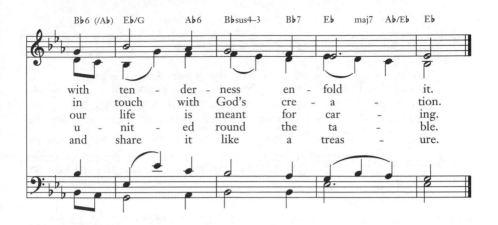

with ten - der - ness en - fold it.
in touch with God's cre - a - tion.
our life is meant for car - ing.
u - nit - ed round the ta - ble.
and share it like a treas - ure.

561   Lord, have mercy

KYRIE (STRATHDEE)   Irregular

Lord, have mer-cy; Christ, have mer-cy; Lord, have mer-cy up - on us.
(or: Lord, have mer-cy, have mer - cy.)

Words: traditional   Music: Jim Strathdee (1941–)

Words: public domain   Music: copyright © Desert Flower Music, 1994. Used by permission.

Communion
562
Now the silence / Then the glory
NOW Irregular

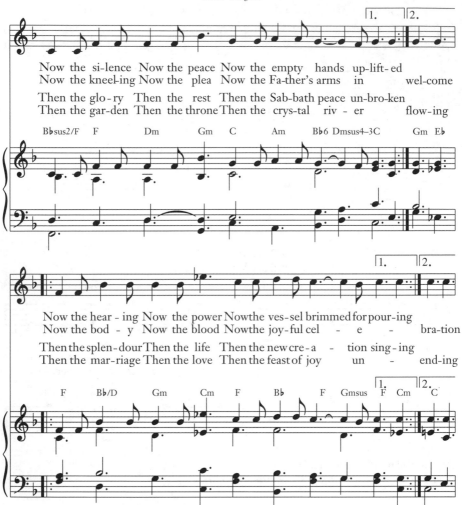

Now the si-lence Now the peace Now the empty hands up-lift-ed
Now the kneel-ing Now the plea Now the Fa-ther's arms in wel-come

Then the glo-ry Then the rest Then the Sab-bath peace un-bro-ken
Then the gar-den Then the throne Then the crys-tal riv - er flow-ing

Now the hear - ing Now the power Now the ves-sel brimmed for pour-ing
Now the bod - y Now the blood Now the joy-ful cel - e - bra-tion

Then the splen-dour Then the life Then the new cre-a - tion sing-ing
Then the mar-riage Then the love Then the feast of joy un - end-ing

Two texts need not be sung together.

Words: Jaroslav J. Vajda (1919–) Music: Carl F. Schalk (1929–)

Now the wed-ding Now the songs Now the heart for-giv - en leap - ing
Then the know-ing Then the light Then the ul - ti-mate ad-ven - ture

Now the Spir - it's vis - i - ta - tion Now the Son's e-piph - an - y
Then the Spir - it's har - vest gath - ered Then the Lamb in maj - es - ty

Now the Fa - ther's bless - ing Now Now Now
Then the Fa - ther's A - men Then Then Then

563 Let us talents and tongues employ

LINSTEAD 8 8 8 8 LM with refrain (5 5 5)

1. Let us tal-ents and tongues em-ploy, reach-ing out with a
2. Christ is a-ble to make us one; at the ta-ble he
3. Je-sus calls us in, sends us out bear-ing fruit in a

shout of joy: bread is bro-ken, the wine is poured,
sets the tone, teach-ing peo-ple to live to bless,
world of doubt, gives us love to tell, bread to share:

Christ is spo-ken and seen and heard.
love in word and in deed ex-press. Je-sus lives a-gain,
God (Im-man-u-el) eve-ry-where!

earth can breathe a-gain, pass the Word a-round: loaves a-bound!

Words: Fred Kaan (1929–) Music: Jamaican folk song; adaptation, Doreen Potter (1925–1980); arrangement, Andrew Donaldson (1951–)

564 The Great Prayer of Thanksgiving

The Lord be with you.
And with you also.
Lift up your hearts.
We lift them up to the Lord.
Let us give thanks to the Lord our God.
It is right to give God thanks and praise.

*The prayer opens with thanksgiving for creation and
for God's mighty acts throughout salvation history.
The people join in the ancient song after these or
similar words:*
... we join with the whole creation
to lift our hearts in joyful praise.

**Holy, Holy, Holy Lord, God of power and might,
heaven and earth are full of your glory.
Hosanna in the highest.**

**Blessed is he who comes in the name of the Lord.
Hosanna in the highest.**

*Prayers of thanksgiving continue for the work of Jesus
Christ, his life, death, and resurrection and for the
institution of the Lord's Supper. The people are invited
to "proclaim the mystery of faith:"*

**Christ has died.
Christ is risen.
Christ will come again.**

*Thanksgiving continues for the gift of the Holy Spirit.
The presence of the Holy Spirit is invoked followed by
a doxology and the people say:*

Amen.

As our Lord taught us, we now pray:

**Our Father in heaven,
hallowed be your name,
your kingdom come,
your will be done
on earth as in heaven.
Give us today our daily bread.
Forgive us our sins
as we forgive those who sin against us.
Save us from the time of trial
and deliver us from evil.
For the kingdom, the power, and the glory are yours
now and forever. Amen**

Words: traditional liturgical text; this version, The Worship Committee of the Board of Congregational
Life, The Presbyterian Church in Canada. Reprinted from The Book of Common Worship, 1991

565 Come, my Way, my Truth, my Life

THE CALL 7 7 7 7

1. Come, my Way, my Truth, my Life:
such a way as gives us breath,
such a truth as ends all strife,
such a life as kill - eth death.

2. Come, my Light, my Feast, my Strength:
such a light as shows a feast,
such a feast as mends in length,
such a strength as makes his guest.

3. Come, my Joy, my Love, my Heart:
such a joy as none can move,
such a love as none can part,
such a heart as joys in love.

Words: George Herbert (1593–1633)   Music: Ralph Vaughan Williams (1872–1958)

Words: public domain   Music: copyright © Stainer & Bell Ltd., 1911

566 O matchless beauty of our God

ST. BOTOLPH 8 6 8 6 CM

1. O match-less beau-ty of our God so an-cient and so new,
2. How late we came to love you, Lord; how strong the hold of sin!
3. You called and cried, yet we were deaf; our stub-born wills you bent;
4. You blazed and spar-kled, yet our hearts to less-er glo-ries turned;

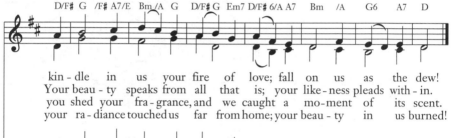

kin-dle in us your fire of love; fall on us as the dew!
Your beau-ty speaks from all that is; your like-ness pleads with-in.
you shed your fra-grance, and we caught a mo-ment of its scent.
your ra-diance touched us far from home; your beau-ty in us burned!

5. And should our faith grow weak and fall,
   tried in the wilderness,
   let beauty blossom out of ash
   and streams of water bless!

6. O matchless beauty of our God
   so ancient and so new,
   enfold in us your fire of love;
   anoint us with your dew!

Alternate tune: Abridge

Words: Augustine of Hippo (354–432); translation, Colin Thompson (1945–)
Music: Gordon Archbold Slater (1896–1979)

Words: translation, copyright © Colin Thompson   Music: copyright © Oxford University Press

567
Eternal light, shine in my heart
HEREFORD 8 8 8 8 LM

1. E - ter - nal light, shine in my heart;
   e - ter - nal hope, lift up my eyes;
   e - ter - nal power, be my sup - port;
   e - ter - nal wis - dom, make me wise.

2. E - ter - nal life, raise me from death;
   e - ter - nal bright - ness, help me see;
   e - ter - nal Spir - it, give me breath;
   e - ter - nal Sav - iour, come to me.

3. Un - til by your most cost - ly grace,
   in - vit - ed by your ho - ly Word,
   at last I come be - fore your face
   to know you, my e - ter - nal God.

Words: Alcuin (735–804); translation, Christopher Idle (1938–)   Music: Samuel Sebastian Wesley
(1810–1876)

568   I sought the Lord, and afterward I knew

PEACE 10 10 10 6

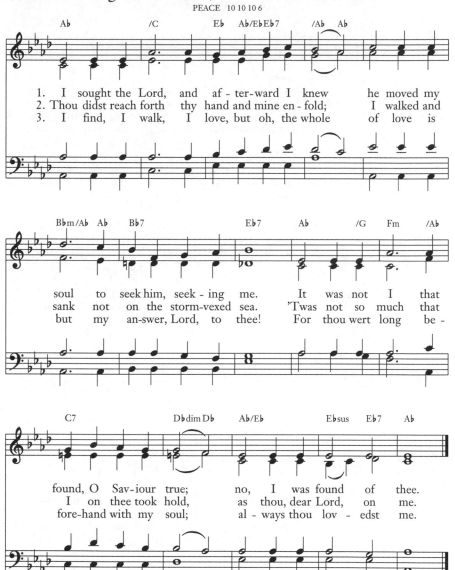

1. I sought the Lord, and af - ter-ward I knew   he moved my soul to seek him, seek - ing me. It was not I that found, O Sav-iour true; no, I was found of thee.

2. Thou didst reach forth thy hand and mine en - fold;   I walked and sank not on the storm-vexed sea. 'Twas not so much that I on thee took hold, as thou, dear Lord, on me.

3. I find, I walk, I love, but oh, the whole   of love is but my an-swer, Lord, to thee! For thou wert long be - fore-hand with my soul; al - ways thou lov - edst me.

Words: anonymous, c. 1890 Music: George W. Chadwick (1854–1931)

Words: public domain Music: public domain

569 O Jesus, I have promised

ANGEL'S STORY 7 6 7 6 D

1. O Je - sus, I have prom - ised to serve thee to the end;
2. Oh let me feel thee near me: the world is ev - er near;
3. Oh let me hear thee speak - ing in ac - cents clear and still,
4. O Je - sus, thou hast prom - ised to all who fol - low thee,

be thou for - ev - er near me, my Sav - iour and my friend:
I see the sights that daz - zle, the tempt - ing sounds I hear.
a - bove the storms of pas - sion, the mur - murs of self - will;
that where thou art in glo - ry there shall thy ser - vant be,

I shall not fear the strug - gle if thou art by my side,
My foes are ev - er near me, a - round me and with - in,
oh speak to re - as - sure me, to has - ten or con - trol;
and, Je - sus, I have prom - ised to serve thee to the end;

Alternate tunes: Thornbury

Words: John Ernest Bode (1816–1874), alt Music: Arthur Henry Mann (1850–1929)

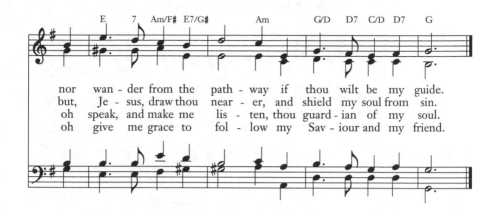

nor wan - der from the path - way if thou wilt be my guide.
but, Je - sus, draw thou near - er, and shield my soul from sin.
oh speak, and make me lis - ten, thou guard - ian of my soul.
oh give me grace to fol - low my Sav - iour and my friend.

570   I have decided to follow Jesus

ASSAM 10 10 10 8

1. I have de - cid - ed to fol-low Je - sus; I have de -
2. The world be - hind me, the cross be - fore me; the world be -
3. Though none go with me, I still will fol - low; though none go
4. Will you de - cide now to fol-low Je - sus? Will you de -

cid - ed to fol-low Je - sus; I have de - cid - ed to fol-low
hind me, the cross be - fore me; the world be - hind me, the cross be -
with me, I still will fol - low; though none go with me, I still will
cide now to fol-low Je - sus? Will you de - cide now to fol-low

Je - sus,
fore me,   No turn-ing back,   no turn-ing back.
fol - low,
Je - sus?

Words: traditional   Music: traditional

571 Lord, I want to be a Christian

I WANT TO BE A CHRISTIAN 14 11 6 11

1. Lord, I want to be a Chris-tian in-a my heart, in-a my heart;
2. Lord, I want to be more lov-ing in-a my heart, in-a my heart;
3. Lord, I want to be more ho-ly in-a my heart, in-a my heart;
4. Lord, I want to be like Je-sus in-a my heart, in-a my heart;

Lord, I want to be a Chris-tian in-a my heart.
Lord, I want to be more lov-ing in-a my heart.
Lord, I want to be more ho-ly in-a my heart.
Lord, I want to be like Je-sus in-a my heart.

In-a my heart, in-a my heart,
In-a my heart, in-a my heart,

Lord, I want to be a Chris-tian in-a my heart.
Lord, I want to be more lov-ing in-a my heart.
Lord, I want to be more ho-ly in-a my heart.
Lord, I want to be like Je-sus in-a my heart.

Words: African–American spiritual   Music: African–American spiritual

Words: public domain   Music: public domain

572

God be in my head

GOD BE IN MY HEAD (NAMETH) Irregular

God be in my head and in my un-der-stand-ing; God be in my eyes and

in my look-ing; God be in my mouth and in my speak-ing;

God be in my heart and in my think-ing; God be at my

end and at my de-part-ing. A - men.

Words: R. Pynson (c. 1514) Music: Bart Nameth (1954–)

Words: public domain Music: copyright © Bart Nameth

573
I'll love the Lord

MACDOWELL 11 10 D 14 D with repeats

1. I'll love the Lord with all that lies in - side me;
2. I'll walk the path that Christ has walked be - fore me;
3. I'll let my life be o - pen to God's Spir - it,
4. I'll love the Lord with all that lies in - side me,

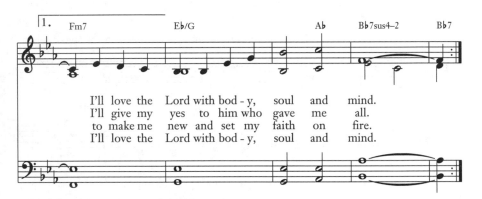

I'll love the Lord with bod - y, soul and mind.
I'll give my yes to him who gave me all.
to make me new and set my faith on fire.
I'll love the Lord with bod - y, soul and mind.

Words: Iona Community (Scotland)   Music: Iona Community (Scotland)

2., 3.

Fm7   Eb/G   Ebdim* Cb/Gb   Fmsus   Bb9   Ebsus4– 3   Fine

I'll love the Lord with bod-y, soul and mind,
I'll give my yes to him who gave me all.
to make me new and set my faith on fire.
I'll love the Lord with bod-y, soul and mind,

* or use B7/F#

Bb/D   Bbm/Db   Ab/C   Abm/Cb

and eve-ry good-ness, eve-ry bless-ing in the
In eve-ry sound and eve-ry si-lence I will
More than all things God's peace and pres-ence are what
and eve-ry good-ness, eve-ry bless-ing in the

1.

Eb/Bb   Bb7

2.

Eb/Bb   F7/A   *D.C. al Fine*   Bb

Lord I'll find. Lord I'll find.
hear his call. hear his call.
I de - sire. I de - sire.
Lord I'll find. Lord I'll find.

574

With the Lord as my guide

RIDGECREST Irregular

Words: Jim Strathdee (1941–)   Music: Jim Strathdee (1941–)

Words: copyright © Desert Flower Music, 1977. Used by permission.   Music: copyright © Desert Flower Music, 1977. Used by permission.

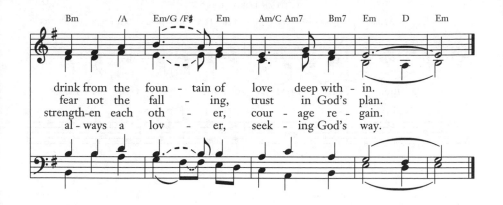

drink from the foun - tain of love deep with - in.
fear not the fall - ing, trust in God's plan.
strength-en each oth - er, cour - age re - gain.
al - ways a lov - er, seek - ing God's way.

575

Lead me, Lord

LEAD ME, LORD 10 8 9 7

Words: Psalm 4:8, Psalm 5:8   Music: Samuel Sebastian Wesley (1810–1876)

Words: public domain   Music: public domain

576

I bind unto myself today

ST. PATRICK, DEIRDRE   Irregular

(return to beginning for vs.2)

1. I bind un-to my-self to-day the strong name of the Trin-i-ty, by in-vo-ca-tion of the same, the Three-in-One, and One-in-Three.
2. I bind this day to me for-ev-er by power of faith, Christ's in-car-na-tion—his bap-tism in the Jor-dan riv-er, his death on Cross for my sal-vation;
3. I bind un-to my-self to-day the vir-tues of the star-lit heaven, the glo-rious sun's life-giv-ing ray, the white-ness of the moon at even,
4. I bind un-to my-self to-day the power of God to hold and lead, God's eye to watch, God's might to stay, God's ear to heark-en to my need,
6. I bind un-to my-self the name, the strong name of the Trin-i-ty, by in-vo-ca-tion of the same, the Three-in-One, the One-in-Three,

Words: St. Patrick of Ireland (372–466); adaptation, Cecil Frances Alexander (1818–1895) Music: Irish traditional hymn; harmony, C.V. Stanford (1852–1924)

Words: public domain Music: public domain

(2.) his burst-ing from the spi - ced tomb, his rid - ing up the
(3.) the flash-ing of the light - ning free, the whirl - ing wind's tem-
(4.) the wis-dom of my God to teach, God's hand to guide, God's
(6.) of whom all na - ture hath cre - a-tion, e - ter - nal Fa - ther,

heaven - ly way, his com - ing at the day of
pes - tuous shocks, the sta - ble earth, the deep salt
shield to ward; the word of God to give me
Spir - it, Word. Praise to the Lord of my sal -

doom I bind un - to my - self to - day.
sea a - round the old e - ter - nal rocks.
speech, the heaven - ly host to be my guard.
va-tion; sal - va - tion is of Christ the Lord!

♮ v.5 (next page)

5. Christ be with me, Christ with-in me, Christ be-
Christ be-neath me, Christ a-bove me, Christ in

hind me, Christ be-fore me, Christ be-side me, Christ to
qui-et, Christ in dan-ger, Christ in hearts of all that

D.C. al Fine
after repeat

win me, Christ to com-fort and re-store me,
love me, Christ in mouth of friend and stran-ger.

Our Father in heaven

PATER NOSTER (DONALDSON) Irregular

Our Fa-ther in heaven, hal-lowed be your name, your king-dom come,

your will be done on earth as in heaven. Give us to-day our dai-ly bread;

for - give us our sins as we for-give those who sin a-gainst us.

Save us from the time of trial and de - liv - er us from e - vil, for the

Words: Luke 11:2–4; translation English Language Liturgical Consultation
Music: Andrew Donaldson (1951–)

king-dom, the pow-er and the glo-ry are yours, now and for-ev - er. A - men.

578   The Nicene Creed

We believe in one God, the Father, the Almighty, maker of heaven and earth, of all that is, seen and unseen.

We believe in one Lord, Jesus Christ, the only Son of God, eternally begotten of the Father, God from God, Light from Light, true God from true God, begotten, not made, of one Being with the Father; through him all things were made. For us and for our salvation he came down from heaven, was incarnate of the Holy Spirit and the Virgin Mary and became truly human. For our sake he was crucified under Pontius Pilate; He suffered death and was buried. On the third day he rose again in accordance with the Scriptures; he ascended into heaven and is seated at the right hand of the Father. He will come again in glory to judge the living and the dead, and his kingdom will have no end.

We believe in the Holy Spirit, the Lord, the giver of life, who proceeds from the Father and the Son, who with the Father and the Son is worshipped and glorified, who has spoken through the prophets.

We believe in one holy catholic and apostolic Church. We acknowledge one baptism for the forgiveness of sins. We look for the resurrection of the dead, and the life of the world to come. Amen.

Words: traditional liturgical text; translation, English Language Liturgical Consultation, 1988

579

Oh, I know the Lord's
laid his hands on me

I KNOW Irregular

1. Did ev-er you see the like be-fore?
   King Je-sus preach-ing to the poor!
2. Oh, was-n't that a hap-py day
   when Je-sus washed my sins a-way!
3. Some seek the Lord and don't seek him right;
   they fool all day and pray at night,
4. My Lord's done just what he said;
   he's healed the sick and raised the dead;

Words: African-American spiritual   Music: African-American Spritual

Words: public domain   Music: public domain

580

God be in my head

GOD BE IN MY HEAD (DAVIES) Irregular

God be in my head and in my un-der-stand-ing; God be in my
eyes and in my look-ing; God be in my mouth and in my speak - ing;
God be in my heart and in my think - ing;
God be at my end and at my de-part - ing.

Words: R. Pynson (c. 1514) Music: H. Walford Davies (1869-1941)

Words: public domain Music: copyright © Oxford University Press

581 Pour out your Spirit from on high

MELCOMBE 8 8 8 8 LM

1. Pour out your Spir - it from on high; Lord, your as - sem - bled serv - ants bless; grac - es and gifts to each sup - ply, and clothe your priests with right - eous - ness.

2. All wis - dom, zeal and faith im - part, and strength, with meek - ness from a - bove, to bear your peo - ple in our heart, and love each soul with faith - ful love.

3. To watch and pray and nev - er faint; by day and night strict guard to keep; to warn and cheer both sin - ner, saint, nour - ish your lambs and feed your sheep.

4. Then, when our work is fin - ished here, in hum - ble hope our charge re - sign: when the good Shep - herd shall ap - pear, in you we rest, O Love di - vine.

Words: James Montgomery (1771–1854), alt   Music: Samuel Webbe, the elder (1740–1816)

Words: public domain   Music: public domain

582 May God's love be fixed above you

TANTUM ERGO 878787

1. May God's love be fixed a - bove you, o - ver - shad - ow
2. May God's love ad - vance be - fore you, vig - i - lant of
3. May God's love be close be - side you, and pre - pare you
4. May God's love re - main up - on you, and your faith - ful -

you with grace; may God's love stand firm be - neath you,
all your ways; may God's love keep watch be - hind you,
for life's race; may God's love live deep with - in you,
ness re - pay with a peace the world can't give you,

wel - come you with glad em - brace!
shield - ing you through all your days!
with as - sur - ance, last - ing grace! Hal - le - lu - jah,
nei - ther shall it take a - way!

1.–3. hal - le - lu - jah, glo - ri - fy the Lord with praise!
4. hal - le - lu - jah, glo - ri - fy the Lord this day!

Alternate tune: Praise, My Soul

Words: John A. Dalles (1954–)   Music: Samuel Webbe's Antiphona 1792

Words: copyright © John A. Dalles, 1992   Music: public domain

583 You are called to tell the story

LARKIN 878787

1. You are called to tell the sto - ry, pass - ing words of
2. You are called to teach the rhy - thm of the dance that
3. You are called to set the tab - le, bless - ing bread as
4. May the One whose love is broad - er than the meas - ure

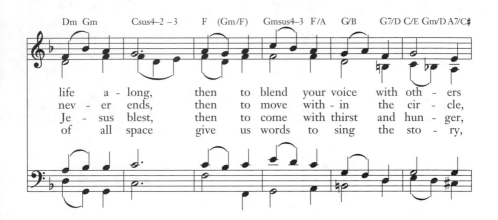

life a - long, then to blend your voice with oth - ers
nev - er ends, then to move with - in the cir - cle,
Je - sus blest, then to come with thirst and hun - ger,
of all space give us words to sing the sto - ry,

as you sing the sac - red song. Christ be known in
hand in hand with stran - gers, friends. Christ be known in
need - ing care like all the rest. Christ be known in
move a - mong us in this place. Christ be known in

Words: Ruth Duck (1947–) Music: Walter MacNutt (1910–1996)

all our sing - ing, fill - ing all with songs of love.
all our danc - ing, touch - ing all with hands of love.
all our shar - ing, feed - ing all with signs of love.
all our liv - ing, fill - ing all with gifts of love.

Descant

4. May the One whose love is broad - er than the

meas - ure of all space give us words to

sing the sto - ry, move a - mong us in this

place. Christ be known in all our liv - ing,

fill - ing all with gifts of love.

584

Give me the faith

COLCHESTER 888888

1. Give me the faith which can re-move and sink the moun-tain
to a plain; give me the child-like pray-ing love, which
longs to build thy house a-gain; thy love, let it my
heart o'er-power, and all my sim-ple soul de-vour.

2. I would the pre-cious time re-deem, and long-er live for
this a-lone, to spend and to be spent for them who
have not yet my Sav-iour known; ful-ly on these my
mis-sion prove, and on-ly breathe, to breathe thy love.

3. My tal-ents, gifts and grac-es, Lord, in-to thy bless-ed
hands re-ceive, and let me live to preach thy word, and
let me to thy glo-ry live; my eve-ry sa-cred
mo-ment spend in pub-lish-ing the sin-ner's Friend.

4. En-large, in-flame and fill my heart with bound-less char-i-
ty di-vine, so shall I all my strength ex-ert, and
love them with a zeal like thine, and lead them to thy
o-pen side, the sheep for whom the Shep-herd died.

Words: Luke 11:20–25; paraphrase, Charles Wesley (1707–1788)
Music: Samuel Sebastian Wesley (1810–1876)

758

585 Christ, you call us all to service

IN BABILONE 8 7 8 7 D

1. Christ, you call us all to ser-vice, call us all who fol-low you;
2. Teach us how to work to-geth-er, bro-ther, sis-ter, side by side,
3. Let us be a serv-ant peo-ple, re-con-cil-ing, end-ing strife,

plant in us a deep com-mit-ment all your work and will to do.
e-qual part-ners in the strug-gle, in the cause of truth al-lied.
seek-ing ways more just of shar-ing and of or-dering hu-man life.

Fire a pas-sion for your jus-tice; in us kin-dle love of peace;
To each one some gift is giv-en— man or wo-man, young or old;
Fill us with a glow-ing vi-sion of this world as it should be;

help us heal the bro-ken-heart-ed; to the cap-tive bring re-lease.
help us use each skill and tal-ent, your great pur-pose to un-fold.
send us forth to change that vi-sion in-to blest re-a-li-ty.

Words: Joy F. Patterson (1931–) Music: Dutch melody; arrangement, Julius Röntgen (1855–1933)

586

You have put on Christ

You have put on Christ, in Christ you have been bap - tized.

Hal - le - lu - jah, hal - le - lu - jah!

Words: ICEL (Rite of Baptism for Children)   Music: Howard Hughes (1930–)

587

Called as partners in Christ's service

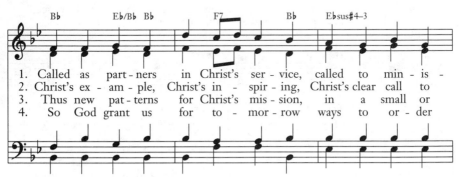

1. Called as part - ners in Christ's ser - vice, called to min - is -
2. Christ's ex - am - ple, Christ's in - spir - ing, Christ's clear call to
3. Thus new pat - terns for Christ's mis - sion, in a small or
4. So God grant us for to - mor - row ways to or - der

Alternate tune: In Babilone

Words: Jane Parker Huber (1926–)   Music: John Zundel (1815–1822)

tries of grace, we res-pond with deep com - mit-ment, fresh new
work and worth, let us fol - low, nev - er fal - tering, rec - on -
glob - al sense, help us bear each oth - er's bur-dens, break-ing
hum - an life that sur-round each per-son's sor - row with a

lines of faith to trace. May we learn the art of shar-ing,
cil - ing folk on earth. Men and wom - en, rich - er, poor - er,
down each wall or fence. Words of com-fort, words of vis - ion,
calm that con-quers strife. Make us part-ners in our liv - ing,

side by side and friend with friend, e - qual part - ners
all God's peo - ple, young and old, blend - ing hum - an
words of chal - lenge, said with care, bring new power and
our com - pas - sion to in - crease, mes - sen - gers of

in our car - ing to ful - fil God's chos - en end.
skills to - geth - er, gra - cious gifts from God un - fold.
strength for ac - tion, make us col-leagues, free and fair.
faith, thus giv - ing hope and con - fi - dence and peace.

588 A prophet–woman broke a jar

MEGERRAN 8 7 8 7 D Iambic

1. A pro - phet-wom - an broke a jar by
2. A faith - ful wom - an left a tomb by
3. Though wom - an-wis - dom, wom - an - truth, for
4. The Spir - it knows, the Spir - it calls, by

Love's di-vine ap-point - ing. With rare per-fume she
Love's di-vine com - mis - sion. She saw, she heard, she
cen - tu-ries were hid - den, un - sung, un-writ - ten
Love's di-vine or - dain - ing, the friends we need, to

filled the room, pre - sid - ing and a - noint - ing. A
preached the Word, a - ris - ing from sub - mis - sion. A
and un - heard, de - rid - ed and for - bid - den, the
serve and lead, their powers and gifts un - chain - ing. The

Alternate tune: The Vicar of Bray

Words: Brian A. Wren (1936–) Music: Walter K. Stanton (1891–1978)

Words: copyright © 1993 by Hope Publishing Co. Music: copyright © Oxford University Press from The BBC Hymn Book

pro - phet-wom - an broke a jar, the sneers of scorn de -
faith - ful wom - an left a tomb, with res - ur - rec - tion
Spir - it's breath, the Spir - it's fire, on free and slave de -
Spir - it knows, the Spir - it calls, from wom - en, men and

fy - ing. With rare per - fume she
gos - pel; she saw, she heard, she
scend - ing, can tum - ble our di -
chil - dren, the friends we need, to

filled the room, pre - par - ing Christ for dy - ing.
preached the Word, a - pos - tle to a - pos - tles.
vid - ing walls, our shame and sad - ness mend - ing.
serve and lead. Re - joice, and make them wel - come!

589 God the Spirit, Guide and Guardian

BETHANY (SMART) 8 7 8 7 D

1. God the Spir - it, Guide and Guard - ian,
2. Christ our Sav - iour, Sov - ereign, Shep - herd,
3. Great Cre - a - tor, Life - be - stow - er,
4. Tri - une God, mys - ter - ious Be - ing,

wind - sped flame and hov - ering dove, breath of life and
Word made flesh, Love cru - ci - fied, teach - er, heal - er,
Truth be - yond all thought's re - call, fount of wis - dom,
un - di - vid - ed and di - verse, deep - er than our

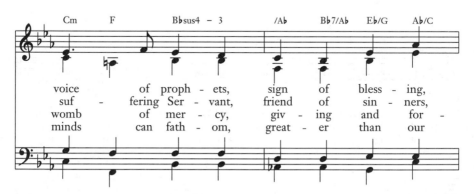

voice of proph - ets, sign of bless - ing,
suf - fering Ser - vant, friend of sin - ners,
womb of mer - cy, giv - ing and for -
minds can fath - om, great - er than our

Words: Carl P. Daw Jr. (1944–) Music: Henry T. Smart (1813–1879)

Words: copyright © 1989 by Hope Publishing Co. Music: public domain

power of love: give to those who lead your peo - ple
foe of pride: in your tend - ing may all pas - tors*
giv - ing all: as you know our strength and weak - ness,
creeds re - hearse: help us in our var - ied call - ings

fresh a - noint - ing of your grace; send them forth as
learn and live a Shep - herd's care: grant them cour - age
so may those the Church ex - alts o - ver - see its
your full im - age to pro - claim, that our min - is -

bold a - pos - tles to your Church in eve - ry place.
and com - pas - sion shown through word and deed and prayer.
life stead - fast - ly yet not o - ver - look its faults.
tries u - nit - ing may give glo - ry to your Name.

* Note: teachers, etc.

765

590

We have this ministry

MINISTRY 13 12 14 13 13

Unison

1. We have this min - is - try and we are not dis - cour - aged;
2. O Christ, the tree of life, our end and our be - gin - ning,
3. The yoke of Christ is ours: the whole world is our par - ish;

it is by God's own power that we may live and serve.
we grow to full - est flower when root - ed in your love.
we dai - ly take the cross, the bur - den and the joy.

O - pen - ly we share God's word, speak - ing truth as we be - lieve,
Broth - ers, sis - ters, cler - gy, lay, called to ser - vice by your grace,
Bear - ing hurts of those we serve, wound - ed, bruised and bowed with pain,

Words: Jim Strathdee (1941–)   Music: Jim Strathdee (1941–)

pray - ing that the shad - owed world may heal - ing light re - ceive.
dif - ferent cul - tures, dif - ferent gifts, the young and old a place.
Ho - ly Spir - it, bread and wine, we die and rise a - gain.

We have this min - is - try; O God, re - ceive our

liv - ing.
giv - ing.
lov - ing.

591   Hallelujah

HALLELUJAH (ZIMBABWE)   Irregular

Descant (may be sung or played an octave higher or lower)

Hal - le - lu - jah,   hal - le - lu,

Hal - le - lu - jah,   hal - le - lu - jah,

Hal - le - lu - jah,   hal - le - lu - jah,

hal - le - lu - jah.   hal - le - lu - jah!

hal - le - lu - jah.   hal - le - lu - jah!

hal - le - lu - jah,   hal - le - lu - jah!

Words: traditional   Music: Abraham Maraire (20th cent.)

Words: public domain   Music: copyright © United Methodist Church Music Service, Mutambara CPS Box 61, Cashel, Zimbabwe

767

592

I, the Lord of sea and sky

HERE I AM, LORD   14 11 14 11 with reefrain (8 9 8 9)

* 1. I, the Lord   of sea and sky,   I have heard   my peo-ple cry.
2. I, the Lord   of snow and rain,   I have borne   my peo-ple's pain.
3. I, the Lord   of wind and flame,   I will tend   the poor and lame.

All who dwell   in dark   and sin   my hand will save.
I have wept   for love   of them: they turn a - way.
I will set   a feast   for them;   my hand will save.

I who made   the stars of night,   I will make their dark-ness bright.
I will break their hearts of stone,   give them hearts for love a - lone.
Fin-est bread   I will pro-vide   till their hearts be sat - is - fied.

Who will bear   my light   to them?   Whom shall I   send?
I will speak   my word   to them.   Whom shall I   send?
I will give   my life   to them.   Whom shall I   send?

* Verses may be sung by a soloist

Words: Daniel L. Schutte (1947–)   Music: Daniel L. Schutte (1947–);
harmony, Michael Pope, John Weissrock

593
As a chalice cast of gold
REBEKAH 77777

Unison

1. As a chal - ice cast of gold, bur - nished,
2. Save me from the sooth - ing sin of the
3. When I bend up - on my knees, clasp my
4. When I dance or chant your praise, when I

bright, and brimmed with wine, make me, Lord, as fit to
emp - ty cult - ic deed and the pi - ous, bab-bling
hands, or bow my head, let my spo - ken, pub-lic
sing a psalm or hymn, when I preach your lov-ing

hold grace and truth and love di - vine. Let my
din of the claimed but un - lived creed. Let my
pleas be dir - ect - ly, sim - ply said, free of
ways, let my heart add its a - men. Let each

praise and wor - ship start with the cleans - ing of my heart.
act - tions, Lord, ex - press what my tongue and lips pro - fess.
tang - led words that mask what my soul would plain - ly ask.
cher - ished out - ward rite thus re - flect your in - ward light.

Words: Thomas H. Troeger (1945–) Music: Rusty Edwards (1955–)

Words: copyright © Oxford University Press, 1985 Music: copyright © 1996 by Hope Publishing Co.

594 Glory be to the Father

GLORIA PATRI (GREATOREX) 6 4 6 8 7 4

Glo - ry be to the Fa-ther, and to the Son, and to the

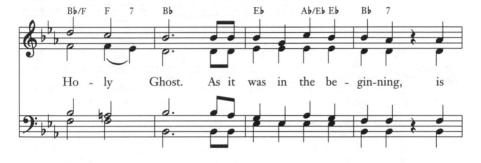

Ho - ly Ghost. As it was in the be - gin-ning, is

now, and ev- er shall be, world with-out end. A - men, a - men.

Words: traditional   Music: Henry W. Greatorex (1813–1858)

Words: public domain   Music: public domain

Marriage

595

Lord and lover of creation

WESTMINSTER ABBEY 8 7 8 7 8 7

1. Lord and lov-er of cre-a-tion, bless the
2. Praise and grat-i-tude we of-fer, for the
3. On your chil-dren wed and wel-come here a-
4. Take them hence, that, in each oth-er, love ful-

mar-riage wit-nessed now: sign of lives no
past which shaped to-day: words which stirred and
mong us, we re-quest health in home and
fill-ing love shall find much to share and

long-er sep-arate, sealed by sym-bol, bound by
deep-ened con-science, fam-i-ly life, good com-pa-
hearts, and hu-mour through which heaven and earth are
more to treas-ure, such that none dare break or

See also: Westminster Abbey 482

Words: Iona Community (Scotland) Music: Henry Purcell (1659–1695);
arrangement, Iona Community (Scotland)

vow,   cel - e - brat - ing   love's   com - mit - ment
ny,   friends   who   touched   and   sum - moned   tal - ent,
blest;   o - pen   doors   and   hu - man   pleas - ure,
bind   those   your   name   has   joined   to - geth - er,

made   to   live   and   last   and   grow.
nour - ished   all   words   can't   con - vey.
time   for   touch   and   trust   and   rest.
one   in   bod - y,   heart   and   mind.

* Purcell's original has G♭

596

As man and woman we are made

SUSSEX CAROL 888888

1. As man and wom - an we are made that love be found and
2. Now Je - sus lived and gave his love to make our life and
3. And Je - sus died to live a - gain, so praise the love that,
4. Then spread the ta - ble, clear the hall and cel - e - brate till

life be - gun: the like - ness of the liv - ing God, u -
lov - ing new; so cel - e - brate with him to - day and
come what may, can bring the dawn and clear the skies, and
day is done; let peace go deep be - tween us all and

nique, yet called to live as one. Praise, praise the love that
drink the joy he of - fers you, that makes the sim - ple
waits to wipe all tears a - way, and let us hope for
joy be shared by eve - ry-one; laugh and make mer - ry

gives us life, through joy or sad - ness, calm or strife.
mo - ment shine and chang - es wa - ter in - to wine.
what shall be, be - liev - ing where we can - not see.
with your friends, and praise the love that nev - er ends!

Words: Brian A. Wren (1936–) Music: English traditional; harmony, Ralph Vaughan Williams (1872–1958)

597

Jesus, the Lord of love and life

WINSCOTT 8 8 8 8 LM

1. Je - sus the Lord of love and life, draw near to
2. Give them each day your peace and joy, let no dark
3. As they have vowed to have and hold, each by the
4. Deep - en, O Lord, their love for you, and in that
5. Be to them both a guide and friend, through all the

bless this hus - band, wife; as they are now in
clouds these gifts de - stroy; in grow - ing trust may
oth - er be con - soled; in wealth or want, in
love, their own re - new; each in the oth - er
years, their home de - fend; Je - sus the Lord of

love made one, let your good will for them be done.
love en - dure, to keep their mar - riage bond se - cure.
health or pain, till death shall part, let love re - main.
find de - light, as lives and in - terests now u - nite.
love and life, stay near and bless this hus - band, wife.

Words: James Seddon (1915–1983), alt Music: Samuel Sebastian Wesley (1810–1876)

O perfect Love

O PERFECT LOVE   11 10 11 10

1. O per - fect Love, all hu - man thought trans - cend - ing,
2. O per - fect Life, be now their full as - sur - ance
3. Grant them the joy which bright-ens earth - ly sor - row;

low - ly we kneel in prayer be - fore your throne,
of ten - der char - i - ty and stead-fast faith,
grant them the peace which calms all earth - ly strife,

that theirs may be the love which knows no end - ing,
of pa - tient hope and qui - et brave en - dur - ance,
and to life's day the glo - rious un-known mor - row

whom you in ho - ly love now join in one.
with child - like trust that fears nor pain nor death.
that dawns up - on e - ter - nal love and life.

Words: Dorothy Frances Gurney (1858–1932)   Music: Joseph Barnby (1838–1896)

Words: public domain   Music: public domain

599

The grace of life is theirs

RHOSYMEDRE 6 6 6 6 8 8 8

1. The grace of life is theirs who on this wed-ding day
   de - light to make their vows and for each oth - er pray.
2. Where love is, God a - bides, and God shall sure - ly bless
   a home where trust and care give birth to hap - pi - ness.

May they, O Lord, to - geth - er prove the last - ing joy of
May they, O Lord, to - geth - er prove the last - ing joy of

Chris-tian love, the last - ing joy of Chris - tian love.
such a love, the last - ing joy of such a love.

3. How slow to take offence
   love is! How quick to heal!
   How ready in distress
   to know how others feel!
   May they, O Lord, together prove
   the lasting joy of such a love,
   the lasting joy of such a love.

4. And when time lays its hand
   on all we hold most dear,
   and life, by life consumed,
   fulfils its purpose here,
   may we, O Lord, together prove
   the lasting joy of Christian love,
   the lasting joy of Christian love.

Words: Fred Pratt Green (1903–)   Music: John David Edwards (1806–1885)

Words: copyright © 1970 by Hope Publishing Co.   Music: public domain

When love is found

O WALY WALY 8 8 8 8 LM

1. When love is found and hope comes home, sing and be glad that two are one. When love ex - plodes and fills the sky, praise God and share our Mak - er's joy.
2. When love has flowered in trust and care, build both each day, that love may dare to reach be - yond home's warmth and light, to serve and strive for truth and right.
3. When love is tried as loved-ones change, hold still to hope though all seems strange, till ease re - turns and love grows wise through lis - tening ears and o - pened eyes.
4. When love is torn and trust be - trayed, pray strength to love till tor-ments fade, till lov - ers keep no score of wrong, but hear through pain love's East - er song.
5. Praise God for love; praise God for life, in age or youth, in calm or strife. Lift up your hearts! Let love be fed through death and life in bro - ken bread.

See Also: O Waly Waly 25 224

Words: Brian A. Wren (1936–)   Music: English traditional; arrangement, Noël Tredinnick (1949–)

Funeral

601 How blest are they who trust in Christ

ROCKINGHAM 8 8 8 8 LM

1. How blest are they who trust in Christ when we and
those we love must part; we yield them up, for
go they must, but do not lose them from our heart.

2. In rip - ened age, their har - vest reaped, or gone from
us in youth or prime, in Christ they have e -
ter - nal life, re - leased from all the bonds of time.

3. In Christ who tast - ed death for us and leads us
through our na - tural grief, we wit - ness to a
strick - en world the strength and prom - ise of be - lief.

Alternate tune: Angelus   See also: Rockingham 231

Words: John 3:13–16, Jude 1:20–21; paraphrase, Fred Pratt Green (1903–)
Music: Psalmody in Miniature, Second Supplement c. 1780; adaptation, Edward Miller (1731–1807)

602 Grief of ending, wordless sorrow

MOUNT AUBURN 8 8 8 8 LM

1. Grief of end - ing, word - less sor - row, pain of
2. Times re - mem - bered, joy dis - cov - ered, love and
3. Word of prom - ise, lift our sing - ing, blend - ing
4. Christ a - mong us, Spir - it - breath - ing, safe com -

part - ing, dry or weep - ing, on our lips and in our
friend - ship, voice and ges - ture, pre - cious, love - ly, one and
griev - ing with be - liev - ing. In your hands is all com -
pan - ion, in your keep - ing, death is birth to res - ur -

bod - ies, lov - ing God, to you we of - fer.
on - ly, giv - ing God, we tell and treas - ure.
plet - ed, last - ing God, our hope and meas - ure.
rec - tion, liv - ing God, our joy for - ev - er.

Words: Brian A. Wren (1936–) Music: Peter Cutts (1937–)

603

Lord of the living

FLEMMING 11 11 11 5

1. Lord of the liv-ing, in your name as-sem-bled, we join to
2. Help us to treas-ure all that will re-mind us of the en-
3. May we, when-ev-er tempt-ed to de-jec-tion, strong-ly re-
4. Lord, you can lift us from the grave of sor-row in-to the

thank you for the life re-mem-bered. Fa-ther have mer-cy,
rich-ment in the days be-hind us. Your love has set us
cap-ture thoughts of res-ur-rec-tion. You gave us Je-sus
pres-ence of your own to-mor-row; give to your peo-ple

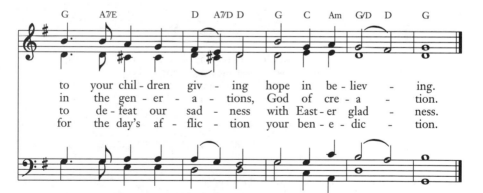

to your chil-dren giv-ing hope in be-liev-ing.
in the gen-er-a-tions, God of cre-a-tion.
to de-feat our sad-ness with East-er glad-ness.
for the day's af-flic-tion your ben-e-dic-tion.

Alternate tune: Christe Sanctorum

Words: Fred Kaan (1929–) Music: Friedrich Ferdinand Flemming (1778–1813)

Funeral

604   O Christ, you wept when grief was raw

PALMER 8 8 8 8 LM with repeats

1. O Christ, you wept when grief was raw, and
2. The well-loved voice is si - lent now, and
3. We try to hold what is not here and
4. In all our lone - li - ness and doubt, through

felt for those who mourned their friend; come
we have much we meant to say; col -
fear for what we do not know; oh,
what we can - not re - al - ize, ad -

close to where we would not be and hold us,
lect our lost and wan - dering words and keep them
take our hands in yours, good Lord, and free us,
dress us from your emp - ty tomb and tell us,

Alternate tunes: Hamburg (Voice Divine) Rockingham

Words: Iona Community (Scotland)   Music: John L. Bell (1949–)

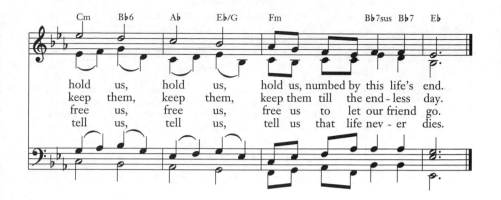

hold us, hold us, hold us, numbed by this life's end.
keep them, keep them, keep them till the end - less day.
free us, free us, free us to let our friend go.
tell us, tell us, tell us that life nev - er dies.

605 Strength to the troubled heart, we come

ELTHAM 8 8 8 8 LM

1. Strength to the trou - bled heart, we come with anx - ious and be - wil - dered minds, striv - ing to reach for mean - ing here: your peace is what we ache to find.

2. Joy of the thank - ful heart, we come; good mem - o - ries are ours to - day, of friend-ship giv - en and re - ceived, of fam - ily care a - long life's way.

3. Friend of the lone - ly heart, we come; the void that's left is hard to fill; strong love stays with your griev - ing ones, sure touch of grace, death's fears to still.

4. Sun of the ris - ing heart, we come; Christ's emp - ty tomb new cour - age gives, for we are sure, em-braced and safe with - in your love, our loved one lives.

Alternate tune: Maryton

Words: David Sparks (20th cent.) Music: Nathaniel Gawthorn (18th cent.);
harmony, Samuel Sebastian Wesley (1810–1876)

606

Ye holy angels bright

DARWALL'S 148TH 666688

1. Ye ho - ly an - gels bright, who wait at God's right hand, or
through the realms of light fly at your Lord's com - mand, as - sist your
song, for else the theme too high doth seem for mor - tal tongue.

2. Ye bless - ed souls at rest, who ran this earth - ly race, and
now, from sin re - leased, be - hold the Sav - iour's face, your prais - es
sound, as in God's sight with sweet de - light ye do a - bound.

3. Ye saints, who toil be - low, a - dore your heaven - ly King, and
on - ward as ye go some joy - ful an - them sing; take all God
gives; through good or ill, praise our God still who ev - er lives!

4. My soul, bear thou thy part, tri - umph in God a - bove, and
with a well-tuned heart sing thou the songs of love! Let all thy
days till life shall end, what - e'er God send, be filled with praise.

Words: Richard Baxter (1615–1691); revision, John Hampden Gurney (1802–1862), alt
Music: John Darwall (1731–1789); harmony, William Henry Monk (1823–1889)

Words: public domain Music: public domain

607

Ye watchers and ye holy ones

LASST UNS ERFREUEN 8 8 4 4 8 8 with hallelujahs

1. Ye watch-ers and ye ho-ly ones, bright ser-aphs, cher-u-bim and thrones, raise the glad strain, Cry
2. Oh high-er than the cher-u-bim, more glo-rious than the ser-a-phim, lead their prais-es, Thou
3. Re-spond, ye souls in end-less rest, ye pa-tri-archs and pro-phets blest, "hal-le-lu-jah, "hal-le-lu-jah!" Ye
4. O friends, in glad-ness let us sing, su-per-nal an-thems ech-o-ing, "hal-le-lu-jah, To

Words: John Athelstan Laurie Riley (1858–1945) Music: Auserlesene Katholische Geistliche Kirchengesänge 1623; harmony, Ralph Vaughan Williams (1872–1958)

Words: copyright © Oxford University Press Music: harmony, copyright © Oxford University Press

Eb /D Cm7 Bb7/D Eb Ab/C Bbsus4 – 3 /Ab Eb/G (/F)

out, do-min-ions, prince-doms, powers, vir -
bear-er of the e-ter-nal word, most
ho-ly twelve, ye mar-tyrs strong, all
God the Fa-ther, God the Son, and

Eb/G Bb7/F Eb Ab/C Eb/Bb Ab Eb/G (Gm Eb Bb/D) Ab/C Cm/Bb

Harmony

tues, arch-an-gels, an-gels' choirs,
gra-cious, mag-ni-fy the Lord,
saints tri-um-phant, raise the song,
God the Spi-rit, Three-in-One,

"Hal - le -

Ab6 Bb Eb/G Fm Eb/G Ab6 Bb7 Cm Bb/D Eb6 F Bb

lu - jah, hal - le - lu - jah, hal - le - lu - jah,

Unison Cm7 (/D) Eb6 Fm Bb7/D C7/E Fm Eb/G Ab6 Bb 7 Eb

hal - le - lu - jah, hal - le - lu - jah!"

787

608

Oh what their joy and their glory must be

O QUANTA QUALIA 10 10 10 10

1. Oh what their joy and their glo - ry must be,
2. Tru - ly, "Je - ru - sa - lem" name we that shore,
3. There, where no trou - bles dis - trac - tion can bring,
4. Now, in the mean - while, with hearts raised on high,
5. Low be - fore God with our prais - es we fall,

those end - less Sab - baths the bless - ed ones see,
cit - y of peace that brings joy ev - er - more;
we the sweet an - thems of Zi - on shall sing,
we for that coun - try must yearn and must sigh,
of whom, and in whom, and through whom are all;

crowns for the val - iant, to wea - ry ones rest:
wish and ful - fil - ment are not sev - ered there,
while for thy grace, Lord, their voic - es of praise
seek - ing Je - ru - sa - lem, dear na - tive land,
of whom, the Fa - ther, and in whom, the Son,

See also: O Quanta Qualia 369

Words: Peter Abelard (1079–1142); translation, John Mason Neale (1818–1866)
Music: Paris Antiphoner 1681; harmony, John Bacchus Dykes (1823–1876)

Words: public domain Music: public domain

God   shall   be   all   and   in   all   ev - er   blest.
nor   do things prayed   for come short   of the   prayer.
thy   bless - ed   peo -   ple   e - ter - nal - ly   raise.
through our   long   ex -   ile on Bab - y - lon's strand.
through whom, the   Spir -   it, with them   ev - er   One.

609   O saints, in splendour sing

STEEPLE ASHTON   6 6 8 6 SM

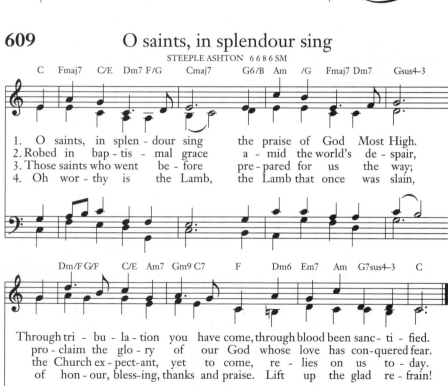

1. O saints, in splen - dour sing   the praise of God   Most High.
2. Robed in bap - tis - mal grace   a - mid the world's   de - spair,
3. Those saints who went   be - fore pre - pared for us   the way;
4. Oh wor - thy is   the Lamb,   the Lamb that once   was slain,

Through tri - bu - la - tion you have come, through blood been sanc - ti - fied.
pro - claim the glo - ry   of   our God whose love has con - quered fear.
the Church ex - pect - ant, yet   to come,   re - lies on us   to - day.
of hon - our, bless - ing, thanks and praise. Lift up the glad   re - frain!

Alternate tune: St. Thomas

Words: Sylvia G. Dunstan (1955–1993)   Music: John Barnard (1948–)

Communion of Saints

610 Light's abode, celestial Salem

RHUDDLAN 878787

1. Light's a-bode, ce-les-tial Sa-lem, vi-sion whence true
2. There for-ev-er and for-ev-er hal-le-lu-jah
3. There no cloud nor pass-ing va-pour dims the bright-ness
4. Oh how glo-rious and re-splen-dent, fra-gile bo-dy,
5. Now with glad-ness, now with cour-age, bear the bur-den

peace doth spring, bright-er than the heart can fan-cy,
is out-poured, for un-end-ing, for un-bro-ken
of the air; end-less noon-day, glo-rious noon-day,
shalt thou be, when en-dued with so much beau-ty,
on thee laid, that here-af-ter these thy la-bours

man-sion of the high-est King; oh how glo-rious
is the feast day of the Lord; all is pure and
from the Sun of suns is there; there no night brings
full of health, and strong and free, full of vi-gour,
may with end-less gifts be paid, and in ev-er-

Alternate tunes: Regent Square Westminster Abbey

Words: Thomas à Kempis (c.1380–1471); translation, John Mason Neale (1818–1866)
Music: Welsh melody

Words: public domain Music: public domain

790

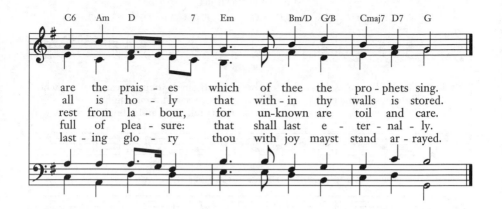

are the prais - es which of thee the pro - phets sing.
all is ho - ly that with - in thy walls is stored.
rest from la - bour, for un-known are toil and care.
full of plea - sure: that shall last e - ter - nal - ly.
last - ing glo - ry thou with joy mayst stand ar - rayed.

Communion of Saints

611

For all the saints

SINE NOMINE 10 10 10 4

1. For all the saints who from their la-bours rest, who
2. Thou wast their rock, their fort-ress and their might,
3. Oh may thy sol - diers, faith-ful, true and bold,

thee by faith be - fore the world con-fessed, thy
thou, Lord, their cap - tain in the well-fought fight, thou
fight as the saints who no-bly fought of old, and

name, O Je - sus, be for - ev - er blest.
in the dark - ness drear their one true light. Hal -
win with them the vic - tor's crown of gold.

- le - lu - jah, hal - le - lu - jah!

Words: William Walsham How (1823–1897)   Music: Ralph Vaughan Williams (1872–1958)

Words: public domain   Music: copyright © Oxford University Press from The English Hymnal

792

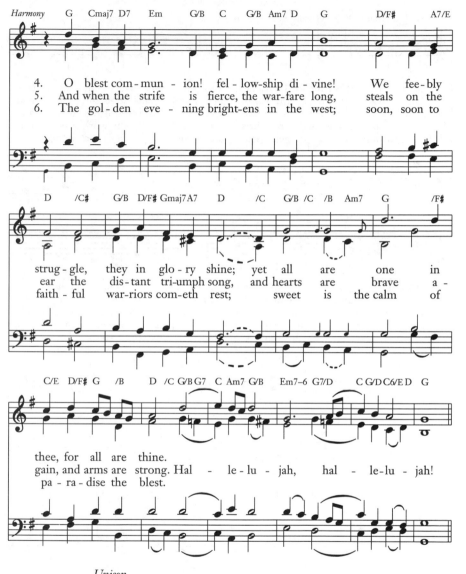

Harmony   G   Cmaj7 D7   Em   G/B   C   G/B Am7 D   G   D/F#   A7/E

4. O blest com - mun - ion! fel - low-ship di - vine!   We   fee-bly
5. And when the strife   is fierce, the war-fare long,   steals on the
6. The gol-den eve - ning bright-ens in the west;   soon, soon to

D   /C#   G/B D/F# Gmaj7 A7   D   /C   G/B /C   /B Am7   G   /F#

strug - gle,   they in glo - ry shine;   yet all   are   one   in
ear   the   dis-tant tri-umph song,   and hearts are   brave   a -
faith - ful   war-riors com-eth rest;   sweet is   the calm   of

C/E D/F# G   /B   D /C G/B G7   C Am7 G/B   Em7-6 G7/D   C G/D C6/E D   G

thee, for   all are   thine.
gain, and arms are strong. Hal - le - lu - jah,   hal - le - lu - jah!
pa - ra - dise the blest.

Unison
7. But lo, there breaks a yet more glorious day;
   the saints triumphant rise in bright array:
   the King of glory passes on his way.
   Hallelujah, hallelujah!

8. From earth's wide bounds, from ocean's farthest coast,
   through gates of pearl streams in the countless host,
   singing to Father, Son and Holy Ghost.
   Hallelujah, hallelujah!

612 Christ is the King

VULPIUS 8 8 8 with hallelujahs

1. Christ is the King! O friends, re-joice; broth-ers and sis - ters,
   with one voice let the world know he is your choice.
2. Oh mag - ni - fy the Lord, and raise an-thems of joy and
   ho - ly praise for Christ's brave saints of an - cient days.
3. They with a faith for - ev - er new fol-lowed the King, and
   round him drew thou-sands of faith - ful serv-ants true.
4. O Chris-tian wom - en, Chris - tian men, all the world o - ver,
   seek a - gain the way dis - ci - ples fol-lowed then.
5. Christ through all a - ges is the same: place the same hope in
   his great name, with the same faith his word pro - claim.

Hal - le - lu - jah, hal - le - lu - jah, hal - le - lu - jah!

6. Let love's unconquerable might
   your scattered companies unite
   in service to the Lord of light.
   Hallelujah, hallelujah, hallelujah!

7. So shall God's will on earth be done,
   new lamps be lit, new tasks begun,
   and the whole church at last be one.
   Hallelujah, hallelujah, hallelujah!

Alternate tune: Victory

Words: G.K.A. Bell (1883–1958) Music: Melchior Vulpius (c.1560–1615);
harmony, Ernest Campbell MacMillan (1893–1973)

613

Give thanks for life,
the measure of our days

CREATION 10 10 10 4

1. Give thanks for life, the meas-ure of our days;
2. Give thanks for those who made their life a light
3. And for our own, our liv-ing and our dead,
4. Give thanks for hope, that like the wheat, the grain

F   Bb   F   Gm/F   C/E   Am/C   Dm   Gm/Bb   C   /Bb

mor-tal, we pass through beau-ty that de-cays, yet sing to
caught from the Christ-flame, burst-ing through the night, who touched the
thanks for the love by which our life is fed, a love not
ly-ing in dark-ness does its life re-tain in res-ur-

F/A   Bb/F   Gm/F   C/E   Am/C   Dm   Gm/Bb   A   /G   /F   A/E   Dm   C

God our hope, our love, our praise:
truth, who burned for what is right: hal-le-lu-jah!
changed by time or death or dread:
rec-tion to grow green a-gain:

F   Bb/D   F/Eb   Bb/D   F7/C   Bb   F/C   C6 – 7   F

Alternate tunes: Engelberg   Sine Nomine
Words: Shirley Murray (1931–)   Music: Beryl Matthews (1926–)
Words: copyright © 1987 by Hope Publishing Co.   Music: copyright © Beryl Matthews

795

614

We gather here to bid farewell

MORNING HYMN 8 8 8 8 LM

1. We gath - er here to bid fare - well to
2. We bless the hand that brought you here and
3. In friend - ship's bonds our souls u - nite in
4. un - til in God's all - glo - rious dawn we

friends who leave for oth - er parts; our prayers we pledge, our
rich - ly blest us all in you: as now you leave for
prayer and praise and ho - ly vow: to God's great heart of
meet be - fore the throne at length, God guide you, keep you,

love we tell, and lift to God our grate - ful hearts.
wid - er sphere God's cov - enant mer - cies we re - view.
love and light your kin in Christ com - mit you now,
lead you on from hope to hope, from strength to strength.

Alternate tune: Winchester New

Words: Margaret Clarkson (1915–)   Music: François H. Barthélémon (1741–1808)

Words: copyright © 1987 by Hope Publishing Co.   Music: public domain

615 Let saints on earth in concert sing

DUNDEE (FRENCH) 8 6 8 6 CM

1. Let saints on earth in con-cert sing with those whose work is done,
2. One fam-i-ly, we dwell in him, one church, a-bove, be-neath,
3. One ar-my of the liv-ing God, to his com-mand we bow:
4. E'en now to their e-ter-nal home there pass some spir-its blest,
5. Je-su be thou our con-stant guide; then, when the word is given,

for all the serv-ants of our King in heaven and earth are one.
though now di-vid-ed by the stream, the nar-row stream of death.
part of the host has crossed the flood, and part is cross-ing now.
while oth-ers to the mar-gin come, wait-ing their call to rest.
bid Jor-dan's nar-row stream di-vide, and bring us safe to heaven.

Fauxbourdon *(melody is in the tenor)*

See Also: Dundee (French) 82

Words: Charles Wesley (1707–1788), alt Music: Scottish Psalter 1615;
harmony, Thomas Ravenscroft (c.1592–c.1635), alt

Words: public domain Music: public domain

616 They did not build in vain

DOLGELLY 666688

1. They did not build in vain who found - ed here a
2. They built up - on the rock that is the ris - en
3. Those who have loved this place, a cloud of wit - ness -
4. Though the hor - i - zon's bend con - ceals the way a -
5. Here is our meet - ing place where doubt finds grounds of

church as wit - ness to God's love a - mid a
Lord, the one foun - da - tion laid which stands each
es, sur - round and urge us on as we now
head, the foot - prints on the road show Christ waits
faith, where hurt finds heal - ing love, our pen - i -

world of pain, for still to those who
earth - ly shock; that, Spir - it filled, we
run our race, and so we lay a -
at the end; in him a - lone our
tence your grace; where bridg - ing time to e -

Words: Alan Luff (1928–)   Music: Welsh traditional

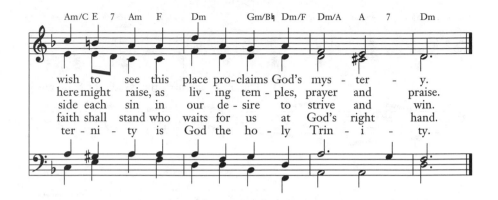

wish to see this place pro-claims God's mys - ter - y.
here might raise, as liv - ing tem - ples, prayer and praise.
side each sin in our de - sire to strive and win.
faith shall stand who waits for us at God's right hand.
ter - ni - ty is God the ho - ly Trin - i - ty.

617 Nothing can trouble

NADA TE TURBE Irregular

Noth-ing can trou - ble, noth-ing can fright-en. Those who seek God shall
Na - da te tur - be; na - da te es-pan - te. Quien a Dios tie - ne,
Rien ne peut trou-bler; ni peut ef - fray - er. Ceux qui cher-chent Dieu

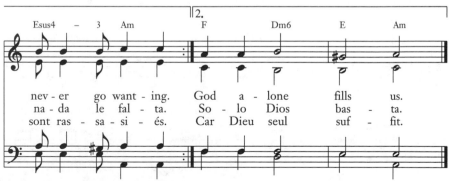

nev - er go want - ing. God a - lone fills us.
na - da le fal - ta. So - lo Dios bas - ta.
sont ras - sa - si - és. Car Dieu seul suf - fit.

Words: Teresa of Ávila (1515-1582); translation, Taizé Community (France); French translation,
Daniel H. Forget (1956-) Music: Taizé Community (France)

618

The blessing of the God of Sarah

BLESSING (NAMETH) Irregular

The bless-ing of the God of Sa-rah as of A-bra-ham, the bless-ing of the Son born of the wom-an Ma - ry, the bless-ing of the Spir - it who broods o - ver us as a mo-ther o-ver her chil-dren

Words: Lois Wilson (20th cent.), alt   Music: Bart Nameth (1954–)

Words: copyright © Lois Wilson   Music: copyright © Bart Nameth

be with you all. A - men.

619   The Lord bless you / Aaronic Blessing

AARONIC BLESSING   Irregular

The Lord bless you and keep you; the Lord make his face shine

up - on you, and be gra - cious un - to you; the

Lord lift up his coun - te - nance up - on you and give you his peace.

Words: traditional   Music: Lowell Mason (1792–1872)

Words: public domain   Music: public domain

620

Go now in peace

TALLIS' CANON 8 8 8 8 LM

May be sung as a round

1. Go now in peace; though friends must part, your
2. Go now in hope, and hope - ful stay, though
3. Go now in faith, through time and chance, un -

pres - ence lives in eve - ry heart. Your
shad - owed val - leys hide your way; through
til we join the wed - ding dance as

gifts to us no words can tell: go
good and e - vil, joy and pain, with
part - ners of the Three - in - One, where

now in peace, in Christ go well.
God, in Spir - it, you re - main.
all is end - ed and be - gun.

Words: Brian A. Wren (1936–)   Music: Thomas Tallis (c.1505–1585)

Words: copyright ©1993 by Hope Publishing Co.   Music: public domain

621

God be with you till we meet again

RANDOLPH 9889

God be with you till we meet a - gain;

1. lov - ing coun - sels guide, up - hold you, with a shep-herd's
2. un - seen wings pro - tect - ing, hide you, dai - ly man - na
3. when life's per - ils thick con - found you, put un - fail - ing
4. keep love's ban - ner float - ing o'er you, smite death's threat-ening

care en - fold you:
still pro - vide you: God be with you till we meet a - gain.
arms a - round you:
wave be - fore you:

Words: Jeremiah Eames Rankin (1828–1904) Music: Ralph Vaughan Williams (1872–1958)

Words: public domain Music: copyright © Oxford University Press from The English Hymnal

622

Go now in peace
GO NOW IN PEACE 8 8 9

Words: Natalie Sleeth (1930–1992) Music: Natalie Sleeth (1930–1992)

Words: copyright © Hinshaw Music Inc., 1976. Reprinted with permission. Music: copyright © Hinshaw Music Inc., 1976. Reprinted with permission.

623

Holy, holy, holy

SANCTUS (SCHUBERT) 11 11 11 11

Ho - ly, ho - ly, ho - ly, God al - might - y, Lord!
Hei - lig, hei - lig, hei - lig, hei - lig ist der Herr!

Ho - ly, ho - ly, ho - ly, eve - ry - where a - dored!
Hei - lig, hei - lig, hei - lig, hei - lig ist nur Er!

1. God with - out be - gin - ning, God, e - ter - nal One
2. Power and love and won - der cir - cling round God's throne,
1. Er der nie be - gon - nen, Er der im - mer war,
2. All - macht, Wun - der, Lie - be, al - les rings - um - her!

reigns and rules for - ev - er all be - neath the sun.
praise our God most ho - ly, Lord of Life a - lone.
e - wig ist und wal - tet, sein wird im - mer dar.
Hei - lig, hei - lig, hei - lig, hei - lig ist der Herr!

Words: traditional   Music: Franz Schubert (1798–1828)

Words: public domain   Music: public domain

Discipleship

624

Blest are they

BLEST ARE THEY 7 7 7 5 with refrain (5 7 5 7)

1. Blest are they, the poor in spir-it; theirs is the king-dom of God.
2. Blest are they, the low-ly ones; they shall in-her-it the earth.
3. Blest are they who show mer-cy; mer-cy shall be theirs.
4. Blest are they who seek peace; they are the chil-dren of God.
5. Blest are you who suf-fer hate all be-cause of me. Re-

Blest are they, full of sor-row, they shall be con-soled.
Blest are they, who hun-ger and thirst; they shall have their fill.
Blest are they, the pure of heart; they shall see God!
Blest are they who suf-fer in faith, the glo-ry of God is theirs.
joice and be glad— yours is the kingdom—shine for all to see.

Refrain

Re-joice and be glad! Bless-ed are you; ho-ly are you! Re-joice and be glad!

Words: Matthew 5:3–12; paraphrase, David R. Haas (1957–) Music: David R. Haas (1957–);
arrangement, Norma de Waal Malefyt

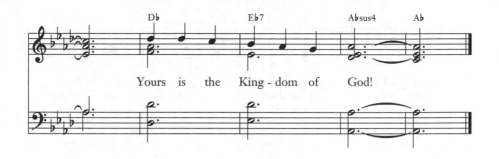

Yours is the King-dom of God!

625   Seek ye first

SEEK YE FIRST Irregular

1. Seek ye first the king-dom of God and his right-eous-ness,
2. Ask, and it shall be giv-en un-to you; seek and ye shall find;
3. We do not live by bread a-lone, but by eve-ry word

and all these things shall be add-ed un-to you.
knock, and the door shall be o-pened un-to you. Al-le-lu, al-le-lu - ia!
that pro - ceeds from the mouth of God.

Words: Karen Lafferty (1948–)   Music: Karen Lafferty (1948–)

626

Lord of all power

SLANE 10 11 11 11

1. Lord of all power, I give you my will,
2. Lord of all wis-dom, I give you my mind,
3. Lord of all boun-ty, I give you my heart;
4. Lord of all be-ing, I give you my all.

in joy-ful o - be-dience your tasks to ful - fil.
rich truth that sur - pass-es our know-ledge to find.
I praise and a - dore you for all you im - part:
If e'er I dis - own you, I stum - ble and fall;

Your bond-age is free-dom, your serv-ice is song,
What eye has not seen and what ear has not heard
your love to in - spire me, your coun-sel to guide,
but, sworn in glad serv-ice your word to o - bey,

and, held in your keep-ing, my weak-ness is strong.
is taught by your Spir - it and shines from your word.
your pres-ence to cheer me, what - ev - er be - tide.
I walk in your free-dom to the end of the way.

Words: Jack C. Winslow (1882–1974) Music: Irish traditional; harmony, Erik Routley (1917–1982)

Discipleship

627 Not for tongues of heaven's angels

BRIDEGROOM 87876

1. Not for tongues of heav-en's an - gels, not for wis-dom to dis -
2. Love is hum - ble; love is gen - tle; love is ten-der, true and
3. Nev-er jeal - ous, nev - er self - ish, love will not re-joice in
4. In the day this world is fad - ing faith and hope will play their

cern, not for faith that mas-ters moun-tains, for this bet - ter gift we
kind; love is gra-cious, ev - er pa - tient, gen - er - ous of heart and
wrong; nev - er boast-ful, nor re - sent - ful, love be-lieves and suf-fers
part, but when Christ is seen in glo - ry love shall reign in eve - ry

yearn:
mind:
long: may   love   be   ours,   O   Lord.
heart:

Words: Timothy Dudley–Smith (1926–) Music: Peter Cutts (1937–)

628
This one thing I do
THIS ONE THING Irregular with Refrain

Unison Refrain

Leader: *This one thing I do,* All: *this one thing I do,* Leader: *this one thing I do,* All: *this one thing I do:*

leav-ing be - hind what lies be - hind, striv-ing to - ward what

lies be-fore, I run to-ward the mark, run to-ward the mark, run to-ward the

mark of the high call - ing of God in Christ Je - sus.

Words: paraphrase, Andrew Donaldson (1951–) Music: Andrew Donaldson (1951–)
Words: copyright © Andrew Donaldson, 1986 Music: copyright © Andrew Donaldson, 1986

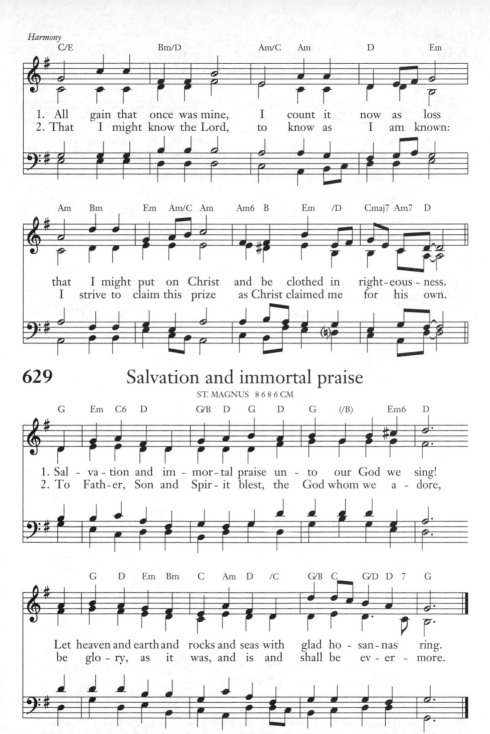

1. All gain that once was mine, I count it now as loss
2. That I might know the Lord, to know as I am known:

that I might put on Christ and be clothed in right-eous-ness.
I strive to claim this prize as Christ claimed me for his own.

629   Salvation and immortal praise

ST. MAGNUS 8 6 8 6 CM

1. Sal - va - tion and im - mor-tal praise un - to our God we sing!
2. To Fath- er, Son and Spir - it blest, the God whom we a - dore,

Let heaven and earth and rocks and seas with glad ho - san-nas ring.
be glo - ry, as it was, and is and shall be ev - er - more.

Words: v.1, Tate and Brady's New Version 1696; v.2, Isaac Watts (1674–1748) Music: Jeremiah Clarke (c.1674–1707), from Divine Companion 1707; harmony, William Henry Monk (1823–1889) after John Pyke Hullah (19th cent.)

Words: public domain Music: public domain

630

When we are living

SOMOS DEL SEÑOR   10 10 10 10

1. When we are liv - ing,   it is in Christ Je - sus,
2. Through all our liv - ing,   we our fruits must give.
3. 'Mid times of sor - row   and in times of pain,
4. A - cross this wide world,   we shall al - ways find

1. Pues si vi - vi - mos   pa - ra Él vi - vi - mos
2. En es - ta vi - da,   fru - tos he - mos de dar.
3. En la tris - te - za   y en el do - lor,
4. En es - te mun - do,   he - mos de en - con - trar

and when we're dy - ing,   it is in the Lord.
Good works of serv - ice   are for of - fer - ing.
when sens - ing beau - ty   or in love's em - brace,
those who are cry - ing   with no peace of mind,

y si mo - ri - mos   pa - ra Él mo - ri - mos.
Las o - bras bue - nas   son pa - ra o - fren - dar.
en la be - lle - za   y en el a - mor,
gen - te que llo - ra   y sin con - so - lar.

Both in our liv - ing   and in our dy - ing,
When we are giv - ing,   or when re - ceiv - ing,
wheth - er we suf - fer,   or sing re - joic - ing,
but when we help them,   or when we feed them,

Sea que vi - va - mos   o que mu - ra - mos,
Ya sea que de - mos   o que re - ci - ba - mos,
sea que su - fra - mos   o que go - ce - mos
Sea que a - yu - de - mos   o que a - li - men - te - mos,

we be-long to God;   we be-long to God.
so-mos del Se - ñor,   so-mos del Se - ñor.

Words: Romans 14:8; paraphrase, v.1, anonymous; translation, Elise S. Eslinger (1942–), v.2–4, Roberto
Escamilla (1931–); translation, George Lockwood (1946–) Music: Hispanic folk song

Words: translation, copyright © The United Methodist Publishing House, 1989 Music: public domain

631 Jesus' hands were kind hands

AU CLAIR DE LA LUNE 11 11 11 11

1. Je - sus' hands were kind hands, do - ing good to all,
2. Take my hands, Lord Je - sus, let them work for you;

heal - ing pain and sick - ness, bless - ing chil - dren small,
make them strong and gen - tle, kind in all I do.

wash - ing tir - ed feet, and sav - ing those who fall;
Let me watch you, Je - sus, till I'm gen - tle too,

Je - sus' hands were kind hands, do - ing good to all.
till my hands are kind hands, quick to work for you.

Words: Margaret Cropper (1886–1980) Music: French traditional

632 Help us accept each other

BARONITA 7 6 7 6 D

1. Help us ac - cept each oth - er as Christ ac - cept-ed us;
2. Teach us, O Lord, your les - sons, as in our dai - ly life
3. Let your ac - cep-tance change us, so that we may be moved
4. Lord, for to-day's en - coun-ters with all who are in need,

teach us as sis - ter, broth-er, each per - son to em - brace.
we strug - gle to be hu - man and search for hope and faith.
in liv - ing sit - u - a - tions to do the truth in love;
who hun - ger for ac - cep-tance, for right - eous - ness and bread,

Be pres - ent, Lord, a - mong us and bring us to be - lieve
Teach us to care for peo - ple, for all— not just for some,
to prac - tice your ac - cep-tance un - til we know by heart
we need new eyes for see - ing, new hands for hold-ing on:

we are our - selves ac - cept - ed and meant to love and live.
to love them as we find them or as they may be - come.
the ta - ble of for-give-ness and laugh - ter's heal-ing art.
re - new us with your Spir - it; Lord, free us, make us one!

Words: Fred Kaan (1929–) Music: Doreen Potter (1925–1980)

633

Who would true valour see

MONKS GATE 6 5 6 5 6 6 6 5

1. Who would true val - our see let them come hith - er:
here's one will con - stant be come wind, come weath - er.
2. Who so be - set me round with dis - mal sto - ries
do but them-selves con-found: my strength the more is.
3. Hob - gob - lin nor foul fiend can daunt my spir - it:
I know I at the end shall life in - her - it.

There's no dis-cour-age - ment shall make me once re - lent
No foes shall stay my might; though I with gi-ants fight,
Then, fan-cies, flee a-way! Fear not what oth-ers say;

my first a - vowed in - tent to be a pil - grim.
but I will have the right to be a pil - grim.
I'll la - bour night and day to be a pil - grim.

Words: John Bunyan (1628–1688), alt Music: English traditional; arrangement, Ralph Vaughan
Williams (1872–1958)

Discipleship

634

Will you come and follow me

KELVINGROVE 76767776

1. Will you come and fol-low me
2. Will you leave your-self be-hind
3. Will you let the blind-ed see   if I but call your   name?
4. Will you love the "you" you hide
5. Lord, your sum-mons ech-oes true when you but call my   name.

Will you go where you don't know
Will you care for cruel and kind
Will you set the pris-oners free   and nev-er be the   same?
Will you quell the fear in-side
Let me turn and fol-low you and nev-er be the   same.

Will you let my love be shown;   will you let my name be known;
Will you risk the hos-tile stare   should your life at-tract or   scare?
Will you kiss the lep-er clean,   and do such as this un-seen,
Will you use the faith you've found   to re-shape the world a-round,
In your com-pa-ny I'll go   where your love and foot-steps show.

Words: Iona Community (Scotland)   Music: John L. Bell (1949–)

will you let my life be grown
Will you let me an-swer prayer in you and you in me?
and ad-mit to what I mean
through my sight and touch and sound
Thus I'll move and live and grow in you and you in me.

635 Brother, sister, let me serve you

SERVANT SONG 8 7 8 7

1. Broth-er, sis-ter, let me serve you; let me be as Christ to you;
2. We are pil-grims on a jour-ney, and com-pan-ions on the road;
3. I will hold the Christ-light for you in the night-time of your fear;
4. I will weep when you are weep-ing; when you laugh I'll laugh with you;

pray that I may have the grace to let you be my serv-ant too.
we are here to help each oth-er walk the mile and bear the load.
I will hold my hand out to you, speak the peace you long to hear.
I will share your joy and sor-row, till we've seen this jour-ney through.

5. When we sing to God in heaven,
we shall find such harmony,
born of all we've known together
of Christ's love and agony.

6. Brother, sister, let me serve you;
let me be as Christ to you;
pray that I may have the grace to
let you be my servant too.

Words: Richard Gillard (1953–) Music: Richard Gillard (1953–)

636

When voices are confusing

WOLVERCOTE 7 6 7 6 D

1. When voic-es are con - fus - ing, when right and wrong are blurred,
2. When truth is hard to fol - low and fact is hard to find,
3. Our lives are yours: oh take us and shape our des - ti - ny;

we need your help in choos - ing the way to be pre - ferred;
when crowd - ap - peals are shal - low, re - shape, re - new our mind.
through will - ing serv - ice make us all you would have us be.

our feet are prone to wan - der in paths un - true, un - tried:
Your ways we would be learn - ing: oh make our choic - es clear,
Con - firm this high en - deav - our a - gainst the reign of strife;

Alternate tune: Lancashire

Words: Miriam Drury (1900–) Music: William Harold Ferguson (1874–1950)

Words: copyright © The Presbyterian Church in Canada, 1972 Music: copyright © Oxford University Press

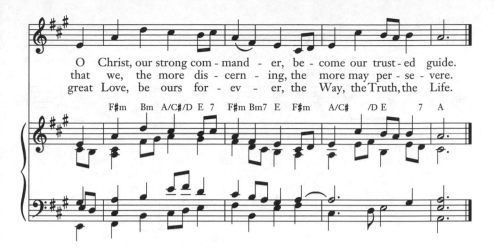

O Christ, our strong com - mand - er, be - come our trust - ed guide.
that we, the more dis - cern - ing, the more may per - se - vere.
great Love, be ours for - ev - er, the Way, the Truth, the Life.

637   Take my life, and let it be consecrated

LÜBECK 7 7 7 7

1. Take my life and let it be con - se - crat - ed, Lord, to thee;
2. Take my hands and let them move at the im - pulse of thy love;
3. Take my voice and let me sing al - ways, on - ly for my King;
4. Take my sil - ver and my gold: not a mite would I with-hold;

take my mo-ments and my days: let them flow in cease-less praise.
take my feet and let them be swift and beau - ti - ful for thee.
take my lips and let them be filled with mes - sa - ges from thee.
take my in - tel - lect, and use eve - ry power as thou shalt choose.

5. Take my will and make it thine;
   it shall be no longer mine;
   take my heart: it is thine own;
   it shall be thy royal throne.

6. Take my love; my Lord, I pour
   at thy feet its treasure store;
   take myself and I will be
   ever, only, all for thee.

Alternate tune: Mozart

Words: Frances Ridley Havergal (1836–1879) Music: Freylinghausen's Geistreiches Gesangbuch 1704

Words: public domain Music: public domain

Take time to be holy

TAKE TIME TO BE HOLY 11 11 11 11

1. Take time to be ho - ly; speak oft with thy Lord.
2. Take time to be ho - ly; the world rush-es on;
3. Take time to be ho - ly; let him be thy guide,
4. Take time to be ho - ly; be calm in thy soul,

A - bide in him al - ways, and feed on his word.
spend much time in se - cret with Je - sus a - lone.
and run not be - fore him, what - ev - er be - tide.
each thought and each mo - tive be - neath his con - trol.

Make friends of God's chil - dren; help those who are weak,
By look-ing to Je - sus, like him thou shalt be;
In joy or in sor - row, still fol - low thy Lord,
Thus led by his Spir - it to foun-tains of love,

for - get - ting in noth - ing his bless-ing to seek.
thy friends in thy con - duct his like-ness shall see.
and, look-ing to Je - sus, still trust in his word.
thou soon shalt be fit - ted for serv-ice a - bove.

Words: W. D. Longstaff (1822–1894)   Music: George C. Stebbins (1846–1945)

Words: public domain   Music: public domain

Discipleship

639

We are marching / Siyahamba

SIYAHAMBA Irregular

We are march-ing in the light of God; we are march-ing in the light of
Si - ya - hamb' e-ku-kha-nyen'kwen-khos', si - ya-hamb' e-ku-kha-nyen'kwen-
Nous mar-chons dans la lu-mière de Dieu, nous mar-chons dans la lu-mière de

1.	2.
	Sop.

God.	We are march-ing,
khos'.	Si - ya - ham - ba,
Dieu.	Oui, nous mar-chons,

God. We are the light of God. We are march-ing, march-ing, we are
khos'. Si - ya - kha-nyen' kwen-khos'. Si - ya - ham - ba, ham - ba, si - ya -
Dieu. Nous mar- lu-mière de Dieu. Oui, nous mar-chons, mar-chons; oui, nous

oo,

march-ing,   march-ing,   we are march-ing in the light of   God.
ham - ba,   ham - ba,   si - ya - hamb' e - ku-kha-nyen' kwen - khos'.
mar-chons,   mar-chons; nous mar-chons dans la lu-mière de   Dieu.

Words: South African (Xhosa) traditional; English translation, Anders Nyberg (1955–); French, Andrew
Donaldson (1951–) Music: South African traditional; arrangement, Anders Nyberg (1955–)

640

Softly and tenderly

THOMPSON 11 7 11 7 with refrain

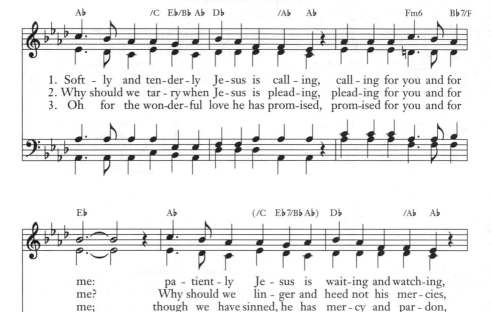

1. Soft - ly and ten-der-ly Je-sus is call - ing, call - ing for you and for
2. Why should we tar - ry when Je-sus is plead-ing, plead-ing for you and for
3. Oh for the won-der-ful love he has prom-ised, prom-ised for you and for

me: pa - tient-ly Je - sus is wait-ing and watch-ing,
me? Why should we lin - ger and heed not his mer - cies,
me; though we have sinned, he has mer - cy and par - don,

watch - ing for you and for me. "Come
mer - cies for you and for me?
par - don for you and for me.

Words: William J. Thompson (1847–1909) Music: William J. Thompson (1847–1909)

Words: public domain Music: public domain

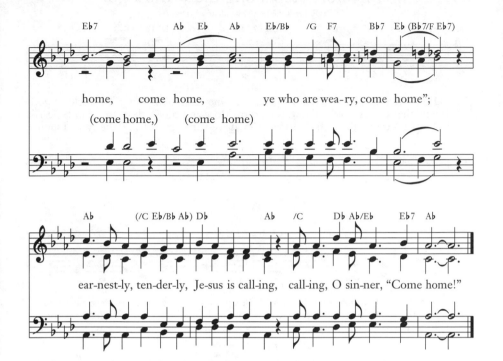

home, come home, ye who are wea-ry, come home";
(come home,) (come home)

ear-nest-ly, ten-der-ly, Je-sus is call-ing, call-ing, O sin-ner, "Come home!"

Discipleship

641 One more step along the world I go

SOUTHCOTE 9 9 9 7 9 with refrain (11 9)

1. One more step a-long the world I go. One more step a-long the world I go.
2. Round the cor-ners of the world I turn. More and more a-bout the world I learn.
3. As I trav-el through the bad and good keep me trav-el-ing the way I should.

From the old things to the new keep me trav-el-ing a-long with you.
All the new things that I see you'll be look-ing at a-long with me.
Where I see no way to go, you'll be tell-ing me the way, I know.

Refrain

And it's from the old I tra-vel to the new. Keep me trav-el-ing a-long with you.

4. Give me courage when the world is rough.
Keep me loving though the world is tough.
Leap and sing in all I do.
Keep me traveling along with you.
Refrain:

5. You are older than the world can be.
You are younger than the life in me.
Ever old and ever new,
keep me traveling along with you.
Refrain:

Words: Sydney Carter (1915–) Music: Sydney Carter (1915–)

642 O Master, let me walk with thee
MARYTON 8 8 8 8 LM

1. O Mas-ter, let me walk with thee in low-ly
2. Help me the slow of heart to move by some clear
3. Teach me thy pa-tience; still with thee in clos-er,
4. in hope that sends a shin-ing ray far down the

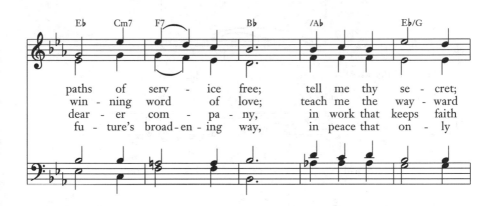

paths of serv-ice free; tell me thy se-cret;
win-ning word of love; teach me the way-ward
dear-er com-pa-ny, in work that keeps faith
fu-ture's broad-en-ing way, in peace that on-ly

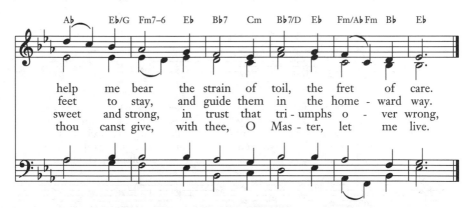

help me bear the strain of toil, the fret of care.
feet to stay, and guide them in the home-ward way.
sweet and strong, in trust that tri-umphs o-ver wrong,
thou canst give, with thee, O Mas-ter, let me live.

Words: Washington Gladden (1836–1918) Music: Henry Percy Smith (1825–1898)

Words: public domain Music: public domain

Discipleship

643

Lift high the cross

CRUCIFER 10 10 with refrain (10 10)

Descant

Lift high the cross, the love of Christ pro - claim

Unison
Refrain

C /E Dm (G7 F/A) G/B C (Am7) C/G D/F♯ Gsus4–3 /A

Lift high the cross, the love of Christ pro - claim

till all the world a - dore his sa - cred name.

G7/B C G7/D C/E Dm7 G6 F/A G/B (F/A G6) F6 Dm7 G7 Csus4–2 – 3   Fine

till all the world a - dore his sa - cred name.

Harmony
Em 7 A6 D /C G/B (Bm) C B Em Am/C B

1. Come, Chris - tians, fol - low where the Mas - ter trod,
2. Led on their way by this tri - um - phant sign,
3. Each new - born serv - ant of the Cru - ci - fied
4. O Lord, once lift - ed on the glo - rious tree,
5. So shall our song of tri - umph ev - er be:

Words: George William Kitchin (1827–1912); revisions, Michael Robert Newbolt (1874–1956)
Music: Sydney H. Nicholson (1875–1947); descant, Richard Proulx (1937–)

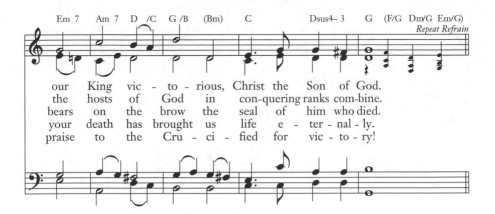

our King vic - to - rious, Christ the Son of God.
the hosts of God in con-quering ranks com-bine.
bears on the brow the seal of him who died.
your death has brought us life e - ter - nal - ly.
praise to the Cru - ci - fied for vic - to - ry!

644 May the mind of Christ my Saviour

ST. LEONARD'S 8 7 8 5

1. May the mind of Christ my Sav - iour live in me from day to day,
2. May the word of God dwell rich - ly in my heart from hour to hour,
3. May the peace of God my Sov-ereign rule my life in eve - ry-thing,
4. May the love of Je - sus fill me, as the wa - ters fill the sea;
5. May I run the race be - fore me, strong and brave to face the foe,

Je - sus' love and power con-trol-ling all I do or say.
so that all may see I tri-umph on - ly through God's power.
that I may be calm to com-fort sick and sor - row - ing.
Christ ex - al - ting, self de - ny - ing, this is vic - to - ry.
look-ing on - ly un - to Je - sus as I on - ward go.

Words: Katie B. Wilkinson (1859–1928) Music: A.C. Barham–Gould (1891–1953)

Follow me, the Master said

FOLLOW ME 7 6 7 6 7 7 7 6

1. "Fol - low me," the Mas - ter said:
2. Should the world and sin op-pose,
3. Though the way may dark ap-pear,
4. Ev - er keep that end in view;

we will fol-low Je - sus.

By his word and Spir - it led,
He is great-er than our foes;
He will make our path-way clear;
All his prom-is - es are true;

we will fol-low Je - sus.

Still for us he lives to plead, at the throne will in - ter - cede,
On his prom-ise we de-pend; he will hear us and de - fend,
In our dai - ly round of care, as we plead with God in prayer,
When this earth-ly course is run, and the Mas - ter says, "Well done!"

Words: anonymous, alt Music: anonymous

Words: public domain Music: public domain

of-fers help in time of need;
help and keep us to the end;
with the cross which we must bear, we will fol-low Je-sus.
life e-ter-nal we have won;

646   Lead me, Jesus; I will follow

LEAD ME, JESUS   Irregular

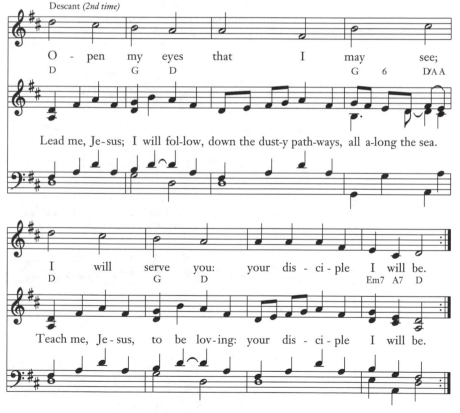

Descant (2nd time)

O-pen my eyes that I may see;

Lead me, Je-sus; I will fol-low, down the dust-y path-ways, all a-long the sea.

I will serve you: your dis-ci-ple I will be.

Teach me, Je-sus, to be lov-ing: your dis-ci-ple I will be.

Words: Ted Creen (1948–)   Music: Ted Creen (1948–)

Lead us, heavenly Father, lead us

MANNHEIM 878787

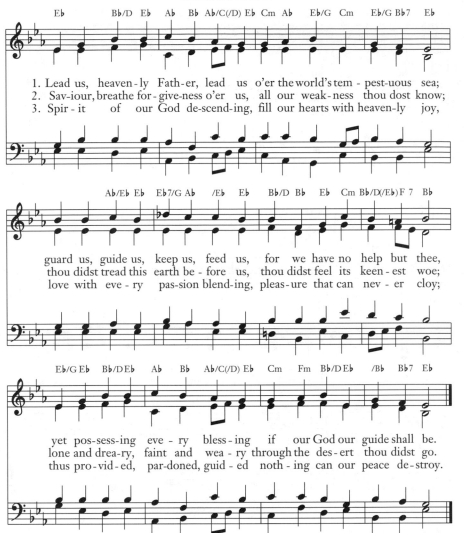

1. Lead us, heaven-ly Fath-er, lead us o'er the world's tem-pest-uous sea;
2. Sav-iour, breathe for-give-ness o'er us, all our weak-ness thou dost know;
3. Spir-it of our God de-scend-ing, fill our hearts with heaven-ly joy,

guard us, guide us, keep us, feed us, for we have no help but thee,
thou didst tread this earth be-fore us, thou didst feel its keen-est woe;
love with eve-ry pas-sion blend-ing, pleas-ure that can nev-er cloy;

yet pos-sess-ing eve-ry bless-ing if our God our guide shall be.
lone and drea-ry, faint and wea-ry through the des-ert thou didst go.
thus pro-vid-ed, par-doned, guid-ed noth-ing can our peace de-stroy.

Words: James Edmeston (1791–1867)   Music: Friedrich Filitz (1804–1876)

Words: public domain   Music: public domain

648

I'm gonna live so God can use me

I'M GONNA LIVE Irregular

Words: African-American spiritual   Music: African-American spiritual; arrangement, Wendell Whalum (1932–1987)

Words: public domain   Music: arrangement, copyright © the estate of Wendell Whalum

Discipleship
649

How clear is our vocation, Lord

REPTON 868866

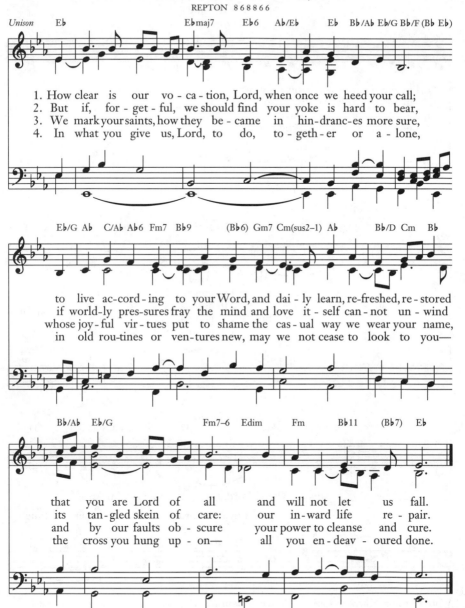

1. How clear is our vo-ca-tion, Lord, when once we heed your call;
2. But if, for-get-ful, we should find your yoke is hard to bear,
3. We mark your saints, how they be-came in hin-dranc-es more sure,
4. In what you give us, Lord, to do, to-geth-er or a-lone,

to live ac-cord-ing to your Word, and dai-ly learn, re-freshed, re-stored
if world-ly pres-sures fray the mind and love it-self can-not un-wind
whose joy-ful vir-tues put to shame the cas-ual way we wear your name,
in old rou-tines or ven-tures new, may we not cease to look to you—

that you are Lord of all and will not let us fall.
its tan-gled skein of care: our in-ward life re-pair.
and by our faults ob-scure your power to cleanse and cure.
the cross you hung up-on— all you en-deav-oured done.

Words: Fred Pratt Green (1903–)   Music: Charles Hubert Hastings Parry (1848–1918)

Words: copyright © 1982 by Hope Publishing Co.   Music: public domain

650

He leadeth me

HE LEADETH ME 8 8 8 8 LM with refrain

1. He lead - eth me: oh bless-ed thought! oh words with heaven-ly com-fort fraught!
2. Some-times 'mid scenes of deep-est gloom, some-times where E-den's flow-ers bloom,
3. Lord, I would clasp thy hand in mine, nor ev - er mur-mur nor re - pine,
4. And when my task on earth is done, when by thy grace the vic-tory's won,

What-e'er I do, wher-e'er I be still 'tis God's hand that lead-eth me.
by wa - ters still, o'er troub-led sea, still 'tis God's hand that lead-eth me!
con - tent, what-ev - er lot I see since 'tis my God that lead-eth me!
e'en death's cold wave I will not flee, since God through Jor - dan lead-eth me.

Refrain

He lead-eth me! He lead-eth me! By his own hand he lead-eth me!

A faith-ful fol-lower I would be, for 'tis God's hand that lead-eth me.

Words: Joseph Henry Gilmore (1834–1918)   Music: William Batchelder Bradbury (1816–1868)

Words: public domain   Music: public domain

651　Guide me, O thou great Redeemer

CWM RHONDDA 8 7 8 7 4 7 7 with repeats

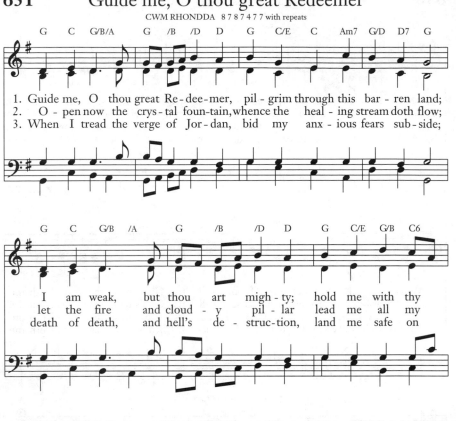

1. Guide me, O thou great Re-dee-mer, pil-grim through this bar-ren land;
2. O-pen now the crys-tal foun-tain, whence the heal-ing stream doth flow;
3. When I tread the verge of Jor-dan, bid my anx-ious fears sub-side;

I am weak, but thou art migh-ty; hold me with thy
let the fire and cloud-y pil-lar lead me all my
death of death, and hell's de-struc-tion, land me safe on

power-ful hand: bread of heav-en, bread of heav-en,
jour-ney through: strong de-liver-er, strong de-liver-er,
Ca-naan's side: songs of prais-es, songs of prais-es,

Words: Welsh, William Williams (1717–1791); translation, William Williams (1717–1791),
Peter Williams (1722–1796), alt   Music: John Hughes (1873–1932)

Words: public domain   Music: public domain

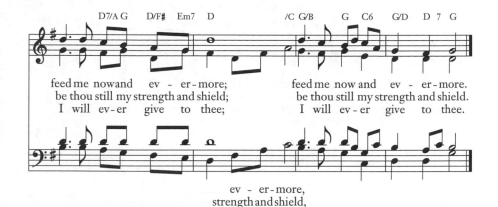

feed me now and ev - er - more;
be thou still my strength and shield;
I will ev - er give to thee;

feed me now and ev - er - more.
be thou still my strength and shield.
I will ev - er give to thee.

ev - er - more,
strength and shield,
give to thee.

652   Forth in thy name, O Lord, I go
CANONBURY 8 8 8 8 LM

1. Forth in thy name, O Lord, I go my dai - ly la - bour to pur - sue;
2. The task thy wis-dom hath as-signed oh let me cheer-ful - ly ful - fil;
3. Thee may I set at my right hand, whose eyes my in-most sub-stance see,
4. Give me to bear thy eas - y yoke, and eve - ry mo-ment watch and pray,

thee, on - ly thee, re - solved to know, in all I think, or speak, or do.
in all my works thy pres-ence find, and prove thy good and per-fect will.
and la-bour on at thy com-mand, and of - fer all my works to thee.
and still to things e - ter - nal look, and has-ten to thy glo-rious day.

Alternate tunes: Gonfalon Royal Song 34

Words: Charles Wesley (1707–1788) Music: Robert Schumann (1810–1856), alt

Words: public domain Music: public domain

653 Fill all my life, O Lord my God

SENNEN COVE 8 6 8 6 CM

1. Fill all my life, O Lord my God,
   in every part with praise,
   that my whole being may proclaim
   your being and your ways:

2. praise in the common things of life,
   our going out and in;
   praise in each duty and each deed,
   however small and plain.

3. Fill every part of me with praise,
   strong though I be or weak;
   of you and of your love, O Lord,
   let all my being speak;

4. then shall each part of day and night
   be sacred to the end,
   and all my life be fellowship
   with you, my Guide and Friend.

Words: Horatius Bonar (1808–1889)   Music: William H. Harris (1883–1973)

Words: public domain   Music: copyright © Oxford University Press from The BBC Hymn Book

654 O God of Bethel, by whose hand

SALZBURG (HAYDN) 8 6 8 6 CM

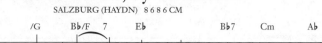
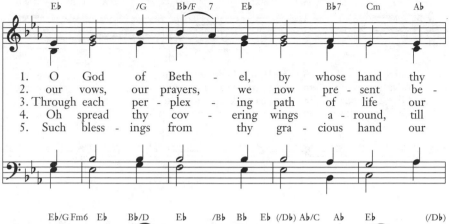

1. O God of Beth - el, by whose hand thy
2. our vows, our prayers, we now pre - sent be -
3. Through each per - plex - ing path of life our
4. Oh spread thy cov - ering wings a - round, till
5. Such bless - ings from thy gra - cious hand our

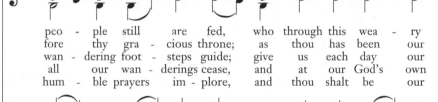

peo - ple still are fed, who through this wea - ry
fore thy gra - cious throne; as thou has been our
wan - dering foot - steps guide; give us each day our
all our wan - derings cease, and at our God's own
hum - ble prayers im - plore, and thou shalt be our

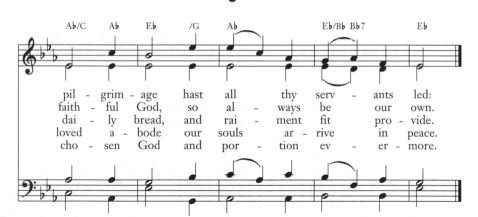

pil - grim - age hast all thy serv - ants led:
faith - ful God, so al - ways be our own.
dai - ly bread, and rai - ment fit pro - vide.
loved a - bode our souls ar - rive in peace.
cho - sen God and por - tion ev - er - more.

Alternate tune: Martyrdom

Words: Philip Doddridge (1702–1751), and John Logan (1748–1788), alt in Scottish Paraphrases 1781
Music: Johann Michael Haydn (1737–1806), alt

Words: public domain   Music: public domain

655

Give me oil in my lamp

GIVE ME OIL   10 8 10 9 with refrain (8 9 8 7)

1. Give me oil   in my lamp; keep me burn-ing; give me
2. Give me joy   in my heart; keep me prais-ing; give me
3. Give me peace in my heart; keep me lov-ing;   give me
4. Give me love in my heart; keep me serv-ing; give me

oil   in my lamp, I pray. Give me oil   in my lamp; keep me
joy   in my heart, I pray. Give me joy   in my heart; keep me
peace in my heart, I pray. Give me peace in my heart; keep me
love in my heart, I pray. Give me love in my heart; keep me

burn-ing;   keep me burn-ing till the break of day.
prais-ing; keep me prais-ing till the break of day.
lov-ing;   keep me lov-ing till the break of day.
serv-ing;   keep me serv-ing till the break of day.

Words: anonymous   Music: traditional; arrangement, Christian Strover (1932–)

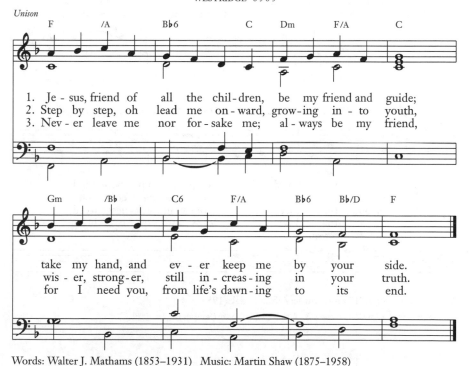

656   Jesus, friend of all the children

WESTRIDGE 8 5 8 3

Unison

1. Je - sus, friend of   all   the chil - dren,   be   my friend and   guide;
2. Step by step, oh   lead me on - ward, grow - ing in - to   youth,
3. Nev - er leave me   nor for - sake me;   al - ways be   my   friend,

take my hand, and   ev - er keep me   by   your   side.
wis - er, strong - er,   still in - creas - ing   in   your   truth.
for   I   need you,   from life's dawn - ing   to   its   end.

Words: Walter J. Mathams (1853–1931)   Music: Martin Shaw (1875–1958)

Discipleship

657

Woman in the night

NEW DISCIPLES   10 10 10 10 with refrain (10 9)

1. Wo-man in the night, spent from giv-ing birth,
2. Wo-man at the well, ques-tion the Mes-siah;
3. Wo-man in the house, nur-tured to be meek,
4. Wo-men on the hill, stand when men have fled;

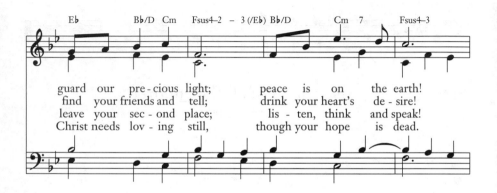

guard our pre-cious light; peace is on the earth!
find your friends and tell; drink your heart's de-sire!
leave your sec-ond place; lis-ten, think and speak!
Christ needs lov-ing still, though your hope is dead.

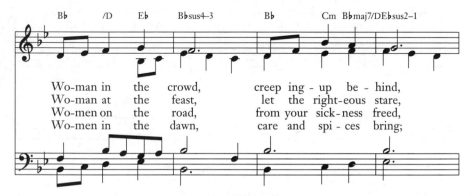

Wo-man in the crowd, creep ing-up be-hind,
Wo-man at the feast, let the right-eous stare,
Wo-men on the road, from your sick-ness freed,
Wo-men in the dawn, care and spi-ces bring;

Words: Brian Wren (1936–) Music: Alfred Fedak (1953–)

touch-ing is al-lowed; seek and you will find!
come and go in peace; love him with your hair!
wit-ness and pro-vide; join-ing word and deed.
ear-li-est to mourn; ear-li-est to sing!

Come and join the song, wom-en, chil-dren, men;

Je - sus makes us free to live a - gain!

658

By gracious powers
so wonderfully sheltered

DONNE SECOURS 11 10 11 10

1. By gra-cious powers so won-der-ful-ly shel-tered, and con-fi-dent-ly
2. Yet is this heart by its old foe tor-ment-ed, still e-vil days bring
3. And when this cup you give is filled to brim-ming with bit-ter sor-row,
4. Yet when a-gain in this same world you give us the joy we had, the

wait-ing come what may, we know that God is with us night and morn-ing,
bur-dens hard to bear; oh give our fright-ened souls the sure sal-va-tion,
hard to un-der-stand, we take it thank-ful-ly and with-out trem-bling,
bright-ness of your sun, we shall re-mem-ber all the days we lived through,

and nev-er fails to greet us each new day.
for which, O Lord, you taught us to pre-pare.
out of so good and so be-loved a hand.
and our whole life shall then be yours a-lone.

Words: Dietrich Bonhoeffer (1906–1945); English versification, Fred Pratt Green (1903–) Music:
Genevan Psalter (1551)

Words: versification, copyright © 1974 by Hope Publishing Co. Music: public domain

659 King of glory, King of peace

GWALCHMAI 7 4 7 4 D

1. King of glo - ry, King of peace, I will love thee,
2. Where-fore with my ut - most art, I will sing thee,
3. Seven whole days, not one in seven, I will praise thee;

and, that love may nev - er cease, I will move thee.
and the cream of all my heart I will bring thee.
in my heart, though not in heaven, I can raise thee.

Thou hast grant - ed my re - quest, thou hast heard me;
Though my sins a - gainst me cried, thou didst clear me,
Small it is, in this poor sort to en - rol thee:

thou didst note my work-ing breast; thou hast spared me.
and a - lone, when they re - plied, thou didst hear me.
e'en e - ter - ni - ty's too short to ex - tol thee.

Words: George Herbert (1593–1633) Music: Joseph David Jones (1827–1870)

Words: public domain Music: public domain

660 Prayer is the soul's sincere desire

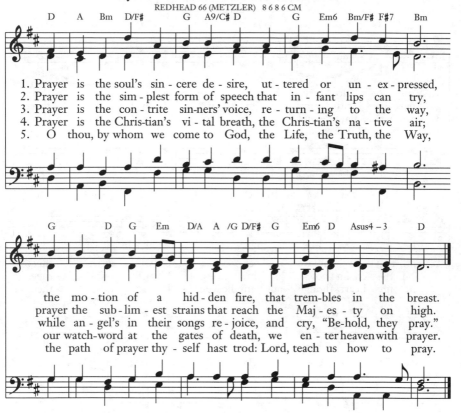

REDHEAD 66 (METZLER) 8 6 8 6 CM

1. Prayer is the soul's sin-cere de-sire, ut-tered or un-ex-pressed,
2. Prayer is the sim-plest form of speech that in-fant lips can try,
3. Prayer is the con-trite sin-ners' voice, re-turn-ing to the way,
4. Prayer is the Chris-tian's vi-tal breath, the Chris-tian's na-tive air;
5. O thou, by whom we come to God, the Life, the Truth, the Way,

the mo-tion of a hid-den fire, that trem-bles in the breast.
prayer the sub-lim-est strains that reach the Maj-es-ty on high.
while an-gel's in their songs re-joice, and cry, "Be-hold, they pray."
our watch-word at the gates of death, we en-ter heaven with prayer.
the path of prayer thy-self hast trod: Lord, teach us how to pray.

Alternate tune: St. Agnes, Durham

Words: James Montgomery (1771–1854) Music: Richard Redhead (1820–1901)

Words: public domain Music: public domain

661

We give thee but thine own

FRANCONIA 6 6 8 6 SM

1. We give thee but thine own, what - e'er the gift may be; all
2. May we thy boun-ties thus as stew-ards true re - ceive, and
3. To com-fort and to bless, to find a balm for woe, to
4. The cap-tive to re - lease, to God the lost to bring, to
5. and we be-lieve thy word, though dim our faith may be: what -

that we have is thine a - lone, a trust, O Lord, from thee.
glad-ly, as thou bless - est us, to thee our first-fruits give.
tend the lone-ly in dis - tress is an-gels' work be - low.
teach the way of life and peace, it is a Christ-like thing,
e'er for thine we do, O Lord, we do it un - to thee.

Words: William Walsham How (1823–1897) Music: König's harmonischer Liederschatz 1738;
arrangement, William Henry Havergal (1793–1870)

Words: public domain Music: public domain

662

Those who wait on the Lord

EAGLE'S WINGS Irregular

1., 6. Those who wait on the Lord
2. Those who serve the suf-fering world
3. Those who live the ris - en life shall re - new their strength;
4. Those who love the Mys - ter - y
5. Those who die on the march

they shall rise up on wings as ea - gles; they shall run and not be wea-ry;

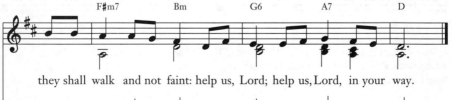

they shall walk and not faint: help us, Lord; help us, Lord, in your way.

Words: traditional   Music: traditional; arrangement, John L. Bell (1949–)

663 God, whose giving knows no ending

RUSTINGTON 8 7 8 7 D

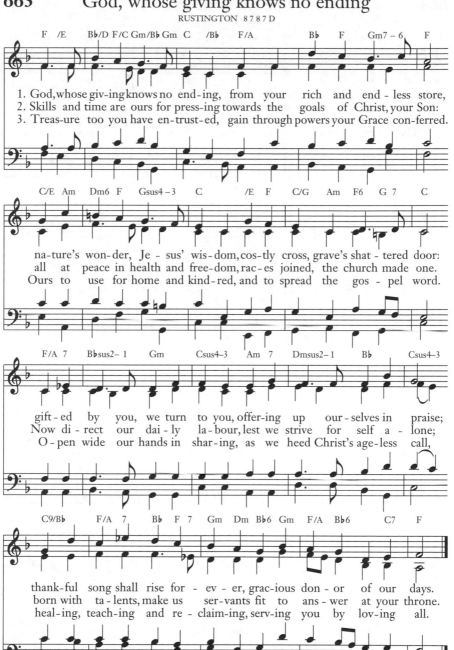

1. God, whose giv-ing knows no end-ing, from your rich and end-less store,
2. Skills and time are ours for press-ing towards the goals of Christ, your Son:
3. Treas-ure too you have en-trust-ed, gain through powers your Grace con-ferred.

na-ture's won-der, Je - sus' wis-dom, cos-tly cross, grave's shat - tered door:
all at peace in health and free-dom, rac - es joined, the church made one.
Ours to use for home and kind-red, and to spread the gos - pel word.

gift-ed by you, we turn to you, offer-ing up our-selves in praise;
Now di - rect our dai - ly la-bour, lest we strive for self a - lone;
O - pen wide our hands in shar-ing, as we heed Christ's age-less call,

thank-ful song shall rise for - ev - er, gra-cious don - or of our days.
born with ta - lents, make us ser-vants fit to ans - wer at your throne.
heal-ing, teach-ing and re - claim-ing, serv-ing you by lov-ing all.

Alternate tunes: Austria Beach Spring

Words: Robert L. Edwards (1915–) Music: Charles Hubert Hastings Parry (1848–1918)

664

The first one ever

BALLAD Irregular

1. The first one ev-er, oh, ev-er to know of the birth of Je-sus was the maid Ma-ry, was Ma-ry the maid of Gal-i-lee, and bless-ed is she, is she who be-lieves. Oh,

2. The first one ev-er, oh, ev-er to know of Mes-si-ah, Je-sus, when he said, "I am he," was the Sa-mar-i-tan wom-an who drew from the well, and bless-ed is she, is she who per-ceives. Oh,

3. The first ones ev-er, oh, ev-er to know of the ris-ing of Je-sus, his glo-ry to be, were Ma-ry, Jo-an-na and Mag-da-lene, and bless-ed are they, are they who see. Oh,

Words: Linda Wilberger Egan (1946–)   Music: Linda Wilberger Egan (1946–)

Words: copyright © Linda Wilberger Egan, 1980. 1983   Music: copyright © Linda Wilberger Egan, 1980, 1983

bless - ed is she who be - lieves in the Lord, oh,
bless - ed is she who per - ceives the Lord, oh,
bless - ed are they who see the Lord, oh,

bless - ed is she who be - lieves. She was
bless - ed is she who per - ceives. 'Twas the Sa -
bless - ed are they who see. They were

Ma - ry the maid of Gal - i - lee, and
mar - i - tan wom-an who drew from the well, and
Ma - ry, Jo - an - na and Mag - da - lene, and

bless - ed is she, is she who be - lieves.
bless - ed is she, is she who per - ceives.
bless - ed are they, are they who see.

665

Lord Jesus, you shall be my song

LES PETITES SOEURS 12 14 12 12

1. Lord Je - sus, you shall be my song as I jour - ney;
2. Lord Je - sus, I'll praise you as long as I jour - ney.
1. Jé - sus, je vou - drais te chan - ter sur ma rou - te;
2. Jé - sus, je vou - drais te lou - er sur ma rou - te;

I'll tell eve-ry-bod-y a - bout you wher-ev - er I go:
May all of my joy be a faith-ful re - flec-tion of you.
Jé - sus, je vou-drais t'an-non-cer à mes voi-sins par - tout,
Jé - sus, je vou-drais que ma voix soit l'é-cho de ta joie,

for our life and our peace and our love is your - self.
May the earth and the sea and the sky join my song.
car toi seul es la vie et la paix et l'a - mour:
et que chan - te la terre et que chan - te le ciel;

Words: Les Petites Soeurs de Jésus and L'Arche Community; translation, Stephen Somerville (1931–)
Music: Les Petites Soeurs de Jésus

Words: copyright © Les Petites Soeurs de Jésus; translation, copyright © Stephen Somerville, 1970 Music: copyright © Les Petites Soeurs de Jésus, 1987

Lord Je - sus, you shall be my song as I jour - ney.
Lord Je - sus, I'll praise you as long as I jour - ney.
Jé - sus, je vou - drais te chan - ter sur ma rou - te.
Jé - sus, je vou - drais te lou - er sur ma rou - te.

3. As long as I live, Jesus, make me your servant,
   to carry your cross and to share all your burdens and tears.
   For you saved me by giving your body and blood.
   As long as I live, Jesus, make me your servant.

4. I fear in the dark and the doubt of my journey;
   but courage will come with the sound of your steps by my side.
   And with all of the family you saved by your love,
   we'll sing to your dawn at the end of our journey.

3. Jésus, je voudrais te servir sur ma route,
   Jésus, je voudrais partager les souffrances de ta croix,
   car tu livres pour moi et ton corps et ton sang;
   Jésus, je voudrais te servir sur ma route.

4. Jésus, je voudrais tout au long de ma route,
   entendre tes pas résonner dans la nuit près de moi,
   jusqu'à l'aube du jour où ton peuple sauvé,
   Jésus, chantera ton retour sur ma route.

666

Living God, your joyful Spirit

REX GLORIAE 8 7 8 7 D

1. Liv - ing God, your joy - ful Spir - it breaks the bounds of time and space,
2. As your bread may we be bro - ken, scat - tered in com - mu - ni - ty;
3. Lord, when we grow tired of giv - ing, feel frus - tra - tion, hurt and strain,
4. Liv - ing God, your power sur-rounds us, as we face the way Christ trod,

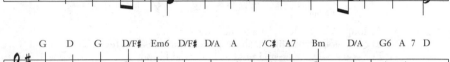

rests in love up - on your peo - ple, drawn to - geth - er in this place.
we who know your great - est bless-ings called to share Christ's min - is - try.
by your Spir - it's quiet com - pul - sion, draw us back to you a - gain.
chal-lenge us to fresh com - mit-ment to the pur - pos - es of God:

Here we join in glad thanks-giv - ing, here re - joice to pray and praise:
May we gen - tly lead each oth - er, share our hun - ger and our thirst;
Guide us through the bit - ter search-ing when our con - fi - dence is lost;
called to share a new cre - a - tion, called to preach a liv - ing word,

Alternate tune: Abbot's Leigh

Words: Jill Jenkins (1937–) Music: Henry T. Smart (1813–1879)

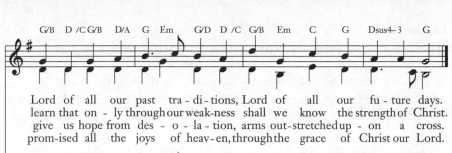

Lord of all our past tra-di-tions, Lord of all our fu-ture days.
learn that on-ly through our weak-ness shall we know the strength of Christ.
give us hope from des-o-la-tion, arms out-stretched up-on a cross.
prom-ised all the joys of heav-en, through the grace of Christ our Lord.

667 God, you touch the earth with beauty

GLEN BERNARD 8 5 8 5

1. God, you touch the earth with beau-ty; make my heart a-new;
2. Like your springs and run-ning wa-ters, make me crys-tal pure;
3. Like your danc-ing waves in sun-light, make me glad and free;
4. Like the arch-ing of the heav-ens, lift my thoughts a-bove;
5. God, you touch the earth with beau-ty; make my heart a-new;

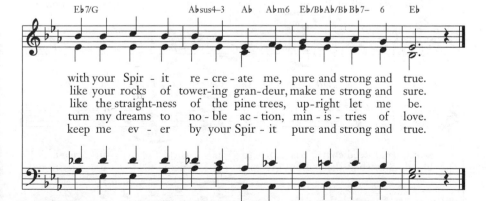

with your Spir-it re-cre-ate me, pure and strong and true.
like your rocks of tow-er-ing gran-deur, make me strong and sure.
like the straight-ness of the pine trees, up-right let me be.
turn my dreams to no-ble ac-tion, min-is-tries of love.
keep me ev-er by your Spir-it pure and strong and true.

Words: Mary S. Edgar (1889–1973) Music: James Edmund Jones (1866–1939)

668

Give us this day our daily bread

BARBARA 12 12 12 12

1. Give us this day our dai - ly bread: this is our prayer.
2. We thank you, Lord, for joy and peace, for lov - ing care.

If by your grace you give us more, Lord, help us share.
As you have loved us, help us, Lord, your love to share.

We are your voice, your hands, your feet; use us to show in
Then we will tell of liv - ing bread: of Je - sus Christ, whose

word and deed com - pas - sion to a world in need.
blood was shed that hun - gry peo - ple might be fed.

Words: Helen Otte (1931–) Music: Harold W. Friedell (1905–1958)

Words: copyright © CRC Publications, 1987 Music: copyright © Belwin-Mills Publishing Corp., 1961

And Jesus said our God
is like a shepherd

AND JESUS SAID Irregular

1. And Je-sus said, our God is like a shep-herd who has lost a sheep, and
2. And Je-sus said, our God is like a wo-man who has lost a coin. She
3. And Je-sus said, our God is like a fath-er who has lost a son. He

leav-ing all the rest, he searched un - til he
lit a lamp and searched all night un - til she
wait-ed eve-ry day for him un - til his

found what had been lost. "Re-joice," he cried, "I've found the
found what had been lost. "Re-joice," she cried, "I've found the
son re-turned to him. "Re-joice," he cried, "my son came

lost!
lost! Re - joice, re - joice with me, re - joice."
home!

Words: Gracia Grindal (1943–) Music: Joy F. Patterson (1931–)

670

Amazing grace

NEW BRITAIN 8 6 8 6 CM

1. A - maz - ing grace, how sweet the sound
2. 'Twas grace that taught my heart to fear
3. Through man - y dan - gers, toils and snares,
1. Grâce in - fi - nie de no - tre Dieu
2. Ma vie fut com - plète - ment chan - gée

that saved a wretch like me! I once was lost,
and grace my fears re - lieved; how pre - cious did
I have al - read - y come; 'tis grace has brought
qui un jour m'a sau - vé. J'é - tais per - du,
du mo - ment où j'ai cru. De - puis ce jour

but now am found, was blind, but now I see.
that grace ap - pear the hour I first be - lieved.
me safe thus far, and grace will lead me home.
er - rant de lieu en lieu quand il m'a re - trou - vé.
de tous les dan - gers, sa grâ - ce m'a se - cou - ru.

Words: John Newton (1725–1807); v.5, A Collection of Sacred Ballads 1790; v.6, William Cowper (1731–1800) Music: anonymous

Words: public domain Music: public domain

4. The Lord has promised good to me:
   this word my hope secures;
   God will my shield and portion be,
   as long as life endures.

5. What thanks I owe you, and what love—
   a boundless, endless store—
   shall echo through the realms above
   when time shall be no more.

6. When we've been there ten thousand years,
   bright shining as the sun,
   we've no less days to sing God's praise than
   when we'd first begun.

3. Dans mes épreuves et mes labeurs
   suffisante est sa grâce.
   Je peux toujours compter sa faveur
   à chaque heure qui passe.

4. Quand nous aurons pendant mille ans
   célébré ses louanges,
   nous pourrons comme au commencement,
   lui offrir nos hommages.

Chinese (Mandarin)

1. Qí yì ēn diǎn! Hé děng gān tián!
   Wǒ zuì yě dé shè miǎn!
   Qián wǒ shī sàng, jīn bèi xún huí;
   Xiā yān jīn dè kàn jiàn.

Cree

1. Mamaskach sakihiwewin
   Kapimachihiwet
   Pikwataw nikiwaihon
   Anoch maka niwap

Mohawk

1. Ioh ne ra a kwat ra o ten raht
   ne se wa ah tsia tah kwen
   wa ka a tsia a tah ton ha tie es kwe
   ses ha tsia a tah tsen rion.

Ojibway

1. Kihcishawencikewin
   kaapimaaci' ikoyaan
   Ninkakippiinkwenaapan hsa
   Nookom itahsh niwaap

671

I heard the voice of Jesus say

KINGSFOLD 8 6 8 6 D CMD

1. I heard the voice of Je - sus say, "Come un - to me and
2. I heard the voice of Je - sus say, "Be - hold, I free - ly
3. I heard the voice of Je - sus say, "I am this dark world's

rest; lay down, thou wea - ry one, lay down thy
give the liv - ing wa - ter; thirst - y one, stoop
light; look un - to me, thy morn shall rise, and

head up - on my breast!" I came to Je - sus as I was,
down, and drink and live!" I came to Je - sus, and I drank
all thy day be bright." I looked to Je - sus, and I found

wea - ry and worn and sad; I found in him a
of that life - giv - ing stream; my thirst was quenched, my
in him my star, my sun, and in that light of

Words: Horatius Bonar (1808–1889)   Music: English traditional; arrangement, Ralph Vaughan Williams (1872–1958)

Words: public domain   Music: arrangement, copyright © Oxford University Press

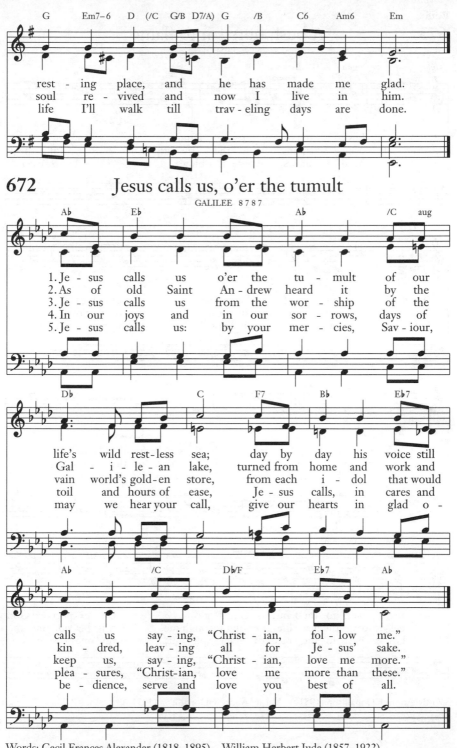

672   Jesus calls us, o'er the tumult

GALILEE 8 7 8 7

Words: Cecil Frances Alexander (1818–1895), William Herbert Jude (1857–1922)

Words: public domain Music: public domain

673

A bush bursts into flame

BURNING BUSH Irregular

1. A bush bursts in - to flame, and the Lord calls a shep - herd by his name; so God calls us, if we will hear. I watch for the flame, I turn my face to the flame of God's glo - ry. Un - ex - pect - ed God

2. Son of Man stands in the riv - er; John the Bap-tist lays hands on him in love; as a dove, the Spir- it comes on him. I come to the wa - ter, cel - e-brate the new life flow-ing through me, Christ be-side me to

3. The wind blows where it blows; who can say where it comes from, where it goes? So is eve - ry-one born of the Spir - it. I wait for the wind; I'm a - live to the voice of the Spir - it, no one sees it, yet

Words: Andrew Donaldson (1951–) Music: Andrew Donaldson (1951–)

Words: copyright © Andrew Donaldson, 1987 Music: copyright © Andrew Donaldson, 1987

en - ters my sto-ry,   I know that God will   call   me by name.
guide me, re-new me,   I know that God has called me by name.   In the com-pa-ny of
still   I can hear it,   I wait for God to   call   me by name.

I fol-low the flame.
all who call on the Lord, I come to the wa - ter.   In the com-pa-ny of all who
I wait for the wind.

I   fol-low,   I   fol-low the flame
call on the Lord,   I   come,   I come to the wa - ter.
I   wait,   I wait for the wind.

In the bulb there is a flower

PROMISE 8 7 8 7 D

Unison

1. In the bulb there is a flow - er, in the seed, an ap-ple tree,
2. There's a song in eve-ry si - lence, seek-ing word and mel-o - dy;
3. In our end is our be-gin - ning, in our time, in - fin-i - ty;

in co-coons, a hid-den prom-ise: but - ter - flies will soon be free!
there's a dawn in eve-ry dark-ness, bring-ing hope to you and me.
in our doubt there is be - liev - ing, in our life, e - ter - ni - ty,

In the cold and snow of win - ter there's a spring that waits to be,
From the past will come the fu - ture; what it holds, a mys-ter - y,
in our death, a res - ur - rec - tion, at the last, a vic - to - ry,

un - re - vealed un - til its sea - son, some-thing God a-lone can see.

Words: Natalie Sleeth (1930–1992) Music: Natalie Sleeth (1930–1992)

Faith

675

Precious Lord, take my hand

PRECIOUS LORD Irregular

1. Pre-cious Lord, take my hand, lead me on, let me
2. When my way grows drear, pre-cious Lord, lin-ger
3. When the dark-ness ap-pears and the night draws

stand; I am tired, I am weak, I am worn;
near; when my life is al-most gone,
near, and the day is past and gone,

through the storm, through the night, lead me on to the
hear my cry, hear my call; hold my hand lest I
at the riv-er I stand, guide my feet, hold my

light:
fall: take my hand, pre-cious Lord, lead me home.
hand:

Words: Thomas A. Dorsey (1899–1993)   Music: Thomas A. Dorsey (1899–1993)

676

Jesus, lover of my soul

ABERYSTWYTH 7 7 7 7 D

1. Je-sus, lov-er of my soul, let me to thy bos-om fly,
2. Oth-er ref-uge have I none; hangs my help-less soul on thee.
3. Thou, O Christ, art all I want; more than all in thee I find:
4. Plen-teous grace with thee is found, grace to cov-er all my sin;

while the near-er wa-ters roll, while the tem-pest
Leave, ah! leave me not a - lone; still sup-port and
raise the fal-len, cheer the faint, heal the sick and
let the heal-ing streams a - bound; make and keep me

still is high: hide me, O my Sav-iour, hide,
com-fort me. All my trust on thee is stayed;
lead the blind. Just and ho - ly is thy name;
pure with - in: thou of life the foun - tain art,

Words: Charles Wesley (1707–1788) Music: Joseph Parry (1841–1903)

Words: public domain Music: public domain

till the storm of life is past, safe in - to the
all my help from thee I bring; cov - er my de -
I am all un - right - eous - ness: false and full of
free - ly let me take of thee; spring thou up with -

ha - ven guide; oh re - ceive my soul at last.
fence - less head with the shad - ow of thy wing.
sin I am; thou art full of truth and grace.
in my heart, rise to all e - ter - ni - ty.

My faith looks up to thee

OLIVET 6646664

1. My faith looks up to thee, thou Lamb of Cal - va - ry,
2. May thy rich grace im - part strength to my faint - ing heart;
3. While life's dark maze I tread, and griefs a - round me spread,
4. When ends life's tran - sient dream, when death's cold sul - len stream

Sav - iour di - vine: now hear me when I pray; take all my
my zeal in - spire; as thou hast died for me, oh may my
be thou my guide; bid dark-ness turn to day, wipe sor-row's
shall o'er me roll, blest Sav-iour, then, in love, fear and dis-

guilt a - way; oh let me from this day be whol - ly thine.
love to thee pure, warm and change-less be, a liv - ing fire.
tears a - way, nor let me ev - er stray from thee a - side.
trust re-move; oh bear me safe a-bove, a ran-somed soul.

Words: Ray Palmer (1808–1887) Music: Lowell Mason (1792–1872);
harmony, Carman H. Milligan (1909–)

Words: public domain Music: harmony, copyright © Carman H. Milligan

678   I greet thee, who my sure Redeemer art

TOULON 10 10 10 10

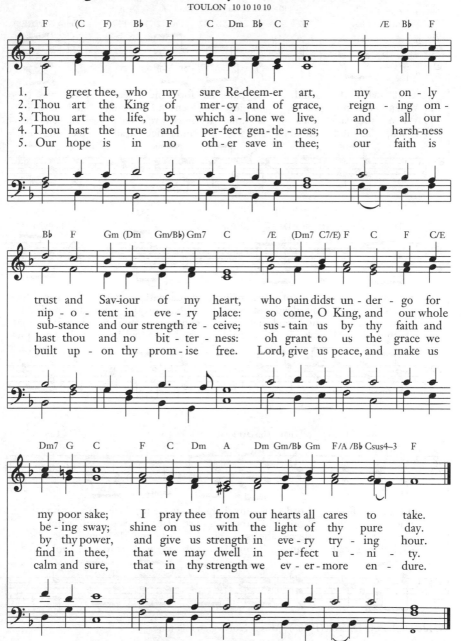

1. I greet thee, who my sure Re-deem-er art, my on-ly
2. Thou art the King of mer-cy and of grace, reign-ing om-
3. Thou art the life, by which a-lone we live, and all our
4. Thou hast the true and per-fect gen-tle-ness; no harsh-ness
5. Our hope is in no oth-er save in thee; our faith is

trust and Sav-iour of my heart, who pain didst un-der-go for
nip-o-tent in eve-ry place: so come, O King, and our whole
sub-stance and our strength re-ceive; sus-tain us by thy faith and
hast thou and no bit-ter-ness: oh grant to us the grace we
built up-on thy prom-ise free. Lord, give us peace, and make us

my poor sake; I pray thee from our hearts all cares to take.
be-ing sway; shine on us with the light of thy pure day.
by thy power, and give us strength in eve-ry try-ing hour.
find in thee, that we may dwell in per-fect u-ni-ty.
calm and sure, that in thy strength we ev-er-more en-dure.

Words: John Calvin (1509–1564); translation, Elizabeth Lee Smith (1817–1898)
Music: French Psalter, Strasbourg 1545

Words: public domain Music: public domain

679 God, when I stand

PRINCESS EUGENIE 10 10 10 10

1. God, when I stand, no path be-fore me clear, when eve-ry
2. When all my prayers no ans-wer seem to bring, and there is
3. When the dark lord of lone-li-ness pre-vails, and, all de-
4. When, as did Thom-as, I pre-sume thee dead, feel-ing and

prayer seems pris-oner of my pain, come with a gen-tle-ness which
si-lence in my deep-est soul, when in the wil-der-ness I
feat-ed, joy and friend-ship die, come, be my joy, such love that
faith it-self with-in me cold, fresh-en my lips with wine, my

calms my fear; Lord of my help-less-ness, my vic-tory gain.
find no spring, Lord of the des-ert plac-es, keep me whole.
nev-er fails; pierce the self-pit-y of my shad-owed sky.
soul with bread; ban-ish my po-ver-ty with heav-en's gold.

Words: Herbert O'Driscoll (1928–) Music: Norwegian folk tune

Words: copyright © T. Herbert O'Driscoll Music: public domain

680 Christ, of all my hopes the ground

MOZART 7 7 7 7

1. Christ, of all my hopes the ground, Christ, the
2. Let thy love my heart in - flame; keep thy
3. Foun - tain of o'er - flow - ing grace, free - ly
4. Thus, O God, an en - trance give to thy

spring of all my joy, still in thee may
fear be - fore my sight; be thy praise my
from thy full - ness give; as I run this
cit - y, draw - ing nigh; hav - ing known it

I be found; still for thee my powers em - ploy.
high - est aim; be thy smile my chief de - light.
earth - ly race, may I prove it Christ to live.
Christ to live, let me know it gain to die.

Words: Ralph Wardlaw (1779–1853) Music: Wolfgang Amadeus Mozart (1756–1791)

Words: public domain Music: public domain

681

We have heard a joyful sound

JESUS SAVES 76767776

1. We have heard a joy-ful sound,
2. Waft it on the roll-ing tide,
3. Sing a-bove the bat-tle's strife,
4. Give the winds a might-y voice,

Je - sus saves, Je - sus saves!

Spread the glad-ness all a-round:
Tell to sin-ners far and wide,
By his death and end-less life,
Let the na-tions now re-joice:

Je - sus saves! Je - sus saves!

Bear the news to eve-ry land, climb the steeps and cross the waves;
Sing, ye is-lands of the sea, ech-o back, ye o-cean's caves;
Sing it soft-ly through the gloom, when the heart for mer-cy craves;
Shout sal-va-tion full and free to eve-ry strand that o-cean laves;

on-ward! 'tis our Lord's com-mand:
earth shall keep her ju-bi-lee:
sing in tri-umph o'er the tomb,
this our song of vic-to-ry,

Je - sus saves! Je - sus saves!

Words: Priscilla Jane Owens (1829–1907) Music: William James Kirkpatrick (1838–1921)

Words: public domain Music: public domain

682 Just as I am, without one plea

WOODWORTH 8 8 8 8

1. Just as I am, with-out one plea, but that thy
2. Just as I am, though tossed a-bout with man-y a
3. Just as I am, poor, wretch-ed, blind; sight,rich-es,
4. Just as I am, thou wilt re-ceive, wilt wel-come,

blood was shed for me, and that thou bid-dest me
con-flict, man-y a doubt, fight-ings and fears with-
heal-ing of the mind, yea, all I need in
par-don, cleanse, re-lieve; be-cause thy prom-ise

come to thee,
in, with-out,
thee I find, O Lamb of God, I come, I come.
I be-lieve,

5. Just as I am, thy love unknown
has broken every barrier down.
Now to be thine, yea, thine alone,
O Lamb of God, I come, I come.

6. Just as I am of that free love
the breadth, length, depth and height to prove,
here for a season, then above,
O Lamb of God, I come, I come.

Words: Charlotte Elliott (1789–1871)   Music: William Batchelder Bradbury (1816–1868)

683 I know not why such wondrous grace

ELNATHA 8 6 8 6 with refrain (9 10 8 7)

1. I know not why such won-drous grace to me God has made
2. I know not why this sav-ing faith to me God did im-
3. I know not how the Spir-it moves, con-vinc-ing me of

known; nor why, un-worth-y as I am, Christ
part, nor how be-liev-ing in the word brought
sin, re-veal-ing Je-sus through the word, cre-

claimed me for his own,
peace in-to my heart, but I know whom I have be-
at-ing faith in him,

liev-ed and am per-suad-ed that Christ is a-ble to

Words: Daniel W. Whittle (1840–1901) Music: James McGranahan (1840–1907)

Words: public domain Music: public domain

keep that which I've com-mit-ted un-to him a-gainst that day.

684 Glory to the Father

GLORIA PATRI (WEAVER) Irregular

Glo-ry to the Fa-ther, and to the

Son, and to the Ho-ly Spir-it: as it was in the be - gin-ning, is

now, and will be for - ev - er. A-men. A - men. A - men.

Words: traditional   Music: John Weaver (1937–)

Words: public domain   Music: copyright © John Weaver, 1978

685

How firm a foundation

ST. DENIO 11 11 11 11

1. How firm a foun - da - tion, ye saints of the Lord,
2. "Fear not, I am with thee; oh be not dis - mayed!
3. "When through the deep wa - ters I call thee to go,
4. "When through fi - ery tri - als thy path - way shall lie,
5. "The soul that on Je - sus hath leaned for re - pose

is laid for your faith in God's ex - cel - lent word!
For I am thy God, and will still give thee aid;
the riv - ers of woe shall not thee o - ver - flow,
my grace, all - suf - fi - cient, shall be thy sup - ply:
I will not— I will not— de - sert to his foes;

What more can God say than to you hath been said,
I'll strength-en thee, help thee, and cause thee to stand
for I will be with thee, thy trou - bles to bless,
the flames shall not hurt thee; I on - ly de - sign
that soul, though all hell should en - deav - our to shake,

Alternate tune: Foundation

Words: K in Rippon's Selection of Hymns 1787   Music: Welsh hymn

Words: public domain   Music: public domain

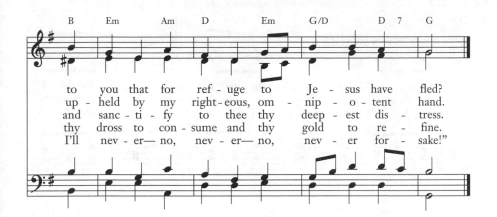

| B | Em | Am | D | Em | G/D | D 7 | G |

to   you   that   for   ref - uge   to   Je - sus   have   fled?
up - held   by   my   right - eous,   om - nip - o - tent   hand.
and   sanc - ti - fy   to   thee   thy   deep - est   dis - tress.
thy   dross   to   con - sume   and   thy   gold   to   re - fine.
I'll   nev - er— no,   nev - er— no,   nev - er   for - sake!"

686   How firm a foundation
FOUNDATION 11 11 11 11

| G (C/G) | C | G/B | G | | D | G (C/G) | C | G/B | Em | G/D | D | | G |

| D/F# | Em | C6 | C | G | | D | G (C/G) | G | C | G/B | Em | G/D | D 7 | G |

Alternate tune: St. Denio

Words: K in Rippon's Selection of Hymns 1787   Music: American Folk melody

Words: public domain   Music: public domain

687 Blessed assurance, Jesus is mine

ASSURANCE 9 10 9 9 with refrain (9 9 9 9)

1. Bless-ed as - sur - ance, Je - sus is mine! Oh what a fore - taste of glo - ry di - vine! Heir of sal - va - tion, pur-chase of God, born of his Spir - it, washed in his blood.
2. Per-fect sub - mis - sion, per-fect de - light, vi - sions of rap - ture now burst on my sight; an - gels de-scend - ing bring from a - bove ech - oes of mer - cy, whis-pers of love.
3. Per-fect sub - mis - sion, all is at rest; I in my Sav - iour am hap-py and blest, watch-ing and wait - ing, look - ing a - bove, filled with his good - ness, lost in his love.

Words: Fanny J. Crosby (1820–1915) Music: Phoebe Knapp (1839–1908)

Words: public domain Music: public domain

Refrain

This is my sto - ry; this is my song:
prais - ing my Sav - iour all the day long;
this is my sto - ry; this is my song:
prais - ing my Sav - iour all the day long.

688

As water to the thirsty

OASIS 767666446

1. As wa - ter to the thirst - y, as beau - ty to the eyes, as
2. Like calm in place of clam - our, like peace that fol-lows pain, like
3. As sleep that fol-lows fe - ver, as gold in-stead of grey, as

strength that fol-lows weak - ness, as truth in-stead of lies, as
meet - ing af - ter part - ing, like sun - shine af - ter rain, like
free - dom af - ter bond - age, as sun - rise to the day, as

song-time and spring-time and sum - mer-time to be,
moon-light and star - light and sun - light on the sea, so
home to the trav - eler and all we long to see,

Words: Timothy Dudley–Smith (1926–) Music: Brian T. Coleman (1920–)

is my Lord, my liv-ing Lord, so is my Lord to me.

Am   Dmsus2–1   Gm   Csus2 – 1   B♭ F/A Gm7   C7   F

Instrumental or vocalized Descant

689 Simply trusting every day

TRUSTING JESUS 7 7 7 7 with refrain

1. Sim-ply trust-ing eve-ry day, trust-ing through a storm-y way,
2. Bright-ly doth his Spir-it shine in-to this poor heart of mine;
3. Sing-ing, if my way be clear, pray-ing, if the path be drear,
4. Trust-ing him while life shall last, trust-ing him till earth be past,

e-ven when my faith is small, trust-ing Je-sus, that is all.
while he leads I can-not fall, trust-ing Je-sus, that is all.
if in dan-ger for him call, trust-ing Je-sus, that is all.
till with-in the jas-per wall, trust-ing Je-sus, that is all.

Refrain

Trust-ing as the mo-ments fly, trust-ing as the days go by,

trust-ing him what-e'er be-fall, trust-ing Je-sus, that is all.

Words: Edgar Page Stites (1836–1921) Music: Ira David Sankey (1840–1908)

Words: public domain Music: public domain

690

Fight the good fight

PENTECOST 8888 LM

1. Fight the good fight with all your might; Christ is your strength and Christ your right; lay hold on life, and it shall be your joy and crown e - ter - nal - ly.
2. Run the straight race through God's good grace; lift up your eyes and seek God's face; the way of life be - fore you lies; Christ is the path and Christ the prize.
3. Cast care a - side; lean on your guide; his bound-less mer - cy will pro - vide; trust, and your trust - ing soul shall prove Christ is its life and Christ its love.
4. Faint not nor fear, those arms are near, and, chang-ing not, still hold you dear; hope and be - lieve, and you shall find Christ is your all: heart, strength and mind.

Words: John Samuel Bewley Monsell (1811–1875), alt Music: William Boyd (1847–1928)

Words: public domain Music: public domain

691 My shepherd is the King of love

DOMINUS REGIT ME 8 7 8 7

1. My shep - herd is the King of love whose
good - ness fails me nev - er; for all things good from
God a - bove re - store my soul for - ev - er.

2. Where streams of liv - ing wa - ter flow, my
ran - somed soul is guid - ed, and where the ver - dant
pas - tures grow, with heaven - ly food pro - vid - ed.

3. Per - verse and fool - ish oft I strayed, but
yet in love you sought me, and on your shoul - der
gen - tly laid, and home, re - joic - ing, brought me.

4. In death's dark vale I fear no ill, with
you, dear Lord, be - side me; your rod and staff my
com - fort still, your cross be - fore to guide me.

5. You spread a table in my sight,
anointing grace bestowing,
and, oh, what rapture of delight:
your cup is overflowing.

6. And so through all the length of days
your goodness fails me never;
Good Shepherd, may I sing your praise
within your house forever!

Alternate tune: St. Columba

Words: Psalm 23, paraphrase Henry Williams Baker (1821–1877), alt
Music: John Bacchus Dykes (1823–1876)

Love

692
Where charity and love prevail
TWENTY-FOURTH 8 6 8 6 CM

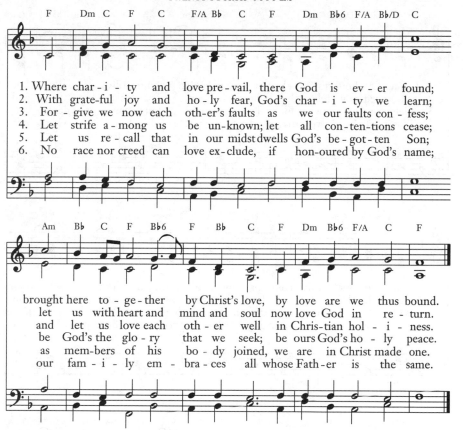

1. Where char-i-ty and love pre-vail, there God is ev-er found;
2. With grate-ful joy and ho-ly fear, God's char-i-ty we learn;
3. For-give we now each oth-er's faults as we our faults con-fess;
4. Let strife a-mong us be un-known; let all con-ten-tions cease;
5. Let us re-call that in our midst dwells God's be-got-ten Son;
6. No race nor creed can love ex-clude, if hon-oured by God's name;

brought here to-ge-ther by Christ's love, by love are we thus bound.
let us with heart and mind and soul now love God in re-turn.
and let us love each oth-er well in Chris-tian hol-i-ness.
be God's the glo-ry that we seek; be ours God's ho-ly peace.
as mem-bers of his bo-dy joined, we are in Christ made one.
our fam-i-ly em-bra-ces all whose Fath-er is the same.

Words: Latin; translation, Omer Westendorf (1916–) Music: Lucius Chapin (19th cent.)

693 Come, O thou traveler unknown

CANDLER 8 8 8 8 LMD

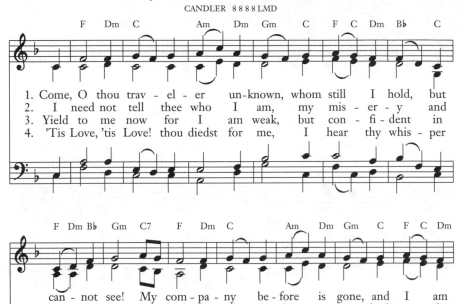

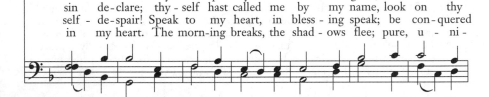

1. Come, O thou trav - el - er un-known, whom still I hold, but can - not see! My com - pa - ny be - fore is gone, and I am left a - lone with thee. With thee all night I mean to stay, and

2. I need not tell thee who I am, my mis - er - y and sin de-clare; thy-self hast called me by my name, look on thy hands and read it there. But who, I ask thee, who art thou? Tell

3. Yield to me now for I am weak, but con - fi - dent in self - de-spair! Speak to my heart, in bless - ing speak; be con - quered by my in - stant prayer. Speak, or thou nev - er hence shalt move, and

4. 'Tis Love, 'tis Love! thou diedst for me, I hear thy whis - per in my heart. The morn-ing breaks, the shad - ows flee; pure, u - ni - ver - sal love thou art. To me, to all, thy mer - cies move; thy

Alternate tune: Carey's (Surrey)

Words: Charles Wesley (1707–1788)   Music: Carlton R. Young (1926–)

Words: public domain   Music: harmony, copyright © Abingdon Press, 1964

| | | | | |
|Gm/Bb|F/A|Gm7 Am Bbmaj7 C|C7|F Dm C|

wres - tle till the break of day. With thee all night I
me thy name and tell me now. But who, I ask thee,
tell me if thy name is Love. Speak, or thou nev - er
na - ture and thy name is Love. To me, to all, thy

| | | | | | | | | | | |
|Acn|Dm|Gm|C|F C|Dm|Gm|Bb|C Bb|Gm7|F|

mean to stay, and wres - tle till the break of day.
who art thou? Tell me thy name and tell me now.
hence shalt move, and tell me if thy name is Love.
mer - cies move; thy na - ture and thy name is Love.

694   This is my commandment

THIS IS MY COMMANDMENT   Irregular

May be sung as a round.

① F   ②

This is my com-mand-ment, that you love one an-oth-er that your

③   C7   1., last time   2.
         F   *Fine*   F   C7

joy may be full. full, that your joy may be

F   C7   *D.C.*

full, that your joy may be full.

Words: John 15:11–12   Music: anonymous

Words: public domain   Music: public domain

Although I speak with angel's tongue

SHE'S LIKE THE SWALLOW 8 8 8 8 LM

1. Al - though I speak with an - gel's tongue, my faith, my
2. For love is pa - tient, love is kind and nev - er
3. For now we peer at dark - ened glass; our vi - sions
4. The gifts, are man-y the bo - dy one, and in - to

knowl - edge all sur - pass, but have no love, my
vain with boast - ing pride; love bears all things, all
end; our tongues all cease. In part we know, in
one are all bap - tized. Be - lov - ed, share one

gifts are vain as clang - ing gong or blar - ing brass.
things en - dures. All things must end; love will a - bide.
part now see: then we will see Love face to face.
heart, one mind, one hope, one faith, one love in Christ.

Alternate tune: O Waly Waly

Words: 1 Corinthians 13; paraphrase, Andrew Donaldson (1951–) Music: Canadian traditional;
arrangement, Andrew Donaldson (1951–)

Words: paraphrase, copyright © Andrew Donaldson, 1995 Music: arrangement, copyright © Andrew Donaldson, 1997

696

In suffering love

BELMONT 8 6 5 9

1. In suf - fering love the thread of life is wo - ven through our care, for God is with us: not a - lone our pain and toil we bear.
2. There is a rock, a place se - cure with - in the storm's cold blast; con - cealed with - in the suf - fering night God's co - ve - nant stands fast.
3. In love's deep womb our fears are held; there God's rich tears are sown and bring to birth, in hope new - born, the strength to jour - ney on.
4. Lord, to our hearts your joy com - mit, in - to our hands your pain, so send us out to touch the world with bless - ings in your name.
5. In suf - fering love our God comes now, hope's vi - sion born in gloom; with tears and laugh - ter shared and blessed the des - ert yet will bloom.

Alternate tune: San Rocco

Words: Rob Johns (1942–1986) Music: William Gardiner's Sacred Melodies 1819

Words: copyright © Elinor F. Johns, 1983 Music: public domain

697
How shall I sing to God

WEAVER MILL Irregular

Words: Brian A. Wren (1936–) Music: Joan Collier Fogg (1949–)

sing it with love.
sing it with love.

sing it with love.

698   Saviour, teach me day by day

SIMPLICITY 7 7 7 7

1. Sav-iour, teach me day by day love's sweet les-son to o-bey;
2. With a child's glad heart of love at thy bid-ding may I move,
3. Teach me thus thy steps to trace, strong to fol-low in thy grace,
4. Love in lov-ing finds em-ploy, in o-be-dience all its joy;

sweet-er les-son can-not be,
prompt to serve and fol-low thee,
learn-ing how to love from thee,
ev-er new that joy will be,

lov-ing God who first loved me.

Words: Jane Eliza Leeson (1807–1882) Music: John Stainer (1840–1901)

Words: public domain Music: public domain

All the way my Saviour leads me

ALL THE WAY 8 7 8 7 D

1. All the way my Sav-iour leads me; what have I to ask be-side?
2. All the way my Sav-iour leads me, cheers each wind-ing path I tread,
3. All the way my Sav-iour leads me, oh the full-ness of his love!

Can I doubt his ten-der mer-cy who through life has been my guide?
gives me grace for eve-ry tri-al, feeds me with the liv-ing bread.
Per-fect rest to me is prom-ised in my Fa-ther's house a-bove.

Heaven-ly peace, di-vin-est com-fort,here by faith in him to dwell;
Though my wea-ry steps may fal-ter, and my soul a-thirst may be,
When my spir-it, clothed im-mor-tal, wings its flight to realms of day,

for I know, what-e'er be-fall me Je-sus do-eth all things well.
gush-ing from the rock be-fore me lo, a spring of joy I see.
this my song through end-less a-ges, "Je-sus led me all the way!"

Words: Fanny J. Crosby (1820–1915) Music: Robert Lowry (1826–1899)
Words: public domain Music: public domain

Love

700 Praise our Maker, peoples of one family

PRAISE OUR MAKER 10 6 10 6

1. Praise our Mak - er, peo - ples of one fam - ily:
2. Love our Sav - iour, fol - low - ers of Je - sus:
3. Care for oth - ers, chil - dren of the Spir - it:

God is love,
God is love, God is love!
God is love, God is love!

Words: Church and School Hymnal 1926; adaptation and v.3, R. Gerald Hobbs (1941–)
Music: E. Rawdon Bailey [Carey Bonner] (1859–1938), alt

Words: adaptation and v.3, copyright © Songs for a Gospel People, 1987. Administered by Wood Lake Books Inc. Music: copyright © National Christian Education Council

701 Gracious Spirit, Holy Ghost

CAPETOWN 7 7 7 5

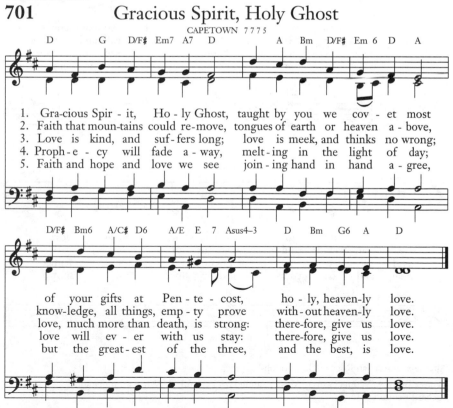

1. Gra-cious Spir - it, Ho - ly Ghost, taught by you we cov - et most
2. Faith that moun-tains could re-move, tongues of earth or heaven a - bove,
3. Love is kind, and suf-fers long; love is meek, and thinks no wrong;
4. Proph-e - cy will fade a - way, melt-ing in the light of day;
5. Faith and hope and love we see join - ing hand in hand a - gree,

of your gifts at Pen - te - cost, ho - ly, heaven-ly love.
know-ledge, all things, emp - ty prove with - out heaven-ly love.
love, much more than death, is strong: there-fore, give us love.
love will ev - er with us stay: there-fore, give us love.
but the great - est of the three, and the best, is love.

Words: 1 Corinthians 13; paraphrase, Christopher Wordsworth (1807–1885)
Music: Friedrich Filitz (1804–1876)

Words: public domain Music: public domain

891

Love
702 Dear Christ, uplifted from the earth

DUNLAP'S CREEK 8 6 8 6 CM

1. Dear Christ, up - lift - ed from the earth, your arms stretched out a - bove through eve - ry cul - ture, eve - ry birth, to draw an an - swering love.

2. Still east and west your love ex - tends, and al - ways, near and far, you call and claim us as your friends and love us as we are.

3. Where age and gen - der, class and race, di - vide us to our shame, you see a per - son and a face, a neigh - bour with a name.

4. May we, ac - cept - ed as we are, yet called in grace to grow, reach out to oth - ers, near and far your heal - ing love to show.

Alternate tunes: San Rocco   St. Botolph

Words: Brian A. Wren (1936–)   Music: Samuel McFarland (fl. 1816); arrangement, Richard Proulx (1938–)

703 Happy the home when God is there

ST. AGNES, DURHAM 8 6 8 6 CM

1. Hap - py the home when God is there,
2. Hap - py the home where Je - sus' name
3. Hap - py the home where prayer is heard
4. Lord, let us in our home a - gree,

and love fills eve - ry breast, where one their
is sweet in eve - ry ear, where chil - dren
and praise is quick to rise, where par - ents
this bless - ed peace to gain; u - nite our

wish, and one their prayer, and one their heaven - ly rest.
ear - ly sing his fame, and par - ents hold him dear.
love the sa - cred word that makes the sim - ple wise.
hearts in love to thee, and love to all will reign.

Words: Henry Ware, the younger (1794–1843) Music: John Bacchus Dykes (1823–1876)

Words: public domain Music: public domain

704 Teach me, God, to wonder

TEACH ME, GOD, TO WONDER   11 9 with refrain (11 9)

1. Teach me, God, to won - der; teach me, God, to see;
2. Let me, God, be o - pen; let me lov - ing be;
1. En - sei - gne - moi, mon Dieu, à voir tes bien - faits,
2. Mets dans mon coeur l'a - mour né de ton Es - prit,

let your world of beau - ty cap - ture me.
let your world of peo - ple speak to me.
à ai - mer la beau - té de ton oeuvre.
pour ce monde que tu as tant ai - mé.

Refrain

Praise to you be giv - en; love for you be lived,
Gloi - re te soit ren - due pour le don de vie;

life be cel - e - brat - ed; joy you give.
nous chan - tons ton a - mour, no - tre joie.

Words: Walter Henry Farquharson (1936–); French translation, Étienne de Peyer; French revised,
R. Gerald Hobbs (1941–)   Music: Ron Klusmeier (1946–)

3. Let me, God, be ready;
   let me be awake,
   in your world of loving, my place take.
   Refrain:

4. Teach me, God, to know you,
   hear you when you speak,
   see you in my neighbour when we
   meet.
   Refrain:

3. Fais de moi l'instrument
   de ta sainte paix,
   qui veut faire s'étendre ton amour.
   Refrain:

4. Fais-moi te connaître,
   apprendre à t'aimer,
   fais-moi te servir, aimant mon
   prochain.
   Refrain:

705   God, who made the earth

SOMMERLIED 5 6 6 4

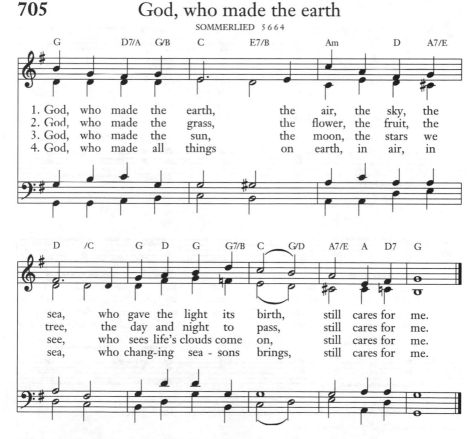

1. God, who made the earth, the air, the sky, the
2. God, who made the grass, the flower, the fruit, the
3. God, who made the sun, the moon, the stars we
4. God, who made all things on earth, in air, in

sea, who gave the light its birth, still cares for me.
tree, the day and night to pass, still cares for me.
see, who sees life's clouds come on, still cares for me.
sea, who chang-ing sea-sons brings, still cares for me.

Words: Sarah Betts Rhodes (1829–1904), alt   Music: Carey Bonner (1859–1938)

706

Come, let us sing

WONDERFUL LOVE 10 8 10 7 8 10

1. Come, let us sing of a won-der-ful love, ten - der and true,
2. Je - sus the Sav-iour this gos-pel to tell joy - ful - ly came,
3. Je - sus is seek-ing the wan-der-ers yet; why do they roam?
4. Come to my heart, O thou won-der-ful love; come and a - bide,

ten - der and true; out of the heart of the
joy - ful - ly came, came with the help - less and
why do they roam? Love on - ly waits to for -
come and a - bide, lift - ing my life till it

Fath - er a - bove, stream - ing to me and to
hope - less to dwell, shar - ing their sor - row and
give and for - get; home, wea - ry wan - der - ers,
ris - es a - bove en - vy and false - hood and

Words: Robert Walmsley (1831–1905) Music: Adam Watson (1845–1912)

Words: public domain Music: public domain

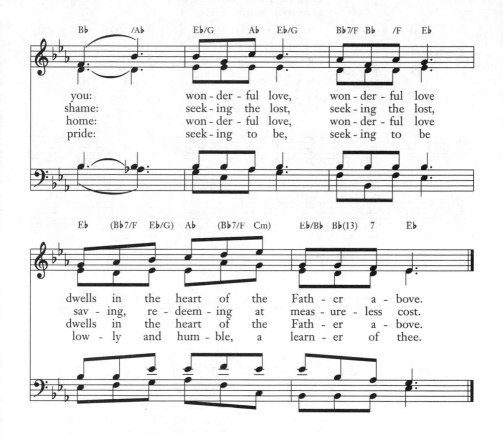

you: won - der - ful love,   won - der - ful love
shame: seek - ing the lost,   seek - ing the lost,
home: won - der - ful love,   won - der - ful love
pride: seek - ing to be,   seek - ing to be

dwells in the heart of the Fath - er a - bove.
sav - ing, re - deem - ing at meas - ure - less cost.
dwells in the heart of the Fath - er a - bove.
low - ly and hum - ble, a learn - er of thee.

More love to thee

MORE LOVE TO THEE 10 10 6 6 4 4

1. More love to thee, O Christ, more love to thee:
hear thou the prayer I make on bend - ed knee;
this is my ear - nest plea: more love, O Christ, to thee,
more love to thee, more love to thee!

2. Through all that life may bring— joy, grief or pain,
work out thy per - fect plan— true heaven ly - gain;
on - ly cre - ate in me more love, O Christ, to thee,

Words: v.1, Elizabeth Prentiss (1818–1878); v.2, Margaret Clarkson (1915–)
Music: William H. Doane (1832–1916)

Words: v.2 copyright © 1990 by Hope Publishing Co. Music: public domain

708
When Israel was in Egypt's land

WHEN ISRAEL WAS 8 5 8 5 with refrain (4 7 4 5)

1. When Is-rael was in E-gypt's land,
2. The Lord told Mo-ses what to do:
3. As Is-rael stood by the wa-ter-side   let my peo-ple go!
4. When they had reached the oth-er shore
5. Lord, help us all from bond-age flee,

op-pressed so hard they could not stand,
to lead the He-brew peo-ple through,
at God's com-mand it did div-ide,   let my peo-ple go!
they let the song of tri-umph soar,
and let us all in Christ be free,

Refrain

Go down,   Mo-ses,
                Mo-ses,   way down in E-gypt's land;
Go down, go down, Mo-ses,

tell old Phar-oah   let my peo-ple go!

Words: African-American spiritual Music: African-American spiritual

Words: public domain Music: public domain

709

What does the Lord require of you

MOON Irregular

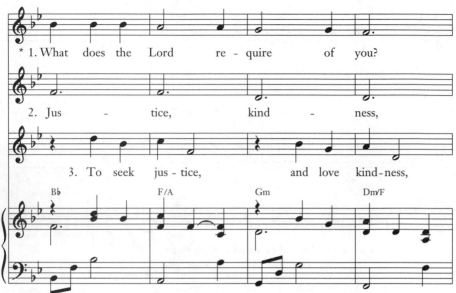

* 1. What does the Lord re - quire of you?

2. Jus - tice, kind - ness,

3. To seek jus - tice, and love kind - ness,

Bb   F/A   Gm   Dm/F

* Verses enter successively; repeat each verse with subsequent verses.

Repeat ad lib   Last time

What does the Lord re - quire of you?   you?

walk hum - bly with your God.   God.

and walk hum - bly with your God.   God.

Eb   Bb/D   Cm7   F   Bb   Bb

Words: Micah 6:8, paraphrase, Jim Strathdee (1941–)   Music: Jim Strathdee (1941–)

Words: paraphrase, copyright © Desert Flower Music, 1986. Used by permission.   Music: copyright © Desert Flower Music, 1986. Used by permission.

Justice
710
What does the Lord require
SHARPTHORNE 666666

1. What does the Lord re - quire for praise and of - fer - ing?
2. Rul - ers of earth, give ear! Should you not jus - tice show?
3. Still down the a - ges ring the pro-phet's stern com-mands.
4. How shall my soul ful - fil God's law so hard and high?

What sac - ri - fice de - sire, or trib - ute bid you
Will God your plead - ing hear, while crime and cruel - ty
To mer-chant, work - er, king he brings God's high de -
Let Christ en - due our will with grace to for - ti -

bring?
grow?   Do just - ly; love mer - cy; walk
mands.
fy.   Then just - ly, in mer - cy we'll

hum - bly with your God.   hum - bly walk with God.

Words: Albert F. Bayly (1901–1984)   Music: Erik Routley (1917–1982)

Words: paraphrase, copyright © Oxford University Press   Music: copyright © 1969 by Hope Publishing Co.

901

711

O holy city, seen of John

MORNING SONG 8 6 8 6 8 6

Unison

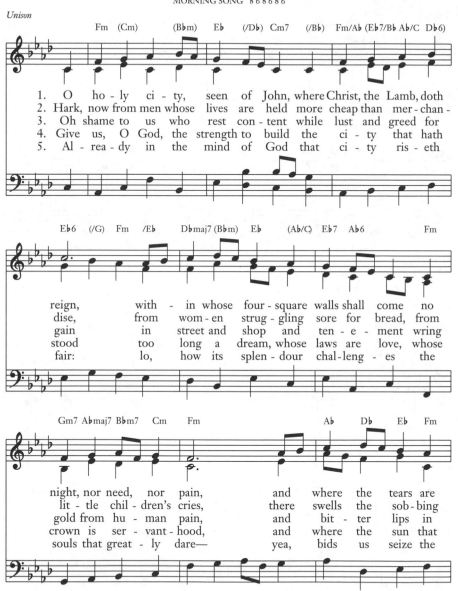

1. O ho-ly ci-ty, seen of John, where Christ, the Lamb, doth
2. Hark, now from men whose lives are held more cheap than mer-chan-
3. Oh shame to us who rest con-tent while lust and greed for
4. Give us, O God, the strength to build the ci-ty that hath
5. Al-rea-dy in the mind of God that ci-ty ris-eth

reign, with-in whose four-square walls shall come no
dise, from wom-en strug-gling sore for bread, from
gain in street and shop and ten-e-ment wring
stood too long a dream, whose laws are love, whose
fair: lo, how its splen-dour chal-leng-es the

night, nor need, nor pain, and where the tears are
lit-tle chil-dren's cries, there swells the sob-bing
gold from hu-man pain, and bit-ter lips in
crown is ser-vant-hood, and where the sun that
souls that great-ly dare— yea, bids us seize the

See also: Morning Song 123

Words: Walter Russell Bowie (1882–1969) from Hymns of the Christian Life 1910, alt
Music: anonymous 1811, in John Wyeth's Repository of Sacred Music, Part Second 1813;
harmony, Charles Winfred Douglas (1867–1944)

Words: public domain Music: harmony, copyright © The Church Pension Fund, 1982. Used by permission.

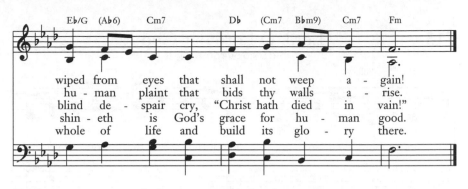

wiped from eyes that shall not weep a - gain!
hu - man plaint that bids thy walls a - rise.
blind de - spair cry, "Christ hath died in vain!"
shin - eth is God's grace for hu - man good.
whole of life and build its glo - ry there.

712   Arise, your light is come

FESTAL SONG 12 14

Descant

4. A - rise, your light is come! The moun-tains burst in song! Rise up! Rise

1. A - rise, your light is come! The Spir - it's call o - bey; show
2. A - rise, your light is come! Fling wide the pris - on door; pro -
3. A - rise, your light is come! All you in sor - row born, bind
4. A - rise, your light is come! The moun-tains burst in song! Rise

up like ea - gles on the wing; God's power will make us strong.

forth the glo - ry of your God which shines on you to - day.
claim the cap-tive's lib - er - ty, good tid - ings to the poor.
up the bro-ken - heart-ed ones and com - fort those who mourn.
up like ea - gles on the wing; God's power will make us strong.

Words: Ruth Duck (1947–)   Music: William H. Walter (1825–1893); descant, Diana McLeod (1931–)

Lord, O Lord our God

LORD, O LORD OUR GOD Irregular

Words: Nicaraguan traditional Music: Nicaraguan traditional; arrangement, Andrew Donaldson (1951–)

Words: public domain Music: arrangement, copyright © The Presbyterian Church in Canada 1996

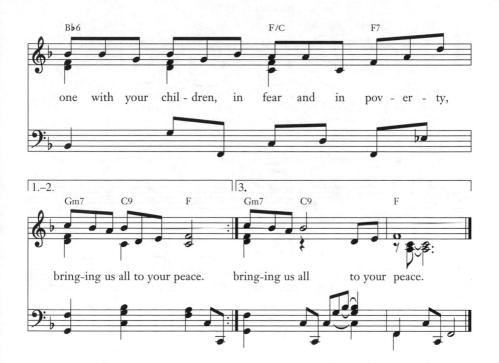

one with your chil-dren, in fear and in pov-er-ty,

1.–2. bring-ing us all to your peace.

3. bring-ing us all to your peace.

714 Wordless, ancient earth's foundations

HELMSLEY 8 7 8 7 4 7

1. Word-less, an - cient earth's foun - da - tions
   speech-less, bound - less con - stel - la - tions
2. We, our earth's stored treas - ures spend - ing,
   we, our hu - man grasp ex - tend - ing,
3. Heal us, feed us by your Spir - it:
   Name us, send us each as serv - ant,

cra - dle fra - gile in your palm;
voice their awe in sound - less psalm:
foul its soil and stain its seas;
land - scapes bruise, proud tow - ers raise.
all earth's tor - ment is your own.
work - ing, bear - ing Christ's sha - lom.

hal - le - lu - jah, hal - le - lu - jah, hal - le -
Ky - ri - e e - lei - son, Chris - te e - lei - son, ky - ri - e e -
Mar - a - na - tha, mar - a - na - tha, mar - a -

Words: Andrew Donaldson (1951–) Music: adapted by Thomas Olivers (1725–1799)

Words: copyright © Andrew Donaldson, 1993 Music: public domain

lu – jah, you are all - cre - at - ing, one.
lei – son, lead us home from wast - ed ways.
na – tha, so we pray: Christ Je - sus, come.

715 Love the Lord your God

LOVE THE LORD Irregular

Love the Lord your God, with all your heart.
Love the Lord your God, with all your soul.

Love the Lord your God with all your

mind. with all that you are.

Words: Jean Strathdee (1944–), Jim Strathdee (1941–) Music: Jean Strathdee (1944–), Jim
Strathdee (1941–)

Pray for the wilderness

WILDERNESS 10 10 10 10

1. Pray for the wil - der - ness, van - ish - ing fast;
2. Learn from the el - e - phant, ea - gle and whale;
3. Work for the jus - tice cre - at - ed things need;
4. Trust that God's Christ o - ver - came nails and wood;
5. Pray for the at - mos-phere; pray for the sea;

pray for the rain for - est, o - pen and vast;
learn from the drag - on - fly, spi - der and snail;
work for the health of each plant and its seed;
trust that earth's peo - ple will turn to the good;
learn from the riv - er, the rock and the tree;

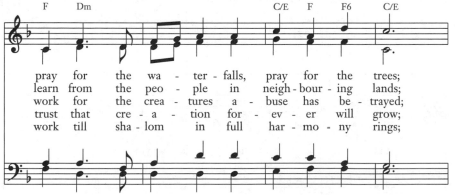

pray for the wa - ter - falls, pray for the trees;
learn from the peo - ple in neigh - bour - ing lands;
work for the crea - tures a - buse has be - trayed;
trust that cre - a - tion for - ev - er will grow;
work till sha - lom in full har - mo - ny rings;

Alternate tune: Slane

Words: Daniel Charles Damon (1955–) Music: Lee Yu San

Words: copyright © 1991 by Hope Publishing Co. Music: copyright © Korean Hymnal Society, 1967

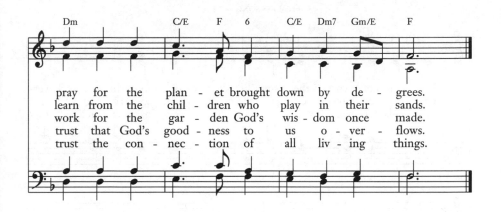

pray for the plan - et brought down by de - grees.
learn from the chil - dren who play in their sands.
work for the gar - den God's wis - dom once made.
trust that God's good - ness to us o - ver - flows.
trust the con - nec - tion of all liv - ing things.

Justice

717

We cannot own the sunlit sky

ENDLESS SONG 8 7 8 7 D

1. We can-not own the sun-lit sky, the moon, the wild - flowers
2. When bod-ies shiv - er in the night, and, wea - ry, wait for
3. God calls hu-man - i - ty to join as part-ners in cre -

grow-ing, for we are part of all that is with -
morn-ing, when chil-dren have no bread but tears, and
a - ting a fu-ture free from want or fear, life's

in life's riv - er flow-ing. With o - pen hands re-
war horns sound their warn-ing, God calls hu - man - i -
good-ness cel - e - brat-ing. That new world beck - ons

ceive and share the gifts of God's cre - a - tion, that
ty to wake, to join in com - mon la - bour, that
from a - far, in - vites our shared en - deav-our, that

Words: Ruth Duck (1947–) Music: attributed to Robert Lowry (1826–1899)

718   Holy, holy, holy Lord

SANCTUS (IONA) Irregular

Words: traditional   Music: Iona Community (Scotland)

719

God in great love for us
lent us this planet

STEWARDSHIP 11 10 11 10

1. God in great love for us lent us this plan-et, gave it a
   pur-pose in time and in space: small as a spark from the
   fire of cre-a-tion, cra-dle of life and the home of our race.

2. Thanks be to God for its boun-ty and beau-ty, life that sus-
   tains us in bo-dy and mind: plen-ty for all, if we
   learn how to share it, rich-es un-dreamed of to fath-om and find.

3. Long have our hu-man wars ru-ined its har-vest; long has earth
   bowed to the ter-ror of force; long have we wast-ed what
   oth-ers have need of, poi-soned the foun-tain of life at its source.

4. Earth is the Lord's: it is ours to en-joy it, ours, as God's
   stew-ards, to farm and de-fend. From its pol-lu-tion, mis-
   use and de-struc-tion, good Lord, de-liv-er us, world with-out end!

Words: Fred Pratt Green (1903–) Music: Valerie Ruddle (1932–)

Justice
720
Our cities cry to you, O God
THE THIRD TUNE 8 6 8 6 D CMD

1. Our cit-ies cry to you, O God, from out their pain and strife;
2. Yet still you walk our streets, O Christ! We know your pres-ence here
3. Your peo-ple are your hands and feet to serve your world to-day,
4. O heal-ing Sav-iour, Prince of Peace, sal-va-tion's source and sum,

you made us for your-self a-lone, but we choose al-ien life.
where hum-ble Chris-tians love and serve in god-ly grace and fear.
our lives the book our cit-ies read to help them find your way.
for you our bro-ken cit-ies cry: Oh come, Lord Je-sus, come!

Our goals are pleas-ure, gold and power; in-jus-tice stalks our earth;
O Word made flesh, be seen in us! May all we say and do
Oh pour your sov-ereign Spir-it out on heart and will and brain:
With truth your roy-al di-a-dem, with right-eous-ness your rod,

in vain we seek for rest, for joy, for sense of hu-man worth.
af-firm you God In-car-nate still and turn sad hearts to you!
in-spire your church with love and power to ease our cit-ies' pain!
oh come, Lord Je-sus, bring to earth the cit-y of our God!

See also: The Third Tune 223

Words: Margaret Clarkson (1915–) Music: Thomas Tallis (c. 1505–1585), melody originally in tenor; arrangement Ralph Vaughan Williams (1872–1958)

721

All who love and serve your city

CHARLESTOWN 8787

1. All who love and serve your cit - y,
2. in your day of loss and sor - row,
3. In your day of wealth and plen - ty,
4. For all days are days of judge - ment,
5. Ris - en Lord, shall yet the cit - y

all who bear its dai - ly stress,
in your day of help - less strife,
wast - ed work and wast - ed play,
and the Lord is wait - ing still,
be the cit - y of de - spair?

all who cry for peace and jus - tice,
hon - our, peace and love re - treat - ing,
call to mind the word of Je - sus,
draw - ing near a world that spurns him,
Come to - day, our Judge, our Glo - ry,

Words: Erik Routley (1917–1982)   Music: Walker's Southern Harmony 1835;
arrangement, Carlton R. Young (1926–)

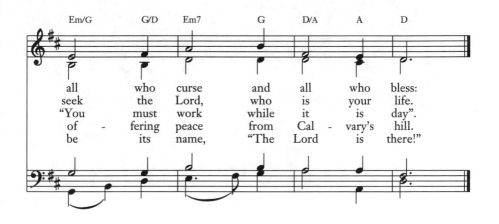

all who curse and all who bless:
seek the Lord, who is your life.
"You must work while it is day".
of - fering peace from Cal - vary's hill.
be its name, "The Lord is there!"

722

Lord, whose love

BEACH SPRING 8 7 8 7 D

1. Lord, whose love through hum-ble ser - vice bore the weight of
2. Still your chil - dren wan-der home - less; still the hun - gry
3. As we wor - ship, grant us vi - sion, till your love's re -
4. Called by wor - ship to your ser - vice, forth in your dear

hu - man need, who up - on the cross, for - sak - en,
cry for bread; still the cap - tives long for free - dom;
veal - ing light in its height and depth and great - ness
name we go to the child, the youth, the a - ged,

of - fered mer - cy's per - fect deed: we, your serv - ants, bring the
still in grief we mourn our dead. As, O Lord, your deep com -
dawns up - on our quick-ened sight, mak-ing known the needs and
love in liv - ing deeds to show; hope and health, good will and

Words: Albert F. Bayly (1901–1984) Music: attributed to Benjamin Franklin White (1800–1879)
from Sacred Harp 1844; harmony, Ronald A. Nelson (1927–)

Words: copyright © Oxford University Press, 1961 Music: harmony, copyright © 1978 Lutheran Book of Worship. Reprinted by permission of Augsburg Fortress.

| Dm | | | Am | F/A | | Bb | (maj7) | C(sus2–1) | Dm |

wor - ship not of voice a - lone, but heart, con - se - crat - ing
pas - sion healed the sick and freed the soul, use the love your
bur - dens your com - pas - sion bids us bear, stir - ring us to
com - fort, coun - sel, aid and peace we give, that your serv - ants,

| /C | Bb6 | (maj7) | F/A | Gm7 | F/A | Bb | F |

to your pur - pose eve - ry gift that you im - part.
Spir - it kin - dles still to save and make us whole.
tire - less striv - ing your a - bun - dant life to share.
Lord, in free - dom may your mer - cy know, and live.

Lord, in this broken world

STELLA ORIENTIS   11 10 11 10 with refrain

1. Lord, in this bro - ken world where you have placed us, o - pen our
2. O - pen our eyes, O Lord, that you can show us how to bring
3. O - pen our hearts, O Lord, show your love through us, tell - ing of

ears to the voic - es that call, cry - ing for help, for di -
heal - ing and help for their pain. Give us the wis - dom and
you who a - lone can re - store; lift - ing and heal - ing the

rec - tion, for com - fort, ease for the pain and re - lief o - ver all.
strength you have prom - ised; speak through your serv - ants, we pray, once a - gain.
bro - ken in spir - it, of - fering your peace and a joy ev - er - more.

Words: Kathleen Rowat (1906–)   Music: Healey Willan (1880–1968)

Words: copyright © Kathleen Rowat, 1995   Music: copyright © Oxford University Press

724 Come now, you blessed, eat at my table

COME NOW, YOU BLESSED 10 10 10 10

Unison

1. "Come now, you bless - ed, eat at my ta - ble,"
2. When did we see you hun - gry or thirs - ty?
3. "When you gave bread to earth's hun - gry chil - dren,
4. Christ, when we see you out on life's road - ways,

said Je - sus Christ to the right - eous a - bove.
When were you home - less, a stran - ger a - lone?
when you gave shel - ter to war's ref - u - gees,
look - ing to us in the fac - es of need,

"When I was hun - gry, thirs - ty and home - less,
When did we see you sick or in pris - on?
when you re - mem - bered those most for - got - ten,
then may we know you, wel - come, and show you

sick and in pris - on, you showed me your love."
What have we done that you call us your own?
you cared for me in the small - est of these." (Optional Interlude)
love that is faith - ful in word and in deed.

Words: Ruth Duck (1947–) Music: Emily R. Brink (1940–)

725
Oh, freedom, freedom is coming
OH, FREEDOM   Irregular with refrain

Words: South African traditional   Music: South African traditional

Words: public domain   Music: public domain

Justice

726 May the God of hope go with us every day

CANTO DE ESPERANZA 11 11 11 11 with refrain (7 7 7 7)

May the God of hope go with us eve-ry day, filling all our
Dios de la es-pe - ran-za, da-nos go - zo y paz! al mun-do en
Que le Dieu de l'es-pé-rance é - claire nos jours rem-plis-sant nos

lives with love and joy and peace. May the God of jus-tice speed us
cri-sis, ha-bla tu ver-dad, Dios de la jus-ti-cia, mán-da-
vi-es de sa joie, sa paix. Que le Dieu de la jus-tice et

on our way, bring-ing light and hope to eve-ry land and race.
nos tu luz, luz y es-pe-ran-za en la os-cu-ri-dad.
de l'a-mour nous mon-tre le che-min de la vé - ri - té.

Words: Alvin Schutmaat (1921–1988); French translation, Andrew Donaldson (1951–)
Music: Hispanic folk song

Words: French translation, copyright © The Presbyterian Church in Canada, 1996   Music: public domain

922

Pray - ing,   let us work for peace,   sing - ing,
O - re - mos   por la paz.   Can - te -
Pri - ons,   oeu-vrons pour la paix;   chan - tons,

share our joy with all.   work - ing   for a
mos de tu a-mor.   lu - che - mos
le coeur plein de joie;   vi - vons   le roy -

world that's new,   faith - ful   when we hear Christ's call.
por la paz,   fie - les   a Ti, Se - ñor.
aume de Dieu,   soy - ons   fi-dèles à sa voix.

Peace

727

Let there be light

CONCORD 4776

1. Let there be light; let there be un-der-stand-ing;
2. O-pen our lips; o-pen our minds to pon-der;
3. Per-ish the sword; per-ish the an-gry judge-ment;
4. Hal-low our love; hal-low the deaths of mar-tyrs;

let all the na-tions ga-ther; let them be face to face.
o-pen the door of con-cord, o-pen-ing in-to grace.
per-ish the bombs and hun-ger; per-ish the fight for gain.
hal-low their ho-ly free-dom; hal-low-ed be your name.

5. Your kingdom come;
your spirit turn to language;
your people speak together;
your spirit never fade.

6. Let there be light;
open our hearts to wonder;
perish the way of terror;
hallow the world God made.

Words: Frances Wheeler Davis (1936–) Music: Robert J.B. Fleming (1921–1976)

Words: copyright © Frances Wheeler Davis Music: copyright © Margaret Fleming

728 The storm is strong; we face the wind

THE KING'S MAJESTY 8 8 8 8 LM

1. The storm is strong; we face the wind.
   The wa - ter ris - es; waves crash in.
   Where are we now? Where will we be?
   There is no mer - cy on this sea.

2. But you, Christ, you are with us here.
   We turn to you in all our fear.
   The sin - gle word you say is "peace",
   and wind and waves and storm all cease.

3. Who can you be? What power your say
   that ev - en winds and sea o - bey?
   Re - move our fear of death and harm.
   Give us your faith and still our storm.

Organ

Alternate tunes: Breslau   Winchester New

Words: Sylvia G. Dunstan (1955–1993)   Music: Graham George (1912–)

Peace

729

Silence! frenzied, unclean spirit

DE JERSEY 8 7 8 7 D

1. "Si-lence! fren-zied, un-clean spir-it," cried God's heal-ing, Ho-ly One.
2. Lord, the de-mons still are thriv-ing in the grey cells of the mind:
3. Si-lence, Lord, the un-clean spir-it in our mind and in our heart;

"Cease your rant-ing! flesh can't bear it. Flee as night be-fore the sun."
ty-rant voic-es, shrill and driv-ing, twist-ed thoughts that grip and bind,
speak your word that when we hear it, all our de-mons shall de-part.

At Christ's voice the de-mon trem-bled, from its vic-tim mad-ly rushed,
doubts that stir the heart to pan-ic, fears dis-tort-ing rea-son's sight,
Clear our thought and calm our feel-ing, still the frac-tured war-ring soul;

while the crowd that was as-sem-bled stood in won-der, stunned and hushed.
guilt that makes our lov-ing fran-tic, dreams that cloud the soul with fright.
by the pow-er of your heal-ing, make us faith-ful, true and whole.

Alternate tune: Ton Y Botel

Words: Thomas H. Troeger (1945–)   Music: Andrew Donaldson (1951–)

Words: copyright © Oxford University Press, 1985   Music: copyright © Andrew Donaldson, 1996
926

730

O for a world where everyone

AZMON 8 6 8 6 CM

1. O   for a world where eve-ry-one re-spects each oth-er's ways,
2. O   for a world where goods are shared and mis-er-y re-lieved,
3. We welcome one world fam-i-ly and strug-gle with each choice
4. The poor are rich, the weak are strong, the fool-ish ones are wise.
5. O   for a world pre-par-ing for God's glo-rious reign of peace,

where love is lived and all is done with jus-tice and with praise.
where truth is spo-ken, chil-dren spared, e-qual-i-ty a-chieved.
that o-pens us to u-ni-ty and gives our vi-sion voice.
Tell all who mourn: out-casts be-long, who per-ish-es will rise.
where time and tears will be no more, and all but love will cease.

Words: Miriam Therese Winter (1938–) Music: Carl G. Gläser (1784–1829);
adaptation, Lowell Mason (1792–1872) in Modern Psalmody, 1839

731

Shalom chaverim

SHALOM 8 4 10 4

Fare-well, dear friends, stay safe, dear friends, have peace, have peace.
Sha-lom cha-ve-rim, sha-lom cha-ve-rim. Sha-lom, sha-lom.
Sja-lom, chers a-mis, sja-lom chers a-mis, sja-lom, sja-lom.

We'll see you a-gain, we'll see you a-gain, have peace, have peace.
Le-hit-ra-ot, le-hit-ra-ot, sha-lom, sha-lom.
jusqu'-au re-voir, jusqu'-au re-voir, sja-lom sja-lom.

Words: traditional Hebrew; translation, Roger N. Deschner (1927–) Music: Jewish traditional

O day of peace that dimly shines

JERUSALEM 8 8 8 8 LMD

1. O day of peace that dim-ly shines through all our
2. Then shall the wolf dwell with the lamb, nor shall the

hopes and prayers and dreams, guide us to jus - tice, truth and
fierce de - vour the small; as beasts and cat - tle calm - ly

Words: Carl P. Daw Jr. (1944–) Music: Charles Hubert Hastings Parry (1848–1918);
arrangement, Gordon Jacob (1895–1984)

love, de-liv-ered from our self - ish schemes. May swords of
graze, a lit-tle child shall lead them all. Then en-e-

Bm   6   F#m   Bm   F#m   E7   Asus4 – 3   Em/G B7/F#

hate fall from our hands, our hearts from en - vy find re-
mies shall learn to love, all crea-tures find their true ac-

Em   (7)   Am   Em   (A7/E) G/D   D7

lease, till by God's grace our war-ring world shall see Christ's
cord; the hope of peace shall be ful-filled, for all the

Gsus2– 1   (D) Em   /A   A7/G   D/F#   D (A/C# Bm)   G

f ——— ff

prom-ised reign of peace.
earth shall know the (Lord.)

Final Ending

Lord.

733
O God of love, true source of peace

EALING 8 8 8 8 LM

1. O God of love, true source of peace, make wars through-out the
2. Re - mem-ber, Lord, your works of old, the won - ders that our
3. Whom shall we trust but you, O God? Where rest but on your
4. Where saints and an - gels dwell a - bove, all hearts are knit in

world to cease; the wrath of sin - ful
fore - bears told; re - mem - ber not our
faith - ful word? None ev - er called on
ho - ly love; oh bind us in that

hearts re - strain:
sin's deep stain: give peace, O God, give peace a - gain.
you in vain:
heaven - ly chain:

Alternate tune: Melcombe

Words: Henry Williams Baker (1821–1877), alt   Music: Herbert S. Oakeley (1830–1903)

Words: public domain   Music: public domain

734 Lord of life and Lord of nations

GOD OF PEACE 877888

1. Lord of life and Lord of na - tions, giv - ing peace, you
2. Lengths of love be - yond all meas - ure, heights of love which
3. Vi - sions new and an-cient dream - ing see the Love be -

make us one: heart of flesh for heart of stone,
now do call, breadth of love as room for all,
yond all death; new the heav - ens, new the earth:

break the walls of all di - vi - sions. Your king - dom come, with
depths of love where hides the treas - ure: through Christ, our Way, we
prom - ise of the king-dom com - ing. Through Christ the wounds of

Words: Anthony Kelly, (1938–)   Music: Christopher Willcock, SJ (1947–)

this its sign: our song this prayer: let   peace now reign.
find true peace,   a world made whole in   God's em-brace.
all this world   in God's own peace will   then be healed.

735   Dona nobis pacem

DONA NOBIS PACEM (IONA) 9 9

Do - na no - bis pa - cem in ter - ra,

do - na no - bis pa - cem, Do - mi - ne.

Words: traditional Latin Music: Iona Community (Scotland)

736 For the healing of the nations
GRAFTON 878787

1. For the heal - ing of the na - tions,
   Lord, we pray with one ac - cord, for a just and
   e - qual shar - ing of the things that earth af - fords.
   To a life of love in ac - tion

2. Lead us for - ward in - to free - dom,
   from de - spair your world re - lease, that, re - deemed from
   war and ha - tred, all may come and go in peace.
   Show us how through care and good - ness

3. All that kills a - bun - dant liv - ing,
   let it from the earth be banned, pride of sta - tus,
   race or school - ing, dog - mas that ob - scure your plan.
   In our com - mon quest for jus - tice

4. You, Cre - a - tor God, have writ - ten
   your great name on hu - man - kind; for our grow - ing
   in your like - ness bring the life of Christ to mind,
   that, by our re - sponse and serv - ice,

Words: Fred Kaan (1929–) Music: Caspar Ett's Cantica Sacra 1840

help us rise and pledge our word.
fear will die and hope in - crease.
may we hal - low life's brief span.
earth its des - ti - ny may find.

737   Dona nobis pacem

DONA NOBIS PACEM   8 6 6 6 6 6

May be sung as a round.

Do - na no - bis pa - cem, pa - cem. Do - na
no - bis pa - cem. Do - na no - bis pa-cem.
Do - na no - bis pa - cem. Do - na
no - bis pa-cem. Do - na no - bis pa - cem.

Words: traditional Latin   Music: traditional

Words: public domain   Music: public domain

738

God the omnipotent

RUSSIAN HYMN 11 10 11 9

1. God the om - ni - po - tent sov-ereign, or - dain - ing great winds your cla - ri - ons and light-nings your sword, show forth your mer - cy: a - lone you are reign - ing. Give to us peace in our time, O Lord.

2. God the all - mer - ci - ful, earth has for - sak - en meek - ness and mer - cy and slight - ed your word; bid not your wrath in its ter - rors a - wak - en. Give to us peace in our time, O Lord.

3. God the all - right - eous, we have de - fied you; yet to e - ter - ni - ty firm stands your word; false - hood and wrong shall not stand long be-side you. Give to us peace in our time, O Lord.

4. God the all - wise, by the fire of your chas-tening earth shall to free - dom and truth be re - stored. Through the thick dark - ness your King - dom is has-tening. You will give peace in your time, O Lord.

5. So shall your chil-dren, with thank - ful de - vo - tion, praise God who saved them from per - il and sword, sing - ing in cho - rus, from o - cean to o - cean, peace to the na - tions and praise to the Lord.

Words: Henry Fothergill Chorley (1808–1872), John Ellerton (1826–1893)
Music: Alexis Feodorovitch Lvov (1798–1870)

Words: public domain Music: public domain

739 Lord, make us servants of your peace

OTTERSPOOR 8 8 8 8 LM

1. Lord, make us serv - ants of your peace: where there is hate, may
2. Where all is doubt, may we sow faith; where all is gloom, may
3. Je - sus, our Lord, may we not seek to be con-soled, but
4. May we not look for love's re - turn, but seek to love un -
5. Dy - ing, we live, and are re - born through death's dark night to

we sow love; where there is hurt, may we for - give; where
we sow hope; where all is night, may we sow light; where
to con - sole, nor look to un - der - stand-ing hearts, but
self - ish - ly, for in our giv - ing we re - ceive, and
end - less day: Lord, make us serv - ants of your peace, to

1.–4.
there is strife, may we make one.
all is tears, may we sow joy.
look for hearts to un - der - stand.
in for - giv - ing are for - given.
wake at last in heav - en's

5.
light.

Words: Francis of Assisi (1182–1226); translation, James Quinn (1919–) Music: Ron Klusmeier (1946–)

740

Make me a channel of your peace

MAKE ME A CHANNEL 8 10 10 8

Make me a chan-nel of your peace:

1. where there is ha-tred,
2. where there's des-pair in
4. it is in par-don-

Make me a chan-nel of your peace:

let me bring your love;
life let me bring hope;
ing that we are par-doned,

where there is in-jur-y, your heal-ing
where there is dark-ness, on-ly
in giv - ing to all that we re-

where there is ha-tred let me bring your love,
where there's des-pair in life let me bring hope;
it is in par-don-ing that we are par-doned,

your heal-ing
on-ly
that we re-

power,
light,
ceive,

and where there's doubt, true faith in you.
and where there's sad - ness, ev - er joy.
and in dy - ing that we're born to e-ter-nal life.

power,
light,
ceive,

and where there's doubt, true faith in you.
and where there's sad - ness, ev - er joy.
and in dy - ing that we're born to e-ter-nal life.

Words: Saint Patrick of Ireland (372–466) Music: Sebastian Temple (1928–);
arrangement, the compilers of Praise Ways

Words: public domain Music: copyright © Franciscan Communications Centre, 1968

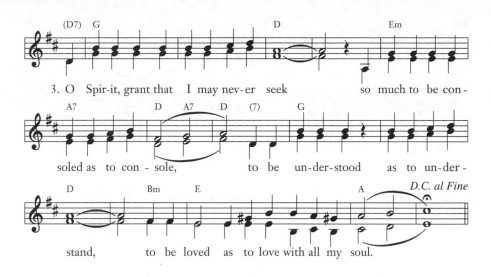

3. O Spir-it, grant that I may nev-er seek so much to be con-soled as to con - sole, to be un-der-stood as to un-der-stand, to be loved as to love with all my soul.

D.C. al Fine

741   Like a mighty river flowing

QUEM PASTORES LAUDAVERE 8 8 8 7

1. Like a might-y riv - er flow-ing, like a flower in beau-ty grow-ing,
2. Like the hills se - rene and e - ven, like the cours-ing clouds of heav-en,
3. Like the sum-mer breez - es play-ing, like the tall trees soft - ly sway-ing,
4. Like the morn-ing sun as - cend-ed, like the scents of eve-ning blend-ed,
5. Like the az - ure o - cean swell-ing, like the jew - el all - ex - cel-ling,

far be-yond all hu - man know-ing
like the heart that's been for - giv - en
like the lips of si - lent pray-ing   is the per - fect peace of God.
like a friend-ship nev - er end - ed
far be-yond our hu - man tell-ing

Words: Michael Perry (1942–1996) Music: German carol melody; arrangement, Ralph Vaughan Williams (1872–1958)

Words: copyright © 1982 by Hope Publishing Co. Music: arrangement, copyright © Oxford University Press

742 Lead on, O King eternal

LANCASHIRE 7 6 7 6 D

1. Lead on, O King e - ter - nal: the day of march has come;
2. Lead on, O King e - ter - nal, till sin's fierce war shall cease,
3. Lead on, O King e - ter - nal: we fol - low, not with fears,

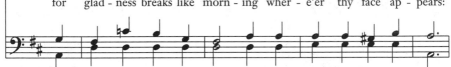

hence - forth in fields of bat - tle thy tents shall be our home:
and ho - li - ness shall whis - per the sweet A - men of peace;
for glad - ness breaks like morn - ing wher - e'er thy face ap - pears:

through days of pre - par - a - tion thy grace has made us strong,
for not with swords' loud clash - ing nor roll of stir - ring drum,
thy cross is lift - ed o'er us; we jour - ney in its light;

Words: Ernest Warburton Shurtleff (1862–1917) Music: Henry T. Smart (1813–1879)

and now, O King e - ter - nal, we lift our bat - tle - song.
but deeds of love and mer - cy, thy reign of peace shall come.
the crown a - waits the con - quest; lead on, O God of might.

743 Lead on, eternal Sovereign

1. Lead on, eternal Sovereign,
   we follow in your way;
   loud rings your cry for justice,
   your call for peace this day:
   through prayerful preparation,
   your grace will make us strong,
   to carry on the struggle
   to triumph over wrong.

2. Lead on, eternal Sovereign,
   we follow not with fear,
   for in each human conflict
   your words of strength we hear:
   that when we serve with gladness,
   you will not let us fall,
   our trust is in your promise
   that love will conquer all.

3. Lead on, eternal Sovereign,
   till sin's fierce war shall cease
   and all your saints together
   will sing a hymn of peace;
   then all in your dominion
   will live with hearts set free,
   to love and serve each other
   for all eternity.

Words: Ernest Warburton Shurtleff (1862–1917), alt
Words: this version, copyright © The Pilgrim Press, 1992

Peace

744

Will your anchor hold

WILL YOUR ANCHOR HOLD 10 9 10 9 with refrain

1. Will your an - chor hold in the storms of life, when the
2. Will your an - chor hold in the straits of fear, when the
3. Will your eyes be - hold through the morn - ing light the

clouds un - fold their wings of strife? When the strong tides lift and the
break-ers roar and the reef is near? While the surg - es rave and the
cit - y of gold and the har-bour bright? Will you an - chor safe by the

ca - bles strain, will your an - chor drift or firm re - main?
wild winds blow, shall the an - gry waves then your bark o'er-flow?
heaven - ly shore, when life's storms are past for - ev - er -more?

Words: Priscilla Jane Owens (1829–1907) Music: William James Kirkpatrick (1838–1921);
harmony, Francis B. Westbrook (1903–1975)

Words: public domain Music: harmony, copyright © Oxford University Press

745   Jesus, Lamb of God

AGNUS DEI (BATEMAN) 10 12 11

We have an an-chor that keeps the soul stead-fast and sure while the bil-lows roll, fast-ened to the rock which can - not move, ground-ed firm and deep in the Sav - iour's love!

Je-sus, Lamb of God: have mer-cy on us. Je-sus, bear-er of our sins: have mer-cy on us. Je-sus, Re-deem-er of the world: grant us peace.

Words: traditional   Music: Paul Bateman (1954–)

Words: public domain   Music: copyright © Paul Bateman

746

What a friend we have in Jesus

WHAT A FRIEND 8 7 8 7 D

1. What a friend we have in Je - sus, all our sins and griefs to bear;
2. Have we tri - als and temp-ta - tions? Is there trou-ble an - y- where?
1. Quel a - mi fi - dèle et ten - dre nous a - vons en Jé - sus- Christ,
2. Quel a - mi fi - dèle et ten - dre nous a - vons en Jé - sus- Christ,

what a priv-i-lege to car - ry eve - ry-thing to God in prayer.
We should nev-er be dis-cour - aged: take it to the Lord in prayer.
tou - jours prêt à nous en - ten - dre, à ré-pondre à no-tre cri!
tou - jours prêt à nous com-pren - dre quand nous som-mes en sou - ci!

Oh what peace we of - ten for - feit, oh what need-less pain we
Can we find a friend so faith - ful, who will all our sor-rows
Il con - naît nos dé - fail - lan - ces, nos chu - tes de cha - que
Di - sons - lui tou-tes nos crain - tes, ou - vrons-lui tout no - tre

Alternate tune: Blaenwern

Words: Joseph Scriven (1820–1886) Music: Charles Crozat Converse (1834–1918)

Words: public domain Music: public domain

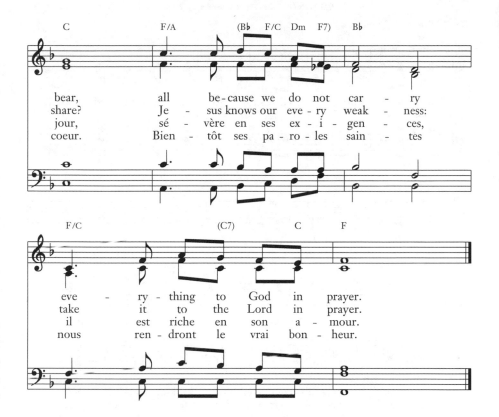

bear, all be-cause we do not car - ry
share? Je - sus knows our eve - ry weak - ness:
jour, sé - vère en ses ex - i - gen - ces,
coeur. Bien - tôt ses pa - ro - les sain - tes

eve - ry - thing to God in prayer.
take it to the Lord in prayer.
il est riche en son a - mour.
nous ren - dront le vrai bon - heur.

3. Are we weak and heavy-laden,
   cumbered with a load of care?
   Precious Saviour, still our refuge:
   take it to the Lord in prayer.
   Do thy friends despise, forsake thee?
   Take it to the Lord in prayer;
   in his arms he'll take and shield thee;
   thou wilt find a solace there.

3. Quel ami fidèle et tendre
   nous avons en Jésus-Christ;
   toujours prêt à nous défendre
   quand nous presse l'ennemi!
   Suivons donc l'étroite voie,
   en comptant sur son secours;
   bientôt nous aurons la joie
   de vivre avec lui toujours!

747

There is a balm in Gilead

BALM IN GILEAD   7 6 7 6 with refrain (8 6 8 6)

Refrain

There is a balm in Gil-e-ad to make the wound-ed whole.

Fine

There is a balm in Gil-e-ad to heal the sin-sick soul.

1. Some - times I feel dis - cour - aged, and think my work's in vain,
2. Don't ev - er feel dis - cour - aged, for Je - sus is your friend,
3. If you can - not preach like Pe - ter, if you can - not pray like Paul,

D.C.

but then the Ho - ly Spir - it re - vives my soul a - gain.
who, if you ask for knowl-edge, will nev - er fail to lend.
you can tell the love of Je - sus, who died to save us all.

Words: African–American spiritual   Music: African–American spiritual

Words: public domain   Music: public domain

Lord of all hopefulness

SNOWSHILL 10 11 11 12

1. Lord of all hope-ful-ness, Lord of all joy, whose trust, ev - er child-like,
2. Lord of all ea - ger-ness, Lord of all faith, whose strong hands were skilled at
3. Lord of all kind - li-ness, Lord of all grace, your hands swift to wel-come,
4. Lord of all gen - tle-ness, Lord of all calm, whose voice is con-tent-ment,

no cares could de-stroy, be there at our wak-ing, and give us, we pray,
the plane and the lathe, be there at our la-bours, and give us, we pray,
your arms to em-brace, be there at our hom-ing, and give us, we pray,
whose pres-ence is balm, be there at our sleep-ing, and give us, we pray,

your bliss in our hearts, Lord, at the break of the day.
your strength in our hearts, Lord, at the noon of the day.
your love in our hearts, Lord, at the eve of the day.
your peace in our hearts, Lord, at the end of the day.

Words: Jan Struther (1901–1953)   Music: Walter K. Stanton (1891–1978)

749
Be still, my soul

FINLANDIA 10 10 10 10 10 10

1. Be still, my soul: the Lord is on thy side;
2. Be still, my soul: thy God doth un - der - take
3. Be still, my soul: when dear - est friends de - part,
4. Be still, my soul: the hour is has - tening on

bear pa - tient - ly the cross of grief or pain;
to guide the fu - ture wise - ly, as the past.
and all is dark - ened in the vale of tears,
when we shall be for - ev - er with the Lord,

leave to thy God to or - der and pro - vide;
Thy hope, thy con - fi - dence let noth - ing shake;
then shalt thou bet - ter know God's love, God's heart,
when dis - ap - point - ment, grief and fear are gone,

Words: Jane L. Borthwick (1813–1897), Katharina von Schlegel (1697–18th cent.)
Music: Jean Sibelius (1865–1957), Finlandia; arrangement, The Hymnal 1933

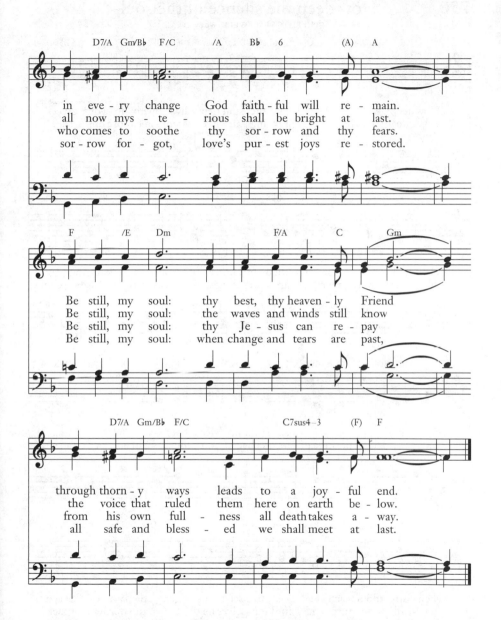

D7/A Gm/Bb F/C   /A   Bb 6   (A) A

in eve-ry change God faith-ful will re - main.
all now mys-te-rious shall be bright at last.
who comes to soothe thy sor-row and thy fears.
sor-row for-got, love's pur-est joys re - stored.

F   /E Dm   F/A   C   Gm

Be still, my soul: thy best, thy heaven-ly Friend
Be still, my soul: the waves and winds still know
Be still, my soul: thy Je-sus can re - pay
Be still, my soul: when change and tears are past,

D7/A Gm/Bb F/C   C7sus4-3   (F) F

through thorn-y ways leads to a joy - ful end.
the voice that ruled them here on earth be - low.
from his own full - ness all death takes a - way.
all safe and bless - ed we shall meet at last.

Peace

750

How deep the silence of the soul

MACPHERSON'S FAREWELL 8 6 8 6 D CMD

1. How deep the si - lence of the soul that lives with-in your grace.
2. Like un - seen chimes on mov-ing air, like warm and morn-ing sun,

How full the grat - i - tude of heart in your a - bid - ing place.
like glad-dening, green-ing, grow-ing things, like trees with blooms be - gun:

What rich se - ren - i - ty is found, what cour - age and re - lease,
such is your pres-ence in our lives, you touch with-out a trace,

when wis - dom teach-es us to seek the gen - tle path to peace.
un - til we turn and find our-selves held fast in your em - brace.

Alternate tune: Kingsfold   See also: MacPherson's Farewell 90

Words: Sylvia G. Dunstan (1955–1993)   Music: Scottish traditional; arrangement, David Iliff (1939–)

Words: copyright © G.I.A. Publications Inc., 1991   Music: arrangement, copyright © 1990 by Hope Publishing Co.

751

Forgive our sins as we forgive

BANGOR 8 6 8 6 CM

1. "For - give our sins as we for - give," you
2. How can your par - don reach and bless the
3. In blaz - ing light your cross re - veals the
4. Lord, cleanse the depths with - in our souls, and

taught us, Lord, to pray, but you a - lone can
un - for - giv - ing heart, that broods on wrongs and
truth we dim - ly knew: what triv - ial debts are
bid re - sent - ment cease; then, bound to all in

grant us grace to live the words we say.
will not let old bit - ter - ness de - part?
owed to us, how great our debt to you!
bonds of love, our lives will spread your peace.

Words: Rosamond E. Herklots (1905–) Music: William Tans'ur's Harmony of Syon 1734

Words: copyright © by permission of Oxford University Press Music: public domain

752

Blest be the God of Israel

MERLE'S TUNE 13 13 13 13

1. Blest be the God of Is - rael, who comes to set us free,
2. Now from the house of Da - vid a child of grace has come,
3. On those who live in dark - ness the sun be - gins to rise,

who vis - its and re - deems us, who grants us lib - er - ty.
a Sav - iour who will lead us to our e - ter - nal home.
the dawn - ing of for - give - ness up - on the sin - ner's eyes;

The proph - ets spoke of mer - cy, of res - cue and re - lease;
Be - fore him goes his her - ald, fore - run - ner in the way,
to guide the feet of pil - grims a - long the paths of peace.

God shall ful - fill the prom - ise to bring the gift of peace.
the proph - et of sal - va - tion, the mes - sen - ger of day.
Oh bless our God and Sav - iour with songs that nev - er cease!

Words: Luke 1:68-79; paraphrase, Michael Perry (1942-1996)   Music: Hal H. Hopson (1933-)

753 You walk along our shoreline

WIE LIEBLICH IST DER MAIEN 7 6 7 6 D

Words: Sylvia G. Dunstan (1955-1993)   Music: Johann Steurlein (1546-1613)

Words: copyright © G.I.A. Publications Inc., 1991   Music: public domain

Mission

754

From the slave pens of the delta

OMNI DIE (LUXEMBOURG) 8 7 8 7 D

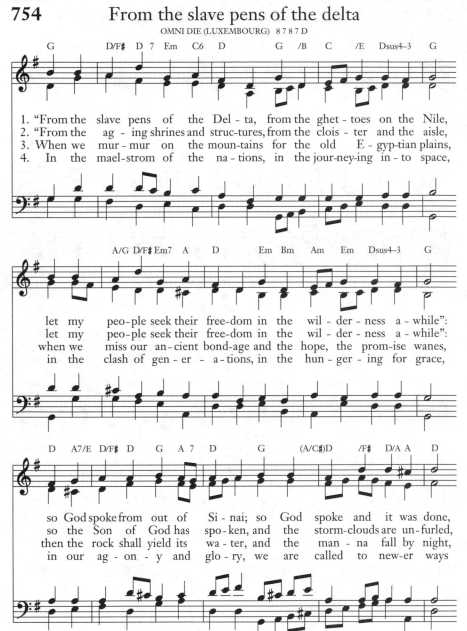

1. "From the slave pens of the Del - ta, from the ghet - toes on the Nile,
2. "From the ag - ing shrines and struc-tures, from the clois - ter and the aisle,
3. When we mur - mur on the moun-tains for the old E - gyp-tian plains,
4. In the mael-strom of the na - tions, in the jour-ney-ing in - to space,

let my peo-ple seek their free-dom in the wil - der - ness a - while":
let my peo-ple seek their free-dom in the wil - der - ness a - while":
when we miss our an - cient bond-age and the hope, the prom-ise wanes,
in the clash of gen - er - a - tions, in the hun - ger - ing for grace,

so God spoke from out of Si - nai; so God spoke and it was done,
so the Son of God has spo - ken, and the storm-clouds are un - furled,
then the rock shall yield its wa - ter, and the man - na fall by night,
in our ag - on - y and glo - ry, we are called to new-er ways

Alternate tune: Bethany (Smart)

Words: Herbert O'Driscoll (1928-) Music: Trier Gesangbuch 1695

Words: copyright © T. Herbert O'Driscoll Music: public domain

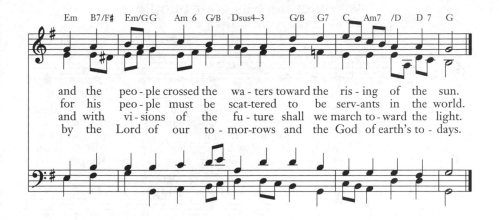

755 Go ye, go ye into the world

GO YE, GO YE 8 10 8 7

Words: Natalie Sleeth (1930-1992) Music: Natalie Sleeth (1930-1992)

Words: copyright © Choristers Guild, 1979 Music: copyright © Choristers Guild, 1979

756

O Christ, our Lord,
we meet here as your people

INTERCESSOR 11 10 11 10

1. O Christ, our Lord, we meet here as your peo - ple, and pray that
we may now ac - cept your grace; for-give us when we seek an earth-ly
king - dom in which we hope to find an hon-oured place.

2. For-give us for our ar - ro-gant as - sump - tions that we a -
lone have found Christ's ho - ly way; for-give us for the cow - ard - ly e -
va - sions that mod - i - fy your chal-lenge to our day.

3. For-give us for the mix - ture of our mo - tives when we are
con - fi - dent our love is pure; for-give us for our un - for - giv - ing
judge - ments when of the Fath - er's will we sound so sure.

4. For-give us, Lord, for all our will - ful blind - ness to hu - man
suf - fering and to hu - man need; for-give us for our cas - u - al un -
kind - ness, the hast - y word and the be-grudg-ing deed.

5. And, in for - giv - ing, grant us of your Spir - it the grace to
lose our selves, and in the loss to find re - demp-tion through a true de -
vo - tion that dares re - flect the pas - sion of your cross.

Words: Ian Alexander (1916-)   Music: Charles Hubert Hastings Parry (1848-1918)

Come sing, O church, in joy!

DARWALL'S 148TH 12 12 4 12

1. Come sing, O church, in joy! Come join, O church, in song!
2. Long years have come and gone, and still God reigns su - preme,
3. Let cour - age be our friend, let wis - don be our guide,
4. Come sing, O church, in joy! Come join, O church, in song!

For Christ the Lord has led us through the a - ges long!
em - pow-ering us to catch the vi - sion, dream the dream!
as we in mis-sion mag - ni - fy the Cru - ci - fied!
For Christ the Lord has tri-umphed o'er the a - ges long!

In bold ac - cord, come cel - e - brate the jour-ney now and praise the Lord!

See also: Darwall's 148th 267 606

Words: Brian Dill (1949-) Music: John Darwall (1731-1789)

Words: copyright © Brian Dill, 1989 Music: public domain

Christ's is the world

DREAM ANGUS 8999

1. Christ's is the world in which we move;
2. Feel for the peo-ple we most a-void—
3. Feel for the par-ents who've lost their child,
4. Feel for the lives by life con-fused,

Christ's are the folk we're sum-moned to love;
strange or be-reaved or nev-er em-ployed.
feel for the wom-en whom men have de-filed,
rid-dled with doubt, in lov-ing a-bused;

Christ's is the voice which calls us to care, and
Feel for the wom-en and feel for the men who
feel for the ba-by for whom there's no breast, and
feel for the lone-ly heart, con-scious of sin, which

Christ is the one who meets us here.
fear that their liv-ing is all in vain.
feel for the wea-ry who find no rest.
longs to be pure but fears to be-gin.

Words: John L. Bell (1949-), Graham Maule (1958-) Music: Scottish traditional; arrangement,
Iona Community (Scotland)

In loving partnership

RIVAULX 8888 LM

1. In lov - ing part - ner - ship we come,
2. We are the hands and feet of Christ,
3. Lov - ing com - mu - ni - ty we seek;
4. In lov - ing part - ner - ship, O God,

seek - ing, O God, your will to do.
serv - ing by grace each oth - er's need.
your hope and strength with - in us move.
help us your fu - ture to pro - claim.

Our prayers and ac - tions now re - ceive;
We dare to risk and sac - ri - fice
The poor and rich, the strong and weak
Jus - tice and peace be our de - sire,

we free - ly of - fer them to you.
with truth - ful word and faith - ful deed.
are brought to - geth - er in your love.
we hum - bly pray in Je - sus' name.

Words: Jim Strathdee (1941-) Music: John Bacchus Dykes (1823-1876)

Mission
760
Where cross the crowded ways of life
WALTON (FULDA) 8 8 8 8 LM

1. Where cross the crowd - ed ways of life, where sound the
2. In haunts of wretch - ed - ness and need, on shad - owed
3. From ten - der child - hood's help - less - ness, from wom - an's
4. The cup of wa - ter given for you still holds the

cries of race and clan, a - bove the noise of
thresh - olds, dark with fears, from paths where hide the
grief, man's bur - dened toil, from fam - ished souls, from
fresh - ness of your grace; yet long these mul - ti -

self - ish strife, we hear your voice, O Son of Man.
lures of greed, we catch the vi - sion of your tears.
sor - row's stress, your heart has nev - er known re - coil.
tudes to view the sweet com - pas - sion of your face.

5. O Saviour, from the mountain side,
make haste to heal these hearts of pain;
among these restless throngs abide,
oh tread the city's streets again;

6. Till human hearts shall learn your love,
and follow where your feet have trod;
till glorious from your heaven above,
shall come the city of our God.

Words: Frank Mason North (1850-1935), alt   Music: William Gardiner's Sacred Melodies 1815
Words: public domain   Music: public domain

Mission

761

Who's goin' to tell the story

WHO'S GOIN' TO TELL THE STORY 10 10 8 13

Words: Natalie Sleeth (1930-1992) Music: Natalie Sleeth (1930-1992)

762

When the poor ones

EL CAMINO Irregular

Unison

1. When the poor ones who have noth-ing share with strang-ers,
2. When at last all those who suf-fer find their com-fort,
1. Cuan-do el po-bre na-da tie-ne y aun re-par-te,
2. Cuan-do su-fre un-hom bre y-lo-gra su con-sue-lo,

when the thirst-y wa-ter give un-to us all,
when they hope though e-ven hope seems hope-less-ness,
cuan-do el hom-bre pa-sa sed y a-gua nos da,
cuan-do es-pe-ra y no se can-sa de es-pe-rar,

when the crip-pled in their weak-ness strength-en oth-ers,
when we love though hate at times seems all a-round us,
cuan-do el dé-bil a su her-ma-no for-ta-le-ce,
cuan-do a-ma-mos, aun que el o-dio nos ro-de-e,

Refrain

then we know that God still goes that road with us,
va Dios mis-mo en nues-tro mis-mo ca-mi-nar,

Words: Miguel Manzano, J.A. Olivar, English translation, George Lockwood (1946-) Music:
Miguel Manzano (20th cent.), J.A. Olivar (20th cent.); arrangement, Alvin Schutmaat (1921-1988)

then we know that God still goes that road with us.
va Dios mis-mo en nues-tro mis - mo ca - mi-nar.

3. When our joy fills up our cup to overflowing,
   when our lips can speak no words other than true,
   when we know that love for simple things is better,
   Refrain:

4. When our homes are filled with goodness in abundance,
   when we learn how to make peace instead of war,
   when each stranger that we meet is called a neighbour,
   Refrain:

3. Cuando crece la alegría y nos inunda,
   cuando dicen nuestros labios la verdad,
   cuando amamos el sentir de los sencillos,
   Refrain:

4. Cuando abunda el bien y llena los hogares,
   cuando un hombre donde hay guerra pone paz,
   cuando "hermano" le llamamos al extraño,
   Refrain:

To show by touch and word

LODWICK 666688

1. To show by touch and word de - vo - tion
2. Re - new our minds to choose the things that
3. Let love from day to day be yard - stick,

to the earth, to hold in full re - gard all
mat - ter most, our hearts to long for truth till
rule and norm, and let our lives por - tray your

life that comes to birth, we need, O God, the
pride - of - self is lost. For eve - ry chal - lenge
word in hu - man form. Now come with us that

will to find the good you had of old in mind.
that we face, we need your guid - ance and your grace.
we may have your wits a - bout us where we live.

Words: Fred Kaan (1929-)   Music: Ron Klusmeier (1946-)

Words: copyright © 1975 by Hope Publishing Co.   Music: copyright © WorshipArts, 1974

Mission

764

There's a spirit in the air

LAUDS 7777

Descant

Praise the love! Praise the love!

F/A Bb Dm Bb F/A C F C6 C F/A C6 Dm Gm Csus4–3

1. There's a spir - it in the air, tell - ing Chris - tians eve - ry-where:
2. Lose your shy - ness, find your tongue, tell the world what God has done:
3. When be - liev - ers break the bread, when a hun - gry child is fed,
4. Still the Spir - it gives us light, see - ing wrong and set - ting right:

Hal - le - lu - jah, hal - le - lu - jah!

Dm Cm 6 Gm6 Dm/F C/F /E F Bb /G F/A /Bb C6 C F

"Praise the love that Christ re-vealed, liv - ing, work - ing, in our world!"
God in Christ has come to stay. Live to - mor - row's life to - day!
praise the love that Christ re-vealed, liv - ing, work - ing, in our world.
God in Christ has come to stay. Live to - mor - row's life to - day!

5. When a stranger's not alone,
   where the homeless find a home,
   praise the love that Christ revealed,
   living, working, in our world.

6. May the Spirit fill our praise,
   guide our thoughts and change our ways.
   God in Christ has come to stay.
   Live tomorrow's life today!

7. There's a Spirit in the air,
   calling people everywhere:
   praise the love that Christ revealed,
   living, working, in our world.

Alternate tune: Monkland

Words: Brian A. Wren (1936-) Music: John W. Wilson (1905-1992)

765 We've a story to tell to the nations

WE'VE A STORY 10 8 8 7 with refrain (9 8 9 7)

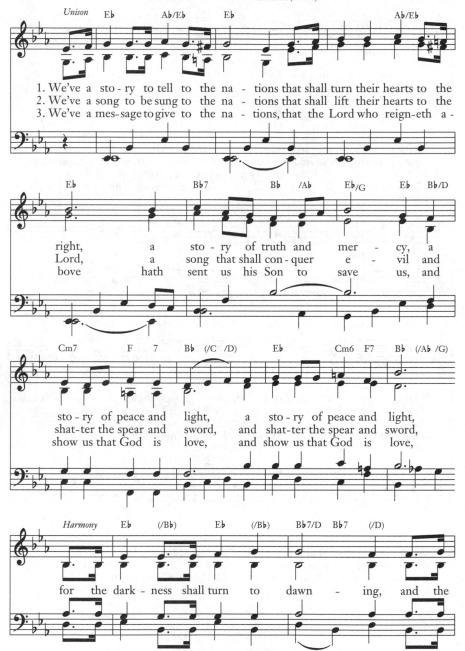

1. We've a sto-ry to tell to the na - tions that shall turn their hearts to the
2. We've a song to be sung to the na - tions that shall lift their hearts to the
3. We've a mes-sage to give to the na - tions, that the Lord who reign-eth a-

right, a sto-ry of truth and mer - cy, a
Lord, a song that shall con - quer e - vil and
bove hath sent us his Son to save us, and

sto - ry of peace and light, a sto - ry of peace and light,
shat - ter the spear and sword, and shat - ter the spear and sword,
show us that God is love, and show us that God is love,

for the dark - ness shall turn to dawn - ing, and the

Words: Colin Sterne (1862-1928) Music: Colin Sterne (1862-1928)

Words: public domain Music: public domain

dawn-ing to noon-day bright, and Christ's great king-dom shall

come on earth, the king-dom of love and light.

766 Amen

AMEN (JOHNSON)

Freely

A - men, a - men,

a - men, a - men.

a - men.

Words: traditional   Music: John Johnson

Lord, speak to me

WINSCOTT 8888 LM

1. Lord, speak to me, that I may speak in liv-ing ech-oes of your tone; as you have sought, so let me seek your err-ing chil-dren lost and lone.
2. Oh lead me, Lord, that I may lead the wan-dering and the wa-vering feet; oh feed me, Lord, that I may feed your hun-gering ones with man-na sweet.
3. Oh teach me, Lord, that I may teach the pre-cious truths that you im-part, and wing my words, that they may reach the hid-den depths of man-y a heart.
4. Oh fill me with your full-ness, Lord, un-til my heart shall o-ver-flow in kin-dling thought and glow-ing word, your love to tell, your praise to show.
5. Oh use me, Lord, use e-ven me just as you will, and when, and where, un-til at last your face I see, your rest, your joy, your glo-ry share.

Words: Frances Ridley Havergal (1836-1879)   Music: Samuel Sebastian Wesley (1810-1876)

Words: public domain   Music: public domain

768 Sometimes a healing word is comfort

WER NUR DEN LIEBEN GOTT 989888

Some-times a heal-ing word

1. is comfort: eas-ing the grieved or anx-ious heart, giv-ing as-sur-ance of our car-ing, treas-ur-ing each and eve-ry part.
2. re-mem-bers: call-ing up days of joy or pain, let-ting the past re-new the pres-ent, till hope can mend and move a-gain.
3. is an-gry: giv-ing a name to dis-con-tent, shin-ing a light on sin or griev-ance, call-ing a peo-ple to re-pent. Come, break the si-lence!
4. takes chanc-es: go-ing where no one yet has been, fac-ing the dan-gers of the des-ert, hop-ing for shel-ter at the inn.
5. will lis-ten: hear-ing the voice-less in-to speech, let-ting the pat-tern of the sto-ry move us to learn what it can teach.

Let us tell the Word that makes us free and well.

Words: Pat Michaels (1954-) Music: George Neumark (1621-1681)

769 Lord of light, whose name and splendour

BETHANY (SMART) 8 7 8 7 D

1. Lord of light, whose name and splen-dour far out-shine the
2. By the faith-ful-ness of work-ers serv-ing you in
3. Grant that know-ledge, still in-creas-ing, at your feet might
4. By pray-ers of faith - ful watch-ers, nev-er si - lent

suns of space, deign to make us your co-work-ers
eve-ry field; by the cour-age where the ra-diance
hum-bly kneel; with your grace our tri - umphs hal-low,
day or night; by the cross of Je - sus bring-ing

in the king-dom of your grace; use us to ful-
of the cross is still re-vealed; by the vic-to-
with your char-i-ty our zeal; lift all na-tions
peace to all, and heal-ing light; by the love that

Words: Howell Elvet Lewis (1860-1953), alt   Music: Henry T. Smart (1813-1879)

Words: copyright © Howell Elvet Lewis. Used by permission of Piers Morgan.   Music: public domain

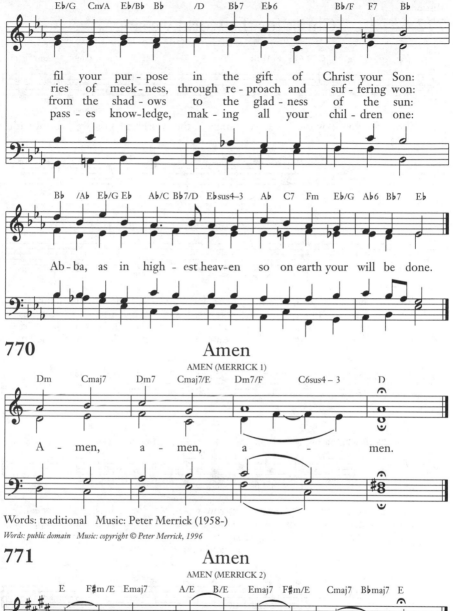

fil your pur - pose in the gift of Christ your Son:
ries of meek - ness, through re - proach and suf - fering won:
from the shad - ows to the glad - ness of the sun:
pass - es know - ledge, mak - ing all your chil - dren one:

Ab - ba, as in high - est heav - en so on earth your will be done.

770 Amen
AMEN (MERRICK 1)

A - men, a - men, a - men.

Words: traditional Music: Peter Merrick (1958-)
Words: public domain Music: copyright © Peter Merrick, 1996

771 Amen
AMEN (MERRICK 2)

A - men, a - men, a - men.

Words: traditional Music: Peter Merrick (1958-)
Words: public domain Music: copyright © Peter Merrick, 1996

772 Christ for the world we sing

MILTON ABBAS 6 6 4 6 6 6 4

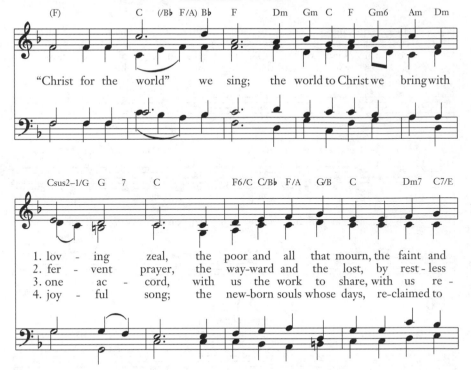

"Christ for the world" we sing; the world to Christ we bring with

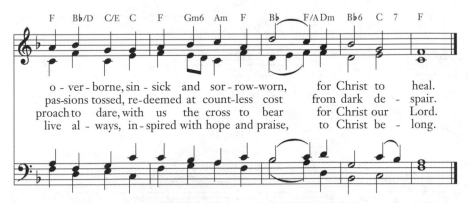

1. lov - ing zeal, the poor and all that mourn, the faint and
2. fer - vent prayer, the way-ward and the lost, by rest-less
3. one ac - cord, with us the work to share, with us re -
4. joy - ful song; the new-born souls whose days, re-claimed to

1. o - ver - borne, sin - sick and sor - row-worn, for Christ to heal.
2. pas-sions tossed, re-deemed at count-less cost from dark de - spair.
3. proach to dare, with us the cross to bear for Christ our Lord.
4. live al - ways, in - spired with hope and praise, to Christ be - long.

Alternate tune: Moscow (Italian Hymn)

Words: Samuel Wolcott (1813-1886)   Music: Eric H. Thiman (1900–1975)

Words: public domain   Music: copyright © estate of Eric H. Thiman

Jesus bids us shine

JESUS BIDS US SHINE 10 11 10 10

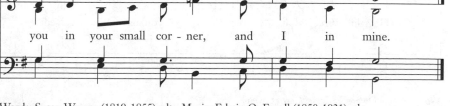

1. Je - sus bids us shine with a pure, clear light,
2. Je - sus bids us shine, first of all for him;
3. Je - sus bids us shine, then, for all a - round;

like a lit - tle can - dle burn - ing in the night.
well he sees and knows it if our light grows dim.
man - y kinds of dark - ness in this world a - bound:

In the world is dark - ness, so we must shine,
He looks down from heav - en to see us shine,
sin and want and sor - row; so we must shine,

you in your small cor - ner, and I in mine.

Words: Susan Warner (1819-1855), alt   Music: Edwin O. Excell (1850-1921), alt

Words: public domain   Music: public domain

God forgave my sin / Freely, freely

FREELY, FREELY 9 9 9 9 with refrain (10 5 10 7)

1. God for-gave my sin in Je-sus' name, I've been
2. All power is given in Je-sus' name, in

born a-gain in Je-sus' name, and in Je-sus' name I
earth and heaven in Je-sus' name, and in Je-sus' name I

come to you to share his love as he told me to.
come to you to share his power as he told me to.

(Org. Ped.)

Refrain *(Unison or improvised harmony)*

He said: "Free - ly, free - ly you have re-ceived;

Words: Carol Owens Music: Carol Owens

freely, freely give. Go in my name and because you believe, others will know that I live."

775

Sent forth by your blessing

ASHGROVE 12 11 12 11 D

1. Sent forth by your bless-ing, our true faith con - fess-ing, your
   The sup - per is end - ed: oh now be ex - tend - ed the
2. With praise and thanks - giv - ing to God ev - er - liv-ing the
   our faith ev - er shar-ing, in love ev - er car-ing, em -

peo - ple, O God, from your ta - ble take leave.
fruits of your ser - vice in all who be - lieve.
task of our eve - ry - day life we will face,
brac - ing as neigh-bours all those of each race.

The seed of your teach - ing, our hun - gry souls
One feast that has fed us, one light that has

Words: Omer Westendorf (1916-)   Music: Welsh traditional

Mission

776 Jesus, life of all the world

GROSSER GOTT 787877

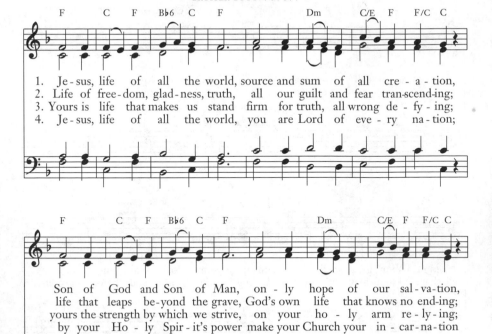

1. Je-sus, life of all the world, source and sum of all cre-a-tion,
2. Life of free-dom, glad-ness, truth, all our guilt and fear tran-scend-ing;
3. Yours is life that makes us stand firm for truth, all wrong de-fy-ing;
4. Je-sus, life of all the world, you are Lord of eve-ry na-tion;

Son of God and Son of Man, on-ly hope of our sal-va-tion,
life that leaps be-yond the grave, God's own life that knows no end-ing;
yours the strength by which we strive, on your ho-ly arm re-ly-ing;
by your Ho-ly Spir-it's power make your Church your in-car-na-tion

Liv-ing Word for all our need, life you give is life in-deed!
life e-ter-nal, gift un-priced, free-ly ours in Je-sus Christ!
yours the war we wage on sin, yours the power by which we win.
till our lives of truth and grace show our world your hu-man face!

Words: Margaret Clarkson (1915-) Music: Katholisches Gesangbuch 1686; harmony, Charles
Winfred Douglas (1867-1944) after Conrad Kocher (1786-1872)

Mission
777
Send me, Lord / Thuma Mina
THUMA MINA Irregular

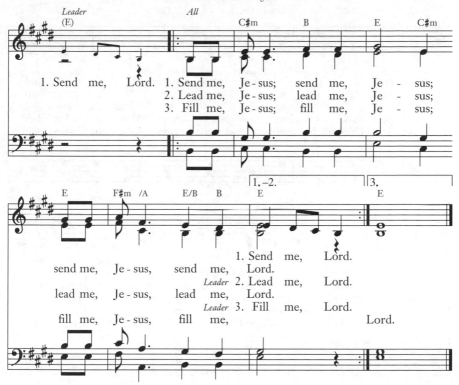

Zulu

Leader Thuma mina.
1. Thuma mina,
thuma mina,
thuma mina, somandla.

Leader Seng' ya vuma.
2. Seng' ya vuma,
seng' ya vuma,
seng' ya vuma, somandla.

French
Leader Prends-moi, Seigneur.
1. Prends-moi, Jé-sus;
prends-moi, Jé-sus;
prends-moi, Jé-sus; oui, prends-moi.

Leader Guide-moi, Seigneur.
2. Guide-moi, Jésus;
guide-moi, Jésus;
guide-moi, Jésus; oui, guide-moi.

Leader Change-moi, Seigneur.
3. Change-moi, Jésus;
change-moi, Jésus;
change-moi, Jésus; oui, change-moi.

Words: South African (Zulu) traditional; French translation, Joëlle Gouël (1943–)
Music: Anders Nyberg (1955–)

Words: French translation, copyright © World Council of Churches, 1990   Music: arrangement, copyright © Walton Music Corporation, 1984

Mission

778
Lord, you give the great commission
HERMON 8 7 8 7 D

1. Lord, you give the great com - mis - sion: "Heal the sick and
2. Lord, you call us to your serv - ice: "In my name bap -
3. Lord, you make the com - mon ho - ly: "This my bo - dy,
4. Lord, you show us love's true meas - ure: "Fath - er, what they
5. Lord, you bless with words as - sur - ing: "I am with you

preach the word." Lest the Church ne - glect its mis - sion
tize and teach." That the world may trust your prom - ise,
this my blood." Let us all for earth's true glo - ry,
do, for - give." Yet we hoard as pri - vate treas - ure
to the end." Faith and hope and love re - stor - ing,

and the Gos - pel go un - heard, help us wit - ness
life a - bun - dant meant for each, give us all new
dai - ly lift life heav - en - ward, ask - ing that the
all that you so free - ly give. May your care and
may we serve as you in - tend, and, a - mid the

Alternate tune: Abbot's Leigh

Words: Jeffery Rowthorn (1934-)   Music: Charles Venn Pilcher (1879-1961); harmony, Walter MacNutt (1910-1996)

to your pur-pose with re-newed in-teg-ri-ty;
fer-vour, draw us clos-er in com-mu-ni-ty;
world a-round us share your chil-dren's lib-er-ty;
mer-cy lead us to a just so-ci-e-ty;
cares that claim us, hold in mind e-ter-ni-ty;

with the Spir-it's gifts em-power us for the work of min-is-try.

779 Amen

AMEN (DRESDEN)

A-men, a - men.

Words: traditional Music: traditional
Words: public domain Music: public domain

780 Amen

AMEN (DANISH)

A-men, a-men, a - men.

Words: traditional Music: traditional
Words: public domain Music: public domain

781 Amen

AMEN (SMITH)

A - men.

A - men.

Words: traditional Music: William Smith (1603-1645)
Words: public domain Music: public domain 983

782   Isaiah the prophet has written of old

ISAIAH THE PROPHET 11 8 11 8 D

1. I - sa - iah the proph - et has writ - ten of old how God's earth - ly king-dom shall come; in - stead of the thorn tree the
2. Yet na - tions still prey on the meek of the world, and con - flict turns par - ent from child. Your peo - ple de - spoil all the

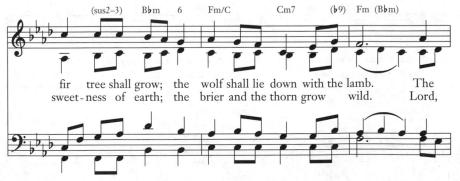

fir tree shall grow; the wolf shall lie down with the lamb. The
sweet-ness of earth; the brier and the thorn grow wild. Lord,

Words: Joy F. Patterson (1931–) Music: American folk melody; arrangement, Alice Parker and Robert Shaw

mountains and hills shall break forth into song, the
hasten to bring in your kingdom on earth, when

peoples be led forth in peace, for the earth shall be filled with the
no one shall hurt or destroy, when wisdom and justice shall

knowledge of God as the waters cover the seas.
reign in the land, and your people shall go forth in joy.

783 The desert shall rejoice and blossom

STERLING 6 6 8 8

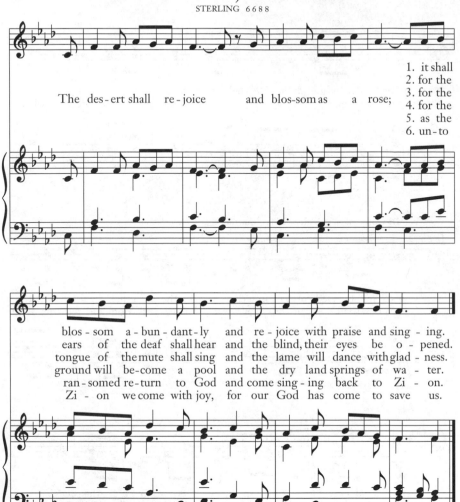

The des-ert shall re-joice and blos-som as a rose;

1. it shall
2. for the
3. for the
4. for the
5. as the
6. un-to

blos-som a-bun-dant-ly and re-joice with praise and sing - ing.
ears of the deaf shall hear and the blind, their eyes be o - pened.
tongue of the mute shall sing and the lame will dance with glad - ness.
ground will be-come a pool and the dry land springs of wa - ter.
ran-somed re-turn to God and come sing - ing back to Zi - on.
Zi - on we come with joy, for our God has come to save us.

Words: Gracia Grindal (1943–) Music: Joy F. Patterson (1931–)

Words: copyright © 1983 by Hope Publishing Co. Music: copyright © 1990 Hope Publishing Co.

784   Thy kingdom come—on bended knee

IRISH 8 6 8 6 CM

1. Thy king - dom come— on bend - ed knee the
2. But the slow watch - es of the night not
3. And lo! al - read - y on the hills the
4. the day in whose clear shin - ing light all
5. when know - ledge, hand in hand with peace, shall

pass - ing a - ges pray, and faith - ful souls have
less to God be - long, and for the ev - er -
flags of dawn ap - pear; gird up your loins, O
wrong shall stand re - vealed, when jus - tice shall be
walk the earth a - broad, the day of per - fect

yearned to see on earth that king - dom's day.
last - ing right the si - lent stars are strong.
proph - et souls; pro - claim the day is near:
clothed with might, and eve - ry hurt be healed,
right - eous - ness, the pro - mised day of God.

Words: Frederick Lucian Hosmer (1840–1929)   Music: Hymns and Sacred Poems, Dublin 1749;
harmony, The English Hymnal 1906

Words: public domain   Music: public domain

785
"Abba, Abba, hear us," we cry
ARIRANG Irregular

1. "Ab - ba, Ab - ba, hear us," we cry; God's Spir-it cries in us
2. with the whole cre - a - tion we cry, groan as in child - birth,
3. As we pray, the Spir - it breathes sighs, sighs far too deep for words;

G   C/G   Gmaj7 (G6   G Am/G)G   D7/A

and pro-claims that we are slaves no more but heirs, the heirs of God.
soon all sin, all death's de - cay will be no more; we shall be free.
God who search - es hearts and knows the Spir-it's mind, hears all our prayer.

G/B   Cmaj7   Am7   D7   G   C/G   G

All cre - a - tion waits, ea - ger and long - ing;

Bm7   Cmaj9   D   G   (G6   G Am/G)G   Am   Bm

Words: Romans 8; paraphrase, Andrew Donaldson (1951–) Music: Korean traditional; harmony, Dale Grotenhuis (1931–)

for the glo-rious free-dom of God's chil-dren soon will be re-vealed.
for the prom-ised glo - ry that we soon shall see, we wait and pray.
as we live in hope we know that in all things God works for good.

786 O day of God, draw nigh

NARENZA 6 6 8 6 SM

1. O   day of God, draw nigh   in beau - ty and in   power;
2. Bring to our trou-bled minds,   un - cer - tain and a - fraid,
3. Bring jus-tice to our land,   that all may dwell se - cure,
4. Bring to our world of strife   your sover-eign word of   peace,
5. O   day of God, draw nigh,   as   at cre - a-tion's   birth,

come with your time-less judge-ment now to match our pres-ent hour.
the qui - et of a stead - fast faith, calm of   a call o - beyed.
and fine - ly build for days to come foun - da - tions that en - dure.
that war may haunt the earth no more and des - o - la-tion cease.
let there be light a - gain, and set your judge-ments in the earth.

Alternate tune: St. Michael

Words: Robert B.Y. Scott (1899–1987) Music: James Hopkirk (1908–1972)

Words: copyright © Emmanuel College Music: copyright © the estate of James Hopkirk, 1938. Used by permission.

787   The kingdom of God is justice and joy

OUT SKERRIES 5 5 5 5 6 5 6 5

1. The king-dom of God is jus - tice and joy,
2. (The) king-dom of God is mer - cy and grace:
3. (The) king-dom of God is chal-lenge and choice;
4. (God's) king-dom is come, the gift and the goal,

for Je - sus re - stores what sin would de - stroy;
the pris-oners are freed, the sin - ners find place,
be - lieve the good news; re - pent and re - joice!
in Je - sus be - gun, in heav - en made whole;

God's pow-er and
the out-cast are
His love for us
the heirs of the

Words: Bryn A. Rees (1911–1983)   Music: Paul Bateman (1954–)

Words: copyright © Mrs. Olwen Scott   Music: copyright © Paul Bateman

Gsus Gm   Bb/C   C7 3   F   Fmaj7   B7   3

glo - ry   in   Je - sus we know,   and here and here-
wel - comed,   God's ban-quet to share,   and hope is a -
sin - ners   brought Christ to his cross,   our cri - sis of
king - dom   shall an-swer his call,   and all things cry,

Gm7   Fsus/C C7 3   Bb   F   Gm7   F   Gm7 F

af – ter   the king-dom shall grow.
wak - ened   in place of de - spair.
judge - ment   for gain or for loss.
"Glo - ry!"   to God all   in   all.

1.–3.   Bbsus   Bb   4.   Bbsus   Bb   Gm7   F

The
The
God's

788
Come, know my joy, the Maker says

FLIGHT OF THE EARLS 8 6 8 6 D CMD

1. "Come, know my joy," the Mak-er says and pours out works of power that
2. The feast we join is long be-gun; God bids us wel-come here to
3. "Come, seek my face," the Giv-er says, "with heart and soul and strength; let
4. "Come, learn of me," the Serv-ant says and mul-ti-plies a feast of

sear the sense, de - fy the mind and fill the soul with awe, and
name and use the sov-ereign gifts with-in our hu-man care. With
fear give way to love; come, step up-on the waves of faith." Dear
loaves and fish, of bread and wine, trans-form-ing eve-ry guest. "Come,"

we with o - pen mouth re-ceive God's gifts with in - fant need, and,
God's own joy some seem to soar, a fierce and ho - ly flame; some
Giv - er, Gift, we seek your face: you share our thorn, our scar. We
says the Host, "from west and east bring gifts to share— come, eat!— none

Alternate tune: Kingsfold

Words: Andrew Donaldson (1951–) Music: Irish traditional melody;
harmony, Francis B. Westbrook (1903–1975)

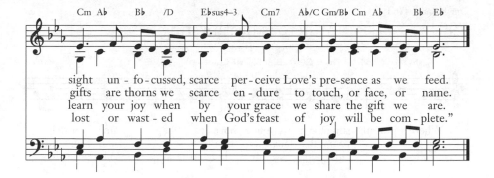

sight un - fo - cussed, scarce per - ceive Love's pre-sence as we feed.
gifts are thorns we scarce en - dure to touch, or face, or name.
learn your joy when by your grace we share the gift we are.
lost or wast - ed when God's feast of joy will be com - plete."

789 O God, our Father in heaven

PATER NOSTER (WEST INDIAN) Irregular

Solo or unison

1. O God, our Fa - ther in heav - en;
2. on earth as it is in heav - en,
3. For - give us our sins, hal-lowed be your name,
4. Save us from the time of tri - al,
5. For the king-dom, the power and the glo - ry,

Unison

your king-dom come, your will be done,
give us to - day our dai - ly bread,
as we for - give those who sin a - gainst us,
and de - liv - er us from e - vil,
are yours now and for - ev - er, a - men,

hal - lowed be your name.

Words: English Language Liturgical Consultation, 1988 Music: West Indian traditional;
arranged by Andrew Donaldson (1951–)

Our Hope in God

790

Where is death's sting

SONG 1   10 10 10 10 10 10

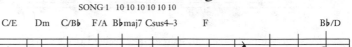

1. Where is death's sting? We were not born to die, nor on - ly
2. Laugh - ter is yours, the laugh-ter free from scorn, and yours the
3. Full - ness of life, in bo - dy, mind and soul; "Who saves their

for the life be - yond the grave; all that is beau - ti -
smile up - on a cheer-ful face: yours, too, the tears, when
life shall lose it," you have said: a great ad - ven - ture

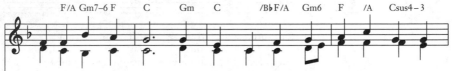

ful in earth and sky, all skill, all know-ledge, all the powers we
love for love must mourn, and death brings si - lence for a lit - tle
with a glo - rious goal; noth - ing that lives in you is ev - er

Words: Godfrey Fox Bradby (1863–c. 1929)   Music: Orlando Gibbons (1583–1625)

Words: public domain   Music: public domain

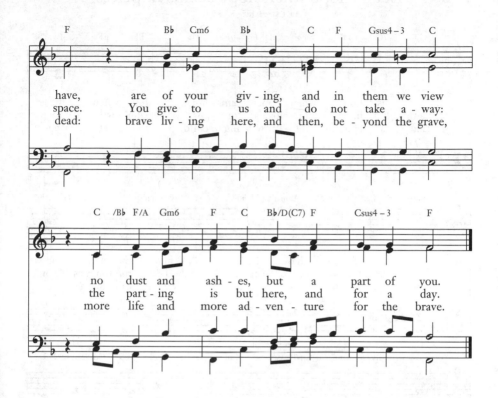

791 Lord God, you now have set
your servant free

SONG 1 10 10 10 10 10 10

Lord God, you now have set your servant free
to go in peace as promised in your word;
my eyes have seen the Saviour Christ the Lord,
prepared by you for all the world to see,
to shine on nations trapped in darkest night,
the glory of your people, and their light.

Words: Luke 2:29–32, paraphrase, Rae E. Whitney (1927–) Music: Orlando Gibbons (1585–1625)
Words: paraphrase, copyright © Church Pension Fund Music: public domain

792 Let us hope when hope seems hopeless

LET US HOPE 8 7 8 7 D

Alternate tune: Hyfrydol

Words: David Beebe (1931–) Music: Emma Lou Diemer (1927–)

Words: copyright © The Pilgrim Press, 1994 Music: copyright © The Pilgrim Press, 1994

sor-row - ing way   and   re - joice   in   har - vest
an - chor sure;   love   shall bloom   in   Love   e -
face   to   face,   un - der - stand   how   love's com -

boun - ty   at   the break - ing   of   the   day.
ter - nal. Faith   and   hope and love   en - dure.
pas - sion blos - soms through a - maz - ing   Grace.

793   Amen

Amen (Robinson)

A - men,   a - men,   a -   men.

Words: traditional   Music: McNeil Robinson II (1943–)

Words: public domain   Music: copyright © Theodore Presser Company, 1984. Reprinted by permission of the publisher

794

Abide with me

EVENTIDE 10 10 10 10

Descant

5. Hold thou thy cross be - fore my clos - ing eyes,
4. Heure a - près heure, il me faut ta pré - sence:

Eb   Bb   7   Cm   Eb/G   Ab   Bb   Cm7 Bb7/D Eb

1. A - bide with me! Fast falls the ev - en - tide;
2. Swift to its close ebbs out life's lit - tle day;
3. I need thy pres - ence eve - ry pass - ing hour;
1. Reste a - vec moi! C'est l'heure où le jour baisse;
2. Le flot des jours ra - pi - de - ment s'é - coule;

shine through the gloom, and point me to the skies; heaven's
le ten - ta - teur ne re - dou - te que toi. Qui

/D Ab/C Eb/Bb Ab   Eb   Fm7 Bb/D Eb Cm6 Bb

the dark - ness deep - ens, Lord, with me a - bide:
earth's joys grow dim; its glo - ries pass a - way;
what but thy grace can foil the tempt-er's power?
l'om - bre gran - dit, Sei - gneur, at - tar - de - toi!
leur gloire est vaine et leur bon - heur dé - çoit;

Words: Henry Francis Lyte (1793–1847)   Music: William Henry Monk (1823–1889)

Words: public domain   Music: public domain

morn - ing breaks and earth's vain shad - ows flee;
donc pren - drait con - tre lui ma de - fense?

Ebsus Bb Cm Eb/G Absus2–1 Caug C7 Fm

when oth - er help - ers fail and com-forts flee,
change and de - cay in all a - round I see:
Who like thy - self my guide and stay can be?
Tous les ap - puis man - quent à ma fai - blesse;
tout change et meurt, tout chan-celle et s'é - croule;

in life, in death, O Lord a - bide with me.
Dans l'om-bre ou la clar - té, reste a - vec moi!

Bb/Ab Eb/G Bb7/F Eb Bb Cm Ab Eb/Ab Bb7 Eb

help of the help-less, oh a - bide with me.
O thou who chang-est not, a - bide with me.
Through cloud and sun-shine, oh a - bide with me.
for - ce du faible, O Christ, reste a - vec moi!
toi qui ne chan-ges point, reste a - vec moi!

4. I fear no foe with thee at hand to bless;
   ills have no weight and tears no bitterness:
   where is death's sting? Where, grave, thy victory?
   I triumph still if thou abide with me.

5. Hold thou thy cross before my closing eyes,
   shine through the gloom, and point me to the skies;
   heaven's morning breaks, and earth's vain shadows flee;
   in life, in death, O Lord, abide with me.

3. J'ose implorer plus qu'un regard qui passe;
   viens, comme à tes disciples autrefois,
   plein de douceur, de tendresse et de grâce,
   et pour toujours, Seigneur, reste avec moi!

4. Heure après heure, il me faut ta présence,
   le tentateur ne redoute que toi.
   Qui donc prendrait contre lui ma défense?
   Dans l'ombre ou la clarté, reste avec moi!

Christ is coming

UNSER HERRSCHER 8 7 8 7 8 7

1. Christ is com - ing! let cre - a - tion from its groans and
2. Earth can now but tell the sto - ry of your bit - ter
3. With that bless - ed hope be - fore us, flutes are tuned and
4. Long your ex - iles have been pin - ing for your prom - ised

la - bour cease; let the glo - rious pro - cla - ma - tion
cross and pain; we shall yet be - hold your glo - ry,
harps are strung; let the might - y ad - vent cho - rus
rest and home, but in heaven - ly glo - ry shin - ing,

hope re - store and faith in - crease:
Lord, when you re - turn to reign:
on - ward roll from tongue to tongue: Christ is com - ing!
soon the ris - en Christ shall come.

Words: John Ross Macduff (1818–1895), alt   Music: Joachim Neander (1650–1680)

Words: public domain   Music: public domain

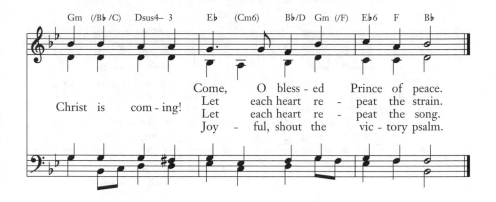

Come, O bless-ed Prince of peace.
Christ is com-ing! Let each heart re-peat the strain.
Let each heart re-peat the song.
Joy-ful, shout the vic-tory psalm.

796 And every one 'neath their vine and fig tree

SHALOM 10 8 8 8

May be sung as a round

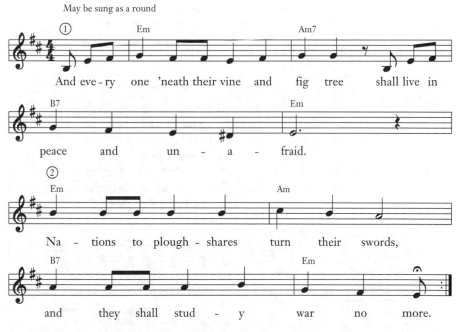

And eve-ry one 'neath their vine and fig tree shall live in

peace and un-a-fraid.

Na-tions to plough-shares turn their swords,

and they shall stud-y war no more.

Words: Micah 4:3–4; paraphrase, Shalom Altman   Music: Shalom Altman

Shall we gather at the river

HANSON PLACE 8 7 8 7 with refrain (8 10 9 7)

1. Shall we gath-er at the riv - er, where bright an - gel feet have trod,
2. On the bos-om of the riv - er, where the Sav-iour King we own,
3. Ere we reach the shin-ing riv - er, lay we eve-ry bur-den down;
4. Soon we'll reach the shin-ing riv - er, soon our pil-grim-age will cease;

with its crys-tal tide for - ev - er flow-ing by the throne of God?
we shall meet, and sor - row nev - er 'neath the glo - ry of the throne.
grace our spir-its will de - liv - er, and pro-vide a robe and crown.
soon our hap - py hearts will quiv - er with the mel - o - dy of peace.

Refrain

Yes, we'll gath-er at the riv - er, the beau-ti-ful, the beau-ti-ful riv - er,

gath-er with the saints at the riv - er that flows by the throne of God.

Words: Robert Lowry (1826–1899) Music: Robert Lowry (1826–1899)

Words: public domain Music: public domain

798
What gift can we bring
ANNIVERSARY SONG 11 11 11 11

1. What gift can we bring, what pres - ent, what to - ken?
2. Give thanks for the past, for those who had vi - sion,
3. Give thanks for to - mor - row, ful of sur - pris - es,
4. This gift we now bring, this pres - ent, this to - ken,

What words can con - vey it, the joy of this day?
who plant - ed and wa - tered so dreams could come true.
for know - ing what - ev - er to - mor - row may bring,
these words can con - vey it, the joy of this day!

When grate - ful we come, re - mem - ber - ing, re - joic - ing,
Give thanks for the now, for stud - y, for wor - ship,
the word is our prom - ise al - ways, for - ev - er;
When grate - ful we come, re - mem - ber - ing, re - joic - ing,

what song can we of - fer in hon - our and praise?
for mis - sion that bids us turn prayer in - to deed.
we rest in God's keep - ing and live in God's love.
this song we now of - fer in hon - our and praise!

Words: Jane Marshall (1924-) Music: Jane Marshall (1924-)

799 God is here! as we your people meet

BLAENWERN 8787D

1. God is here! As we your peo - ple meet to of - fer
2. Here are sym - bols to re - mind us of our life - long
3. Here our chil - dren find a wel - come in the Shep - herd's
4. Sov - ereign God of Church and King - dom, in an age of

praise and prayer, may we find in full - er mea - sure
need of grace; here are ta - ble, font and pul - pit,
flock and fold; here, as bread and wine are tak - en,
change and doubt keep us faith - ful to the gos - pel;

what it is in Christ we share. Here, as in the world a -
here the cross has cen - tral place. Here in hon - es - ty of
Christ sus - tains us, as of old. Here the ser - vants of the
help us work your pur - pose out. Here, in this day's ded - i -

Alternate tune: Abbot's Leigh

Words: Fred Pratt Green (1903-)   Music: William P. Rowlands (1860-1937)

Words: copyright © 1979 by Hope Publishing Co.   Music: public domain

round us, all our var - ied skills and arts wait the
preach - ing, here in si - lence, as in speech, here, in
Ser - vant seek in wor - ship to ex - plore what it
ca - tion, all we have to give, re - ceive; we, who

com - ing of the Spir - it in - to o - pen minds and hearts.
new - ness and re - new - al, God the Spir - it comes to each.
means in dai - ly liv - ing to be - lieve and to a - dore.
can - not live with - out you, we a - dore you; we be - lieve.

800   O Canada

O CANADA 10 10 8 6 8 6 8 10 10

1. O Can - a - da our home and na - tive land,
2. Al - might - y Love, by thy mys - te - rious power,
1. Ô Ca - na - da! Ter - re de nos aï - eux,

true pa - triot love in all our hearts com - mand.
in wis - dom guide, with faith and free - dom dower,
ton front est ceint de fleu - rons glo - ri - eux.

With glow - ing hearts, thy chil - dren stand,
be ours a na - tion ev - er - more
Car ta main, de paix in - spir - é - e,

the true north strong and free; from far and wide,
that no op - pres - sion blights, where jus - tice rules
sait main - te - nir le droit, ton his - toire est une

Words: French, Adolphe B. Routhier (1839–1920), alt; English v. 1, Robert Stanley Weir (1856-1926), alt;
v.2, Albert C. Watson (1859-1926) Music: Calixa Lavallée (1842-1891); arrangement, Frederick C.
Silvester (1901-1966)

801 From ocean unto ocean

ELLACOMBE 7 6 7 6 D

1. From o - cean un - to o - cean our land shall name you Lord,
2. O Christ, we pray be - fore you: come in your power to dwell.
3. Our Sav - our King, de - fend us, and guide where we should go;

and, filled with true de - vo - tion, o - bey your sov-ereign word;
Now hum-bly we im - plore you: make this land whole and well,
forth with your mes-sage send us, your love and light to show;

our prair - ies and our moun - tains, for - est and fer - tile field, our
and may we know, Lord Je - sus, the touch of your dear hand, and,
till, fired with true de - vo - tion and kin-dled by your word, from

riv - ers. lakes and foun - tains to you shall trib - ute yield.
healed of our dis - eas - es, the tempt-er's power with-stand.
o - cean un - to o - cean our land shall name you Lord.

Words: Robert Murray (1832-1909) Music: Mainz Song Book 1833

Words: public domain Music: public domain

802   For the fruits of all creation

AR HYD Y NOS 12 12 8 8 12

1. For the fruits of all cre - a - tion,
   for the gifts to eve - ry na - tion, thanks be to God;
2. In the just re - ward of la - bour,
   in the help we give our neigh-bour, God's will is done;
3. For the har-vests of the Spir - it,
   for the good we all in - her - it, thanks be to God;

for the plough-ing, sow-ing, reap-ing, si - lent growth while we are sleep-ing,
in our world-wide task of car - ing for the hun - gry and des - pair-ing,
for the won - ders that as-tound us, for the truths that still con-found us,

fu - ture needs in earth's safe-keep-ing, thanks be to God.
in the har-vests we are shar-ing, God's will is done.
most of all, that love has found us, thanks be to God.

Words: Fred Pratt Green (1903–)   Music: Welsh traditional

Words: copyright © 1970 by Hope Publishing Co.   Music: public domain

Harvest Thanksgiving

803   Come, ye thankful people, come

ST. GEORGE'S, WINDSOR   7 7 7 7 D

1. Come, ye thank-ful peo - ple, come, raise the song of har - vest home;
2. All the world is God's own field, fruit un - to God's praise to yield;
3. For the Lord our God shall come and shall take the har - vest home;
4. E - ven so, Lord, quick - ly come to thy fi - nal har - vest home:

all is safe - ly gath - ered in, ere the win - ter storms be - gin;
wheat and weeds to - geth - er sown, un - to joy or sor - row grown;
from the field shall in that day all of - fenc - es purge a - way,
gath - er thou thy peo - ple in, free from sor - row, free from sin;

Descant

4. there, for - ev - er pu - ri - fied, in thy pres - ence

God, our Mak - er, doth pro - vide for our wants to
first the blade and then the ear, then the full corn
give the an - gels charge at last in the fire the
there, for - ev - er pu - ri - fied, in thy pres - ence

Words: Henry Alford (1810–1871) Music: George Job Elvey (1816–1893); descant, C.S. Lang
(1891–1971)

Words: public domain Music: descant, copyright © Novello & Co. Ltd.

to a - bide. Come with all thine an - gels,

be sup - plied. Come, to God's own tem - ple,
shall ap - pear. Lord of har - vest, grant that
tares to cast, but the fruit - ful ears to
to a - bide. Come, with all thine an - gels,

come: raise the glo - rious har - vest home.

come: raise the song of har - vest home.
we whole - some grain and pure may be.
store in God's store - house ev - er - more.
come: raise the glo - rious har - vest home.

804   For all your goodness, God

FOR ALL YOUR GOODNESS, LORD   10 6 6 10

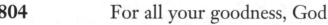

May be sung as a round

① For all your good - ness, God, we give you thanks.

② Thanks for the food we eat, and for the friends we meet;

③ for each new day we greet, we give you thanks.

Words: traditional American   Music: German traditional; arrangement, Darryl Nixon (1952–)

805

Give thanks, my soul, for harvest

CRÜGER 7 6 7 6 D

1. Give thanks, my soul, for har - vest, for store of fruit and grain,
2. Give thanks, my soul, for rich - es of wood-land, mine and hill,
3. Give thanks, my soul, for la - bours that strength and days em - ploy,
4. Give thanks, my soul, for beau - ty, for vi - sion, hope and skill,

but know the own - er gives us that we may share a - gain;
but know that gold and tim - ber are the Cre - a - tor's still,
but know your Mak-er's pur - pose brings toil as well as joy.
for Christ, di - vine re - veal - er of God's re - deem-ing will.

where souls are lone and hun - gry, where need - y chil-dren cry,
and God's on loan to stew - ards to fash-ion and to share,
Where leads the path to er - ror, where jus - tice lies in chain,
Show forth, O God, your pur - pose; di - rect our will and hand

Alternate tune: Wolvercote

Words: William Watkins Reid (1890–) Music: Johann Crüger (1598–1662);
arrangement, William H. Monk (1823–1889)

Words: copyright © The Hymn Society, 1961, renewal 1989. All rights reserved. Used by permission of Hope Publishing Co. Music: public domain

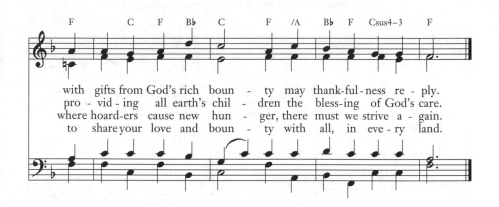

with gifts from God's rich boun - ty may thank-ful-ness re - ply.
pro - vid - ing all earth's chil - dren the bless-ing of God's care.
where hoard-ers cause new hun - ger, there must we strive a - gain.
to share your love and boun - ty with all, in eve - ry land.

806   To bless the earth

CHRISTUS, DER IST MEIN LEBEN 7 6 7 6

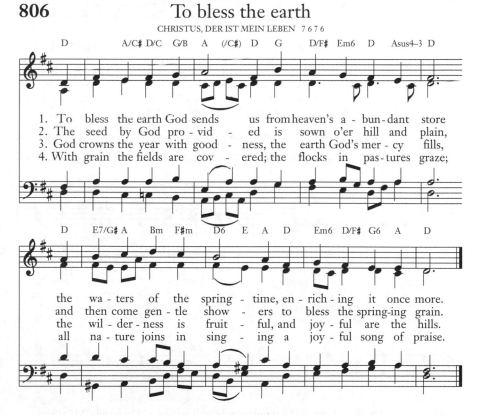

1. To bless the earth God sends us from heaven's a - bun-dant store
2. The seed by God pro - vid - ed is sown o'er hill and plain,
3. God crowns the year with good - ness, the earth God's mer - cy fills,
4. With grain the fields are cov - ered; the flocks in pas - tures graze;

the wa - ters of the spring - time, en - rich - ing it once more.
and then come gen - tle show - ers to bless the spring-ing grain.
the wil - der - ness is fruit - ful, and joy - ful are the hills.
all na - ture joins in sing - ing a joy - ful song of praise.

Words: Psalm 65; paraphrase, Psalter, 1912   Music: Melchior Vulpius (c.1570–1615),
arrangement, Johann Sebastian Bach (1685–1750)

Words: public domain   Music: public domain

807 We plough the fields and scatter

WIR PFLÜGEN (DRESDEN) 7 6 7 6 D with refrain

1. We plough the fields and scat - ter the good seed on the
2. You on - ly are the Mak - er of all things near and
3. We thank you, our pro - vid - er, for all things bright and
1. Les as - tres dans leur cour - se, l'o - rage et les é -
2. La per - le de ro - sé - e, les grap - pes de rai -
3. Bé - nis, bé - nis, mon â - me, le Dieu de Jé - sus -

land, but it is fed and wa - tered by
far; you paint the way - side flow - er, you
good, the seed - time and the har - vest, our
clairs, le gai ba - bil des sour - ces, le
sin, le chant de l'é - pou - sé - e, l'a -
Christ, et ses bien - faits pro - cla - me, bien -

God's al - migh - ty hand: you send the snow in win - ter, the
light the eve - ning star; the winds and waves o - bey you; by
life, our health, our food. No gifts have we to of - fer for
vol de l'ai - gle fier', le tendre a - mour d'un pè - re, un
rô - me du bon pain et le joy - eux cor - tè - ge des
faits d'un si grand prix. Il sème en a - bon - dan - ce, le

Words: Matthias Claudius (1740–1815); translation, Jane Montgomery Campbell (1817–1878)
Music: Johann Abraham Schulz (1747–1800)

Words: public domain Music: public domain

warmth to swell the grain, the breez - es and the
you the birds are fed; much more to us, your
all your love im - parts, but that which you most
beau re - gard d'en - fant, le sang dans nos ar -
mois et des sai - sons, les fins cris - taux de
long de tes sen - tiers, les dons qu'en sa clé -

sun - shine, and soft re - fresh - ing rain.
chil - dren, you give our dai - ly bread.
wel - come: our hum - ble, thank - ful hearts.
tè - res: tout vient du Dieu vi - vant. Bé -
nei - ge, à Dieu nous les de - vons. Bé -
men - ce il veut mul - ti - pli - er. Bé -

Refrain

All good gifts a - round us are sent from heaven a - bove; we
nis ton Dieu sans ces - se, ô peu - ple des chré - tiens, fais

thank you, Lord, we thank you, Lord for all your love.
tien - nes ses pro - mes - ses, jou - is de tous ses biens.

808 Come in, come in, New Year

CROFT'S 136TH 666688

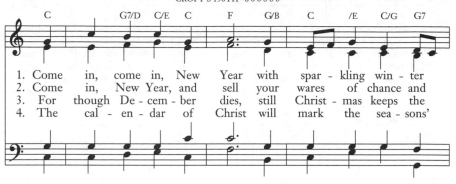

1. Come in, come in, New Year with spar - kling win - ter
2. Come in, New Year, and sell your wares of chance and
3. For though De - cem - ber dies, still Christ - mas keeps the
4. The cal - en - dar of Christ will mark the sea - sons'

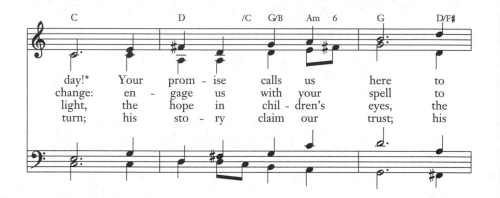

day!* Your prom - ise calls us here to
change: en - gage us with your spell to
light, the hope in chil - dren's eyes, the
turn; his sto - ry claim our trust; his

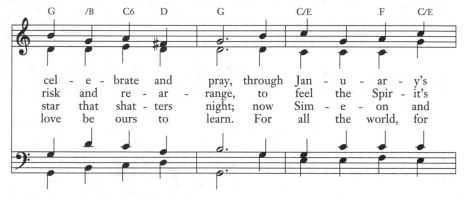

cel - e - brate and pray, through Jan - u - ar - y's
risk and re - ar - range, to feel the Spir - it's
star that shat - ters night; now Sim - e - on and
love be ours to learn. For all the world, for

* original words: shining summer day

Words: Shirley Murray (1931–) Music: William Croft (1678–1727); harmony, Hymns Ancient and Modern, revised 1950

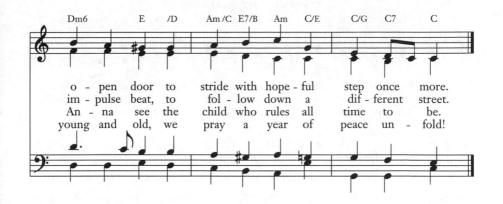

o - pen door to stride with hope - ful step once more.
im - pulse beat, to fol - low down a dif - ferent street.
An - na see the child who rules all time to be.
young and old, we pray a year of peace un - fold!

Old and New Year

809

All beautiful the march of days

CHRISTMAS CAROL 8 6 8 6 D CMD

1. All beau-ti-ful the march of days, as sea-sons come and go;
2. O'er white ex-pans-es spar-kling pure the ra-diant morns un-fold;
3. O thou from whose un-fath-omed law the year in beau-ty flows,

the hand that shaped the rose hath wrought the cry-stal of the snow,
the sol-emn splen-dours of the night burn bright-er through the cold;
thy-self the vi-sion pas-sing by in cry-stal and in rose;

hath sent the hoar-y frost of heaven, the flow-ing wa-ters sealed,
life mounts in eve-ry throb-bing vein, love deep-ens round the hearth,
day un-to day doth ut-ter speech, and night to night pro-claim

and laid a si-lent love-li-ness on hill and wood and field.
and clear-er sounds the an-gel hymn, good will to all on earth.
in ev-er-chang-ing words of light the won - der of thy name.

Words: Frances Whitmarsh Wile (1878–1939) Music: Henry Walford Davies (1869–1941)

810   Now greet the swiftly changing year

SIXTH NIGHT 8886

1. Now greet the swift - ly chang - ing year with
2. Christ's love a - bun - dant far ex - ceeds the
3. With such a God to lead our way in
4. "All glo - ry be to God on high and

joy and pen - i - tence sin - cere; re - joice, re - joice, with
vol - ume of a whole year's needs; re - joice, re - joice, with
haz - ard and pros - per - i - ty, what need we fear in
peace on earth," the an - gels cry; re - joice, re - joice, with

thanks em - brace an - oth - er year of grace.
thanks em - brace an - oth - er year of grace.
earth or space in this new year of grace?
thanks em - brace an - oth - er year of grace.

Words: anonymous 17th century Slovak; translation, Jaroslav J. Vajda (1919–)
Music: Alfred V. Fedak (1953–)

Words: translation, copyright © Jaroslav J. Vajda, 1990, alt Music: copyright © Selah Publishing Co., Inc., 1990

811

Standing at the portal

ST. ALBAN'S 6 5 6 5 D with refrain

1. Stand-ing at the por - tal of the o-pening year,
words of com-fort meet us hush-ing eve-ry fear,
spo-ken through the si - lence by God's lov-ing voice,
ten - der, strong and faith - ful, mak-ing us re - joice.

2. "I, your God, am with you: do not be a - fraid;
I will help and strength - en; do not be dis-mayed,
for I will up - hold you with my own right hand;
you are called and cho - sen in my sight to stand."

3. God will not for - sake us and will nev - er fail;
God's e - ter - nal cov - enant ev - er will pre - vail.
Rest-ing on this prom - ise, what have we to fear?
God is all - suf - fi - cient for the com - ing year.

Words: Frances Ridley Havergal (1836–1879) Music: Franz Joseph Haydn (1732–1809)

Words: public domain Music: public domain

Refrain

On-ward, then, and fear not, chil-dren of the day, for God's word shall nev - er, nev - er pass a - way.

812 Glory to God

GLORIA (TAIZÉ) Irregular

① Dm Gm C F ② Dm Gm C F

Glo-ry to God, glo-ry to God, glo-ry in the high-est!
Glo - ri - a, glo - ri - a, in ex-cel - sis De - o!
Gloi-re à Dieu, gloi-re à Dieu, gloi-re dans les hauts-lieux!

③ Dm Gm C F ④ Dm Gm C F

Glo-ry to God, glo-ry to God. Hal-le-lu-jah, hal-le-lu-jah!
Glo - ri - a, glo - ri - a. Al-le-lu-ia, al-le-lu-ia!
Gloi-re à Dieu, gloi-re à Dieu. Al-lé-lu-ia, al-le-lu-ia!

May be sung as a round.

Accompaniment

Instrumental Descant

Fine

Words: Luke 2:4; paraphrase, traditional   Music: Taizé Community (France)

813

Father, we praise thee

CHRISTE SANCTORUM 11 11 11 5

1. Fa - ther, we praise thee, now the night is o - ver; ac - tive and watch - ful, stand we all be - fore thee; sing - ing, we of - fer prayer and med - i - ta - tion: thus we a - dore thee.
2. Mon - arch of all things, fit us for thy man - sions; ban - ish our weak - ness, health and whole - ness send - ing; bring us to heav - en, where thy saints u - nit - ed joy with - out end - ing.
3. All - ho - ly Fa - ther, Son and e - qual Spir - it, trin - i - ty bless - ed, send us thy sal - va - tion; thine is the glo - ry, gleam - ing and re - sound - ing through all cre - a - tion.

Words: ascribed to Gregory the Great (540–604); translation, Percy Dearmer (1867–1936)
Music: Paris Antiphoner 1681; harmony, Ralph Vaughan Williams (1872–1958)

Words: translation, copyright © Oxford University Press   Music: harmony, copyright © Oxford University Press from The English Hymnal

814

Morning has broken

BUNESSAN 5 5 5 4 D

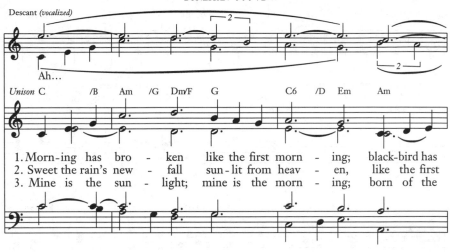

Words: Eleanor Farjeon (1881–1965), Enlarged Songs of Praise 1931   Music: Gaelic melody; arrangement, John Wilson (1905–1992)

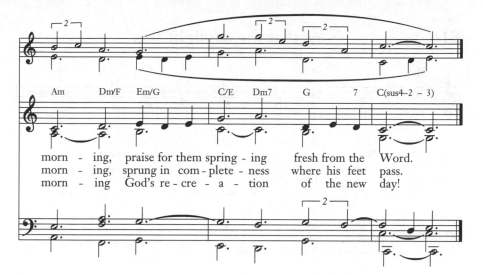

Am   Dm/F   Em/G   C/E   Dm7   G   7   C(sus4–2 – 3)

morn - ing,   praise for them spring - ing   fresh from the   Word.
morn - ing,   sprung in com - plete - ness   where his feet   pass.
morn - ing   God's re - cre - a - tion   of   the new   day!

815   New every morning is the love
MELCOMBE 8 8 8 8 LM

D   /F#   Em6   D   A   Bm   G   D   A/C#   Bm6   A/C# D(E7)   F#m   D6   E7   A

1. New eve - ry morn - ing   is   the love our wak - ing and up - ris - ing prove;
2. New mer - cies each   re - turn - ing   day   a - round us hov - er while we pray,
3. If on our dai - ly   course our mind be   set   to hal - low   all   we find,
4. The triv - ial round, the com - mon task, will   fur - nish all   we ought to   ask,
5. On - ly, O Lord, in   thy dear love, fit   us   for per - fect rest a - bove,

D   Bm   G   D/F#   D   A   D/F#   Em   A7/C#   D   A/G D/F#   G   D/A   A 7   D

through sleep and dark - ness safe - ly brought, re - stored   to   life   and power and thought.
new per - ils past, new sins for - given, new thoughts of God, new hopes of heaven.
new treas - ures still of count - less price God   will   pro - vide for   sac - ri - fice.
room to de - ny our - selves, a road to   bring   us dai - ly   near - er   God.
and help us, this and eve - ry day   to   live more near - ly   as   we pray.

Words: John Keble (1792–1866) Music: Samuel Webbe, the elder (1740–1816)

816 Now that the daylight fills

HERR, JESU CHRIST 8 8 8 8 LM

1. Now that the day - light fills the sky, we lift our hearts to heaven on high, that God, in all we do or say, would keep us free from harm this day.

2. Our hearts and lips may God re - strain; keep us from caus - ing oth - ers pain, that we may see and serve the Son, and grow in love for eve - ry - one.

3. From e - vil may God guard our eyes, our ears from emp - ty praise and lies; from self - ish - ness our hearts re - lease, that we may serve, and know God's peace,

4. that we, when this new day is gone, and night in turn is draw - ing on, with con - science free from sin and blame, may praise and bless the ho - ly Name.

5. To God the Fa - ther, heaven - ly Light, to Christ, re - vealed in earth - ly night, to God the Ho - ly Ghost we raise our e - qual and un - ceas - ing praise.

Alternate tune: Warrington

Words: Ambrose of Milan (340–397); translation, John Mason Neale (1818–1866)
Music: melody from Cantionale Germanicum 1628; harmony, Gothaischer Cantional 1651, alt

Words: public domain Music: public domain

Morning

817 O splendour of God's glory bright

SOLEMNIS HAEC FESTIVITAS 8 8 8 8 LM

1. O splen - dour of God's glo - ry bright, from light e -
2. Come, ver - y Sun of heav - en's love, in last - ing
3. And now to you our prayers as - cend, Cre - a - tor,
4. Con - firm our will to do the right, and keep our
5. Dawn's glo - ry gilds the earth and skies: let him, our

ter - nal bring - ing light! O Light of Light, light's
ra - diance from a - bove, and to our in - ward
glo - rious with - out end; we plead your sov - ereign
hearts from en - vy's blight; let faith its ea - ger
per - fect morn, a - rise— the Word in God the

liv - ing spring, true day, all days il - lu - min - ing.
hearts con - vey the Ho - ly Spir - it's cloud - less ray.
grace for power to con - quer in temp - ta - tion's hour.
fires re - new, and hate the false, and love the true.
Fa - ther one, the Fa - ther im - aged in the Son.

Words: Ambrose of Milan (340–397); translation, Louis Fitzgerald Benson (1855–1930)
Music: Paris Gradual 1685; harmony, Arthur Hutchings (1906–1989)

Words: public domain Music: harmony, copyright © Oxford University Press

O Jesus, Lord of heavenly grace

GONFALON ROYAL 8 8 8 8 LM

1. O Je - sus, Lord of heaven - ly grace,
2. Come, ho - ly Sun of heaven - ly love,
3. May faith, deep - root - ed in the soul,
4. Oh hal - lowed be the ap - proach - ing day;
5. O Christ, with each re - turn - ing morn,

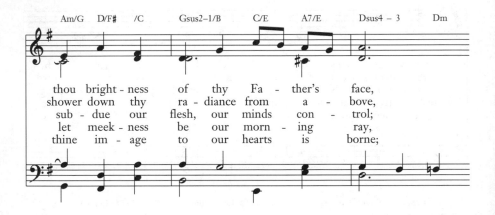

thou bright - ness of thy Fa - ther's face,
shower down thy ra - diance from a - bove,
sub - due our flesh, our minds con - trol;
let meek - ness be our morn - ing ray,
thine im - age to our hearts is borne;

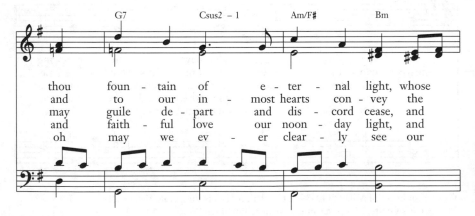

thou foun - tain of e - ter - nal light, whose
and to our in - most hearts con - vey the
may guile de - part and dis - cord cease, and
and faith - ful love our noon - day light, and
oh may we ev - er clear - ly see our

Alternate tunes: Melcombe   Solothurn

Words: anonymous Latin, 4th cent.; translation, John Chandler (1806–1876) and anonymous
Music: Percy Carter Buck (1871–1947)

Words: public domain   Music: harmony, copyright © Oxford University Press from The English Hymnal

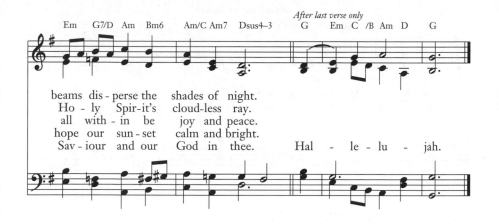

beams dis-perse the shades of night.
Ho-ly Spir-it's cloud-less ray.
all with-in be joy and peace.
hope our sun-set calm and bright.
Sav-iour and our God in thee. Hal - le - lu - jah.

819 Awake, arise, oh sing a new song

AWAKE, ARISE Irregular

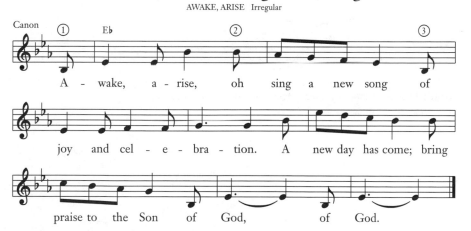

A - wake, a - rise, oh sing a new song of
joy and cel - e - bra - tion. A new day has come; bring
praise to the Son of God, of God.

Words: Marna Leasure (20th cent.)   Music: Marna Leasure (20th cent.)

820

Holy God, holy and mighty

TRISAGION 8 1118,668

Ho - ly, ho - ly, ho - ly God, ho - ly and might - y,
A - gi - os O The - os, a - gi - os is - chi - ros.

ho - ly and e - ter - nal, have mer - cy on us.
a - gi - os a - tha - na - tos, e - le - i - son i - mas.

Words: Russian Orthodox Liturgy   Music: Russian Orthodox Liturgy

Words: public domain   Music: public domain

821

Sun of my soul, my Saviour dear

HURSLEY 8 8 8 8 LM

1. Sun of my soul, my Sav - iour dear, it is not night if you are near; oh may no earth - born cloud a - rise to hide you from your serv - ant's eyes.

2. When the soft dews of kind - ly sleep my wea - ried eye - lids gent - ly steep, be my last thought: How sweet to rest for - ev - er on my Sav - iour's breast.

3. Watch by the sick; en - rich the poor with bless - ings from your bound - less store; be eve - ry mourn - er's sleep to - night, like in - fants' slum - bers, pure and light.

4. Come near and bless us when we wake, as through the world our way we take, till in the o - cean of your love we lose our - selves in heav - en a - bove.

Words: John Keble (1792–1866) Music: Katholisches Gesangbuch c. 1774;
harmony, Carman H. Milligan (1909–)

Words: public domain Music: harmony, copyright © Carman H. Milligan

822 All praise to thee, my God, this night

TALLIS' CANON 8 8 8 8 LM

May be sung as a round

1. All praise to thee, my God, this night, for all the bless-ings
2. For-give me, Lord, through Christ, I pray, the wrong that I have
3. Oh may my soul on thee re-pose, and with sweet sleep mine
4. Praise God, from whom all bless-ings flow; praise God, all crea-tures

of the light; keep me, oh keep me, safe from harm with-
done this day, that I, be-fore I sleep, may be at
eye-lids close. Sleep that shall me more vig-orous make to
here be-low; praise God a-bove, ye heav-enly host; praise

for canon only

in the shel-ter of thine arm. (-ter of thine arm)
peace with neigh-bour, self and thee. (-bour, self and thee.)
serve thee, God, when I a-wake. (when I a-wake.)
Fa-ther, Son and Ho-ly Ghost. (and Ho-ly Ghost.)

Words: Thomas Ken (1637–1711) Music: Thomas Tallis (c. 1505–1585)

Words: public domain Music: public domain

823 O Laughing Light, O firstborn of creation

ANGERS 11 11 11 5

1. O Laugh-ing Light, O first - born of cre - a - tion,
2. Day's light is frag - ile. Your light is e - ter - nal.
3. Light of the world, O Je - sus, you are wor - thy!

ra - diance of glo - ry, light from light be - got - ten, God self-re-
We look to you, our light with - in the sha - dow. We sing to
Giv - er of Life and Child of God we praise you. Here as the

veal - ing, ho - ly, bright and bless - ed, you shine up - on us.
you Cre - a - tor, Christ and Spir - it; you shine be - fore us.
u - ni - verse pro-claims your glo - ry! You shine a - mong us.

Words: Sylvia G. Dunstan (1955–1993) Music: Chartres Antiphoner 1784,
harmony, Gerald H. Knight (1908–1979)

824 At evening, when the sun had set

ANGELUS 8 8 8 8 LM

1. At eve - ning, when the sun had set, the sick, O
2. Once more the eve - ning falls, and we, op - pressed with
3. O Sav - iour Christ, our cares dis - pel, for some are
4. and all de - sire your per - fect rest, for none is
5. O Sav - iour Christ, O Son of Man, you have been

Lord, a - round you lay: in such dis - tress and
ma - ny ills, draw near, and though your form we
sick, and some are sad, and some have nev - er
whol - ly free from sin, and those who long to
trou - bled, tempt - ed, tried; your kind but search - ing

pain they met, but with what joy they went a - way!
can - not see, we know and feel that you are here.
loved you well, and some have lost the love they had,
serve you best are most a - ware of wrong with - in.
glance can scan the ver - y wounds that shame would hide.

6. Your touch still holds its ancient power;
   no word from you can fruitless fall:
   hear us, touch us in this hour,
   and in your mercy heal us all.

Words: Henry Twells (1823–1900), alt Music: Cantica Spiritualia 1847; melody, Georg Joseph (d.1668)

825 Saviour, again to your dear name

ELLERS 10 10 10 10

1. Sav - iour, a - gain to your dear name we raise
2. Grant us your peace up - on our home-ward way;
3. Grant us your peace as day turns in - to night;
4. Grant us your peace through - out our earth - ly life,

with one ac - cord our part - ing hymn of praise:
with you be - gan, with you shall end the day;
stay with us till the com - ing of the light;
our balm in sor - row and our stay in strife;

we join to bless you, ere our wor - ship cease,
guard all the lips from sin, the hearts from shame
keep safe all those who call up - on your name,
then, when your voice shall bid our con - flict cease,

then, in the si - lence, wait your word of peace.
that in this house have called up - on your name.
for dark and light to you are both the same.
call us, O God, to your e - ter - nal peace.

Words: John Ellerton (1826–1893) Music: Edward John Hopkins (1818–1901);
harmony, Carman H. Milligan (1909–)

Words: public domain Music: harmony, copyright © Carman H. Milligan

826

The day you gave us, Lord, has ended

ST. CLEMENT 9 8 9 8

5. So be it, Lord, your throne shall nev - er,

1. The day you gave us, Lord, has end - ed;
2. We thank you that your church, un - sleep - ing
3. As to each con - ti - nent and is - land
4. The sun that bids us rest is wak - ing
5. So be it, Lord, your throne shall nev - er,

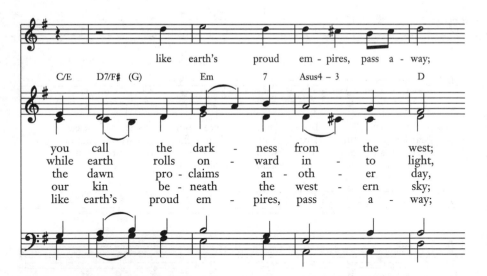

like earth's proud em - pires, pass a - way;

you call the dark - ness from the west;
while earth rolls on - ward in - to light,
the dawn pro - claims an - oth - er day,
our kin be - neath the west - ern sky;
like earth's proud em - pires, pass a - way;

Words: John Ellerton (1826–1893), alt   Music: Clement Cotterill Scholefield (1839–1904);
descant, Christopher Gower (1939–)

your sov - ereign reign will stand for - ev - er,

D/F#   G   (C/G)   D   7   Em Am /C   Dsus4 – 3

our morn - ing hymns to you as - cend - ed;
through all the world its watch is keep - ing,
the voice of prayer is nev - er si - lent,
fresh voic - es hour by hour are mak - ing
your sov - ereign reign will stand for - ev - er,

till dawns your glo - rious day.

D/C   G/B   D7   Em G/B   C6   Am 7   D   G

your praise now sanc - ti - fies our rest.
nor will it rest by day or night.
nor fade the sounds of praise a - way.
your won - drous deeds re - sound on high.
and grow, till dawns your glo - rious day.

827

Holy, holy Lord

SANCTUS (STRATHDEE) Irregular

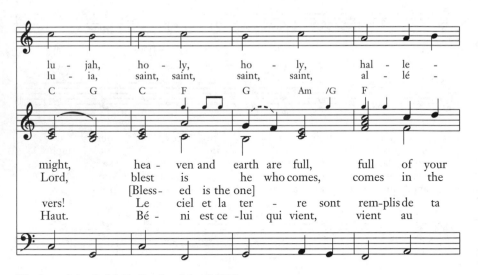

Words: traditional   Music: Jim Strathdee (1941-)

Words: public domain   Music: copyright © Desert Flower Music, 1978. Used by permission.

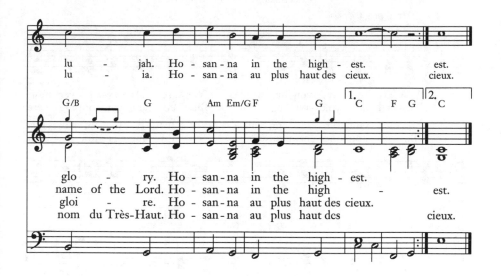

lu - jah. Ho - san - na in the high - est. est.
lu - ia. Ho - san - na au plus haut des cieux. cieux.

G/B   G   Am Em/G F   G   1. C   F   G   2. C

glo - ry. Ho - san - na in the high - est.
name of the Lord. Ho - san - na in the high - est.
gloi - re. Ho - san - na au plus haut des cieux.
nom du Très-Haut. Ho - san - na au plus haut des cieux.

828

You are holy, you are whole

DU ÄR HELIG 7 7 7 7 7 7 7 7 8 11 14

May be sung as a round.

① Dm

You are ho - ly, you are whole. You are al - ways e - ver more
Bless-ed are you com-ing near. Bless-ed are you com-ing here

Tu es saint et a - bon-dance et tu es tou - te puis-sance,
Bé - nis ton pro-chain re - tour, en nos âm - es ton la - bour,

F   Bb   (Dm)   Gm   A7sus   A

[1.]

than we e - ver un - der-stand. You are al - ways at hand.
to your church in wine and bread, raised from

plus que nous ne com-pren-ions. En toi nous nous con - fions.
pour ton peu - ple, vin et pain, de la

[2.]

A7sus   A7   Dm   ②   Dm   Gm

You are ho - ly; you are
soil, raised from dead. tu es saint, saint, plé - ni -
terr', don di - vin.

You are ho - ly, you are whole, you are
Tu es saint et a - bon - dance et tu

Words: Per Harling (1945-); French words, Joëlle Gouël Music: Per Harling (1945-)

Words: copyright © Per Harling, 1991; French words, copyright © World Council of Churches, 1991 Music: copyright © Per Harling, 1991;
French translation, copyright © World Council of Churches, 1991

whole - ness. You are pre - sent;
tu - de, tu es pré - sent,

al - ways e - ver - more than we e - ver un - der - stand.
es tou - te puis - sance, plus que nous ne com - pren - ions.

let the cos - mos praise you, Lord. Hal - le -
que l'un - i - vers te loue, Seign - eur. Al - lé -

You are al - ways at hand. Bless - ed
En toi nous nous con - fions. Bé - nis

lu - jah, hal - le - lu - jah, hal - le -
lu - ia, al - lé - lu - ia, al - lé -

are you com - ing near, bless - ed are you com - ing here to your
ton pro - chain re - tour, en nos âm - es ton la - bour, pour ton

lu - jah, hal - le - lu - jah, our Lord.
lu - ia, al - lé - lu - ia Seign - eur.

church in wine and bread, raised from soil, raised from dead.
peu - ple, vin et pain, de la terr', don di - vin.

Swedish

Du är helig; Du är hel.
Du är alltid mycket mer,
än vi nånsin kan förstå,
Du är nära ändå.
Välsignad vare Du,
Som kommer hit just nu,
Välsignande vår jord,
Blir till bröd på vårt bord.

Du är helig, Du är helhet,
Du är närhet,
Hela kosmos lovar Dig!
Halleluja, halleluja, halleluja, halleluja, vår Gud.

829

Holy, holy, holy Lord

LAND OF REST 5 5 10 5

1. Ho - ly, ho - ly, ho - ly Lord,
2. Bless - ed is the one who comes
[Bless - ed is he]
1. Saint, saint, saint est l'É - ter - nel,
2. Bé - ni soit ce - lui qui vient

God of pow-er and might, heaven and earth are
in the name of the Lord. Ho - san - na in the
Dieu de l'u - ni - vers! Le ciel et la terre sont rem -
au nom de l'É - ter - nel. Ho - san - na au plus

full of your glo - ry. Ho - san - na in the high - est.
high - est, ho - san - na in the high - est.
plis de ta gloi - re. Ho - san - na au plus haut des cieux.
haut des cieux, ho - san - na au plus haut des cieux.

Words: American folk hymn   Music: American folk hymn; arrangement, Marcia Pruner

Words: public domain   Music: arrangement © The Church Pension Fund, 1985

830   Praise God from whom all blessings flow

OLD 100TH   8 8 8 8 LM

Praise God from whom all bless - ings flow; praise
La grâ - ce de no - tre Sau - veur, l'a -

him all crea - tures here be - low; praise
mour du Père et sa fa - veur, et

him a - bove, ye heaven - ly host; praise
l'onc - ti - on du Saint - Es - prit, soient

Fa - ther, Son and Ho - ly Ghost.
a - vec nous par Jé - sus - Christ!

Words: Thomas Ken (1637-1711)   Music: Genevan Psalter 1551; last line, Ravenscroft's Psalter 1621

Words: public domain   Music: public domain

831 Our Father who art in heaven

PATER NOSTER (LANGDON) Irregular

Our Fath-er who art in heaven, hal-low-ed be thy name; thy king-dom come; thy will be done on earth, as it is in heaven; give us this day our dai-ly bread, and for- give us our debts, as we for-give our debt-ors, as

Words: Luke 11:2-4; paraphrase, traditional   Music: Richard Langdon (1729-1803)

Words: public domain   Music: public domain

we for - give our debt-ors, and lead us not in - to temp -
ta - tion, but de - liv - er us from e - vil, for thine is the
king-dom, and the power and the glo-ry for - ev - er. A - men.

832 The Lord bless you / Aaronic Blessing

AARONIC BLESSING (NAMETH) Irregular

The Lord bless you and keep you; the
Lord make his face shine up - on you, and be gra - cious un - to you; the
Lord lift up his coun - te-nance up - on you and give you his peace,

Words: traditional   Music: Bart Nameth (1954–)

Words: public domain   Music: copyright © Bart Nameth

give you his peace. A - men.

National Anthems

833   O Canada, our home and native land

O CANADA   10 10 8 6 8 6 8 10 10

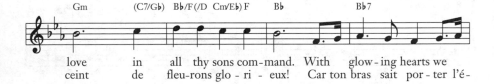

O Ca - na - da!	our home and na - tive land!	True pa - triot
O Ca - na - da!	ter - re de nos aï - eux,	ton front est

love in	all thy sons com - mand. With	glow - ing hearts we
ceint de	fleu-rons glo - ri - eux!	Car ton bras sait por - ter l'é-

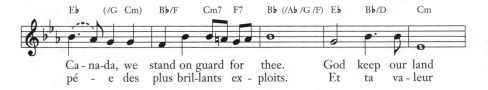

see thee rise, the	true north strong and free; from	far and wide, O
pé - e, il	sait por - ter la croix!	Ton his-toire est une é-po-

Ca - na - da, we	stand on guard for thee.	God keep our land
pé - e des	plus bril-lants ex - ploits.	Et ta va - leur

glo - rious and free!	O Ca-na-da! we stand on	guard for
de foi trem-pée,	pro - té-ge-ra nos foy - ers	et nos

thee.	O Ca - na - da! we stand on	guard for thee.
droits,	pro - té - ge-ra nos foy-ers	et nos droits.

Words: French, Adolphe B. Routhier (1839–1920); English, Robert Stanley Weir (1856–1926)
Music: Calixa Lavallée (1842–1891)

Words: public domain   Music: public domain

834

God save our gracious Queen

GOD SAVE THE QUEEN 6 6 4 6 6 6 4

God save our gra-cious Queen; long live our no-ble Queen; God save the Queen:

send her vic - to - ri-ous, hap - py and glo - ri-ous,

long to reign o - ver us: God save the Queen.

Words: anonymous c. 1745   Music: Thesaurus Musicus, London 1745

Words: public domain   Music: public domain

835   Musical Amens in Various Keys

Copyright Holders
(* indicates music)

NB: *All copyright material remains the property of the copyright owner(s) and permission to copy any copyright item can be granted only by the copyright owner(s). All such material in this edition is reproduced by permission of the copyright owner(s). Any reproduction of the material contained herein is strictly forbidden without the permission of all applicable copyright holders and The Presbyterian Church in Canada. The Presbyterian Church in Canada retains graphic rights to the material contained in this volume. Items which are otherwise in the public domain may be freely reproduced for use in a worship bulletin.*

Abingdon Press, 201 Eighth Avenue S, PO Box 801, Nashville, USA, TN, 37202-0801, Ph: (615) 749-6422, Fax: (615) 749-6512
Hymn(s): 41*, 46*, 105*, 109, 215*, 215, 485*, 530*, 630, 693*, 721*, 731, 762

Alexander, Rev Ian P, 7 Hay Meadow Lane, Burghill, Hereford, UK, HR4 7RZ, Ph: (01432) 761921
Hymn(s): 756

Anderson, Fred, Madison Ave Presbyterian Church, 921 Madison Ave, New York, NY, USA, 10021, Ph: (212) 288-8920, Fax: (212) 249-1466
Hymn(s): 49

Anglican Church of Canada, 600 Jarvis St, Toronto, ON, Canada, M4Y 2J6, Ph: (416) 924-9192, Fax: (416) 968-7983
Hymn(s): 423*, 548*

Arnéra, H, information sought
Hymn(s): 299

Association for Promoting Christian Knowledge, Church of Ireland House, Church Ave, Rathmines, Mr Keith Dungan, Dublin 6, Ireland, Ph: 011-353-1-496-6981, Fax: 011-353-1-497-2865
Hymn(s): 134*, 556*

Augsburg Fortress Publishers, 426 S 5th St, Karen Merrick, PO Box 1209, Minneapolis, MN, USA, 55440, Ph: (800) 328-4648, Fax: (612) 330-3455
Hymn(s): 144*, 219*, 534*, 722*

Austin, David, 3 Imperial Avenue, Westcliff on Sea, Essex, UK, SS0 8ND
Hymn(s): 455*

Barham-Gould Estate, 34 Pollards Dr, c/o D R Gould, Horsham, West Sussex, UK, RH 13 5 HH, Ph: 011-44-140-325-2083
Hymn(s): 644*

Barnes, Gerald L, 35 Dollis Ave, London, UK, N3 1BY
Hymn(s): 107*

Bartlett, L F, 2 New South Head Road, Vaucluse, NSW, Australia, 2030
Hymn(s): 225*

Bateman, Paul, 134 Conway Road, London, UK, N14 7BJ
Hymn(s): 745*, 787*

Beaudon, Rev Londa, 1153 Blvd Perrot, N D de L'Ile Perrot, PQ, Canada, J7V 3J1, Ph: (514) 667-2618
Hymn(s): 438

Belwin-Mills Publishing Corp, 15800 NW 48th Ave, c/o Columbia Pictures Publications, PO Box 4340, Miami, FL, USA, 33014, Ph: (305) 620-1500, Fax: (305) 625-3480
Hymn(s): 157*, 276*, 531*, 668*, 728*

Black, George, 507 Princess Ave, London, ON, Canada, N6B 2B7, Ph: (519) 439-0977, Fax: (519) 439-8704
Hymn(s): 295*

Fred Bock Music Company, PO Box 570567, Tarzana, CA, USA, 91356, Ph: (818) 996-6181, Fax: (818) 996-2043
Hymn(s): 392*, 392, 472*, 472

Boosey & Hawkes Music Publishers, 35 East 21st Street, New York, USA, NY, 10010-6212, Ph: (212) 358-5300, Fax: (212) 358-5301
Hymn(s): 732*

Bowers, The Reverend Canon J E, 13 Bathurst, Orton Goldhay, Peterborough, Cambs, UK, PE2 5QH, Ph: 011-44-173-336-1834
Hymn(s): 536

Breitkopf & Härtel, Walkmühlstr. 52, Wiesbaden, Germany, D-65195, Ph: 011-49-611-45008-0, Fax: 011-49-611-4500859
Hymn(s): 749*

Bridge, Basil E, 124 Linacre Ave, Sprowston, Norwich, UK, NR7 8JS
Hymn(s): 56, 280, 558

Broadman Press (SESAC), 127 Ninth Ave N, Nashville, TN, USA, 37234, Ph: (615) 251-2533
Hymn(s): 188*, 262*

C A Music, 209 Chapelwood Dr, c/o Music Services, Franklin, TN, USA, 37069, Fax: (615) 794-0793
Hymn(s): 114*, 114

Cabena, Barrie, 1-60 Allen Street West, Waterloo, ON, Canada, N2L 6H5, Ph: (519) 579-8827
Hymn(s): 426*

Caird, Mrs V M, The G B Caird Memorial Trust, Mansfield College, Oxford, England, UK, OX1 3TF
Hymn(s): 503

Cambridge University Press, 40 West 20th Street, Permissions Controller, New York, NY, USA, 10011-4211, Ph: (212) 924-3900, Fax: (212) 691-3239
Hymn(s): 138*, 313*

Carlson, Dosia, 555 W Glendale Ave, Phoenix, AZ, USA, 85021, Ph: (602) 264-1221
Hymn(s): 124*, 124

Cartford, Gerhard M, 2279 Commonwealth Ave, St Paul, MN, USA, 55108
Hymn(s): 453

Chatto and Windus Ltd, Random House, 20 Vauxhall Bridge Road, London, UK, SW1V 2SA, Ph: 011-44-171-973-9000, Fax: 011-44-171-233-8791
Hymn(s): 461

Chávez, Juan Francisco, Arenal 48, Depto. 10, Mexico (San Angel), D F Mexico, 01050
Hymn(s): 109*

Chinese Christian Literature Council, Flat A 4/F St Andrew's Christian Centre, 138 Nathan Road, Kowloon, Hong Kong, Ph: (852) 2367 8031-3, Fax: (852) 2739 6030
Hymn(s): 335*, 335

Chorister's Guild, 2834 W Kingsley Road, Garland, TX, USA, 75041, Ph: (214) 271-1521, Fax: (214) 840-3113
Hymn(s): 755*, 755, 819*, 819

Christian Conference of Asia, Pak Tin Village, Mei Tin Road, attn: Rev. Toshitsugu Arai, Shatin, N T, Hong Kong
Hymn(s): 346

Christian Marketing Canada Limited, 590 York Rd, PO Box 7000, Niagara-on-the-Lake, ON, Canada, L0S 1J0, Ph: (905) 641-0631, Fax: (905) 641-8824
Hymn(s): 79*, 358*, 358, 400*, 400, 409*, 409, 496*, 496, 774*, 774

Church Pension Fund, The Church Hymnal Corporation, 445 Fifth Ave, Attn: Pamela Tang, New York, NY, USA, 10016, Ph: (212) 592-1800, Fax: (212) 779-3392
Hymn(s): 183, 186*, 232, 261*, 273, 343, 711*, 791, 829*

Copyright Holders

Church Society for Bible, Church and Nation, Dean Wace House, 16 Rosslyn Road, Watford, Herts, UK, WD1 7EY, Ph: 011-44-192-323-5111, Fax: 011-44-192-380-0362
Hymn(s): 482*, 507*

Clellamin, Doreen, PO Box 498, Bella Coola, Canada, BC, V0T 1C0, Ph: (604) 799-5557
Hymn(s): 447*, 447

Cleveland, J Jefferson, 2119 E 96th Street #2, attn: Paul J Cleveland, Chicago, IL, USA, 60617, Ph: (773) 933-0997
Hymn(s): 108*, 108

Cole-Turner, Ronald S, Pittsburgh Theological Seminary, 616 North Highland Ave, Pittsburgh, PA, USA, 15206-2596, Ph: (412) 362-5610 x2170, Fax: (412) 363-3260
Hymn(s): 521

Common Cup Company, 7591 Gray Ave, c/o Ian Macdonald, Burnaby, BC, Canada, V5J 3Z4, Ph: (604) 434-8323, Fax: (604) 430-3697
Hymn(s): 403*, 403

Concordia Publishing House, 3558 S Jefferson Ave, St Louis, MO, USA, 63118, Ph: (314) 268-1000, Fax: (314) 268-1329
Hymn(s): 246, 279*, 418*, 418, 429, 464

The Copyright Company, 40 Music Square East, Nashville, TN, USA, 37302, Ph: (615) 244-5588, Fax: (615) 244-5591
Hymn(s): 20*, 20, 27*, 27, 36*, 36, 56*, 260*, 260, 292*, 292, 300*, 300, 445*, 445, 625*, 625

Costen, Melva Wilson, PO Box 42479, Atlanta, GA, USA, 30311, Ph: (404) 527-7729, Fax: (404) 527-0901
Hymn(s): 233*

Cousins, John, 188 Elmwood Ave, North York, ON, Canada, M2N 3M6, Ph: (416) 221-4081
Hymn(s): 547*

CRC Publications, 2850 Kalamazoo Ave SE, Grand Rapids, MI, USA, 49560, Ph: (616) 224-0785, Fax: (616) 224-0834
Hymn(s): 7*, 7, 22, 38*, 38, 42, 50*, 50, 74, 75, 163, 421*, 668, 724*, 785*

Creen, Ted, St Andrew's Presbyterian Church, 865 2nd Ave, Owen Sound, ON, Canada, N4K 4M6, Ph: (519) 376-7886
Hymn(s): 646*, 646

J Curwen & Sons, Ltd, Stockley Close, Stockley Road, West Drayton, Middlesex, UK, UB7 9DE
Hymn(s): 121*, 448*

Dakota Conference, United Church of Christ, c/o Winifred E Boub, PO Box 567, Pierre, SD, USA, 58501, Ph: (605) 224-8676, Fax: (605) 224-0850
Hymn(s): 301

Dalles, John A, Wekiva Presbyterian Church, 211 Wekiva Springs Lane, Longwood, FL, USA, 32779, Ph: (407) 869-1608, Fax: (407) 869-8256
Hymn(s): 276, 491, 582

Davies, Mr William, 10 Fayre Meadow, Robertsbridge, East Sussex, England, TN32 5AU, Ph: 01580 880380
Hymn(s): 288*

Davis, Frances Wheeler, 5205 Belmore Ave, Montréal, PQ, Canada, H4V 2C7
Hymn(s): 727

Davison, Rev. Dr Peter, All Saints Anglican Church, 3205-27th Street, Vernon, BC, Canada, V1T 4V8, Ph: (250) 542-3179, Fax: (250) 542-5139
Hymn(s): 295*, 295

Dill, Brian, King's Grant Presbyterian Church, 745 Little Neck Road, Virginia Beach, VA, USA, 23452, Ph: (757) 340-2840, Fax: (757) 431-1770
Hymn(s): 757

Donaldson, Andrew, Seraph Music, 14 Hambly Ave, Toronto, ON, Canada, M4E 2R6, Ph: (416) 691-1158, Fax: (416) 690-9967
Hymn(s): 66*, 66, 76, 169*, 190, 225, 278*, 278, 339*, 346*, 403*, 545*, 577*, 628*, 628, 673*, 673, 695*, 695, 714, 729*, 785

Downing, Edith Sinclair, 1703 Circle Loop SE, Lacey, WA, USA, 98503, Ph: (360) 438-5358
Hymn(s): 262

Duba, Arlo D, 111 Lakesouth Terrace, Hotsprings, AR, USA, 71913-9723
Hymn(s): 12

Dunn, John, St Paul's Parish, 29 Mount Auburn St, Cambridge, MA, USA, 02138, Ph: (617) 491-8400, Fax: (617) 354-7092
Hymn(s): 97

Edgar, Mary S, Estate Executor, 10 Wychwood Park, c/o Mr J W Gilchrist, Toronto, ON, Canada, M6G 2V5
Hymn(s): 667

Edwards, Paul, information sought
Hymn(s): 44*

Egan, Linda Wilberger, 302 Woodward Road, Moylan, PA, USA, 19063, Ph: (610) 566-6305, Fax: (610) 566-6305
Hymn(s): 664*, 664

Emmanuel College, 75 Queen's Park Cres E, Office of the Principal, Toronto, ON, Canada, M5B 1K7, Fax: (416) 585-4516
Hymn(s): 222, 337, 423, 786

Escamilla, Roberto, information sought
Hymn(s): 630

Faber Music Limited, 3 Queen Square, London, UK, WC1N 3AU, Ph: 011-44-171-278-7436, Fax: 011-44-171-278-3817
Hymn(s): 4, 70, 387

Farquharson, Walter, PO Box 126, Saltcoats, SK, Canada, S0A 3R0, Ph: (306) 744-2214
Hymn(s): 334

Fetter, Ms Judy, 3450 Cook Street, Victoria, BC, Canada, V8X 1B3, Ph: (250) 920-9935, Fax: (250) 479-8243
Hymn(s): 478

Fitch, William, Estate of, Christie Gardens, 602 Melita Cres Apt #325, c/o Mary Fitch, Toronto, Canada, ON, M5G 3Z5
Hymn(s): 518

Fleming, Margaret, 57-8889 212th St, Langley, BC, Canada, V1M 2E8
Hymn(s): 484*, 727*

Forget, Daniel H, L'église presbytérienne de St Andrew, 1169 route 243 RR #2, BP 2, Melbourne, QC, Canada, J0B 2B0, Ph: (819) 816-3184, Fax: (819) 816-3184
Hymn(s): 453, 617

Fox, Rev. David, 1 Tone Close, Bettws, Newport, UK, NP9 6AT
Hymn(s): 512

Franciscan Communications Center, 1229 S Santee Street, Los Angeles, CA, USA, 90015, Ph: (213) 764-2916
Hymn(s): 740*

Fraysse, Claude, Allée de la grande Muzenne, 26750 Genissieux, France, 26750, Ph: 011-33-75 02 71 93, Fax: 011-33-75 02 71 93
Hymn(s): 420*, 420

Gélineau, Joseph, 43 rue Georges Villette, 77250 Eculles, Moret sur Loing, France, Ph: 011-33-60-70-53-77, Fax: 011-33-1-64-31-18-16
Hymn(s): 346

Geyer, John B, 335 Blackness Road, Dundee, Scotland, UK, DD2 1SN
Hymn(s): 522

Copyright Holders

G I A Publications, 7404 S Mason Ave, Chicago, IL,
USA, 60638, Ph: (708) 496-3800, Fax: (708) 496-3828
Hymn(s): 24*, 24, 59*, 59, 71*, 71, 87, 112*, 167*,
202, 206*, 254*, 254, 272, 289, 303*, 307*, 322,
341*, 341, 356, 383*, 383, 417*, 417, 424*, 430*,
430, 446*, 446, 474, 492*, 492, 501*, 501, 520,
525*, 527*, 527, 528*, 528, 532*, 534, 557*, 557,
573*, 573, 583, 595*, 595, 604*, 604, 609, 617*,
617, 624*, 624, 634*, 634, 643*, 662*, 702*, 712,
717, 718*, 724, 728, 735*, 750, 753, 758*, 758,
812*, 823

Green, Judee Archer, 1471 Old Hwy. 99, Ancaster,
ON, Canada, L9H 5E3, Ph: (905) 628-3307,
Fax: (905) 628-2492
Hymn(s): 540

Gregory, Philip E — information sought
Hymn(s): 519

Harcourt Brace Jovanovich Inc., PO Box 860630,
Orlando, FL, USA, 32886-0630, Ph: (407) 345-
3983, Fax: (407) 352-8860
Hymn(s): 219

Harling, Per, PO Box 92, Sigtuna, LC, Sweden, 193
22, Fax: 011-46-8-592-562-70
Hymn(s): 828*, 828

The Fredrick Harris Music Co, Limited, Unit 1
5865 McLaughlin Road, Chris Luce, Mississauga,
ON, Canada, L5R 1B8, Ph: (905) 501-1595,
Fax: (905) 501-0929
Hymn(s): 144

Harwood, Basil, Estate of, c/o The Public Trustee
M4582, Stewart House, 24 Kingsway, Ms Elizabeth
Paterson, Trust Officer, London, UK, WC2B 6JX,
Ph: 0171-664-7187, Fax: 0171-664-7704
Hymn(s): 271*, 477*, 478*

Hedges, Anthony, 76 Walkergate, Berkeley, East
Yorkshire, UK, HU17 9ER, Ph: 011-44-148-286-
0580, Fax: 011-44-148-288-8503
Hymn(s): 289*

Held, Wilbur, 3340 Woodbend Dr, Clearmont, CA,
USA, 91711, Ph: (909) 624-0623
Hymn(s): 140*

David Higham Associates Ltd, 5-8 Lower John St, Golden
Square, London, England, W1R 4HA,
Ph: 011-44-171-437-7888, Fax: 011-44-171-437-1072
Hymn(s): 125, 814

Hillert, Richard, 1620 Clay Ct, Melrose Park, IL,
USA, 60160, Ph: (708) 681-5598
Hymn(s): 246*

Hinshaw Music, Inc, PO Box 470, Chapel Hill, NC,
USA, 27514, Ph: (919) 933-1691, Fax: (919) 967-3399
Hymn(s): 87*, 178*, 466*, 466, 622*, 622, 761*,
761

Hobbs, R Gerald, Vancouver School of Theology,
6000 Iona Drive, Vancouver, BC, Canada, V6T
1L4, Ph: (604) 822-9815, Fax: (604) 822-9212
Hymn(s): 299, 388, 704

Holman, Dr Derek, 75 George Henry Blvd, Willowdale,
ON, Canada, M2J 1E8, Ph: (416) 494-7068
Hymn(s): 160*, 243*

Hope Publishing Company, 380 South Main Place,
Carol Stream, IL, USA, 60188, Ph: (800) 323-
1049, Fax: (708) 665-2552
Hymn(s): 2, 3*, 3, 6, 8*, 8, 10, 14*, 14, 16*, 16,
25*, 35*, 35, 45*, 45, 46, 48, 49*, 53*, 53, 62, 68*,
68, 72*, 72, 74*, 80*, 83*, 83, 86, 88, 89, 90*, 90,
91, 92, 94*, 94, 100, 102*, 102, 106, 117*, 119*,
119, 121, 127, 130*, 130, 131, 137*, 137, 155*,
155, 159*, 162*, 179, 182, 185*, 185, 187, 196,
203*, 203, 223*, 223, 224*, 224, 226*, 226, 229*,
229, 248*, 250*, 250, 251, 252*, 263, 267*, 282,
283, 285*, 288, 305, 306, 309*, 309, 310*, 310,
314*, 317*, 317, 324*, 324, 329, 345*, 345, 351,
354, 355, 361*, 361, 365*, 365, 385*, 385, 400,
437, 439, 448, 449*, 449, 461*, 470*, 470, 475*,
475, 486, 497, 504*, 504, 509*, 509, 510, 515, 524,
529*, 530, 555, 556, 559, 562*, 562, 563*, 563,
567, 585, 588, 589, 593*, 596*, 596, 597, 599,
600*, 600, 601, 602*, 602, 603, 605, 609*, 613,
614, 616, 620, 626*, 627*, 627, 631, 632*, 632,
641*, 641, 643*, 643, 649, 655*, 657, 658, 663,
674*, 674, 688*, 688, 697*, 697, 702, 707, 710*,
716, 719*, 719, 720, 721, 732, 736, 741, 750*,
752*, 752, 763, 764*, 764, 776, 778, 782, 783*,
783, 798*, 798, 799, 802, 805, 808, 814*, 823*

Hopkirk, James, Estate of, 131 Brenda Cres., c/o
Arthur E B Armstrong, Scarborough, ON,
Canada, M1K 3C8, Ph: (416) 261-2539
Hymn(s): 375*, 786*

Hurd, David, General Theological Seminary, 175 Ninth
Ave, New York, NY, USA, 10011, Ph: (212) 243-5150
Hymn(s): 287*

Integrity Music, Inc., 1000 Cody Road, Mobile, AL,
USA, 36695, Ph: (334) 633-9000, Fax: (334) 633-5202
Hymn(s): 95*, 95, 376*, 376, 379*, 379, 427*,
427, 546*, 546, 635*, 635

International Commission on English in the
Liturgy, 1275 K Street NW, Suite 1000,
Washington, DC, USA, 20005-12-2, Ph:
(202) 347-0800, Fax: (202) 347-1839
Hymn(s): 469, 577, 586*, 586, 789

Ireland, The John, Trust, 35 St Mary's Mansion, St Mary's
Terrace, Mr P B A Taylor, London, UK, W2 1SQ
Hymn(s): 220*

Janzen, Jean Wiebe, 5508 E Lane, Fresno, CA, USA,
93727, Ph: (209) 251-9006
Hymn(s): 312, 391

Jenkins, Jill, 61 Lakeside Road, London, UK, N13 4PS
Hymn(s): 666

Johns, Elinor F, 38 Ruttan Bay, Winnipeg, MB,
Canada, R3T 0H6, Ph: (204) 475-4509
Hymn(s): 178, 696

Jones, W Thomas, 508 South 5th Street, Mebane,
NC, USA, 27302
Hymn(s): 178*

Kansfield, Norman, New Brunswick Theological
Seminary, 17 Seminary Place, New Brunswick, NJ,
USA, 08901, Ph: (908) 247-5241, Fax: (908) 249-5412
Hymn(s): 41

Korean Hymnal Society, 501 Sung Woo Building,
51-3 Do-wha Dong, Ma-po Gu, Seoul, Korea, Ph:
011-82-2-715-7871, Fax: 011-82-2-702-3341
Hymn(s): 716*

Kriewald, James A, information sought
Hymn(s): 523*, 544*

Lawson-Gould
Hymn(s): 782*

Lorenz Publishing Co, 501 East 3rd St, PO Box 802,
Dayton, OH, USA, 45401-0802, Ph: (513) 228-6118,
Fax: (513) 223-2042
Hymn(s): 471*, 471, 766*

Lumko Institute, PO Box 5058, Delmenville, South Africa,
1403
Hymn(s): 264*, 264

MacMillan, Ernest Campbell, 1671 Lakeshore Rd, c/o
Ross A MacMillan, Sarnia, ON, Canada, N7X 1B7
Hymn(s): 612*

MacNutt, Walter, The estate of, 161 St George St,
Apt 507, Toronto, ON, Canada, M5R 2M3
Hymn(s): 334*

Manley, James K, 434 Ives Terrace, Sunnyvale, CA,
USA, 94087, Fax: (415) 948-8430
Hymn(s): 399*, 399

Copyright Holders

Manna Music, PO Box 218, Pacific City, OR, USA, 97135, Ph: (503) 965-6112, Fax: (503) 965-6880
Hymn(s): 294*, 332*, 332

Maranatha! Music, 40 Music Square East, c/o The Copyright Co, Nashville, TN, USA, 37203, Ph: (615) 244-5588, Fax: (615) 244-5591
Hymn(s): 266

Martin, James P, 30-900 West 17th Street, North Vancouver, BC, Canada, V7P 3KS, Ph: (604) 986-4557, Fax: (604) 985-0982
Hymn(s): 120

Matsikenyiri, Patrick, Africa University, PO Box 1320, Mutare, Zimbabwe, Africa
Hymn(s): 514*, 514

Kevin Mayhew Ltd, Rattlesden, Jane Rayson, Bury-St-Edmunds, Suffolk, UK, IP30 0SZ, Ph: 011-44-144-973-7978, Fax: 011-44-144-973-7834
Hymn(s): 490*

McGuire, Cherie, 87 Gardiner Cres, Chatham, ON, Canada, N7L 3V4
Hymn(s): 373

McKay, Stan, Dr Jessie Salteaux Social Centre, Beauséjour, MB, R0E 0C0, Ph. (204) 268-3913, Fax. (204) 268-4463
Hymn(s): 301

McLeod, Diana, 352 Park St North, Peterborough, ON, Canada, K9H 4P5, Ph: (705) 748-4044, Fax: (705) 748-3141
Hymn(s): 712*

Mealy, Margaret W, 1404 Summit Rd, Berkeley, CA, USA, 94708
Hymn(s): 132*

Medical Mission Sisters, 92 Sherman St, Hartford, CT, USA, 06105, Ph: (860) 233-0875, Fax: (860) 509-9509
Hymn(s): 123, 730

Mennonite World Conference, 50 Kent Ave, Kitchener, ON, Canada, N2G 3R1, Ph: (519) 571-0060, Fax: (519) 571-1980
Hymn(s): 398

Mercy Publishing, 209 Chapelwood Dr, c/o Music Services, Franklin, TN, USA, 37064, Ph: (615) 794-9015, Fax: (615) 794-0793
Hymn(s): 216*, 216

Merrick, Peter, 44 Benlamond Ave, Toronto, ON, Canada, M4E 1Y9, Ph: (416) 690-3880, Fax: (416) 481-8999
Hymn(s): 770*, 771*

Michaels, Patrick, 88 Lexington Ave, Somerville, MA, USA, 02144, Ph: (617) 776-5604
Hymn(s): 768

Miller, Lynette, 801 Regent Ave W, PO Box 45032, Winnipeg, MB, Canada, R2C 5C7
Hymn(s): 513

Milligan, Carman H, Riverpark Place, 1 Corkstown Road Rm 416, c/o Leatta Milligan, Nepean, Canada, ON, K2H 1B6, Ph: (613) 828-6886
Hymn(s): 434*, 677*, 821*, 825*

A R Mowbray & Co Ltd, Wellington House, 125 Strand, London, England, WC2R 2BB, Ph: 011-44-171-420-5555, Fax: 011-44-171-240-7261
Hymn(s): 170*, 205*, 259, 314

Murray, A Gregory, Estate of, Downside Abbey, Stratton-on-the-Fosse, Bath, England, BA3 4RH, Ph: 011-44-176-123-2226, Fax: 011-44-176-123-2973
Hymn(s): 227*

Nameth, Bart, 64 Bond St N, Hamilton, ON, Canada, L8S 3W2, Ph: (905) 528-9492
Hymn(s): 213*, 572*, 618*, 832*

National Christian Education Council, 1020 Bristol Road, Selly Oak, Birmingham, UK, B29 6LB, Ph: 011-44-121-472-4242, Fax: 011-44-121-472-7575
Hymn(s): 348*, 348, 381, 700*, 705*

Neswick, Bruce, 3401 38th Street NW, #423, Washington, DC, USA, 20016-3041, Ph: (202) 537-6420, Fax: (202) 537-5613
Hymn(s): 111*

Novello & Co Ltd, c/o Music Sales Corporation, 257 Park Ave S, c/o Shawnee Press, New York, NY, USA, 10010
Hymn(s): 96*, 166*, 247*, 290*, 291*, 298*, 299*, 321*, 374*, 462*, 569*, 803*

OCP Publications, 5536 NE Hassalo, Portland, OR, USA, 97213, Ph: (800)547-8992, Fax: (503) 282-3486
Hymn(s): 12, 57*, 57, 109*, 109, 201*, 201, 214*, 422*, 422, 540*, 540, 592*, 592, 734*, 734, 762*, 762

O'Driscoll, Rev. Herbert, 1000 Jasmine Ave, Victoria, BC, Canada, V8Z 2P4, Ph: (250) 479-9847, Fax: (250) 479-8556
Hymn(s): 679, 754

OMF International, 2 Cluny Road, Singapore, Singapore, 259570, Ph: 011-65-473-5755, Fax: 011-65-472-2398
Hymn(s): 134

Oxford University Press, Great Clarendon Street, Oxford, UK, OX2 6DP, Ph: 011-44-186-555-6767, Fax: 011-44-186-555-6646
Hymn(s): 125*, 147*, 191*, 256*, 256, 552*

Oxford University Press, London, Permissions Department, 70 Baker Street, Miss Joyce Horn, London, UK, W1M 1DJ, Ph: 011-44-171-616-5900, Fax: 011-44-171-616-5901
Hymn(s): 4*, 11*, 17*, 60*, 85*, 92*, 100*, 110*, 140, 145*, 149*, 160, 164*, 183*, 191, 192, 244*, 249*, 263*, 273*, 284*, 302*, 302, 311, 333*, 340*, 362*, 362, 363*, 370*, 375, 386*, 395, 433*, 438*, 480*, 483*, 488, 493*, 508*, 508, 510*, 512*, 524*, 531, 560*, 560, 566*, 580*, 588*, 607*, 607, 611*, 612, 621*, 633*, 636*, 653*, 656*, 656, 671*, 710, 720*, 722, 741*, 744*, 748*, 748, 751, 772*, 788*, 809*, 813*, 813, 817*, 818*

Oxford University Press, New York, Attn: Brian Hill, 198 Madison Ave, New York, NY, USA, 10016-4314, Ph: (212) 726-6000, Fax: (212) 726-6444
Hymn(s): 136*, 158, 175*, 184, 186, 212, 281, 593, 723*, 729

Patterson, Joy F, 325 Broadway, Wausau, WI, USA, 54403, Ph: (715) 842-2664
Hymn(s): 31, 104

Peyer, Étienne de, Bd Tranchées 14, 1206 Geneva, Switzerland, Ph: 011-41-22-346-5572
Hymn(s): 704

Archdiocese of Philadelphia, Music Office, 222 N 17th St, Philadelphia, PA, USA, 19103, Ph: (215) 587-3696, Fax: (215) 587-3561
Hymn(s): 538*, 538

Pilcher, Charles Venn, information sought
Hymn(s): 334*

The Pilgrim Press, 700 Prospect Ave East, Cleveland, Ohio, USA, 44115-1100, Ph: (216) 736-3700, Fax: (216) 736-3703
Hymn(s): 184*, 199, 244, 743, 792*, 792

Pitt-Watson, Ian, Estate of, 47 Boundary Road, St John's Wood, c/o David Pitt-Watson, London, England, UK, NW8 0JE
Hymn(s): 101

The Presbyterian Church in Canada, 50 Wynford Dr, North York, ON, Canada, M3C 1J7, Ph: (416) 441-1111 Fax: (416) 441-2825
Hymn(s): 18, 21, 23, 28, 30, 33, 40*, 43, 52, 63, 67, 69, 84, 93, 103, 111, 120, 135, 168, 218, 230,

Copyright Holders

234, 269, 298, 304, 315, 321, 327, 328, 342, 348, 350, 353, 377, 378*, 384, 398, 399, 406, 410, 414, 430, 433, 441, 462, 467, 473, 493, 564, 636, 691, 713*, 726, 731, 769, 788, 789*

Theodore Presser Company, 1 Presser Place, Bryn Mawr, PA, USA, 19010-3490, Ph: (215) 525-3636, Fax: (215) 527-7841
Hymn(s): 486*, 793*

Proulx, Richard, 3300 NorthLake Shore Drive, #11-D, Chicago, IL, USA, 60657-3947, Ph: (773) 883-9417
Hymn(s): 274*

Reith, Angela, 47 Mayton Street, London, UK, N7 6QP, Ph: 011-44-171-609-8153, Fax: 011-44-171-609-8153
Hymn(s): 260*

Ridout, Michael, 22 Enderby Road, Toronto, ON, Canada, M4E 2S3, Ph: (416) 690-7833
Hymn(s): 311*

Röntgen, Julius, Estate of, c/o F E Röntgen
Hymn(s): 585*

Rosevear, Henry, Estate of, 31 Killdeer Cres, c/o Marilyn Broughton, Toronto, ON, Canada, M4G 2W7, Ph: (416) 421-5490
Hymn(s): 13*, 153*

Rowat, Kathleen, Manoir Westmount, 4646 Sherbrooke West, Montréal, PQ, Canada, H3Z 2Z8
Hymn(s): 723

Royal School of Church Music, Cleveland Lodge, Westhumble, Dorking, Surrey, UK, RH5 6BW, Ph: 011-44-130-687-7676, Fax: 011-44-130-688-7260
Hymn(s): 172*, 283*, 338*, 433*, 826*

Rusbridge, Rosalind, 9 Springfield House, Cotham Road, Bristol, England, UK, BS6 6DQ
Hymn(s): 143*

Sacred Music Press, 501 East 3rd Street, c/o The Lorenz Co, Dayton, OH, USA, 45401, Ph: 1 (800) 444-1144, Fax: (513) 223-2042
Hymn(s): 553*

Schalk, Carl F, 1208 Park Dr, Melrose Park, IL, USA, 60160, Ph: (708) 344-7167, Fax: (708) 344-7130
Hymn(s): 440*

E C Schirmer Music Co, 138 Ipswich St, Boston, MA, USA, 02215, Ph: (617) 236-1935, Fax: (617) 236-0261
Hymn(s): 338

G Schirmer Inc, 24 E 22nd St, New York, NY, USA, 10010, Ph: (212) 254-2100, Fax: (212) 254-2013
Hymn(s): 131*, 142*, 142

Selah Publishing Co, PO Box 3037, Kingston, NY, USA, 12401, Fax: (914) 338-2991
Hymn(s): 187*, 227, 241*, 241, 296*, 296, 305*, 312*, 657*, 669*, 669, 739, 810*

Sheldon, Robin, 151 Bath Road, Hounslow, Middlesex, UK, TW3 3BU, Ph: 011-44-181-570-1465
Hymn(s): 91*

Silvester, Frederick, Estate of, c/o Mrs W Verduij
Hymn(s): 800*

Smith, Doris Wright, Estate of, 817 Landis Ave CN 1501, c/o Gerald Spall, Vineland, NJ, USA, 08360
Hymn(s): 101*

Society for Promoting Christian Knowledge, Holy Trinity Church, Marylebone Road, Pat Phillips, General Secretary, London, UK, NW1 4DU, Ph: 011-44-171-387-5989, Fax: 011-44-171-388-1947
Hymn(s): 285

Somerville, Stephen, St Ambrose Church, 782 Brown's Line, Etobicoke, ON, Canada, M8W 3W2, Ph: (416) 251-8282, Fax: (416) 251-4400
Hymn(s): 665

Sosa, Pablo, Camacuá 282, 1406 Buenos Aires, Argentina
Hymn(s): 93*, 93, 199*

Sovereign Music UK, PO Box 356, Leighton Buzzard, Beds, UK, LU7 8WP, Ph: 011-44-152-538-5578, Fax: 011-44-152-537-2743
Hymn(s): 550*, 550

Speers, Rev. Canon John E, 76 Puget St, Barrie, Canada, ON, L4M 4N4, Ph: (705) 726-1072
Hymn(s): 279

Stainer & Bell Ltd, Victoria House, 23 Gruneisen Road, Finchley, PO Box 110, London, UK, N3 1DZ, Ph: 011-44-181-343-3303, Fax: 011-181-343-3024
Hymn(s): 322*, 565*

Stassen, Linda, New Songs Ministries, RR 1, PO Box 454, Erin, TN, USA, 37061, Ph: (615) 289-3853
Hymn(s): 526*, 526

St Martin's Publishing (re Tomlinson) Information sought
Hymn(s): 529

Stone, Carol C, 940 Channing Way, Berkeley, CA, USA, 94710, Ph: (510) 849-2351
Hymn(s): 132

Strathdee, Jim and Jean, Desert Flower Music, PO Box 1476, Carmichael, CA, USA, 95609, Ph: (916) 481-2999, Fax: (916) 481-2999
Hymn(s): 412*, 412, 436*, 436, 561*, 574*, 574, 590*, 590, 709*, 709, 715*, 715, 759, 827*

Stright, Ken and Jeanne, PO Box 254, Pictou, NS, Canada, B0K 1H0, Ph: (902) 485-5818
Hymn(s): 124

Stuempfle, Herman G Jr., 330 Ridge Ave, Gettysburg, PA, USA, 17325, Ph: (717) 334-2893
Hymn(s): 188, 287

Tempo Music Publications, 3773 West 95th Street, Leawood, KS, USA, 66206, Ph: (913) 381-5088, Fax: (913) 381-5081
Hymn(s): 268*, 268

Thiman, Eric, estate of see Oxford University Press (London)

Thompson, The Rev. Dr Colin P, St Catherine's College, Oxford, UK, OX1 3UJ
Hymn(s): 566

Tyrrell, Mrs J, 41 Minster Road, Godalming, Surrey, England, GU7 1SR
Hymn(s): 626

Unichappell Music, Inc, Div of Hal Leonard Publishing Corp, 7777 W Bluemound Road, PO Box 13819, Milwaukee, WI, USA, 53213-0819, Ph: (414) 774-3630, Fax: (414) 774-3259
Hymn(s): 675*, 675

United Church Press, 132 W 31st St, New York, NY, USA, 10001, Ph: (718) 937-9515, Fax: (718) 937-9804
Hymn(s): 12*

The United Church Publishing House, 3250 Bloor Street West, attn: Copyright Permissions, Etobicoke, ON, Canada, M8X 2Y4, Fax: (416) 232-6004
Hymn(s): 423*, 548*

United Methodist Church Music Service, Mutambara CPS Box 61, c/o Univ. of Zimbabwe, Cashel, Zimbabwe, Ph: 011-263-4-3032-11, Fax: 011-263-4-3334-02
Hymn(s): 591*

United Reformed Church see Oxford University Press (London)

Vajda, Jaroslav J, 3534 Brookstone South Dr, St Louis, MO, USA, 63129-2900, Ph: (314) 892-9473
Hymn(s): 167, 307, 810

Van Maanen, John R, 27 Foster St, Simcoe, ON, Canada, N3Y 2C3
Hymn(s): 356*

Walton Music Corp., 170 NE 33rd Street, Fort Lauderdale, USA, Florida, 33334, Ph: (954) 563-1844, Fax: (954) 563-9006
Hymn(s): 152*, 152, 639*, 639, 777*

Waterloo Music Co Ltd, 3 Regina St N, Waterloo,
ON, Canada, N2J 4A5, Ph: (519) 886-4990,
Fax: (519) 886-4999
Hymn(s): 337*, 402*, 520*, 536*, 541*, 583*, 778*

Waters, Margaret, 134 St Lawrence Blvd, London,
ON, Canada, N6J 2X1, Ph: (519) 685-1714
Hymn(s): 117
Weaver, John, Madison Ave Presbyterian Church,
921 Madison Ave, New York, NY, USA, 10021,
Ph: (212) 288-8920, Fax: (212) 249-1466
Hymn(s): 684*
Josef Weinberger Ltd, 12-14 Mortimer Street, London,
England, W1N 7RD, Ph: 011-44-171-580-2827,
Fax: 011-44-171-436-9616
Hymn(s): 248
The Westminster/John Knox Press, 100 Witherspoon
St, Louisville, KY, USA, 40202-1396,
Ph: (502) 569-5060, Fax: (502) 569-5113
Hymn(s): 286, 319, 435*, 471*, 484, 587, 749*
Whalum, Wendell, Estate of, 2439 Greenwood
Circle, c/o Mrs Clarie G Whalum, East Point,
GA, USA, 30344
Hymn(s): 648*
Wilkinson, Katie B, Estate of—information sought,
Hymn(s): 644
Willan, Healey, Estate of, 101-350 Lonsdale Rd, c/o Mary
Willan Mason, Toronto, ON, Canada, M5P 1R6
Hymn(s): 122*, 163*
Williams, Derek, 44 High Street, Little
Walsingham, Norfolk, UK, NR22 6AA,
Ph: 011-44-132-882-0216
Hymn(s): 70*, 332
Williams, Stanley, West Bay Indian Mission,
Excelsior, Manitoulin Island, ON, P0P 1G0,
Ph. (705) 377-4971
Hymn(s): 332
Wilson, Lois, 40 Glen Rd Apt 310, Toronto, ON,
Canada, M4W 2V1, Ph: (416) 975-0395,
Fax: (416) 975-0848
Hymn(s): 618
Wood Lake Books, 10162 Newene Road, Winfield,
BC, Canada, V4V 1R2, Ph: (250) 766-2778,
Fax: (250) 766-2736
Hymn(s): 40, 73, 98*, 469*, 700, 796, 804*
Word Music Inc., 3319 West End Ave Suite 200,
Nashville, TN, USA, 37203, Ph: (615) 385-9673,
Fax: (615) 297-6128
Hymn(s): 25
Work, Mrs John W III, 1030 17th Avenue North,
Nashville, TN, USA, 37208
Hymn(s): 133*, 133
World Council of Churches, 150 route de Ferney,
Terry MacArthur, 1211 Geneva 2, Switzerland,
Fax: 011-41-22-791-0361
Hymn(s): 242*, 388*, 388, 777, 828
World Library Publications, 3815 N Willow Road, a
div. of J S Paluch, Schiller Park, IL, USA, 60176,
Ph: (847) 678-0621, Fax: (847) 671-5715
Hymn(s): 316, 692, 775
WorshipArts, Ron Klusmeier, Fax: (250) 468-7172
Hymn(s): 73*, 73, 391*, 515*, 555*, 704*, 704,
739*, 763*

PSALMS
Lift up the gates eternal 12
Oh look and wonder 93
Praise to the Lord 73
Praise ye the Lord 108
Safe in your hands, O God who made me 14
Shout for joy to the Lord 66
ADVENT
All earth is waiting to see the promised One .. 109
Hope is a star 119
People in darkness 124
CHRISTMAS
Away in a manger 149
Go, tell it on the mountain 133
Infant holy, Infant lowly 143
Jesus, our brother, kind and good 150
Joy to the world 153
Once in royal David's city 166
Silent night 154
Still, still, still 152
That boy-child of Mary 155
The first nowell 136
Twas in the moon of wintertime 144
EPIPHANY
We three kings 173
LENT
We come to ask your forgiveness 201
When Jesus the healer passed through Galilee 203
PALM/PASSION SUNDAY
Filled with excitement 215
Hosanna 213
Hosanna, loud hosanna 218
MAUNDY THURSDAY
Jesu, Jesu, fill us with your love 229
GOOD FRIDAY
Were you there when they crucified my Lord 233
EASTER
Alleluia, alleluia, give thanks to the risen Lord /
Alleluia No. 1 260
I danced in the morning / Lord of the dance 250
Jesus is risen from the grave 254
DAY OF PENTECOST
That day in Jerusalem 278
GOD CREATOR AND RULER
God of many names 309
God of the sparrow, God of the whale 307
Many and great, O God, are your works 301
This is my Father's world 328
Wherever I may wander 319
Who made the earth and the heavens / He's got
the whole world 339
GOD IN CHRIST
A holy baby 345
Come, children, join to sing 377
Jesus loves me, this I know 373
Jesus the Christ said: I am the bread 346
Jesus, Jesus, Jesus in the morning 378
Lord, the light of your love is shining 376
Praise him, praise him, Jesus our blessed
Redeemer 372
Tell me the stories of Jesus 348
GOD THE HOLY SPIRIT
Holy Spirit, hear us 381
Spirit, Spirit of gentleness 399
When the spirit of the Lord moves in my soul 398
WORSHIP
All things bright and beautiful 435
Can a little child like me 441
Children of Jerusalem 415
Come, let us sing to the Lord our song 412

Items for Children & Youth

Languages other than English

Descants & Fauxbourdons

Topics

Affirmation of Faith see Baptism; Profession of Faith; Faith; Commitment

Ascension see also Ascension / Reign of Christ section 265ff; Jesus Christ: Kingship / Reign

Ash Wednesday see Lent; Repentance
Bless / Blessing see also Service Music

Canticles and Scripture Paraphrases see also Psalm section 1ff; Scripture indexes

Topics

Change see Growth in Faith; Christian Nurture / Teaching

Children's Hymns see separate index of items suitable for children and youth

Choruses and Meditative Songs

Christian Nurture / Teaching see also Growth in Faith

Christmas see also Christmas section 133ff

Church see also Church section 469ff

Topics

Topics

Topics

Topics

Topics

Topics

Topics

Topics

Topics

Topics

Topics

Love divine, all loves excelling 371
There is a balm in Gilead 747
What king would wade through
murky streams 184

Holy Spirit: Comforter
Come down, O Love divine 386
Come, thou almighty King 293
God, we praise you for the morning 436
Holy Spirit, come, confirm us 387
O love, how deep, how broad, how high 205
Spirit, come, dispel our sadness 380

Holy Spirit: Gifts of
Come, holy spirit / Veni Sancte Spiritus 383
Holy Spirit, come, confirm us 387
Lord, you give the great commission 778
O Lord of heaven and earth and sea 432
Pour out your Spirit from on high 581
They did not build in vain 616

Holy Spirit: Illuminator / Teacher
Break now the bread of life 507
Come down, O Love divine 386
God, we praise you for the morning 436
O Holy Spirit, by whose breath 402
O Lord of every shining constellation 302
On this assembled host 277
Open my eyes, that I may see 500
The Spirit breathes upon the word 506
There's a spirit in the air 764
Thou whose almighty word 291

Holy Spirit: Indwelling
O holy Dove of God descending 392
Spirit, come, dispel our sadness 380
Thanks to God whose word was spoken 509

Holy Spirit: Power of
Filled with the Spirit's power 282
God the Spirit, Guide and Guardian 589
I'll love the Lord 573
Jesus, life of all the world 776
Let every Christian pray 283
Lord, you give the great commission 778
Spirit divine, attend our prayers 390
Spirit, come, dispel our sadness 380
They did not build in vain 616
What was your vow and vision 182

Holy Week see also Palm / Passion Sunday; Maundy Thursday; Good Friday; Easter / Eastertide
Behold the Lamb of God 525
From heaven you came, helpless babe 379
O Christ, our Lord, we meet here as your people
756

Holy / Holiness see also God: Holiness of
Colourful Creator, God of mystery 317
Fire of God, O sacred flame 395
For the bread which you have broken 549
Lord, I want to be a Christian 571
Lord, you give the great commission 778
Take time to be holy 638
Worship the Lord in the beauty of holiness 174
You are holy, you are whole 828

Home see also Family
Amazing grace 670
Happy the home when God is there 703
O Lord of heaven and earth and sea 432
Precious Lord, take my hand 675
When love is found 600

Hope see also Our Hope in God
All earth is waiting to see the promised One 109
All my hope on God is founded 462
As comes the breath of spring 396
As longs the hart 25
As pants the hart 26
Be still, my soul 749
Before the Lord my soul is bowed 92
Blest be the everlasting God 454
Blest be the tie that binds 481
Born in the night 137
Christ is coming 795
Christ is the King 612
Come in, come in, New Year 808
Come, ye disconsolate 195
Deep in the shadows of the past 510
For all the love 440
Give thanks for life, the measure of our days .. 613
Give thanks, my soul, for harvest 805
God bless your church with strength 491
God, we praise you for the morning 436
Hope is a star 119
I greet thee, who my sure Redeemer art 678
I rest in God alone 36
I'll praise my Maker while I've breath 105
In suffering love 696
In the bulb there is a flower 674
Jesus, the very thought of thee 367
Let Christian faith and hope dispel 368
Lord of all hopefulness 748
My hope is built on nothing less 349
O day of peace that dimly shines 732
O God, our help in ages past 330
O Lord, hear my prayer / The Lord is my song . 446
O Love that wilt not let me go 209
O saints, in splendour sing 609
Oh give thanks, for God is gracious 72
Oh send thy light forth 29
People in darkness 124
Praise the Lord 418
Sleepers, wake! 127
Sometimes a healing word is comfort 768
The steadfast love of the Lord 20
There's a voice in the wilderness crying 128
This joyful Eastertide 259
Up from the depths I cry to you 90
We have come at Christ's own bidding 187
When the poor ones 762

Hunger see also Feast / Food; Social Concerns
All who hunger, gather gladly 534
I hunger and I thirst 198
Living God, your joyful Spirit 666
Oh give thanks, for God is gracious 72
You are called to tell the story 583
You satisfy the hungry heart 538

Inner Peace see Calm / Serenity; Peace

Invitation see also Call / Calling; Jesus Christ: Call of
All who hunger, gather gladly 534
I have decided to follow Jesus 570
Softly and tenderly 640
To God be the glory 350
Woman in the night 657
You thirsty ones 190

Jesus Christ: Alpha and Omega see Jesus Christ: First and Last

Jesus Christ: Baptism of see Baptism of Jesus

Jesus Christ: Bread of Life see Bread / Manna
Deck thyself, my soul, with gladness 533

Topics

Topics

Topics

Topics

Topics

Topics

Maundy Thursday see also Maundy Thursday section 224ff

Mercy see also God: Mercy of

Mission see also Mission section 753ff; Evangelism; Social Concerns / Social Justice

Morning see also Morning section 813ff

Music / Singing / Song

Mystery

Name see also God: Name of; Jesus Christ: Name of

National Occasions see also National Occasions section 800ff

Nations see also National Occasions

Topics

Topics

Topics

Topics

Topics

Topics

Topics

Topics

Topics

Tunes

Tunes

Tunes

Tunes

Tunes

Tunes

Tunes

Tunes

Tunes

Tunes

Meters

Meters

Meters

Meters

Meters

Meters

Meters

Meters

Meters

Meters

1111

Meters

Meters

Meters

References to Scripture: By Book

References to Scripture: By Book

JOHN (cont'd)

Authors, Composers & Sources
(* indicates music)

Authors, Composers & Sources

Authors, Composers & Sources

Authors, Composers & Sources

Authors, Composers & Sources

Authors, Composers & Sources

Authors, Composers & Sources

First Lines & Common Titles

First Lines & Common Titles

First Lines & Common Titles

God of grace and God of glory 490
God of hosts, you chose a vine 48
God of many names 309
God of mercy, God of grace 39
God of the sparrow, God of the whale 307
God, of your goodness give me yourself 458
God, our Sovereign Lord remaining 60
God, reveal your presence 414
God reveals His presence see God, reveal your presence
God save our gracious Queen 834
God the omnipotent 738
God the Spirit, Guide and Guardian 589
God, we praise you for the morning 436
God, when I stand 679
God who gives to life its goodness 334
God, who made the earth 705
God, who stretched the spangled heavens 305
God, Who touchest earth with beauty see God, you touch the earth with beauty
God, whose giving knows no ending 663
God, you touch the earth with beauty 667
God's glory fills the heavens 10
God's law is perfect 9
God's name forever shall endure 43
Good Christian men, rejoice see Good Christians, all rejoice
Good Christians, all rejoice 141
Gracious Spirit, Holy Ghost 701
Grant us peace see Dona nobis pacem
Great God, arise 41
Great God, your love has called us here 226
Great is thy faithfulness 324
Great Shepherd of your people, hear 450
Grief of ending, wordless sorrow 602
Guide me, O thou great Redeemer 651
Hail, O festival day 244
Hail, our once-rejected Jesus 353
Hail the day that sees Him rise see Hail the day that sees Christ rise
Hail the day that sees Christ rise 265
Hail, Thou once despised Jesus! see Hail, our once-rejected Jesus
Hail to the Lord's Anointed 115
Hallelujah (Iona) 532
Hallelujah 591
Hallelujah (Sinclair) 294
Hallelujah! Hallelujah! Hallelujah! 261
Hallelujah! sing to Jesus 370
Happy the home when God is there 703
Hark! a thrilling voice is sounding 116
Hark how the adoring see Come let us join our cheerful songs
Hark the glad sound 118
Hark! the herald angels sing 139
He is born! Now the child has come see Il est Né
He is Lord 252
He leadeth me 650
He who would valiant be see Who would true valour see
Help us accept each other 632
Help us to help each other, Lord 489
Herald! Sound the note of judgement 117
Here I Am, Lord see I, the Lord of sea and sky
Here is bread: here is wine 546
Here, O my Lord, I see thee 543
High in the heavens, eternal God 19

Ho ye that thirst see You thirsty ones
Holy Ghost, dispel our sadness see Spirit, come, dispel our sadness
Holy God, holy and mighty 820
Holy Spirit, come, confirm us 387
Holy Spirit, hear us 381
Holy Spirit, truth divine 394
Holy, holy, holy (Argentina) 303
Holy, holy, holy (Cabena) 426
Holy, holy, holy (Dykes) 299
Holy, holy, holy (Schubert) 623
Holy, holy, holy Lord (Iona) 718
Holy, holy, holy Lord (Pruner) 829
Holy, holy Lord (Strathdee) 827
Hope is a star 119
Hosanna, loud hosanna 218
Hosanna (Nameth) 213
Hosanna (Tuttle) 216
How blessed are the ones who hear 493
How blest are they who trust in Christ 601
How blest are they whose trespass 17
How blest are they, who, fearing God 1
How brightly beams the morning star 180
How clear is our vocation, Lord 649
How deep the silence of the soul 750
How firm a foundation 685
How firm a foundation 686
How great thou art see O Lord my God! / How great thou art
How long will you forget me, Lord 6
How lovely is thy dwelling place 52
How lovely, Lord, how lovely 53
How many are against me, Lord 2
How shall I sing to God 697
How sweet the name of Jesus sounds 357
I am the church! You are the church! 475
I bind unto myself today 576
I come with joy 530
I cried out for heaven to hear me 45
I danced in the morning / Lord of the dance 250
I greet thee, who my sure Redeemer art 678
I have decided to follow Jesus 570
I heard the voice of Jesus say 671
I hunger and I thirst 198
I joyed when to the house of God 84
I know not why God's wondrous grace see I know not why such wondrous grace
I know not why such wondrous grace 683
I love the Lord, for he has heard my voice see I love you, Lord, for you have heard my voice
I love the Lord 76
I love Thy kingdom, Lord see We love your kingdom, Lord
I love you, Lord, for you have heard my voice 75
I rest in God alone 36
I sing the almighty power of God 333
I sought the Lord, and afterward I knew 568
I, the Lord of sea and sky 592
I to the hills will lift my eyes 82
I waited for the Lord my God 23
I waited, I waited on you, Lord 24
I was glad when they said to me 83
I will call upon the Lord 408
I wonder as I wander 142
I worship you, O Lord 16

First Lines & Common Titles

First Lines & Common Titles

First Lines & Common Titles

First Lines & Common Titles